ADDISON – WESLEY MATHEMATICS 11
Québec Edition

Brendan Kelly
Professor of Mathematics
University of Toronto
Toronto, Ontario

Bob Alexander
Assistant Coordinator
of Mathematics
Toronto Board of Education
Toronto, Ontario

Paul Atkinson
Principal
Cameron Heights
Collegiate Institute
Kitchener, Ontario

Contributing Authors

Michael Cassidy
Mathematics Coordinator
Baldwin-Cartier School Commission
Pointe Claire, Québec

John Di Domenico
Resource Teacher
Laval Catholic High School
Laval, Québec

Joan Ebbett
Protestant School Board of
Greater Montreal
Montreal, Québec

Elaine Whitton
Protestant School Board of
Greater Montreal
Montreal, Québec

Addison-Wesley Publishers Limited

Don Mills, Ontario • Reading, Massachusetts
Menlo Park, California • New York
Wokingham, England • Amsterdam
Bonn • Sydney • Singapore
Tokyo • Madrid • San Juan

Design
John Zehethofer

Editorial
Lesley Haynes

Photo Credits

The publisher wishes to thank the following sources for photographs and other illustrative materials used in this book. We will gladly receive information enabling us to rectify any errors or references in credits.

Cover, Richard Simpson; 1, © Daily Telegraph/Masterfile; 15, B. Brooks/Masterfile; 21, B. Brooks/Masterfile; 32, Lesley Haynes; 41, Mel DiGiacomo/Image Bank; 42, Addison-Wesley photo library, Metropolitan Toronto Police College; 59, Toronto Blue Jays Baseball Club; 60, Masterfile; 99, Metropolitan Toronto Police College; 120, Ontario Department of Transportation and Communications; 141, Paul Atkinson; 146, © R. Kinne/Science Source/Masterfile; 148, Roberts/Miller Comstock Inc.; 151, J.A. Kraulis/Masterfile; 161, Global Television Network; 165, A. McKim/Masterfile; 171, Allsport/Masterfile; 177, A. Smith/Masterfile; 181, Allsport/Masterfile; 189, Canapress Photo Service; 193, Bob Alexander; 203, Vincent Van Gogh Foundation/National Museum, Vincent Van Gogh, Amsterdam; 210, The Toronto Star; 269, Roberts/Miller Comstock Inc.; 281, Addison-Wesley photo library; 287, N. Schmidt/Masterfile; 323, Miller Comstock Inc.; 335, Nova-Scotia Power Corporation; 338, Roberts/Miller Comstock Inc.; 391, THE BETTMANN ARCHIVE; 439, Swiss National Tourist Office; 452, CP Rail; 453, Addison-Wesley photo library; 458, Stanford News Service

Written, printed, and bound in Canada

A B C D E F— BP —98 97 96 95 94 93

ISBN 0-201-55323-6

Features of Mathematics 11

CONCEPT DEVELOPMENT

Mathematics 11 is carefully sequenced to develop concepts in mathematics. Concepts are explained with several examples, each of which has a detailed solution.

1-2 RADICAL ARITHMETIC

Although the ancient Greeks discovered irrational numbers, they never developed the symbols needed to use radicals. It wasn't until 1525 that the square root symbol appeared, possibly derived from the written letter "r" (for *root*).

$$\kappa \longrightarrow \kappa\!/ \longrightarrow \sqrt{} \longrightarrow \sqrt{}$$

To add or subtract radicals, first simplify each radical by extracting all perfect-square factors. Then combine like radicals.

Example 1. Simplify.　a) $\sqrt{12} + \sqrt{27}$　b) $3\sqrt{8} + 2\sqrt{3} - 2\sqrt{75} + 4\sqrt{50}$

Solution.　a) $\sqrt{12} + \sqrt{27} = \sqrt{4 \times 3} + \sqrt{9 \times 3}$
$$= 2\sqrt{3} + 3\sqrt{3}$$
$$= 5\sqrt{3}$$

　b)　$3\sqrt{8} + 2\sqrt{3} - 2\sqrt{75} + 4\sqrt{50}$
$$= 3 \times 2\sqrt{2} + 2\sqrt{3} - 2 \times 5\sqrt{3} + 4 \times 5\sqrt{2}$$
$$= 6\sqrt{2} + 20\sqrt{2} + 2\sqrt{3} - 10\sqrt{3}$$
$$= 26\sqrt{2} - 8\sqrt{3}$$

Products involving radicals can be expanded using the distributive law.

Example 2. Expand and simplify.
　a) $5\sqrt{2}(2\sqrt{3} - \sqrt{8})$　　　　b) $(5\sqrt{7} - 2\sqrt{3})(\sqrt{7} + 4\sqrt{3})$
　c) $(\sqrt{x} - 2)^2$　　　　　　　　d) $(3 - 2\sqrt{5})(3 + 2\sqrt{5})$

Solution.　a) $5\sqrt{2}(2\sqrt{3} - \sqrt{8}) = 10\sqrt{6} - 5\sqrt{16}$
$$= 10\sqrt{6} - 20$$

REINFORCEMENT

An abundance of exercises is provided to reinforce skills and concepts. These exercises are graded by difficulty with an appropriate balance of A, B, and C exercises. The A exercises may sometimes be completed mentally and the answers given orally or the questions may be used as additional examples when teaching the lesson. The B exercises are intended for the students to consolidate their learning of the concepts that were taught. The C exercises present a challenge and usually involve extensions of the concepts taught in that section.

Review Exercises and *Cumulative Reviews* provide additional practice. Answers to all questions are included in the text.

TECHNOLOGY

A contemporary mathematics program must reflect the impact of calculators and computers on society.

Mathematics 11 assumes that students will use scientific calculators where appropriate. It is up to the students to familiarize themselves with their calculators.

USING TECHNOLOGY

Graphical Solutions

Mathematical Models

When solving problems dealing with real-world phenomena, it is often helpful to construct a model to help us visualize what is happening. This model may be a solid object such as a wind tunnel or an airplane cockpit simulator.

Sometimes the model we construct may be semi-abstract such as a computer program that uses animation. These programs are often helpful, for example, to demonstrate chemistry experiments.

At other times, the model is abstract and consists of an equation or a set of equations. In creating these equations we define the relationships between two or more components of the real-world problem we are studying. Sometimes the relationships are easy to define; for example, the equation relating the amount of money A invested, the annual rate of interest R, and the amount of money P at the end of one year: $P = A(1 + R)$. Often, the relationships are difficult to define; for example, the various forces that cause a liquid to cool or an airplane to withstand the stresses of flight.

It is important to be able to manipulate the equations of our model both algebraically and graphically. Graphing calculators have many helpful features that can be used to analyze graphs of equations.

Solving Equations

Previously, we have found the roots of a polynomial equation $f(x) = 0$ by graphing $y = f(x)$ and observing the points at which the graph crossed the x-axis. In effect, we were discovering the points of intersection of the two functions $Y_1 = f(x)$ and $Y_2 = 0$.

To solve the equation $2x - 1 = 5$ graphically, the left side of the equation can be entered as Y_1 and the right side as Y_2 on the functions menu. These two separate functions, $Y_1 = 2x - 1$ and $Y_2 = 5$, are graphed on the same screen. The point of intersection $(3, 5)$ indicates the solution $(x = 3)$ to the equation.

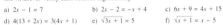

Solve each equation graphically by the method shown above. Verify each solution algebraically.

　a) $2x - 1 = 7$　　　　b) $2x - 2 = -x + 4$　　　c) $6x + 9 = 4x + 15$

　d) $4(13 + 2x) = 3(4x + 1)$　　e) $\sqrt{3x + 1} = 5$　　f) $\sqrt{x + 1} = x - 5$

Average Marks

A student has marks of 64 and 78 on recent math tests. What mark on a third test would give the student an average of 60? 80? 90?

USING TECHNOLOGY features provide opportunities for students to explore mathematical problems using graphing calculators. It is assumed that students know how to operate their graphing calculators.

APPLICATIONS OF MATHEMATICS

Students can better understand mathematical principles when they are related to their applications. For this reason, applications are integrated throughout *Mathematics 11*.

Every chapter begins with an applied problem that is solved as an example in the chapter.

1 Algebraic Operations and Equations

Modern communications systems depend on geosynchronous satellites which are placed in orbit above the equator. Such a satellite is synchronized with the Earth's rotation, and appears to be stationary. Its height and speed are adjusted so that it travels once around the Earth in exactly 24 h. How high should a communications satellite be placed? (See Section 1-6 *Example 3*.)

Many sections begin with an application which illustrates the necessity for the mathematics that follows.

5-13 APPLICATIONS OF EXPONENTIAL AND LOGARITHMIC FUNCTIONS: PART TWO

Growth of Populations

Occasionally we see statements such as this, in magazines and newspapers.

In favorable breeding conditions, the population of a swarm of desert locusts can multiply 10-fold in 20 days.

This information is not sufficient to calculate the population of a swarm of locusts, since an initial population figure is not given. But we can still use the statement to compare the populations of a swarm at two different times.

Example 1. Use the information above to compare the population of a swarm of locusts after 30 days with its population after 20 days.

Applications are also included throughout the exercises.

Acid Rain

7. Between 1956 and 1976 the annual average pH of precipitation at Sault Ste. Marie, Ontario, dropped from 5.6 to 4.3. How many times as acidic as the precipitation in 1956 was the precipitation in 1976?

8. In the spring, the pH of a stream dropped from 6.5 to 5.5 during a 3-week period in April.
   a) How many times as acidic did the stream become?
   b) Why would this happen in April?
   c) The mean pH of Lake Huron is 8.2. How many times as acidic was the stream:
      i) before the 3-week period   ii) after the 3-week period?

9. When the pH of the water in a lake falls below 4.7, nearly all species of fish in the lake are deformed or killed. How many times as acidic as clean rainwater, which has a pH of 5.6, is such a lake?

PROBLEM SOLVING

Problem solving is integrated throughout the program, with many of the exercises providing challenging problems for the students to solve. In addition, a variety of special features are included which promote the development of problem-solving skills.

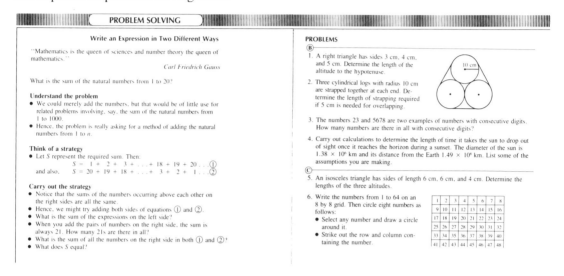

The *PROBLEM SOLVING* feature is a two-page spread in every chapter which extends the strategies that were developed in earlier grades. The problems are graded by difficulty into B, C, and D problems. The B problems may require some ingenuity to solve. The C problems are challenging, and are similar to the problems that are found in mathematics contests. Some of the D problems are extremely difficult, and may approach the level of difficulty of the problems that occur in olympiad competitions. It is not expected that many students will solve the D problems.

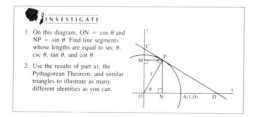

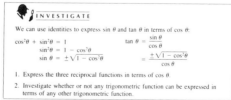

Frequent *INVESTIGATE* features are starting points for mathematical investigations to help the student develop analytic skills. These features always relate to the concepts that are developed in the sections in which they occur.

The *MATHEMATICS AROUND US* features outline applications of mathematics in the sciences, the arts, business, and industry.

MATHEMATICS AROUND US

The Loudness of Sounds

The range of sounds detectable by the human ear is enormous. A rock group can be *10 trillion* times as loud as a leaf rustling in a breeze. The loudness of sounds is measured in units called *decibels* (dB).

> Every increase of 10 dB corresponds to a 10-fold increase in loudness.

For example, the increase from the hum of a refrigerator to an air conditioner is 20 dB. This is 2 increases of 10 dB, so the increase in loudness is $(10)^2$, or 100. Hence, an air conditioner is 100 times as loud as a refrigerator.

The Decibel Scale
Decibels

140 — Jet engine at 25 m

— Jet engine at 100 m
— Threshold of pain
120 —

— Rock group
100 — Chain saw

— Heavy truck
— Average street traffic
80 —

— Air conditioner
60 — Conversational speech

— Refrigerator hum
40 —

— Quiet whisper

20 —

QUESTIONS

1. a) How many times as loud as conversational speech is a chain saw?
   b) How many times as loud as a quiet whisper is a chain saw?

2. Let L_1 and L_2 represent the loudnesses of sounds of S_1 decibels and S_2 decibels respectively. Show that
   $$\frac{L_2}{L_1} = 10^{0.1(S_2 - S_1)}$$
   Use this equation in the questions below.

3. How many times as loud as:
   a) an air conditioner is a heavy truck
   b) a refrigerator hum is average street traffic
   c) average street traffic is a jet at 100 m?

THE MATHEMATICAL MIND features offer insights into the work of mathematicians and the historical development of mathematics. Anecdotes of human interest that are part of history are included. In this feature, problems related to the topic are presented for the student to solve.

THE MATHEMATICAL MIND

The Origin of the Function Concept

The concept of a function originated in the seventeenth century, when scientists and mathematicians became interested in the study of motion.

- Galileo showed that the path of a projectile fired into the air is a parabola.

- The moon's motion was studied because knowledge of its position was used to determine longitude at sea.

Since moving objects follow a single line or a curve, mathematicians thought that a function was defined by a single equation. For example, this definition was given by James Gregory in 1667.

Leonhard Euler 1707–1783

As late as 1734, Leonhard Euler defined a function as any expression formed in any manner from a variable quantity and constants. He also introduced the $f(x)$ notation.

By 1750, scientists studying vibrating strings had encountered an example of a function that could not be defined by a single equation. This caused a controversy over the question of what a function was. Euler extended the definition to include cases where there were different expressions in different intervals of the domain. For example, Euler would have considered the following expression to be a single function.

$$f(x) = \begin{cases} x + 6, & \text{if } x \le -2 \\ x^2, & \text{if } -2 \le x \le 2 \\ x + 2, & \text{if } x \ge 2 \end{cases}$$

Contents

List of symbols and notations

$\mathbb{N}$ the set of natural numbers including zero

$\mathbb{Z}$ the set of integers

$\mathbb{Q}$ the set of rational numbers

$\mathbb{Q}'$ the set of irrational numbers

$\mathbb{R}$ the set of real numbers

$\mathbb{N}^*, \mathbb{Z}^*, \mathbb{Q}^*, \mathbb{R}^*$ the set of numbers excluding zero

$\mathbb{Z}_+, \mathbb{Q}_+, \mathbb{Q}'_+, \mathbb{R}_+$ the set of positive numbers

$\mathbb{Z}_-, \mathbb{Q}_-, \mathbb{Q}'_-, \mathbb{R}_-$ the set of negative numbers

$\mathbb{Z}_+^*, \mathbb{Q}_+^*, \mathbb{R}_+^*$ the set of strictly positive numbers

$\mathbb{Z}_-^*, \mathbb{Q}_-^*, \mathbb{R}_-^*$ the set of strictly negative numbers

$]a, +\infty$ the set of real numbers greater than a

$[a, b]$ the closed interval with endpoints a and b

$]a, b[$ the open interval with endpoints a and b

$-\infty, a[$ the set of real numbers less than a

$]a, b]$ half-open interval

$[a, b[$ half-open interval

$[a, +\infty$ the set of real numbers greater than or equal to a

$-\infty, a]$ the set of real numbers less than or equal to a

$\forall x$ for each $x,\ldots$ for all $x,\ldots$

$|a|$ the absolute value of a

$[a]$ the greatest integer less than or equal to a

$\rightarrow$ if$\ldots$ then$\ldots$

$\leftrightarrow$ if and only if

(a, b) ordered pair

y^{-1} the reciprocal or inverse of y

$f(x)$ the image of x under function f

$f: A \rightarrow B$ f is a function that maps A onto B

$\log$ logarithm to base 10

$\log_b$ logarithm to base b

$\ln$ logarithm to base e

$\overline{AB}$ segment AB

$m\overline{AB}$ the measure of segment AB

$m\angle ABC$ the measure of angle ABC

$\overset{\frown}{AB}$ arc AB

$m\overset{\frown}{AB}$ the measure of arc AB

$\cong$ is congruent to

$\sim$ is similar to

1 Algebraic Operations and Equations

Modern communications systems depend on geosynchronous satellites which are placed in orbit above the equator. Such a satellite is synchronized with the Earth's rotation, and appears to be stationary. Its height and speed are adjusted so that it travels once around the Earth in exactly 24 h. How high should a communications satellite be placed? (See Section 1-6 *Example 3*.)

1-1 FROM RATIONALS TO IRRATIONALS

The followers of the Greek mathematician Pythagoras made a considerable study of numbers. These Pythagoreans were a secret society who combined mathematical investigation with numerology and mysticism. To them is attributed the discovery of many geometrical theorems, as well as the analysis of triangular, square, and other numbers discussed earlier.

The Pythagoreans found points on the number line which do not correspond to any rational numbers. New numbers had to be defined to represent such points. Since they are not rational numbers, they are called irrational numbers.

> An *irrational number* is one that cannot be represented in the form $\dfrac{m}{n}$, where m and n are integers and $n \neq 0$. The decimal expansion of an irrational number neither terminates nor repeats.

The Greeks found several examples of irrational numbers, and it was eventually proved that any number of the form $\sqrt{n}$, where n is not a perfect square, is irrational. An irrational number in this form is called a *radical*.

Example 1. Which of these numbers are irrational?

a) $\sqrt{7}$ b) $\sqrt{144}$ c) $\sqrt{p}$, where p is prime d) $\sqrt{11} - 1$

Solution. a) Since 7 is not a perfect square, $\sqrt{7}$ is irrational.
b) Since $144 = 12^2$, $\sqrt{144} = 12$, which is rational.
c) Primes are not perfect squares, therefore $\sqrt{p}$ is irrational.
d) Since 11 is not a perfect square, $\sqrt{11}$ is irrational. Subtracting 1 does not affect the decimal portion of the expansion of $\sqrt{11}$, therefore $\sqrt{11} - 1$ is irrational.

Example 1 suggests that the result of adding a rational number to, or subtracting it from an irrational number is an irrational number.

Example 2. Show that $\sqrt{2} \times \sqrt{5} = \sqrt{2 \times 5}$

Solution.
$$(\sqrt{2} \times \sqrt{5})^2 = \sqrt{2} \times \sqrt{5} \times \sqrt{2} \times \sqrt{5}$$
$$= (\sqrt{2})^2 \times (\sqrt{5})^2$$
$$= 2 \times 5$$

Take the square root of each side.
$$\sqrt{2} \times \sqrt{5} = \sqrt{2 \times 5}$$

The above result suggests the following property for radicals.

> $$\sqrt{a} \times \sqrt{b} = \sqrt{a \times b} \qquad a, b \geqslant 0$$

The next example applies this property, and shows that the product of two or more irrational numbers is not necessarily irrational.

Example 3. Simplify.

a) $3\sqrt{2} \times 2\sqrt{7}$

b) $5\sqrt{6} \times \sqrt{10} \times 2\sqrt{15}$

Solution.   a) $3\sqrt{2} \times 2\sqrt{7} = 3 \times 2 \times \sqrt{2 \times 7}$
$$= 6\sqrt{14}$$

b) $5\sqrt{6} \times \sqrt{10} \times 2\sqrt{15} = 2 \times 5 \times \sqrt{6 \times 10 \times 15}$
$$= 10\sqrt{900}$$
$$= 10 \times 30$$
$$= 300$$

The same property can be used to express radicals in simplest form.

Example 4. Simplify.

a) $\sqrt{44}$

b) $\sqrt{72}$

Solution.   a) $\sqrt{44} = \sqrt{4 \times 11}$
$$= \sqrt{4} \times \sqrt{11}$$
$$= 2\sqrt{11}$$

b) $\sqrt{72} = \sqrt{36} \times \sqrt{2}$
$$= 6\sqrt{2}$$

Many irrational numbers are not radicals. The best known of the non-radical irrational numbers is the number we denote by π. In 1761, the German mathematician Lambert proved that π was irrational. In 1986, a computer generated a 29 360 129-digit decimal expansion of π and, as expected, it never repeats.

Radicals like $\sqrt{44}$ and $\sqrt{72}$ are known as *entire radicals*, while radicals like $2\sqrt{11}$ and $6\sqrt{2}$ are called *mixed radicals*. It is often necessary to change from one form to the other.

Example 5. Identify each number as a mixed radical or an entire radical, then change it to the other form.

a) $4\sqrt{3}$

b) $\sqrt{18}$

c) $\sqrt{75}$

d) $2\sqrt{5}$

e) $\sqrt{80}$

f) $12\sqrt{3}$

Solution.   a) $4\sqrt{3}$ is a mixed radical.
$$4\sqrt{3} = \sqrt{4} \times \sqrt{4} \times \sqrt{3}$$
$$= \sqrt{48}$$

b) $\sqrt{18}$ is an entire radical.
$$\sqrt{18} = \sqrt{9} \times \sqrt{2}$$
$$= 3\sqrt{2}$$

c) $\sqrt{75}$ is an entire radical.
$$\sqrt{75} = \sqrt{25} \times \sqrt{3}$$
$$= 5\sqrt{3}$$

d) $2\sqrt{5}$ is a mixed radical.
$$2\sqrt{5} = \sqrt{2} \times \sqrt{2} \times \sqrt{5}$$
$$= \sqrt{20}$$

e) $\sqrt{80}$ is an entire radical.
$$\sqrt{80} = \sqrt{16} \times \sqrt{5}$$
$$= 4\sqrt{5}$$

f) $12\sqrt{3}$ is a mixed radical.
$$12\sqrt{3} = \sqrt{12} \times \sqrt{12} \times \sqrt{3}$$
$$= \sqrt{432}$$

EXERCISES 1-1

Ⓐ

1. Which of these numbers are irrational?
   a) $\sqrt{17}$ b) $\sqrt{196}$ c) $\sqrt{21} + 1$ d) $\sqrt{7} + \sqrt{9}$ e) $\sqrt{51} \times \sqrt{51}$

2. Simplify.

   a) $\sqrt{36 + 64}$ b) $\sqrt{2.56}$ c) $\sqrt{0.09}$ d) $\sqrt{\dfrac{49}{81}}$ e) $\sqrt{\dfrac{121}{36}}$

3. Simplify.
   a) $\sqrt{6} \times \sqrt{5}$ b) $\sqrt{7} \times \sqrt{3}$ c) $(8\sqrt{3})(7\sqrt{2})$
   d) $(-5\sqrt{6})(-3\sqrt{7})$ e) $(12\sqrt{7})(-8\sqrt{11})$ f) $(-15\sqrt{7})(-5\sqrt{10})$

4. Simplify.
   a) $\sqrt{18}$ b) $\sqrt{12}$ c) $\sqrt{50}$ d) $\sqrt{80}$ e) $\sqrt{112}$ f) $\sqrt{132}$

5. Simplify.
   a) $2\sqrt{6} \times 5\sqrt{3}$ b) $4\sqrt{5} \times 7\sqrt{10}$ c) $8\sqrt{10} \times 3\sqrt{6}$
   d) $(9\sqrt{15})(-4\sqrt{6})$ e) $(-6\sqrt{6})(5\sqrt{12})$ f) $(-5\sqrt{10})(-7\sqrt{8})$

6. Identify each number as a mixed radical or an entire radical, then change it to its other form.
   a) $\sqrt{32}$ b) $2\sqrt{6}$ c) $\sqrt{98}$ d) $3\sqrt{5}$ e) $\sqrt{320}$ f) $9\sqrt{5}$

Ⓑ

7. Simplify.
   a) $2\sqrt{3} \times 5\sqrt{6} \times 3\sqrt{2}$ b) $4\sqrt{10} \times 6\sqrt{6} \times 3\sqrt{5}$
   c) $3\sqrt{6} \times 2\sqrt{18} \times \sqrt{15}$ d) $(5\sqrt{8})(-3\sqrt{6})(2\sqrt{15})$

8. Estimate.
   a) $\sqrt{30}$ b) $\sqrt{200}$ c) $\sqrt{125}$ d) $\sqrt{0.9}$ e) $\sqrt{150}$ f) $\sqrt{2.52}$

9. Use a calculator to arrange each set in order from least to greatest.
   a) $5\sqrt{2}, 4\sqrt{3}, 3\sqrt{6}, 2\sqrt{14}, 2\sqrt{10}$
   b) $-6\sqrt{2}, -4\sqrt{5}, -2\sqrt{17}, -5\sqrt{3}, -4\sqrt{6}$
   c) $4\sqrt{7}, 5\sqrt{5}, 6\sqrt{3}, 8\sqrt{2}, 3\sqrt{14}$

10. Use the diagram to show that $\sqrt{20} = 2\sqrt{5}$ and $\sqrt{45} = 3\sqrt{5}$.

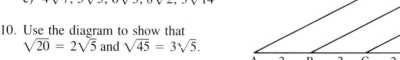

11. P, Q, R, and S are the midpoints of the sides of a square ABCD. If AB $= 4\sqrt{2}$ cm, find the area of PQRS.

Ⓒ

12. Which number of each pair is the greater? (Do not use a calculator.)
   a) $5\sqrt{3}, 6\sqrt{2}$ b) $7\sqrt{2}, 4\sqrt{6}$ c) $3\sqrt{5}, 4\sqrt{3}$
   d) $-8\sqrt{3}, -10\sqrt{2}$ e) $2\sqrt[3]{7}, 3\sqrt[3]{2}$ f) $\dfrac{3}{4}\sqrt{12}, \dfrac{2}{3}\sqrt{14}$

THE MATHEMATICAL MIND

The Dilemma of the Pythagoreans

The Pythagoreans knew how to represent points on a number line by rational numbers. They believed intuitively that since a rational number can be written as a ratio of any two natural numbers, all points on the line can be represented in this way.

However, by the end of the fifth century B.C., the Pythagoreans found a point on the number line that does not correspond to a rational number. They proved that the length of the diagonal of a unit square cannot be written in the form $\frac{m}{n}$. This means there is no rational number for the point P on the number line shown.

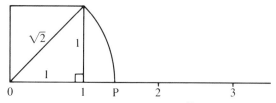

The Pythagoreans proved that $\sqrt{2}$ is not a rational number by the technique known as "indirect proof", or "proof by contradiction". If $\sqrt{2}$ is a rational number, then there are natural numbers m and n such that $\sqrt{2} = \frac{m}{n}$.

Square both sides.

$$(\sqrt{2})^2 = \left(\frac{m}{n}\right)^2$$
$$2 = \frac{m^2}{n^2}$$
$$2n^2 = m^2$$

Since a perfect square has an even number of prime factors, then m^2 has an even number of prime factors and $2n^2$ has an odd number. This is impossible. Therefore, $\sqrt{2}$ cannot be a rational number.

This, then, was the dilemma of the Pythagoreans. The number $\sqrt{2}$ existed because it was the length of the diagonal of a unit square. Yet, they did not see how it could exist since it was not a rational number.

QUESTIONS

1. Prove that $\sqrt{3}$ is irrational by indirect proof.

2. Use the fact that $\sqrt{2}$ is irrational to prove that $\sqrt{2} + 5$ is irrational.

3. Can the length, width, and diagonal of a rectangle all be rational numbers? Explain your answer.

1-2 RADICAL ARITHMETIC

Although the ancient Greeks discovered irrational numbers, they never developed the symbols needed to use radicals. It wasn't until 1525 that the square root symbol appeared, possibly derived from the written letter "r" (for *root*).

To add or subtract radicals, first simplify each radical by extracting all perfect-square factors. Then combine like radicals.

Example 1. Simplify. a) $\sqrt{12} + \sqrt{27}$ b) $3\sqrt{8} + 2\sqrt{3} - 2\sqrt{75} + 4\sqrt{50}$

Solution. a) $\sqrt{12} + \sqrt{27} = \sqrt{4 \times 3} + \sqrt{9 \times 3}$
$$= 2\sqrt{3} + 3\sqrt{3}$$
$$= 5\sqrt{3}$$

b) $3\sqrt{8} + 2\sqrt{3} - 2\sqrt{75} + 4\sqrt{50}$
$$= 3 \times 2\sqrt{2} + 2\sqrt{3} - 2 \times 5\sqrt{3} + 4 \times 5\sqrt{2}$$
$$= 6\sqrt{2} + 20\sqrt{2} + 2\sqrt{3} - 10\sqrt{3}$$
$$= 26\sqrt{2} - 8\sqrt{3}$$

Products involving radicals can be expanded using the distributive law.

Example 2. Expand and simplify.
a) $5\sqrt{2}(2\sqrt{3} - \sqrt{8})$ b) $(5\sqrt{7} - 2\sqrt{3})(\sqrt{7} + 4\sqrt{3})$
c) $(\sqrt{x} - 2)^2$ d) $(3 - 2\sqrt{5})(3 + 2\sqrt{5})$

Solution. a) $5\sqrt{2}(2\sqrt{3} - \sqrt{8}) = 10\sqrt{6} - 5\sqrt{16}$
$$= 10\sqrt{6} - 20$$

b) $(5\sqrt{7} - 2\sqrt{3})(\sqrt{7} + 4\sqrt{3}) = 5(\sqrt{7})^2 + 20\sqrt{21} - 2\sqrt{21} - 8(\sqrt{3})^2$
$$= 35 + 18\sqrt{21} - 24$$
$$= 11 + 18\sqrt{21}$$

c) $(\sqrt{x} - 2)^2 = (\sqrt{x} - 2)(\sqrt{x} - 2)$
$$= (\sqrt{x})^2 - 2\sqrt{x} - 2\sqrt{x} + 4$$
$$= x - 4\sqrt{x} + 4$$

d) $(3 - 2\sqrt{5})(3 + 2\sqrt{5}) = 3^2 - (2\sqrt{5})^2$
$$= 9 - 20$$
$$= -11$$

Example 2d shows that the product of expressions involving radicals can be a rational number.

Division is the inverse of multiplication.

$54 \div 6 = 9$ since $9 \times 6 = 54$

Likewise, $\sqrt{21} \div \sqrt{3} = \sqrt{7}$ since $\sqrt{7} \times \sqrt{3} = \sqrt{21}$

Example 3. Simplify.

a) $\dfrac{\sqrt{76}}{\sqrt{2}}$ b) $\dfrac{12\sqrt{42}}{4\sqrt{6}}$ c) $\dfrac{4\sqrt{90}}{3\sqrt{72}}$

Solution.   a) $\dfrac{\sqrt{76}}{\sqrt{2}} = \sqrt{38}$

b) $\dfrac{12\sqrt{42}}{4\sqrt{6}} = \dfrac{12}{4} \times \sqrt{\dfrac{42}{6}}$

$= 3\sqrt{7}$

c) It is often best to express radicals in simplest form before dividing.

$\dfrac{4\sqrt{90}}{3\sqrt{72}} = \dfrac{4 \times 3\sqrt{10}}{3 \times 6\sqrt{2}}$

$= \dfrac{2\sqrt{10}}{3\sqrt{2}}$

$= \dfrac{2\sqrt{5}}{3}$

Example 4. The time it takes for a pendulum to swing back and forth once depends only on the length of the pendulum. This period T seconds is given by the formula $T = 2\pi\sqrt{\dfrac{l}{9.8}}$, where l is the length of the pendulum in metres. By what factor is the period increased when the pendulum length is tripled?

Solution.   For pendulum length l: $T_1 = 2\pi\sqrt{\dfrac{l}{9.8}}$

$\doteq 2\sqrt{l}$

For pendulum length $3l$: $T_2 = 2\pi\sqrt{\dfrac{3l}{9.8}}$

$\doteq 2\sqrt{3l}$

$\dfrac{T_2}{T_1} = \dfrac{2\sqrt{3l}}{2\sqrt{l}}$

$= \sqrt{3}$

The period is increased by a factor of $\sqrt{3}$ when the length of the pendulum is tripled.

EXERCISES 1-2

(A)

1. Simplify.
   a) $\sqrt{20} + \sqrt{5}$ b) $\sqrt{12} + \sqrt{3}$ c) $2\sqrt{18} - \sqrt{2}$
   d) $3\sqrt{7} + 5\sqrt{28}$ e) $3\sqrt{40} + 2\sqrt{10}$ f) $5\sqrt{48} - 11\sqrt{3}$

2. Simplify.
   a) $\sqrt{50} - \sqrt{18}$ b) $\sqrt{12} + \sqrt{75}$ c) $\sqrt{24} + \sqrt{54}$
   d) $\sqrt{8} - \sqrt{32}$ e) $\sqrt{175} + \sqrt{63}$ f) $\sqrt{80} - \sqrt{45}$

3. Simplify.
   a) $5\sqrt{12} - 2\sqrt{48}$ b) $7\sqrt{24} + 3\sqrt{96}$ c) $8\sqrt{63} - 3\sqrt{175}$
   d) $9\sqrt{32} - 12\sqrt{18}$ e) $11\sqrt{54} + 6\sqrt{150}$ f) $7\sqrt{20} - 6\sqrt{45}$

4. Simplify.
   a) $\sqrt{3}(\sqrt{5} + \sqrt{7})$ b) $4\sqrt{3}(7\sqrt{2} - 3\sqrt{5})$ c) $5\sqrt{6}(2\sqrt{a} + 4\sqrt{b})$
   d) $9\sqrt{5}(2\sqrt{15} - 7\sqrt{3})$ e) $2\sqrt{y}(4\sqrt{2} - 3\sqrt{y})$ f) $7\sqrt{2}(3\sqrt{18} + 2\sqrt{2})$

5. Simplify.
   a) $(\sqrt{3} + \sqrt{5})(2\sqrt{3} - \sqrt{5})$ b) $(2\sqrt{5} - 3\sqrt{7})(\sqrt{5} + 2\sqrt{7})$
   c) $(3\sqrt{x} - 2\sqrt{y})(5\sqrt{x} + 3\sqrt{y})$ d) $(2\sqrt{3} - 3\sqrt{2})(4\sqrt{3} - \sqrt{2})$
   e) $(4\sqrt{6} + 2\sqrt{3})(7\sqrt{6} + 4\sqrt{3})$ f) $(8\sqrt{m} - 3\sqrt{n})(2\sqrt{m} - 5\sqrt{n})$

6. Simplify.
   a) $\dfrac{24\sqrt{14}}{8\sqrt{2}}$ b) $\dfrac{-15\sqrt{30}}{45\sqrt{6}}$ c) $\dfrac{18\sqrt{39}}{-6\sqrt{3}}$ d) $\dfrac{54\sqrt{70}}{9\sqrt{5}}$
   e) $\dfrac{36\sqrt{22}}{-90\sqrt{2}}$ f) $\dfrac{60\sqrt{51}}{-4\sqrt{3}}$ g) $\dfrac{32\sqrt{35}}{4\sqrt{7}}$ h) $\dfrac{28\sqrt{55}}{42\sqrt{11}}$

(B)

7. Simplify.
   a) $4\sqrt{45} + 3\sqrt{80} - 11\sqrt{20}$ b) $3\sqrt{50} + 6\sqrt{32} - 4\sqrt{18}$
   c) $2\sqrt{150} - 5\sqrt{54} - 3\sqrt{24}$ d) $5\sqrt{18} + 6\sqrt{8} - 2\sqrt{32}$
   e) $3\sqrt{40} - 5\sqrt{90} - 2\sqrt{160}$ f) $9\sqrt{45} + 5\sqrt{125} - 6\sqrt{245}$

8. Simplify.
   a) $3\sqrt{2}(4\sqrt{7} - 5\sqrt{2})$ b) $6\sqrt{3}(3\sqrt{12} - 2\sqrt{75})$
   c) $-5\sqrt{6}(2\sqrt{3} - 3\sqrt{2})$ d) $4\sqrt{3}(3\sqrt{6} + 2\sqrt{7} - 5\sqrt{3})$
   e) $5\sqrt{a}(\sqrt{18} + 7\sqrt{a} - 5\sqrt{8})$ f) $8\sqrt{b}(4\sqrt{2} - 2\sqrt{3} - 3\sqrt{b})$

9. Simplify.
   a) $(\sqrt{5} + \sqrt{2})(\sqrt{5} - \sqrt{2})$ b) $(3\sqrt{m} - 2\sqrt{n})(3\sqrt{m} + 2\sqrt{n})$
   c) $(4\sqrt{6} + 8\sqrt{2})(4\sqrt{6} - 8\sqrt{2})$ d) $(5\sqrt{2} - 3\sqrt{6})^2$
   e) $(7\sqrt{x} + 4\sqrt{y})^2$ f) $2\sqrt{2}(3\sqrt{3} + 5\sqrt{7})^2$

10. Simplify.

a) $\dfrac{12\sqrt{20}}{3\sqrt{5}}$

b) $\dfrac{18\sqrt{24}}{-3\sqrt{8}}$

c) $\dfrac{-24\sqrt{45}}{72\sqrt{20}}$

d) $\dfrac{-30\sqrt{40}}{-5\sqrt{18}}$

e) $\dfrac{45\sqrt{54}}{18\sqrt{12}}$

f) $\dfrac{-60\sqrt{96}}{12\sqrt{27}}$

g) $\dfrac{12\sqrt{40}}{8\sqrt{45}}$

h) $\dfrac{15\sqrt{84}}{10\sqrt{63}}$

11. From a height of h metres, the distance d kilometres to the horizon is given by the formula $d \doteq 3.6\sqrt{h}$.
   a) By what factor is the distance to the horizon increased when:
      i) the height is doubled
      ii) the height is tripled?
   b) By what factor must the height be increased so that the distance to the horizon is doubled?

12. The period of a pendulum T seconds is given by the formula $T = 2\pi\sqrt{\dfrac{l}{9.8}}$, where l is the length of the pendulum in metres.
   a) By what factor is the period increased when the length is:
      i) quadrupled
      ii) increased fivefold?
   b) By what factor must the length be increased for the period:
      i) to triple
      ii) to increase by a factor of $2\sqrt{2}$?

Ⓒ

13. When at rest, a meson decays radioactively in t_0 μs (microsecond). At a speed v, the time for decay is increased to t μs where $t = \dfrac{t_0}{\sqrt{1 - \left(\dfrac{v}{c}\right)^2}}$, c being the speed of light. By what factor is the decay time increased when the meson is travelling at half the speed of light?

14. a) By substituting convenient values for a and b, show that, in general, $\sqrt{a} + \sqrt{b} \neq \sqrt{a + b}$.
   b) Are there any values of a and b such that $\sqrt{a} + \sqrt{b} = \sqrt{a + b}$?

 INVESTIGATE

If n is a perfect square, what is the next perfect square?

1-3 RATIONALIZING THE DENOMINATOR

When radicals were first used, mathematicians quickly discovered that not all expressions with radicals in the denominator, such as $\dfrac{5}{\sqrt{2}}$, could be simplified by division. The division operation was impossible to perform because the divisor was an infinite non-repeating decimal. So, they rewrote the expression, multiplying numerator and denominator by the radical in the denominator. This makes the denominator a rational number.

$$\frac{5}{\sqrt{2}} = \frac{5}{\sqrt{2}} \times \frac{\sqrt{2}}{\sqrt{2}} \qquad \text{Equivalent to}$$
$$\text{multiplying by 1.}$$
$$= \frac{5\sqrt{2}}{2}$$

This procedure is called *rationalizing the denominator*.

Example 1. Rationalize the denominator.

a) $\dfrac{3}{\sqrt{6}}$ b) $\dfrac{2}{\sqrt{18}}$ c) $\dfrac{3\sqrt{2} - 5}{\sqrt{2}}$

Solution.

a) $\dfrac{3}{\sqrt{6}} = \dfrac{3}{\sqrt{6}} \times \dfrac{\sqrt{6}}{\sqrt{6}}$

$= 3\dfrac{\sqrt{6}}{6}$

$= \dfrac{\sqrt{6}}{2}$

b) $\dfrac{2}{\sqrt{18}} = \dfrac{2}{3\sqrt{2}}$

$= \dfrac{2}{3\sqrt{2}} \times \dfrac{\sqrt{2}}{\sqrt{2}}$

$= \dfrac{2\sqrt{2}}{6}$

$= \dfrac{\sqrt{2}}{3}$

c) $\dfrac{3\sqrt{2} - 5}{\sqrt{2}} = \dfrac{3\sqrt{2} - 5}{\sqrt{2}} \times \dfrac{\sqrt{2}}{\sqrt{2}}$

$= \dfrac{6 - 5\sqrt{2}}{2}$

$= 3 - \dfrac{5}{2}\sqrt{2}$

In *Example 2d)* of the previous section, we found that the result of simplifying $(3 - 2\sqrt{5})(3 + 2\sqrt{5})$ was -11, a rational number. $(3 - 2\sqrt{5})$ and $(3 + 2\sqrt{5})$ are called *conjugates*, and the fact that the product of conjugates is a rational number can be used to simplify expressions having binomial denominators with radical terms.

Example 2. Simplify.

a) $\dfrac{14}{3 + \sqrt{2}}$ b) $\dfrac{3\sqrt{2} - 2\sqrt{5}}{2\sqrt{2} - \sqrt{5}}$

Solution. a) The conjugate of $3 + \sqrt{2}$ is $3 - \sqrt{2}$. Multiply the numerator and the denominator by $3 - \sqrt{2}$.

$$\frac{14}{3 + \sqrt{2}} = \frac{14}{3 + \sqrt{2}} \times \frac{3 - \sqrt{2}}{3 - \sqrt{2}}$$

$$= \frac{14(3 - \sqrt{2})}{9 - 2}$$

$$= 2(3 - \sqrt{2})$$

$$= 6 - 2\sqrt{2}$$

b) Multiply the numerator and the denominator by $2\sqrt{2} + \sqrt{5}$.

$$\frac{3\sqrt{2} - 2\sqrt{5}}{2\sqrt{2} - \sqrt{5}} = \frac{3\sqrt{2} - 2\sqrt{5}}{2\sqrt{2} - \sqrt{5}} \times \frac{2\sqrt{2} + \sqrt{5}}{2\sqrt{2} + \sqrt{5}}$$

$$= \frac{12 + 3\sqrt{10} - 4\sqrt{10} - 10}{8 - 5}$$

$$= \frac{2 - \sqrt{10}}{3}$$

When the denominator contains algebraic expressions involving radicals, the same methods can be used to write an equivalent expression with no radicals in the denominator. The resulting denominator is not necessarily a rational number.

Example 3. Write an equivalent expression with no radicals in the denominator.

a) $\dfrac{3}{\sqrt{x}}, x \neq 0$ 　　　　　　b) $\dfrac{2x}{\sqrt{x} - y}, \sqrt{x} \neq y$

Solution. a) $\dfrac{3}{\sqrt{x}} = \dfrac{3}{\sqrt{x}} \times \dfrac{\sqrt{x}}{\sqrt{x}}$ 　　b) $\dfrac{2x}{\sqrt{x} - y} = \dfrac{2x}{\sqrt{x} - y} \times \dfrac{\sqrt{x} + y}{\sqrt{x} + y}$

$$= \frac{3\sqrt{x}}{x} \qquad\qquad\qquad = \frac{2x(\sqrt{x} + y)}{x - y^2}$$

EXERCISES 1-3

Ⓐ

1. Rationalize the denominator.

a) $\dfrac{2}{\sqrt{5}}$ 　　b) $\dfrac{7}{\sqrt{11}}$ 　　c) $\dfrac{-4}{\sqrt{3}}$ 　　d) $\dfrac{5\sqrt{2}}{\sqrt{7}}$

e) $\dfrac{6\sqrt{10}}{-\sqrt{3}}$ 　　f) $\dfrac{12\sqrt{7}}{7\sqrt{5}}$ 　　g) $\dfrac{18\sqrt{5}}{3\sqrt{2}}$ 　　h) $\dfrac{20\sqrt{7}}{-4\sqrt{3}}$

2. Express in simplest form.

a) $\dfrac{3\sqrt{6}}{\sqrt{20}}$ 　　b) $\dfrac{4\sqrt{5}}{\sqrt{8}}$ 　　c) $\dfrac{-9\sqrt{12}}{\sqrt{18}}$ 　　d) $\dfrac{15\sqrt{3}}{3\sqrt{8}}$

e) $\dfrac{-24\sqrt{7}}{-3\sqrt{12}}$ 　　f) $\dfrac{14\sqrt{3}}{2\sqrt{28}}$ 　　g) $\dfrac{20\sqrt{24}}{3\sqrt{20}}$ 　　h) $\dfrac{36\sqrt{18}}{8\sqrt{8}}$

(B)

3. Simplify.

a) $\dfrac{2\sqrt{3} + 4}{\sqrt{3}}$

b) $\dfrac{5\sqrt{7} - 3}{\sqrt{7}}$

c) $\dfrac{4\sqrt{5} - 2}{\sqrt{5}}$

d) $\dfrac{6\sqrt{2} - \sqrt{3}}{\sqrt{3}}$

e) $\dfrac{8\sqrt{6} + \sqrt{5}}{\sqrt{5}}$

f) $\dfrac{3\sqrt{10} - \sqrt{2}}{\sqrt{2}}$

g) $\dfrac{5\sqrt{8} + 2\sqrt{3}}{\sqrt{6}}$

h) $\dfrac{3\sqrt{12} - 4\sqrt{3}}{2\sqrt{2}}$

4. Rationalize the denominator.

a) $\dfrac{\sqrt{3}}{\sqrt{5} - \sqrt{2}}$

b) $\dfrac{\sqrt{5}}{\sqrt{7} + \sqrt{3}}$

c) $\dfrac{\sqrt{11}}{8 - \sqrt{5}}$

d) $\dfrac{2\sqrt{5}}{\sqrt{6} + \sqrt{3}}$

e) $\dfrac{5\sqrt{6}}{\sqrt{12} - 5}$

f) $\dfrac{4\sqrt{7}}{\sqrt{15} - \sqrt{10}}$

g) $\dfrac{6\sqrt{3}}{5 + \sqrt{2}}$

h) $\dfrac{9\sqrt{5}}{\sqrt{11} - \sqrt{5}}$

5. Simplify.

a) $\dfrac{3\sqrt{2} + \sqrt{3}}{2\sqrt{3} + \sqrt{2}}$

b) $\dfrac{5\sqrt{3} + \sqrt{2}}{2\sqrt{3} - \sqrt{2}}$

c) $\dfrac{5\sqrt{3} - 3\sqrt{5}}{\sqrt{5} - \sqrt{3}}$

d) $\dfrac{3 + 2\sqrt{5}}{3\sqrt{5} - 4}$

e) $\dfrac{2\sqrt{7} - 4\sqrt{3}}{3\sqrt{7} + \sqrt{3}}$

f) $\dfrac{\sqrt{7} + 3\sqrt{2}}{9 + 2\sqrt{14}}$

6. Find an equivalent expression with no radicals in the denominator.

a) $\dfrac{5x}{\sqrt{y}}$

b) $\dfrac{3\sqrt{m}}{\sqrt{m} - n}$

c) $\dfrac{3}{\sqrt{2a + b}}$

d) $\dfrac{x}{\sqrt{x} + 1}$

e) $\dfrac{2\sqrt{3}}{\sqrt{2x} - 1}$

f) $\dfrac{-1}{3 - \sqrt{x}}$

g) $\dfrac{2a}{\sqrt{5} - \sqrt{a}}$

h) $\dfrac{5x}{\sqrt{x} + \sqrt{3}}$

(C)

7. Rationalize the denominator of the reciprocal.

a) $\sqrt{2}$

b) $\sqrt{12}$

c) $\sqrt{50}$

d) $\sqrt{2} - 1$

e) $\sqrt{3} + \sqrt{2}$

f) $2\sqrt{5} - 3\sqrt{2}$

8. Simplify.

a) $\dfrac{1}{2 + \sqrt{3}} + \dfrac{1}{2 - \sqrt{3}}$

b) $\dfrac{3}{\sqrt{5} - \sqrt{2}} - \dfrac{1}{\sqrt{5} + \sqrt{2}}$

c) $\dfrac{6}{\sqrt{2}} + \dfrac{2}{\sqrt{2} + 1}$

d) $\dfrac{1}{\sqrt{x} - \sqrt{y}} + \dfrac{1}{\sqrt{x} + \sqrt{y}}$

e) $\dfrac{m}{\sqrt{m} - \sqrt{n}} - \dfrac{m}{\sqrt{m} + \sqrt{n}}$

f) $\dfrac{4a}{\sqrt{2a} - b} - \dfrac{a}{\sqrt{2a} + b}$

9. Rationalize the numerator.

a) $\dfrac{\sqrt{2}}{4}$

b) $\dfrac{\sqrt{5}}{3}$

c) $\dfrac{\sqrt{x}}{xy}$

d) $\dfrac{\sqrt{x} + 1}{x}$

e) $\dfrac{\sqrt{a} + 2\sqrt{b}}{\sqrt{a}}$

f) $\dfrac{-\sqrt{m} + 2n}{\sqrt{m} - \sqrt{n}}$

g) $\dfrac{\sqrt{x} - \sqrt{y}}{\sqrt{x} + \sqrt{y}}$

h) $\dfrac{2\sqrt{a} - 3\sqrt{b}}{2\sqrt{a} + 3\sqrt{b}}$

1-4 THE REAL NUMBERS

In the fifth century B.C., the Pythagoreans found points on the number line that did not correspond to rational numbers. In the nineteenth century A.D., mathematicians wondered if there were points on the number line with no corresponding decimals. It wasn't until 1876 that the German mathematician Richard Dedekind proved that every point on the number line has a corresponding decimal, and conversely, every decimal corresponds to a point on the number line.

> All numbers that can be represented by decimals are real numbers. These numbers correspond to every point on the number line.

This diagram shows how the various types of numbers are related.

The Real Numbers

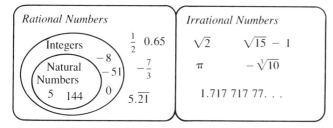

Example.   Classify each number as rational or irrational.

a) $7.3\overline{756}$ b) $0.010\ 010\ 001\ 000\ 010\ \ldots$ c) $\dfrac{\sqrt{3}}{\sqrt{48}}$ d) 7π

Solution.   a) $7.3\overline{756}$ is a repeating decimal and therefore a rational number.
b) The digits follow a pattern, but a non-repeating pattern.
   $0.010\ 010\ 001\ 000\ 010\ \ldots$ is irrational.

c) $\dfrac{\sqrt{3}}{\sqrt{48}} = \sqrt{\dfrac{1}{16}}$

   $= \dfrac{1}{4}$, which is rational

d) If 7π were rational, we could write $7\pi = \dfrac{a}{b}$, where a and b are natural numbers.
   It would follow that $\pi = \dfrac{a}{7b}$, which is rational. But π is irrational.

   Therefore, 7π cannot be rational; it is irrational.

EXERCISES 1-4

Ⓐ

1. Which numbers appear to be irrational?
   a) 2.363 663 666 3 . . .
   b) −0.123 456 78 . . .
   c) 1.407 240 724 . . .
   d) 5.312 312 231 . . .
   e) −17.717 171 71 . . .
   f) 4.925 925 92 . . .
   g) 8.069 069 069 . . .
   h) −24.734 659 28 . . .

2. Which numbers are irrational?
   a) $\sqrt{34}$
   b) $\sqrt{256}$
   c) $\sqrt{36 + 49}$
   d) $2\sqrt{18} - \sqrt{3}$
   e) $\sqrt{25 + 56}$
   f) $\sqrt{6.25}$
   g) $\sqrt{16} - \sqrt{12}$
   h) $\sqrt{\dfrac{65}{9}}$
   i) $7 - \sqrt{169}$

3. Which numbers are rational and which are irrational?
   a) 0.010 120 230 123 4 . . .
   b) 3.131 313 131 313 . . .
   c) −1.357 957 957 957 . . .
   d) 0.707 007 000 700 . . .
   e) 2.179 652 389 57 . . .
   f) −5.246 810 121 4 . . .

Ⓑ

4. To which of the sets of numbers listed does each number belong?
   a) $\sqrt{37}$
   b) $-5.1\overline{62}$
   c) $\sqrt{169}$
   d) $-2.357\ 911\ 13$ . . .
   e) $-\dfrac{29}{5}$
   f) $\sqrt{2}$
   g) $\sqrt{49 + 16}$
   h) $\sqrt{48} - \sqrt{18}$

   | Natural numbers, $\mathbb{N}$ |
   | Integers, $\mathbb{Z}$ |
   | Rational numbers, $\mathbb{Q}$ |
   | Irrational numbers, $\mathbb{Q}'$ |
   | Real numbers, $\mathbb{R}$ |

5. Using the [√] key on a calculator, $\sqrt{5} = 2.236\ 067\ 9$. This is a rational number, but $\sqrt{5}$ is irrational. Can a number be both rational and irrational? Explain.

6. Find a rational number and an irrational number between each pair of numbers.
   a) $2.\overline{5791}$ and $2.\overline{5792}$
   b) $-6.\overline{327}$ and $-6.327\ 332\ 733\ 2$ . . .
   c) $4.190\ 119\ 011\ 190$ . . . and $4.190\ 219\ 021\ 190$ . . .

Ⓒ

7. Using the [√] key on a calculator, $\sqrt{0.444\ 444\ 4} = 0.666\ 666\ 6$
   a) Write fractions in the form $\dfrac{m}{n}$ for 0.444 444 4 and 0.666 666 6, and use them to explain the calculator result.
   b) Find another number which gives a similar result.

8. The solution of $3x + 12 = 3$ is real, rational, and an integer. Describe the solution(s) of each equation.
   a) $3x + 5 = 17$
   b) $19 + 6x = 7$
   c) $5 + 4x = 11$
   d) $x^2 + 3 = 12$
   e) $x^2 + 1 = 4$
   f) $x^2 + 4 = 1$

1-5 SOLVING QUADRATIC EQUATIONS

Have you ever wondered how high you would have to go to be able to see from one coast of Canada to the other? If you were in Vancouver, the answer to this question, h kilometres, is the positive root of the equation $h^2 + 12\,740h - 20\,000\,000 = 0$. If you were in Winnipeg, the equation to solve is $h^2 + 12\,740h - 6\,000\,000 = 0$. These are examples of *quadratic equations*.

Quadratic equations without a first-degree term can always be reduced to the form $x^2 = c$. The solution is completed by taking the square root of both sides.

Example 1.   Solve the equation $3.5x^2 = 9.1$. Express the roots to three decimal places.

Solution. $3.5x^2 = 9.1$
Divide both sides by 3.5.
$$x^2 = 2.6$$
$$x = \pm\sqrt{2.6}$$
$$\doteq \pm 1.612$$

Quadratic equations usually have first-degree terms, and many of these equations can be solved by factoring.

Example 2.   Solve.

a) $x^2 - x - 12 = 0$ b) $4t^2 - 20t + 25 = 0$

Solution.   a) $x^2 - x - 12 = 0$
$(x - 4)(x + 3) = 0$
Either $x - 4 = 0$ or $x + 3 = 0$
$x = 4$ $x = -3$

b) $4t^2 - 20t + 25 = 0$
$(2t - 5)(2t - 5) = 0$
$2t - 5 = 0$
$t = 2.5$

In *Example 1* and *Example 2a*, the quadratic equations have two different roots. In *Example 2b*, we say that the quadratic equation has two equal roots.

Many quadratic equations cannot be solved by factoring. But all quadratic equations can be solved using the method of *completing the square*.

Example 3.   Solve. $x^2 + 8x + 2 = 0$

Solution. $x^2 + 8x + 2 = 0$

Isolate the constant term.

$$x^2 + 8x = -2$$

Add the square of one-half the coefficient of x to both sides.

$$x^2 + 8x + 16 = -2 + 16$$
$$(x + 4)^2 = 14$$

Take the square root of both sides.

$$x + 4 = \pm\sqrt{14}$$
$$x = -4 \pm \sqrt{14}$$

The method of completing the square can be used to prove the formula for solving any quadratic equation.

Given:

The general quadratic equation $ax^2 + bx + c = 0$, where $a \neq 0$

Required to Prove:

$$x = \frac{-b \pm \sqrt{b^2 - 4ac}}{2a}$$

Proof:

Statement	Reason
$ax^2 + bx + c = 0$	
$x^2 + \dfrac{b}{a}x + \dfrac{c}{a} = 0$	Dividing both sides by a
$x^2 + \dfrac{b}{a}x = -\dfrac{c}{a}$	Isolating the constant term
$x^2 + \dfrac{bx}{a} + \dfrac{b^2}{4a^2} = \dfrac{b^2}{4a^2} - \dfrac{c}{a}$	Completing the square on the left side, and adding the same term to the right side
$\left(x + \dfrac{b}{2a}\right)^2 = \dfrac{b^2 - 4ac}{4a^2}$	Writing the left side as a complete square
$x + \dfrac{b}{2a} = \pm\dfrac{\sqrt{b^2 - 4ac}}{2a}$	Taking the square root of both sides
$x = \dfrac{-b}{2a} \pm \dfrac{\sqrt{b^2 - 4ac}}{2a}$	
$x = \dfrac{-b \pm \sqrt{b^2 - 4ac}}{2a}$	

This result is called the quadratic formula.

Quadratic Formula

The roots of the equation $ax^2 + bx + c = 0$ are $x = \dfrac{-b \pm \sqrt{b^2 - 4ac}}{2a}$.

Example 4. Find the roots of each equation.

a) $9x^2 - 12x + 2 = 0$ b) $9x^2 - 12x + 3 = 0$

c) $9x^2 - 12x + 4 = 0$ d) $9x^2 - 12x + 5 = 0$

Solution. Compare each equation with the general equation $ax^2 + bx + c = 0$.

a) $9x^2 - 12x + 2 = 0$ $a = 9, b = -12, c = 2$

$$x = \frac{-b \pm \sqrt{b^2 - 4ac}}{2a}$$

$$= \frac{-(-12) \pm \sqrt{(-12)^2 - 4(9)(2)}}{2(9)}$$

$$= \frac{12 \pm \sqrt{72}}{18}$$

$$= \frac{12 \pm 6\sqrt{2}}{18}$$

$$= \frac{2 \pm \sqrt{2}}{3}$$

The roots of the equation are $\dfrac{2 + \sqrt{2}}{3}$ and $\dfrac{2 - \sqrt{2}}{3}$.

b) $9x^2 - 12x + 3 = 0$ $a = 9, b = -12, c = 3$

$$x = \frac{-(-12) \pm \sqrt{(-12)^2 - 4(9)(3)}}{2(9)}$$

$$= \frac{12 \pm \sqrt{36}}{18}$$

$$= \frac{12 \pm 6}{18}$$

$$= 1 \text{ or } \frac{1}{3}$$

The roots are 1 and $\dfrac{1}{3}$.

c) $9x^2 - 12x + 4 = 0$ $a = 9, b = -12, c = 4$

$$x = \frac{-(-12) \pm \sqrt{(-12)^2 - 4(9)(4)}}{2(9)}$$

$$= \frac{12 \pm 0}{18}$$

$$= \frac{2}{3}$$

The equation has two equal roots, $\dfrac{2}{3}$.

d) $9x^2 - 12x + 5 = 0$

$a = 9, b = -12, c = 5$

$$x = \frac{-(-12) \pm \sqrt{(-12)^2 - 4(9)(5)}}{2(9)}$$

$$= \frac{12 \pm \sqrt{-36}}{18}$$

Since the square root of a negative number is not defined as a real number, the equation has no real roots.

As *Example 4* suggests, the number under the radical sign indicates the types of roots the equation has. The quantity $b^2 - 4ac$ in the quadratic formula is called the *discriminant* of the quadratic equation. This quantity is denoted D, and it is named for discriminating among the three cases that can occur.

Nature of the Roots of a Quadratic Equation
The roots of the quadratic equation $ax^2 + bx + c = 0$, $a \neq 0$, are:

$$x = \frac{-b \pm \sqrt{D}}{2a}, \text{ where } D = b^2 - 4ac \text{ is the discriminant}$$

If $D > 0$, there are two distinct real roots.
If $D = 0$, there is only one real root, called a double root.
If $D < 0$, the roots are not real numbers.

Example 5. Determine the nature of the roots of $2x^2 - 7x + 3 = 0$.

Solution. The nature of the roots is determined by the value of the discriminant
$D = b^2 - 4ac$.
$2x^2 - 7x + 3 = 0$
$a = 2, b = -7, c = 3$
$D = b^2 - 4ac$
$\quad = (-7)^2 - 4(2)(3)$
$\quad = 49 - 24$
$\quad = 25 > 0$
Since $D > 0$, there are two distinct real roots.

It is worth noting that when D is a perfect square, then $\sqrt{D}$ is a rational number. Hence, the two roots are rational numbers. Furthermore, this implies that if we were required to solve the equation, it could be done by factoring.

For *Example 5*, D is 25, which is a perfect square. Solving $2x^2 - 7x + 3 = 0$ in two ways:

By factoring

$$2x^2 - 7x + 3 = 0$$
$$(x - 3)(2x - 1) = 0$$
$$x = 3 \text{ or } x = \frac{1}{2}$$

By using the formula

$$x = \frac{-(-7) \pm \sqrt{25}}{2(2)}$$
$$= \frac{7 \pm 5}{4}$$
$$x = 3 \text{ or } x = \frac{1}{2}$$

Example 6. Find a quadratic equation with roots -2 and 5.

Solution. Let r and s represent the roots of the equation $ax^2 + bx + c = 0$.
Then $x - r$ and $x - s$ are factors of $ax^2 + bx + c$.
Hence, $ax^2 + bx + c = a(x - r)(x - s)$
Substitute $r = -2$ and $s = 5$.
$(x + 2)(x - 5) = x^2 - 3x - 10$
So $x^2 - 3x - 10 = 0$ has roots -2 and 5.

In *Example 6*, the equation is in its simplest form. Any equation of the form $a(x^2 - 3x - 10) = 0$, $a \neq 0$ has roots -2 and 5.

EXERCISES 1-5

(A)

1. Solve, expressing the roots to 2 decimal places.
   a) $6x^2 = 45$
   b) $5.8c^2 - 29 = 0$
   c) $2.7t^2 - 13.77 = 0$

2. Solve by factoring.
   a) $x^2 - 9x + 14 = 0$
   b) $m^2 - 2m = 15$
   c) $2x^2 + 11x + 15 = 0$
   d) $5t^2 - 11t = 12$

3. Solve by using the quadratic formula.
   a) $x^2 - 4x + 1 = 0$
   b) $2x^2 - 11x + 10 = 0$
   c) $4x^2 + 7x + 5 = 0$

4. Solve.
   a) $x^2 - 24x - 112 = 0$
   b) $12a^2 - 25a - 7 = 0$
   c) $5x^2 + 4x - 1 = 0$
   d) $2x^2 - 4x + 5 = 0$
   e) $\dfrac{1}{x} + \dfrac{x}{2} = \dfrac{3}{2}$
   f) $\dfrac{3}{x + 1} - \dfrac{3}{4} = \dfrac{x - 1}{3x + 1}$

5. In the open sea, the distance between the waves, the wavelength L metres, is approximated by the formula $L = 0.64v^2$, where v is the velocity in metres per second of the waves.
   a) What is the wavelength when the velocity is: i) 2 m/s   ii) 3 m/s?
   b) What is the velocity to 1 decimal place when the wavelength is:
      i) 10 m   ii) 15 m?

6. The speed with which water flows out of a hole at the bottom of a reservoir is related to the depth of the water. According to Torricelli's theorem, $d \doteq 0.05s^2$, where d is the depth of the water in metres and s is the speed in metres per second. What is the speed, to 1 decimal place, of the water if the depth is:
   a) 1 m   b) 2 m   c) 5 m?

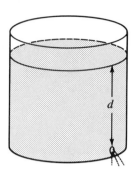

(B)

7. Determine the nature of the roots of each equation.
   a) $3x^2 + 7x + 4 = 0$ b) $2x^2 + 3x - 8 = 0$ c) $5x^2 - x + 2 = 0$
   d) $4x^2 + 12x + 9 = 0$ e) $2x^2 - 9x - 5 = 0$ f) $3x^2 + 4x + 7 = 0$

8. Write a quadratic equation with these roots.
   a) $3, 7$ b) $-4, 9$ c) $\frac{2}{3}, -5$ d) $-\frac{1}{2}, -\frac{3}{4}$ e) $0, -\frac{3}{2}$ f) $2 + \sqrt{5}, 2 - \sqrt{5}$

9. For what value(s) of k does each equation have two equal real roots?
   a) $3x^2 - kx + 8 = 0$ b) $5x^2 + 8x - 2k = 0$ c) $kx^2 + 9 = 18x$

10. For what value(s) of m does each equation have a double root?
    a) $2x^2 + mx + 9 = 0$ b) $5mx^2 + 6x + 2 = 0$ c) $4x^2 - 2mx + 3 = 0$

11. Find a value of k so that each quadratic equation can be solved by factoring.
    a) $x^2 + kx + 12 = 0$ b) $kx^2 + 12x + 9 = 0$ c) $x^2 - 3x = k$

12. Solve the equations given on page 15 to determine how high you would have to go until you could see from one coast of Canada to the other coast:
    a) from above Vancouver   b) from above Winnipeg.

(C)

13. In a certain programming language, the instruction CALL—856 executes a delay loop of length t microseconds, where $t = 2.5x^2 + 13.5x + 13$, and x is a number stored in memory. What number x should be stored to have a delay loop of length: a) 1 s   b) 30 s?

14. A square with sides of length 6 cm is divided into 3 right triangles and a larger isosceles triangle. The three right triangles have equal areas.
    a) Find the value of x.
    b) Find the area of the larger isosceles triangle.

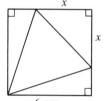

6 cm

15. Explain why the equation $(x - 1)^2 + (x + 1)^2 = 0$ has no real roots.

16. Determine whether or not there are any real numbers x and y with the property that the reciprocal of their sum is equal to the sum of their reciprocals.

1-6 SOLVING RADICAL EQUATIONS

The design of a domed stadium calls for a roof which is part of a sphere. If the diameter of the base of the stadium is 200 m, and the roof is 75 m above the centre of the playing field, what is the radius of the sphere?

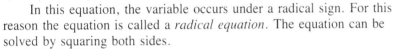

    This problem can be answered by solving the following equation for r, where h is the height of the roof, and c is the diameter of the base.

$$\sqrt{4h(2r - h)} = c$$

Substitute 200 for c and 75 for h.

$$\sqrt{300(2r - 75)} = 200$$

    In this equation, the variable occurs under a radical sign. For this reason the equation is called a *radical equation*. The equation can be solved by squaring both sides.

$$(\sqrt{300(2r - 75)})^2 = 200^2$$
$$300(2r - 75) = 40\ 000$$
$$6r - 225 = 400$$
$$6r = 625$$
$$r \doteq 104.2$$

The radius of the sphere is approximately 104 m.

    The steps used in solving the above equation are used to solve other radical equations.

Example 1. Solve.

  a) $\sqrt{x - 3} - 3 = 0$ b) $\sqrt{x - 3} + 3 = 0$

Solution.

a) $\sqrt{x - 3} - 3 = 0$
Isolate the radical.
$$\sqrt{x - 3} = 3$$
Square both sides.
$$(\sqrt{x - 3})^2 = 3^2$$
$$x - 3 = 9$$
$$x = 12$$

b) $\sqrt{x - 3} + 3 = 0$
Isolate the radical.
$$\sqrt{x - 3} = -3$$
Square both sides.
$$(\sqrt{x - 3})^2 = (-3)^2$$
$$x - 3 = 9$$
$$x = 12$$

Check.

When $x = 12$,
L.S. $= \sqrt{x - 3} - 3$
$= \sqrt{9} - 3$
$= 0$
R.S. $= 0$
The solution is correct.
That is, 12 is the only root of the equation
$\sqrt{x - 3} - 3 = 0$.

When $x = 12$,
L.S. $= \sqrt{x - 3} + 3$
$= \sqrt{9} + 3$
$= 6$
R.S. $= 0$
The solution is not correct.
That is, 12 is not a root of the equation $\sqrt{x - 3} + 3 = 0$. This equation has no real roots.

In *Example 1b* we could have predicted that the equation has no real roots. Since the radical sign always denotes the positive square root, it is impossible for the left side of the equation, $\sqrt{x-3}+3$, to be equal to 0. This example shows that the operation of squaring both sides of an equation may lead to numbers that do not satisfy the original equation. These are called *extraneous roots*. They are roots of the equation that was obtained after squaring, but they are not roots of the original equation.

Extraneous roots are often introduced when you square both sides of an equation. For this reason, you must identify extraneous roots.

To solve a radical equation, follow these steps.
Step 1. Isolate the radical on one side of the equation.
Step 2. Square both sides of the equation.
Step 3. Identify extraneous roots and reject them.

Example 2. Solve.

a) $4 + \sqrt{2+x} = x$ b) $4 - \sqrt{2+x} = x$

Solution.   a) $4 + \sqrt{2+x} = x$

Isolate the radical.
$$\sqrt{2+x} = x - 4$$
Square both sides.
$$(\sqrt{2+x})^2 = (x-4)^2$$
$$2 + x = x^2 - 8x + 16$$
$$x^2 - 9x + 14 = 0$$
$$(x-7)(x-2) = 0$$
Either $x - 7 = 0$ or $x - 2 = 0$
$$x = 7 \qquad\qquad x = 2$$

Check.

When $x = 7$,
L.S. $= 4 + \sqrt{2+7}$
$ = 4 + 3$
$ = 7$
R.S. $= 7$
7 is a root.

When $x = 2$,
L.S. $= 4 + \sqrt{2+2}$
$ = 4 + 2$
$ = 6$
R.S. $= 2$
2 is an extraneous root.

The equation has only one root, $x = 7$.

b) $4 - \sqrt{2+x} = x$

Isolate the radical.
$$-\sqrt{2+x} = x - 4$$
Square both sides.
$$(-\sqrt{2+x})^2 = (x-4)^2$$
$$2 + x = x^2 - 8x + 16$$
The same equation was obtained in part a), and the solution from here on is the same. The possible roots are 7 and 2.

Check.

When $x = 7$,
L.S. $= 4 - \sqrt{2 + 7}$
$= 4 - 3$
$= 1$
R.S. $= 7$
7 is an extraneous root.

When $x = 2$,
L.S. $= 4 - \sqrt{2 + 2}$
$= 4 - 2$
$= 2$
R.S. $= 2$
2 is a root.

The equation has only one root, $x = 2$.

In *Example 2*, the extraneous roots were identified by checking the possible roots obtained. Another method is to identify the possible values of x after the radical has been isolated. For example, this equation was obtained in *Example 2a*, $\sqrt{2 + x} = x - 4$.
Since the left side of the equation cannot be negative, the right side cannot be negative either. This introduces a restriction on x, namely, $x - 4 \geq 0$, or $x \geq 4$. From this point on, the solution is valid only if $x \geq 4$. Since 2 was one of the possible roots, it can then be rejected. If this method is used, it is not necessary to check the roots.

Example 3. When a satellite is h kilometres above the Earth the period, or time for one complete orbit, T minutes is given by this formula.
$T = 1.66 \times 10^{-4} \sqrt{(6370 + h)^3}$.
How high should a satellite be placed above the equator so that it always appears to be above the same point on the ground? Give your answer to the nearest hundred kilometres.

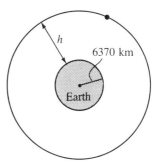

Solution. The period of the satellite has to equal the period of the Earth's rotation, which is 24 h, or 1440 min.
Substitute 1440 for T in the formula.
$$1440 = 1.66 \times 10^{-4} \sqrt{(6370 + h)^3}$$
Isolate the radical.
$$\frac{1440}{1.66 \times 10^{-4}} = \sqrt{(6370 + h)^3}$$
Since the left side is positive, there are no restrictions on h.
Therefore, there are no extraneous roots.
Square both sides.
$7.525\ 039\ 9 \times 10^{13} = (6370 + h)^3$
Solve by taking the cube root of both sides.
$$42\ 219 = 6370 + h$$
$$35\ 849 = h$$
To the nearest hundred kilometres, the satellite should be placed 35 800 km above the ground.

EXERCISES 1-6

1. Solve.
   a) $\sqrt{3x + 1} = 7$ b) $\sqrt{2x + 7} = 5$
   c) $2\sqrt{x} = 8$ d) $12\sqrt{x} = 30$
   e) $\sqrt{x} + 3 = 4$ f) $\sqrt{x} - 6 = -3$

2. Solve.
   a) $\sqrt{x + 2} - 5 = 0$ b) $\sqrt{x - 4} - 7 = 0$
   c) $\sqrt{2x + 7} - 9 = 0$ d) $\sqrt{2x + 1} + 5 = 8$
   e) $\sqrt{7x - 3} - 2 = 3$ f) $\sqrt{3x - 1} + 7 = 10$

3. Solve.
   a) $2 = 3\sqrt{2x - 5}$ b) $\sqrt{5x + 2} - 3 = 1$
   c) $-2\sqrt{6x + 1} = 14$ d) $5 + \sqrt{4x - 3} = 9$
   e) $-7 + 5\sqrt{2x + 3} = 8$ f) $-3\sqrt{2x + 1} + 5 = -4$

4. Determine, by inspection, which of the following equations have extraneous roots.
   a) $\sqrt{x + 3} + 5 = 0$ b) $\sqrt{3x - 2} - 2 = 3$
   c) $4 + \sqrt{2x - 7} = 0$ d) $-4 + \sqrt{3x + 1} = 0$
   e) $7 + 5\sqrt{2x + 3} = 4$ f) $3\sqrt{x + 1} + 2 = 8$

Ⓑ

5. The formula for the length d of the diagonal of a rectangle with sides of length a and b is $d = \sqrt{a^2 + b^2}$. Solve the formula for a.

6. Solve.
   a) $4\sqrt{2x + 7} - 5 = 7$ b) $4 + 2\sqrt{5x - 3} = 12$
   c) $3 + 4\sqrt{8x - 3} = 15$ d) $-5\sqrt{8x - 4} + 3 = 18$
   e) $7\sqrt{9x + 12} - 5 = 16$ f) $-20 + 6\sqrt{2x + 17} = -2$

7. Solve.
   a) $x + \sqrt{x - 5} = 7$ b) $x - \sqrt{x - 5} = 7$
   c) $\sqrt{x + 7} + 5 = x$ d) $\sqrt{x^2 + 3} = x + 1$
   e) $6 - \sqrt{x + 6} = x$ f) $\sqrt{x - 2} - x = -8$

8. Solve.
   a) $x + \sqrt{3 + x} = 3$ b) $x - \sqrt{2x - 5} = 4$
   c) $1 + \sqrt{6 - 2x} = x + 2$ d) $5 + \sqrt{x + 1} = 2x + 1$
   e) $\sqrt{3x + 4} + 9 = 2x$ f) $x + \sqrt{3x + 1} = 9$

9. Solve.
   a) $x - 3 = \sqrt{3x - 11}$ b) $2\sqrt{5 - 4x} + x = 3$
   c) $3\sqrt{2x + 9} - x = 7$ d) $\sqrt{2x + 7} + x - 4 = 10$
   e) $2x - \sqrt{4x + 1} = 7$ f) $\sqrt{3x + 4} + x = 12$

10. At the scene of an accident, police can estimate the speed a car had been travelling by the length of the skid marks. One formula used for this purpose is $v = -7 + 8.2\sqrt{d}$, where v is the speed in kilometres per hour and d is the length of the skid marks in metres.
    a) Solve the formula for d.
    b) How long would be the skid marks of a car braking from:
       i)   60 km/h   ii)   90 km/h   iii)   120 km/h?
    c) What was the speed of the car if the length of its skid marks were:
       i)   50 m   ii)   100 m   iii)   150 m?

11. Solve for the variable indicated.

    a) $T = 2\pi\sqrt{\dfrac{l}{g}}$, l

    b) $u = \sqrt{v^2 - 2as}$, a

    c) $V = \sqrt{\dfrac{2gE}{W}}$, W

    d) $m = \dfrac{M}{\sqrt{1 - \dfrac{v^2}{c^2}}}$, c

    e) $v = \sqrt{\dfrac{F}{mk} - u^2}$, k

    f) $e = \sqrt{\dfrac{h^2 - 2ma^2E}{2ma}}$, E

12. The total surface area A of a cone with base radius r and height h is given by the formula $A = \pi r(r + \sqrt{r^2 + h^2})$. Solve this formula for h.

13. In $\triangle ABC$, $\angle B = 90°$, and AB is 1 cm longer than BC. If the perimeter of the triangle is 70 cm, find the lengths of the three sides.

Ⓒ
14. Solve the equation $x - 7\sqrt{x} + 12 = 0$ in two different ways.
    a) As a radical equation   b) As a quadratic equation in $\sqrt{x}$

15. The diagram shows a sector of a circle with radius r. If h is as defined on the diagram, then the chord length c is given by this formula.
$c = \sqrt{4h(2r - h)}$
Solve the formula for h.

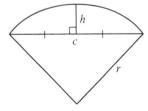

16. Check the results of *Exercise 15* as follows.
    a) Substitute the value of c which would result if the sector were a semicircle.
    b) Determine a condition that must be satisfied by r and c.

17. Without solving, find 3 equations that have no real roots.
    a) $\sqrt{x - 5} = 8 - x$
    b) $\sqrt{2x + 10} = -2 - x$
    c) $2x - 12 = \sqrt{17 - 3x}$
    d) $\sqrt{-7 - 3x} = 5x + 4$
    e) $4 + \sqrt{6 - 20x} = 10x$
    f) $-100x = \sqrt{15x - 1.5} - 11$

18. Explain the difference between an equation having extraneous roots and one having no real roots. Illustrate your answer with specific examples.

1-7 SOLVING POLYNOMIAL EQUATIONS BY GRAPHING

When we drop a stone into a well, a certain amount of time passes before we hear it hit the water. The time interval t seconds for a well 100 m deep can be calculated from this equation.

$0.015t^3 - 4.9t^2 + 100 = 0$

This is an example of a cubic equation. Quadratic and cubic equations are special cases of a more general type of equation called a *polynomial equation*. Here are some other examples of polynomial equations.

Quartic equation (fourth degree): $x^4 + 2x^3 - 6x^2 + 3x + 1 = 0$

Quintic equation (fifth degree): $3x^5 + 2x^4 - 5x^2 - 3 = 0$

Polynomial equations with a cubic term, such as $x^3 - 12x + 8 = 0$, first appeared in Babylonian tablets dated about 2000 B.C. Although the Babylonians lacked a general technique for solving such equations, they developed numerical methods for solving certain types of cubic equations. During the last four thousand years, a number of different methods have been developed to solve such equations. The most useful method is one that has been employed only recently — in most practical applications, computers are now used to solve polynomial equations.

One method of solving a polynomial equation is to use a grid. When the graph of the polynomial expression is plotted, the expression equals zero where the graph intersects the *x*-axis.

Example 1.   Solve by graphing. $x^3 - 12x + 8 = 0$

Solution.   Let $y = x^3 - 12x + 8$. Make a table of values for various values of x, plot the ordered pairs (x,y) on a grid, and draw a smooth curve through them.

x	y
-5	-57
-4	-8
-3	17
-2	24
-1	19
0	8
1	-3
2	-8
3	-1
4	24
5	73

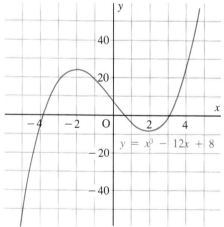

The expression is equal to 0 where the graph intersects the *x*-axis. The roots of the equation $x^3 - 12x + 8 = 0$ are approximately -3.8, 0.7, and 3.1.

Example 2. Solve graphically. a) $x^3 - 12x - 16 = 0$ b) $x^3 - 12x + 32 = 0$

Solution. Compare the given equation with the equation in *Example 1*.

a) Since the constant term in $y = x^3 - 12x - 16$ is 24 less than the constant term in $y = x^3 - 12x + 8$, the table of values can be written directly. Each y-value for $y = x^3 - 12x - 16$ is 24 less than the corresponding y-value for $y = x^3 - 12x + 8$.

b) Similarly, each y-value for $y = x^3 - 12x + 32$ is 24 greater than the corresponding y-value for $y = x^3 - 12x + 8$.

Plot the ordered pairs and draw the graphs.

	a)	b)
x	y	y
-5	-81	-33
-4	-32	16
-3	-7	41
-2	0	48
-1	-5	43
0	-16	32
1	-27	21
2	-32	16
3	-25	23
4	0	48
5	49	97

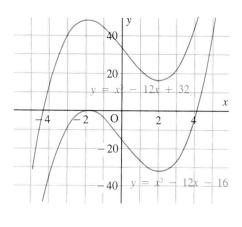

a) The graph of $y = x^3 - 12x - 16$ appears to cross the x-axis at one point and touch it at another. The equation $x^3 - 12x - 16 = 0$ has three real roots, two of which are equal: -2, -2, and 4.

b) The graph of $y = x^3 - 12x + 32$ intersects the x-axis at only one point. The equation $x^3 - 12x + 32 = 0$ has one real root, which is approximately -4.4.

Example 3. Solve graphically. $x^4 - 20x^2 + 10x + 30 = 0$

Solution. Make a table of values for the equation $y = x^4 - 20x^2 + 10x + 30$ and graph the ordered pairs.

x	y
-5	105
-4	-74
-3	-99
-2	-54
-1	1
0	30
1	21
2	-14
3	-39
4	6

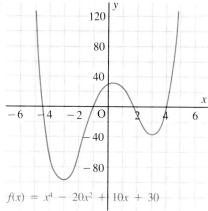

The roots of the equation $x^4 - 20x^2 + 10x + 30 = 0$ are approximately $-4.6, -1.0, 1.6,$ and 3.9. There are four real roots.

EXERCISES 1-7

Ⓐ

1. Use the graph to estimate the root(s) of the equation.

   a) $x^3 + 2x^2 - 10 = 0$

   b) $-x^3 - 3x^2 + 5x + 16 = 0$

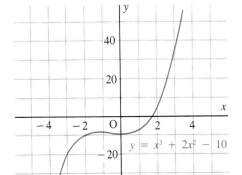

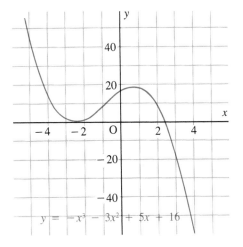

   c) $x^4 - 10x^2 - 5x + 5 = 0$

   d) $x^5 - 10x^3 + 15x = 0$

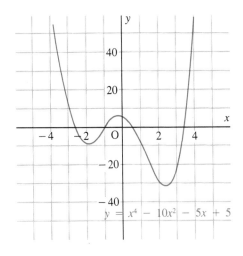

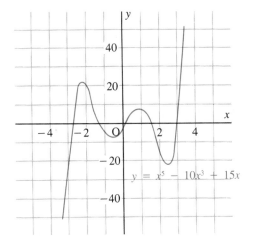

Ⓑ

2. Solve graphically.

   a) $x^3 - 10x = 0$

   b) $x^3 - 10x + 12 = 0$

   c) $x^3 - 10x - 12 = 0$

   d) $x^3 - 10x - 24 = 0$

3. Solve graphically.
   a) $x^3 - 15x - 10 = 0$ b) $x^3 + x - 15 = 0$
   c) $x^4 - 15x^2 + 20 = 0$ d) $x^4 - 5x^2 - 10x - 25 = 0$

4. Use a graph to find the x-intercepts of the graph of each function.
   a) $f(x) = x^3 + 10x - 20$ b) $f(x) = x^3 - 3x^2 + x - 10$
   c) $f(x) = x^4 - 10x^2 + 5x + 7$ d) $f(x) = x^4 - 4x^3 + 16x - 25$

5. In *Exercise 1 b)*, is it possible to tell for certain if there are two equal negative roots? If there are not two equal negative roots, then what other possibilities are there for this equation?

6. Explain why every cubic equation has at least one real root.

7. Sketch an example of a cubic function which has:
   a) three equal roots
   b) two equal roots and a third root which is less than they are
   c) two equal roots and a third root which is greater than they are
   d) one real root

8. Sketch an example of a quartic function which has:
   a) four equal roots
   b) two pairs of two equal roots
   c) one pair of equal roots and two other real roots
   d) one pair of equal roots

9. Solve the equation on page 26 to determine how long it is between dropping a stone into a well 100 m deep and hearing the stone hit the water.

10. It is given that the equations $x^3 - 12x + 16 = 0$ and $x^3 - 12x - 16 = 0$ both have two different real roots.
    a) Which of the equations below have:
       i) three different real roots   ii) only one real root?
       $$x^3 - 12x + 20 = 0 \qquad x^3 - 12x + 10 = 0 \qquad x^3 - 12x - 20 = 0$$
    b) For what values of k does the equation $x^3 - 12x + k = 0$ have:
       i) 3 different real roots   ii) 2 different real roots   iii) only 1 real root?

Ⓒ

11. A Babylonian tablet gives the values of $n^3 + n^2$ for integral values of n from 1 to 30.
    a) Make a table of values for $n = 1$ to 10.
    b) Use your table to find a root of the equation $x^3 + 2x^2 = 441$.
    c) Determine whether or not the equation $x^3 + 2x^2 = 441$ has any other real roots.

12. Individual packets of juice measure 6.4 cm by 3.8 cm by 10.3 cm. The packets contain 250 mL of juice. The manufacturer plans to introduce a new line of juice in packets containing twice as much juice. If each dimension of the original packets is increased by the same amount, find the dimensions of the new packets.

10.3 cm
6.4 cm   3.8 cm

USING TECHNOLOGY

Graphical Solutions

Mathematical Models

When solving problems dealing with real-world phenomena, it is often helpful to construct a model to help us visualize what is happening. This model may be a solid object such as a wind tunnel or an airplane cockpit simulator.

Sometimes the model we construct may be semi-abstract such as a computer program that uses animation. These programs are often helpful, for example, to demonstrate chemistry experiments.

At other times, the model is abstract and consists of an equation or a set of equations. In creating these equations we define the relationships between two or more components of the real-world problem we are studying. Sometimes the relationships are easy to define; for example, the equation relating the amount of money A invested, the annual rate of interest R, and the amount of money P at the end of one year: $P = A(1 + R)$. Often, the relationships are difficult to define; for example, the various forces that cause a liquid to cool or an airplane to withstand the stresses of flight.

It is important to be able to manipulate the equations of our model both algebraically and graphically. Graphing calculators have many helpful features that can be used to analyze graphs of equations.

Temperature Readings

The relationship between the temperature readings on the Celsius (C) and Fahrenheit (F) scales is given by $C = \frac{5}{9}(F - 32)$ and $F = \frac{9}{5}C + 32$.

a) Enter $Y_1 = \frac{5}{9}(X - 32)$ on the functions menu of your graphing calculator. With the TRACE feature find the Fahrenheit temperatures equivalent to $-20°C$, $-10°C$, $0°C$, $10°C$, and $20°C$. You will have to adjust the settings for the viewing window of your calculator.

b) The boiling point of water at sea level is $100°C$. What is this reading on the Fahrenheit scale?

Enter $Y_2 = \frac{9}{5}X + 32$ on the functions menu and display both Y_1 and Y_2 on the same screen.

c) At what temperature is the reading the same on both scales?

d) What reading on the Fahrenheit scale is twice the reading on the Celsius scale?

e) What reading on the Celsius scale is twice the reading on the Fahrenheit scale?

f) Verify your answers to b), c), d) and e) algebraically.

Solving Equations

Previously, we have found the roots of a polynomial equation $f(x) = 0$ by graphing $y = f(x)$ and observing the points at which the graph crossed the x-axis. In effect, we were discovering the points of intersection of the two functions $Y_1 = f(x)$ and $Y_2 = 0$.

To solve the equation $2x - 1 = 5$ graphically, the left side of the equation can be entered as Y_1 and the right side as Y_2 on the functions menu. These two separate functions, $Y_1 = 2x - 1$ and $Y_2 = 5$, are graphed on the same screen. The point of intersection $(3, 5)$ indicates the solution $(x = 3)$ to the equation.

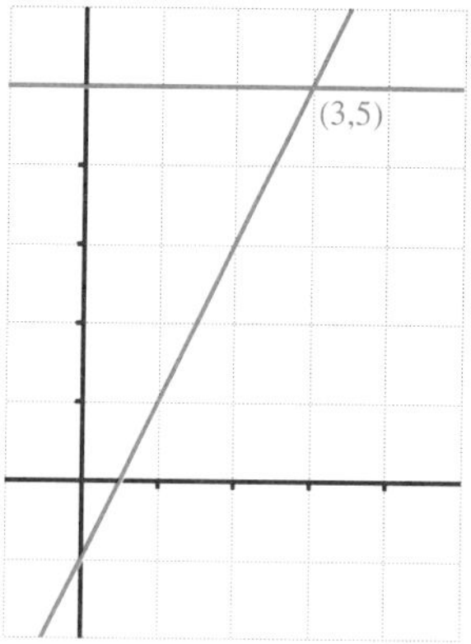

Solve each equation graphically by the method shown above. Verify each solution algebraically.

a) $2x - 1 = 7$

b) $2x - 2 = -x + 4$

c) $6x + 9 = 4x + 15$

d) $4(13 + 2x) = 3(4x + 1)$

e) $\sqrt{3x + 1} = 5$

f) $\sqrt{x + 1} = x - 5$

Average Marks

A student has marks of 64 and 78 on recent math tests. What mark on a third test would give the student an average of 60? 80? 90?

Let x represent the mark on the third test.

The average of the 3 marks is $\dfrac{64 + 78 + x}{3}$.

To find the mark needed to obtain an average of 60, we solve the equation $\dfrac{64 + 78 + x}{3} = 60$. In a similar way, we can find the marks needed to obtain averages of 80 and 90.

An interesting way to solve this problem graphically is to enter $Y_1 = \dfrac{64 + 78 + x}{3}$, $Y_2 = 60$, $Y_3 = 80$, and $Y_4 = 90$ on the functions menu of your graphing calculator.

a) Adjust the viewing window to be $[-1, 150]$ by $[-1, 100]$. Graph Y_1, Y_2, Y_3, and Y_4 together on your screen. Use the TRACE feature and position the screen cursor to determine the mark needed in the third test for each average value.

b) What is the maximum average the student can obtain on these three tests?

c) What is the minimum average?

MATHEMATICS AROUND US

The Waggle Dance of Honeybees

In 1973, Karl von Frisch received a Nobel Prize for his research in animal behaviour. One of his discoveries concerns a method used by honeybees to communicate the location of a food source to other bees inside a hive. Von Frisch observed bees returning to the hive when they had discovered a food source. Shortly after a bee returned, hundreds of bees left the hive, and went directly to the food source, although the bee which had found the food remained inside the hive. Somehow, the bee had informed the others where the food was located.

By marking the bees with paint, and using glass-walled hives, von Frisch learned how they do this. The bee which found the food performs a dance on the honeycomb inside the hive. It follows a figure-8 pattern and wags its body in the central part. Von Frisch observed that:

- the orientation of the central portion indicates the direction of the food source,
- the speed of the dance indicates the distance to the food.

Von Frisch made thousands of observations, comparing the speeds of the bees' dances with the distances to the food, and summarized his results on a graph like the one shown.

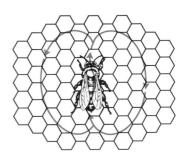

QUESTIONS

1. If the food is 1 km away, how many complete cycles does the bee make in 15 s? in 1 min?

2. If the bee makes 10 complete cycles in one minute, how far away is the food?

3. How would the graph differ if it were drawn to show the number of complete cycles in one minute instead of 15 s?

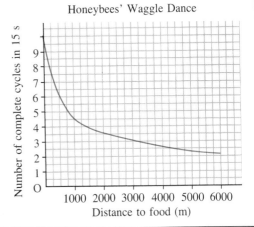

Honeybees' Waggle Dance

1-8 SOLVING POLYNOMIAL EQUATIONS BY FACTORING

Although there are formulas for solving cubic and quartic equations, they involve cube and fourth roots, and are too complicated to be of practical significance. There are no formulas for solving polynomial equations of degree higher than the fourth. (See *THE MATHEMATICAL MIND*, page 37.)

Some polynomial equations can be solved by factoring.

Example 1. Solve for x. $x^3 - x = 0$

Solution.   The left side of the equation has a common factor.
$$x^3 - x = 0$$
$$x(x^2 - 1) = 0$$
$$x(x - 1)(x + 1) = 0$$
Either $x = 0$ or $x - 1 = 0$ or $x + 1 = 0$
$$x = 1 \qquad\qquad x = -1$$

Example 2. Solve for x. $x^3 - 3x^2 - 4x + 12 = 0$

Solution.   We recognize that the left side can be factored by grouping because a factor of $x - 3$ remains when common factors are removed from the first two terms and from the last two terms.
$$x^3 - 3x^2 - 4x + 12 = 0$$
$$x^2(x - 3) - 4(x - 3) = 0$$
$$(x - 3)(x^2 - 4) = 0$$
$$(x - 3)(x + 2)(x - 2) = 0$$
Either $x - 3 = 0$ or $x + 2 = 0$ or $x - 2 = 0$
$$x = 3 \qquad\qquad x = -2 \qquad\qquad x = 2$$

Example 3. Solve for x. $x^3 + 9x^2 + 13x + 5 = 0$

Solution.   Since grouping does not produce a common factor, we try the factor theorem.

Let $f(x) = x^3 + 9x^2 + 13x + 5$.

The factors of 5 are ± 1 and ± 5.

By inspection, we see that $f(1) \neq 0$. All the terms are positive and hence cannot have a sum of zero.
$$f(-1) = (-1)^3 + 9(-1)^2 + 13(-1) + 5$$
$$= -1 + 9 - 13 + 5$$
$$= 0$$
Since $f(-1) = 0$, $x + 1$ is a factor of the left side of the given equation. Also, 5 is the last term in the quadratic factor. The quadratic factor can be found by long division, or by equating coefficients.

Let $(x + 1)(x^2 + bx + 5) = x^3 + 9x^2 + 13x + 5$.

The term containing x is $5x + bx$ on the left side, and $13x$ on the right side. Since the coefficients are equal,
$$5 + b = 13$$
$$b = 8$$
Therefore, the given equation can be written in the form
$$(x + 1)(x^2 + 8x + 5) = 0$$
Either $x + 1 = 0$ or $x^2 + 8x + 5 = 0$
$$x = -1$$
$$x = \frac{-8 \pm \sqrt{8^2 - 4(1)(5)}}{2}$$
$$= \frac{-8 \pm \sqrt{64 - 20}}{2}$$
$$= \frac{-8 \pm \sqrt{44}}{2}$$
$$= -4 \pm \sqrt{11}$$

Example 4.   Solve for x. $x^3 + 1 = 0$

Solution.   The left side of the equation is a sum of cubes.
$$x^3 + 1 = 0$$
$$(x + 1)(x^2 - x + 1) = 0$$
Either $x + 1 = 0$ or $x^2 - x + 1 = 0$
$$x = -1$$
$$x = \frac{1 \pm \sqrt{(-1)^2 - 4(1)(1)}}{2}$$
$$= \frac{1 \pm \sqrt{-3}}{2}$$
There is only one root, $x = -1$, in the set of real numbers.

Example 5.   A rectangular piece of cardboard measuring 10 cm by 8 cm is made into an open box by cutting squares from the corners and turning up the sides. If the box is to hold a volume of 48 cm³, what size of square must be removed?

Solution.   Draw a diagram.
Let the side of the square to be removed be represented by x centimetres. Then the volume of the box is given by this expression.
$$V = x(10 - 2x)(8 - 2x)$$
Since the volume is 48 cm³,
$$x(10 - 2x)(8 - 2x) = 48$$
$$4x(5 - x)(4 - x) = 48$$
$$x(20 - 9x + x^2) = 12$$
$$x^3 - 9x^2 + 20x = 12$$
$$x^3 - 9x^2 + 20x - 12 = 0 \quad \cdots \text{①}$$

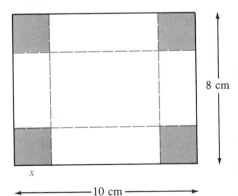

Solve using the factor theorem.
Let $f(x) = x^3 - 9x^2 + 20x - 12$.

$$f(1) = 1^3 - 9(1)^2 + 20(1) - 12$$
$$= 1 - 9 + 20 - 12$$
$$= 0$$

Since $f(1) = 0$, $x - 1$ is a factor of the left side of equation ①. The other factors can be found by division, by inspection, or by using the factor theorem again.

$$f(2) = 2^3 - 9(2)^2 + 20(2) - 12$$
$$= 8 - 36 + 40 - 12$$
$$= 0$$

Since $f(2) = 0$, $x - 2$ is a factor of the left side of equation ①.
Since $x - 1$ and $x - 2$ are factors, using the factor property the third factor has the form $x - a$, where

$$(-1)(-2)(-a) = -12$$
$$a = 6$$

Therefore, the third factor is $x - 6$.
That is, the equation may be written $(x - 1)(x - 2)(x - 6) = 0$.
Either $x = 1$, $x = 2$, or $x = 6$

When $x = 1$, the dimensions of the box are 8 cm by 6 cm by 1 cm, and it has a volume of 48 cm³.

When $x = 2$, the dimensions are 6 cm by 4 cm by 2 cm, and the volume is also 48 cm³.

It is impossible for x to be 6 since four squares with sides of this length cannot be cut from the cardboard.

Therefore, four squares with 1 cm sides, or four squares with 2 cm sides can be removed to form a box with a volume of 48 cm³.

As the above examples suggest, only certain polynomial equations can be solved by factoring. More general methods are needed to solve other polynomial equations.

EXERCISES 1-8

1. Solve for x.
   a) $x(x - 2)(x + 5) = 0$
   b) $x(2x + 3)(x - 4) = 0$
   c) $x(x^2 + 10x + 21) = 0$
   d) $x(6x^2 + 5x - 21) = 0$
   e) $x^3 - 4x = 0$
   f) $2x^3 + 10x^2 + 12x = 0$

2. a) One root of each equation below is the same for every equation. What is this root?
   i) $10x^3 - 25x^2 - 15x = 0$
   ii) $12x^3 = 27x$
   iii) $6x^3 + 45x = 33x^2$
   iv) $3x^4 + 14x^3 + 8x^2 = 0$
   v) $18x^4 - 50x^2 = 0$
   vi) $35x^2 - 5x^3 = 60x$
   b) Find the other roots of each equation in part a).

Ⓑ

3. Solve.
   a) $x^3 - 2x^2 + 3x - 6 = 0$
   b) $x^3 + 5x^2 - 9x - 45 = 0$
   c) $2x^3 - 3x^2 - 11x + 6 = 0$
   d) $3x^3 - 2x^2 - 12x + 8 = 0$

4. Solve.
   a) $x^3 + 3x^2 - 10x - 24 = 0$
   b) $x^3 - x^2 + 9x - 9 = 0$
   c) $2x^3 - 3x^2 - 5x + 6 = 0$
   d) $8x^3 + 4x^2 - 18x - 9 = 0$

5. Solve.
   a) $x^3 + x - 10 = 0$
   b) $2x^3 - 4x^2 - 18x + 36 = 0$
   c) $2x^3 + 10x^2 + 13x + 5 = 0$
   d) $3x^3 - 2x^2 + 75x - 50 = 0$

6. Find three consecutive integers with a product of: a) -24 b) -120.

7. What number and its cube differ by: a) 24 b) -120?

8. A rectangular piece of cardboard measuring 12 cm by 8 cm is made into an open box by cutting squares from the corners and turning up the sides. If the volume of the box is 60 cm³, what are its dimensions?

Ⓒ

9. The product of the squares of two consecutive integers is 256 036. Find the integers.

10. Write a polynomial equation with these roots.
    a) 2, 5, 1
    b) $-1, 2 + \sqrt{3}, 2 - \sqrt{3}$
    c) $-\dfrac{1}{2}, 3, -3, 1$
    d) $-1, \dfrac{3 + 2\sqrt{5}}{2}, \dfrac{3 - 2\sqrt{5}}{2}$

11. If one root is 2, find each value of k, and the other roots.
    a) $2x^3 - 13x^2 + kx + 10 = 0$
    b) $25x^4 + kx^2 + 16 = 0$
    c) $3x^3 - 15x^2 + kx - 4 = 0$
    d) $3x^4 - kx^3 + 49x^2 - 23x - 14 = 0$

12. Solve.
    a) $3x^4 - 15x^2 + 12 = 0$
    b) $\dfrac{3}{x^2} + \dfrac{2x}{x + 2} = \dfrac{3x}{x + 2} + \dfrac{1}{x^2}$

13. The diagrams show the first four pyramidal numbers. The number of balls in each layer of the pyramids is a perfect square. An expression for the nth pyramidal number is $\dfrac{n(n + 1)(2n + 1)}{6}$.

     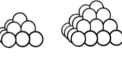

    a) Verify that the expression is correct by using it to find the number of balls in the pyramids shown in the diagrams.
    b) The only pyramidal number (other than 1) which is a perfect square is 4900. How many layers are in the pyramid for this number?

THE MATHEMATICAL MIND

The Cubic Equation Controversy

One of the most important mathematical achievements of the sixteenth century was the discovery by Italian mathematicians of formulas for the solution of cubic and quartic equations. This accomplishment occurred at a time when discoveries were often kept secret, and rivals were challenged to solve the same problem.

About 1510, a professor at the University of Bologna revealed to a student a method he had found of solving cubic equations without a quadratic term, such as $x^3 + 5x = 8$.

Nicolo Tartaglia
1499-1557

In 1535, when Nicolo Tartaglia claimed to have found a method of solving cubic equations without a linear term, such as $x^3 + 2x^2 = 6$, the former student challenged him to a public equation-solving contest. But before the contest, Tartaglia learned how to solve an equation of the first type as well, and he won the contest triumphantly.

Tartaglia knew that, by substituting $y - \dfrac{b}{3a}$ for x, any cubic equation

$ax^3 + bx^2 + cx + d = 0$ could be reduced to the form $y^3 + my = n$.

He proved that a root of this equation is

$$y = \sqrt[3]{\sqrt{\left(\frac{m}{3}\right)^3 + \left(\frac{n}{2}\right)^2} + \frac{n}{2}} - \sqrt[3]{\sqrt{\left(\frac{m}{3}\right)^3 + \left(\frac{n}{2}\right)^2} - \frac{n}{2}}.$$

Girolamo Cardano
1501-1576

Later, Girolamo Cardano urged Tartaglia to show him his method. When Cardano promised to keep it secret, Tartaglia gave it to him. But in 1545 Cardano published his *Ars Magna*, a Latin text on algebra, and included Tartaglia's solution of cubic equations. When Tartaglia protested the breach of his promise, Cardano claimed to have received his information from another party, and accused Tartaglia of plagiarism from the same source. There followed a bitter dispute between the two men over the question of who was the first to discover the formula for solving cubic equations.

Tartaglia's solution gave only one root, and later mathematicians found improved solutions. They also discovered formulas for quartic equations. Much work was done attempting to find a formula for quintic equations, but without success. This was proved to be impossible in 1824 by the Norwegian mathematician, Niels Henrik Abel.

QUESTIONS

1. Use a calculator and the formula given above to solve these cubic equations. Verify each solution.
   a) $y^3 + 6y = 2$
   b) $y^3 + 4y + 3 = 0$
   c) $x^3 - 3x^2 + 5x + 4 = 0$

PROBLEM SOLVING

The Most Famous Problem in Mathematics

"I have discovered a truly marvelous demonstration of this proposition which this margin is too narrow to contain."

Pierre de Fermat

Pierre de Fermat was one of the great mathematicians of the seventeenth century. He had the habit of writing his results, often without the proofs, in the margins of his books. Therefore, his successors had to discover the proofs for themselves. But there is one result that no one has been able to prove, and because of the above quotation in which Fermat claimed to have a proof, this problem has become perhaps the most famous problem in mathematics. It is called Fermat's Last Theorem.

Fermat's Last Theorem
If x, y, z, and n are natural numbers, the equation $x^n + y^n = z^n$ has no solution if $n > 2$.

Since Fermat's time, many great mathematicians have spent years trying to prove this theorem. A few even claimed to have proofs, which turned out to contain errors! We know now that if the equation $x^n + y^n = z^n$ has any integral solutions, then n must be greater than 125 000. Although Fermat's Last Theorem is so difficult that it has never been proved, several related problems are much easier to solve.

Prove that if Fermat's Last Theorem can be proved for any exponent k, then it is true for all multiples of k.

Think of a strategy and carry it out
- Suppose there is a natural number $k > 2$ such that $x^k + y^k = z^k$ has no solutions which are natural numbers.
- Let m be a multiple of k; that is, $m = dk$. Can you prove that $x^m + y^m = z^m$ has no solutions which are natural numbers?

Look back
- By 1825, various mathematicians had found elaborate proofs of the theorem for $n = 3, 4, 5,$ and 7. This meant that the theorem was true for many other values of n. What values of n were they?
- To prove Fermat's Last Theorem, it is only necessary to consider the cases where n is a prime number.
- Is it correct to call Fermat's Last Theorem a "theorem"? Explain.

PROBLEMS

Ⓑ

1. Give examples of natural numbers that satisfy each equation.
   a) $x^2 + y^2 + z^2 = w^2$
   b) $x^3 + y^3 + z^3 = w^3$
   c) $x^2 + y^2 = z^2 + w^2$
   d) $x^3 + y^3 = z^3 + w^3$

2. Two numbers have a sum of 9 and a product of 12. Find their difference.

3. If $x = y$, prove that $4xy = (x + y)^2$.

4. The diagram shows a cross section through a torus. The dimensions of the torus are as follows: d, inside diameter; D, outside diameter; r, radius of circular cross section; R, radius from centre of torus to centre of cross section.
   a) Express in terms of R and r.
      i) D ii) d
   b) Express in terms of D and d.
      i) R ii) r
   c) The formulas for the surface area A and volume V of a torus are $A = 4\pi^2 Rr$ and $V = 2\pi^2 Rr^2$. Express these formulas in terms of D and d.
   d) Substitute the results of part a) into the formulas obtained in part c), and simplify the results.

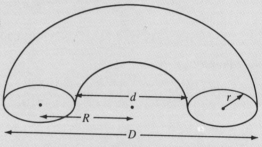

5. The ancient oriental Yin-Yang symbol consists of a circular region bisected by a curve passing through the centre, formed by two semicircles. Show how to draw a curve which bisects both regions.

Ⓒ

6. Find values of A and B such that $\dfrac{7x - 11}{(x + 2)(x - 3)} = \dfrac{A}{x + 2} + \dfrac{B}{x - 3}$ $x \neq -2, 3$.

7. Prove that $\dfrac{1}{2} \times \dfrac{3}{4} \times \dfrac{5}{6} \times \ \dots \ \times \dfrac{35}{36} < \dfrac{1}{6}$.

8. In *Problem 5*, show how to draw a straight line which bisects both regions.

Ⓓ

9. Observe that both $x^2 + 5x + 6$ and $x^2 + 6x + 5$ can be factored. Are there other trinomials of the form $x^2 + bx + c$ and $x^2 + cx + b$ which can be factored? Either obtain an algorithm to generate all of them, or prove that there are no others.

Review Exercises

1. a) Change to mixed radicals.
   i) $\sqrt{24}$ ii) $\sqrt{45}$ iii) $\sqrt{112}$ iv) $\sqrt{605}$
   b) Change to entire radicals.
   i) $3\sqrt{7}$ ii) $5\sqrt{2}$ iii) $4\sqrt{5}$ iv) $7\sqrt{6}$

2. Simplify.
   a) $2\sqrt{5} \times 3\sqrt{2} \times \sqrt{10}$ b) $5\sqrt{3} \times 2\sqrt{2} \times 2\sqrt{6}$ c) $(-4\sqrt{3})(-3\sqrt{2})(-5\sqrt{7})$

3. Simplify.
   a) $3\sqrt{30} + 2\sqrt{64} - 5\sqrt{12}$ b) $4\sqrt{40} + 8\sqrt{24} - 3\sqrt{48}$ c) $7\sqrt{120} - 3\sqrt{52} - 2\sqrt{28}$

4. Simplify.
   a) $3\sqrt{x} - 7\sqrt{x} + \sqrt{x}$ b) $\sqrt{8x} + \sqrt{12y} + \sqrt{18x} - \sqrt{75y}$ c) $3\sqrt{2}(\sqrt{2x} + 1)^2$

5. Simplify.
   a) $2\sqrt{3}(3\sqrt{8} - 4\sqrt{2})$ b) $7\sqrt{3}(4\sqrt{24} - 3\sqrt{50})$ c) $(6\sqrt{3} - 2\sqrt{6})^2$

6. Simplify.
   a) $\dfrac{12\sqrt{12}}{4\sqrt{2}}$ b) $\dfrac{16\sqrt{50}}{-5\sqrt{10}}$ c) $\dfrac{-40\sqrt{50}}{-8\sqrt{125}}$

   d) $\dfrac{3\sqrt{5} + 5}{\sqrt{5}}$ e) $\dfrac{6\sqrt{7} - 4}{\sqrt{7} - \sqrt{2}}$ f) $\dfrac{4\sqrt{18} - 3\sqrt{2}}{\sqrt{5} + \sqrt{3}}$

7. Solve.
   a) $x^2 - 5x - 14 = 0$ b) $m^2 + 4m - 32 = 0$
   c) $3v^2 - 2v - 1 = 0$ d) $6t^2 - 11t - 10 = 0$

8. Solve.
   a) $\sqrt{3x - 2} = 4$ b) $4\sqrt{2x - 1} - 3 = 9$ c) $2\sqrt{5x + 7} + 3 = 0$

9. For what values of m will $x^2 - 2mx + m + 12 = 0$ have:
   a) equal roots   b) real roots   c) no real roots?

10. If m is a positive number less than 4, which of these equations has equal roots?
    a) $x^2 + mx + 1 = 0$ b) $mx^2 + 3x - 5 = 0$ c) $3x^2 + 2mx + 7 = 0$

11. A grappling iron is thrown vertically to catch on a ledge 7.5 m above the thrower. If its height h metres t seconds after being thrown is given by $h = -4.9t^2 + 11t + 1.5$, will it reach the ledge?

12. Solve graphically.   a) $x^3 - 5x + 9 = 0$ b) $\dfrac{x^3}{3} - 3x = 0$

13. Solve.
    a) $x^3 - x^2 - 4x + 4 = 0$ b) $x^3 - 4x^2 + x + 6 = 0$
    c) $x^3 - x^2 - 3x + 6 = 0$ d) $x^4 - 3x^3 - 2x^2 + 12x - 8 = 0$

Supermarket cashiers try to memorize current sale prices while they work. If the percent they memorize is a known function of time, what is the greatest percent they can memorize and how long does it take them? (See Section 2-8 *Example 3.*)

2-1 FUNCTIONS

In mathematics, the word "function" is used to express the idea that one quantity depends on another. For each illustration below, try to express the accompanying statement without using "function".

The distance to the horizon is a function of the observer's height above the ground.

Stopping distance is a function of speed.

The length of a tree's shadow is a function of the time of day. It was measured at 2 h intervals on a summer day. The results are shown in the table and graph.

Time of day	Shadow length (m)
08:00	12.0
10:00	7.7
12:00	5.7
14:00	6.0
16:00	7.7
18:00	10.3
20:00	14.2

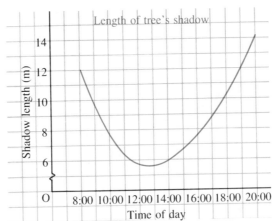

The relation between time of day and shadow length can be expressed as a set of ordered pairs.
$R = \{(8, 12.0), (10, 7.7), (12, 5.7), (14, 6.0), (16, 7.7), (18, 10.3), (20, 14.2)\}$
Since the tree's shadow cannot have two different lengths at the same time, this relation has a special property. No two ordered pairs have the same first coordinate. For this reason, this relation is called a function.

> A *function* is a relation in which no two ordered pairs have the same first coordinate.

Example 1. Is each relation a function?

a) $\{(2, 1), (3, 5), (3, 6), (4, -2), (5, -1)\}$

b) $\{(3, -2), (4, 1), (5, 1), (6, 0), (7, -2)\}$

Solution. a) Two ordered pairs, (3, 5) and (3, 6), have the same first coordinate. Therefore, the relation is not a function.

b) Since every ordered pair has a different first coordinate, the relation is a function.

From the graphs of the relations in *Example 1*, we can find a simple way to determine if a relation is a function.

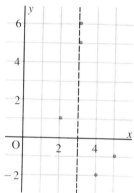

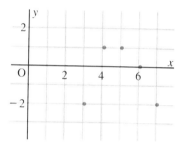

Since the points (3, 5) and (3, 6) have the same first coordinate, they can be joined by a vertical line. The relation is not a function.

No two points can be joined by a vertical line. The relation is a function.

Vertical-line test for a function

If no two points on a graph can be joined by a vertical line, the graph represents a function.

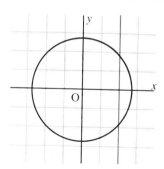

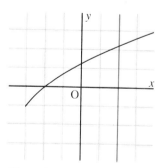

Since there is a vertical line which intersects the graph more than once, the relation is *not* a function.

Since there is no vertical line which intersects the graph more than once, the relation *is* a function.

The *domain* of a function is the set of all the first components of the ordered pairs of the function. The set of all the second components of the ordered pairs is the *range* of the function. For example, for the function {(1, 2), (2, 5), (3, 6), (4, 6)}, the domain is {1, 2, 3, 4} and the range is {2, 5, 6}.

When the domain and range of a function are sets of real numbers, the function is said to be a *real* function. A real function f is often defined by a rule (equation) which assigns to each element x of the domain *one and only one* element y of the range. The value of x is chosen arbitrarily, while the value of y is determined by the choice of x. For this reason, x is called the *independent variable* and y is called the *dependent variable*.

This dependence is expressed symbolically as $y = f(x)$, using a special notation called *function notation*. The symbol $f(x)$ is read as "*f* of *x*." It is the value of f at x or the image of x under f; $f(x)$ is another name for the dependent variable y. We use simply f, when describing a function.

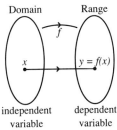

Example 2. Given the linear function $f(x) = 2x - 1$, find:

   a) $f(2)$ b) $f(t)$ c) $f(x + 2)$.

Solution.   a) To compute $f(2)$ we substitute 2 for x in the expression.
$$f(x) = 2x - 1$$
$$f(2) = 2(2) - 1$$
$$= 4 - 1$$
$$= 3$$

   b) $f(x) = 2x - 1$
   $$f(t) = 2(t) - 1$$
   $$= 2t - 1$$

   c) $f(x) = 2x - 1$
   $$f(x + 2) = 2(x + 2) - 1$$
   $$= 2x + 4 - 1$$
   $$= 2x + 3$$

In *Example 2a)*, if we write $f(2) = 3$, we can say when $x = 2$, $y = 3$. Another way to write this is $(2, 3) \in f$. In *Example 2b)* and *c)*, notice that algebraic expressions were substituted for the variable in the equation of a function.

Unless otherwise specified, the domain of a real function is the set of admissible real values of the independent variable for which the function is defined.

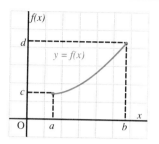

Domain of f is $[a, b]$.
Range of f is $[c, d]$.

Example 3. Find the domain and range of the function f whose graph is shown at the right.

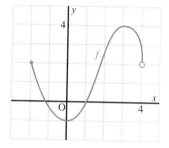

Solution. Since there is a solid dot at $x = -2$, this value is included. Since there is an empty dot at $x = 4$, this value is excluded. The domain of f is $[-2, 4[$. The function has a minimum value of -1 and a maximum value of 4. The range of f is $[-1, 4]$.

Example 4. What are the domain and range of the constant function $f(x) = 2$?

Solution. For any value of x, y is always equal to 2.
The domain of f is $\mathbb{R}$, the set of real numbers.
The range of f is $\{2\}$.

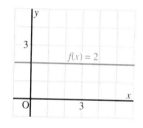

Example 5. Determine the domain and range of the function $g(x) = \dfrac{1}{x}$.

Solution. We know that $g(0) = \dfrac{1}{0}$, which is undefined.
So 0 is not an admissible value for x.
Hence, the domain of g is $\mathbb{R}^*$, the set of nonzero real numbers.
To find the range we express x in terms of y.
We write $g(x) = \dfrac{1}{x}$ as $y = \dfrac{1}{x}$
$$xy = 1$$
$$x = \dfrac{1}{y}$$
So y cannot equal 0.
Hence, the range of g is $\mathbb{R}^*$.

EXERCISES 2-1

A

1. Does each graph represent a function?

a)

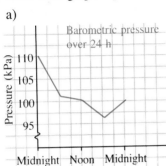

b)

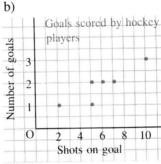

c)

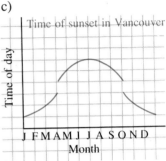

2. For each graph, if it represents a function, state its domain and range.

a)

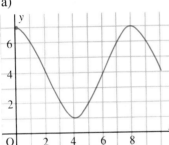

b)

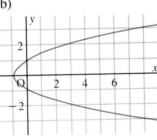

c)

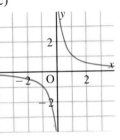

3. Does each set of ordered pairs represent a function?

a) $\{(2, 5), (3, 10), (5, 26), (7, 50)\}$

b) $\{(9, 2), (6, 5), (3, 1), (6, 8), (7, 11)\}$

c) $\{(0, 4), (1, 5), (2, 8), (3, 13), (-1, 5), (-2, 8), (-3, 13)\}$

B

4. For each graph, find the domain and range of the function it represents.

a)

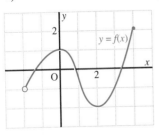

b)

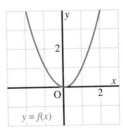

c)

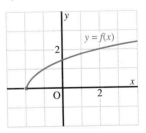

5. Graph each relation, and state its domain and range. Is each relation a function?

a) $y = 3x - 1$ b) $y = -5$ c) $x = 4$

6) If $g(x) = 1 - 2x$, find:

a) $g(1)$ b) $g(-2)$ c) $g(-5)$ d) $g(0)$ e) $g(6)$ f) $g\left(-\dfrac{1}{2}\right)$.

7) Find $f(-3)$, $f(4)$, and $f(-0.5)$ for each function.
a) $f(x) = 5x - 2$ b) $f(x) = x^2 - 5$ c) $f(x) = x^2 + x$

8) For each graph of $y = f(x)$, find $f(-4)$, $f(0)$, and $f(6)$.

a)

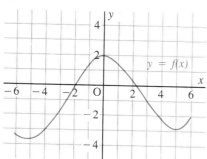

b)

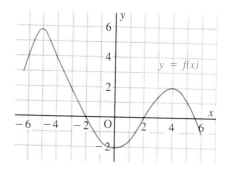

9) If $f(x) = 3x^2 - 5x + 2$, find:
a) $f(4)$ b) $f(-2)$ c) $f(1)$ d) $f(-1)$ e) $f(0)$ f) $f(1.5)$.

10) If $g(x) = -2x^2 + 3x - 6$, find:
a) $g(1)$ b) $g(2)$ c) $g(-2)$ d) $g(0)$ e) $g(-4)$ f) $g(-0.5)$.

11) If $f(x) = 2x + 1$, and $g(x) = 3 - x$, find:
a) $f(a)$ b) $f(3a)$ c) $f(1 + y)$ d) $f(x + 1)$
e) $g(y)$ f) $g(2 - y)$ g) $g(z - 1)$ h) $g(2x - 3)$
i) $2f(x)$ j) $5g(n)$ k) $-3f(x)$ l) $-2g(a)$.

12) Graph each function and state its domain and range.
a) $f(x) = 2x + 1$ b) $f(x) = x^2$
c) $f(x) = \sqrt{x}$

13) If $f(x) = 2 - 5x$, and $g(x) = x^2 - x - 1$, evaluate each expression.
a) $f(1) + g(1)$ b) $f(2) + g(2)$ c) $f(-1) + g(-1)$
d) $f(-1) - g(-1)$ e) $f(-3) - g(-3)$ f) $f(0) - g(0)$

14) If $f(x) = 2x - 3$ and $g(x) = 1 - 4x$, find a value of x that satisfies each equation.
a) $f(x) = 0$ b) $g(x) = -7$ c) $f(x) = g(x)$ d) $f(x - 1) = g(-x)$

2-2 QUADRATIC FUNCTIONS

In case of a forced landing, private and military aircraft often carry a flare pistol which can be used to attract the attention of those looking for them. The height of the flare above the ground is a function of the elapsed time since firing. A typical expression for the height might be $h = -5t^2 + 100t$.

The table of values and the graph show how h depends on t.

Time, t (s)	Height, h (m)
0	0
2	180
5	375
10	500
15	375
18	180
20	0

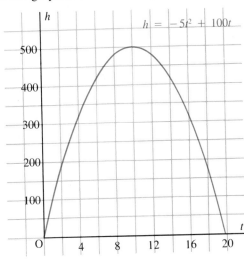

Since there is only one value of h for each value of t, the relation between h and t is a function. It is called a quadratic function because the equation contains a term $-5t^2$ in which the variable is squared.

The graph of every quadratic function is a *parabola*. Parabolic curves arise in many areas of science, and they are used in art and architecture.

A *quadratic function* has a defining equation which can be written in the form:

$$y = ax^2 + bx + c \qquad \text{or} \qquad f(x) = ax^2 + bx + c$$

where a, b, and c are constants and $a \neq 0$. The graph of a quadratic function is a parabola.

These are quadratic functions because they can be expressed in the form $f(x) = ax^2 + bx + c$.

$$f(x) = x^2 - 6$$
$$f(x) = 3x - 0.5x^2$$
$$f(t) = 2(t - 1)^2 + 5$$

These are not quadratic functions because they cannot be expressed in the form $f(x) = ax^2 + bx + c$.

$$f(x) = \frac{1}{x^2 - 4}$$
$$f(z) = \sqrt{z}$$

Example 1. a) Graph the quadratic function $y = 2x^2 - 4x - 11$ for $-3 \leqslant x \leqslant 5$.
b) What are the domain and range of the function?

Solution.   a)

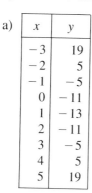

x	y
-3	19
-2	5
-1	-5
0	-11
1	-13
2	-11
3	-5
4	5
5	19

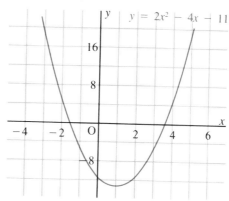

b) The domain of the function, the set of all possible values of x, is the set of all real numbers. The range is the set of all possible values of y. The table and the graph suggest that this is the set $\{y \mid y \geqslant -13\}$.

In many applications of quadratic functions, the graph shows only that part of a parabola which is in the first quadrant. This happens when the variables are restricted to positive numbers.

Example 2. In the open sea, the approximate height h metres of the waves is given by the formula $h = 0.008v^2$, where v is the speed of the wind in knots.
a) Graph h as a function of v for $0 \leqslant v \leqslant 80$.
b) The highest wave ever measured at sea was 34 m. Use the graph to estimate the wind speed at the time.

Solution.   a)

Wind speed, v (knots)	Wave height, h (m)
0	0
20	3.2
40	12.8
60	28.8
80	51.2

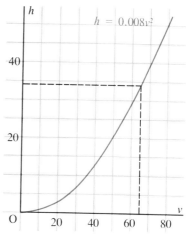

b) From the graph, a wave height of 34 m corresponds to a wind speed of about 65 knots.

EXERCISES 2-2

(A)

1. Is each function a quadratic function?
   a) $y = 3x^2 + 7x - 2$ b) $f(x) = x^2 + \sqrt{x}$ c) $f(x) = 25 - 9x^2$
   d) $y = 7 - 5x^2$ e) $y = 2x^2 + 11 - 4x$ f) $f(x) = \dfrac{1}{4x^2 - 9x + 12}$

(B)

2. a) Graph the function $y = 2x^2 + 5$.
   b) What are the domain and range of the function?

3. a) Graph the function $y = x^2 - 6x + 2$.
   b) What are the domain and range of the function?

4. A pebble is dropped from a bridge into a river. Its height h metres above the river t seconds after the moment of release is given by $h = 82 - 4.9t^2$.
   a) Graph the function for reasonable values of t.
   b) State the domain and range.
   c) How high is the pebble after 2.5 s?

5. The shape of a parabolic mirror in a certain reflecting telescope is defined by the equation $y = 0.1x^2 - 20$, where x and y are measured in centimetres.
   a) Graph the function for $0 \leqslant x \leqslant 25$.
   b) How deep is the mirror if the diameter AB is 50 cm?

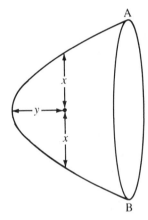

6. Graph each function and state its domain and range.
   a) $f(x) = 2x^2 - 6x + 5$ b) $g(t) = 3 + 2t - 0.5t^2$

7. The Viking 1 spacecraft made a soft landing on Mars on July 20, 1976. Its speed v metres per second t seconds before touchdown was given by $v = 1.2 + 3.2t$. Its height h metres t seconds before touchdown was given by $h = 1.2t + 1.6t^2$.
   a) Draw graphs of the speed and the height as functions of time.
   b) Determine the speed and the height of the spacecraft 90 s before touchdown.

8. When a flare is fired vertically, its height h metres after t seconds is given by $h = -4.9t^2 + 143.2t$.
   a) How high is the flare after 5 s?
   b) How long does it take the flare to reach a height of 1 km?

9. In *Example 2*, what is the effect on the height of the waves if the windspeed is:
   a) doubled
   b) tripled?

10. A landscape architect plans a circular flowerbed with a bordering pathway. The total diameter of the flowerbed and pathway is 20 m.

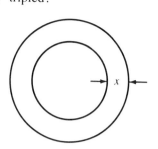

   a) If the width of the pathway is x metres, express the area A of the flowerbed as a function of x.
   b) Graph the function.
   c) What is the domain of the function?

11. If each small circle has radius r, express the area of the shaded region as a function of r.
   a)

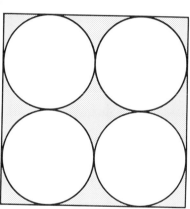

   b)

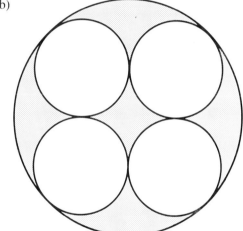

12. The velocity v millimetres per second of a particle falling through water is a function of its diameter d millimetres. The formula is $v = 655d^2$. How long will it take each particle listed to reach the seafloor where the ocean is 5000 m deep?

Particle	Diameter (mm)
Pebble	8.0
Coarse sand	0.5
Fine sand	0.1
Clay	0.004

13. The wavelength L metres of an ocean wave is a quadratic function of the form $L = kT^2$, where T is the period in seconds and k is a constant.
   a) Find the value of k if a wave with wavelength 25 m has a period of 4.0 s.
   b) What is the wavelength of a wave if its period is 6.5 s?

2-3 COMPARING THE GRAPHS OF $y = x^2$ AND $y = x^2 + q$

In this and the following sections, we shall develop a technique for graphing quadratic functions without making a table of values. The first step is to investigate the effect on the graph of $y = x^2$ of adding some number q to get $y = x^2 + q$. We do this by substituting different values for q and graphing the resulting parabolas.

When $q = 0$, the equation becomes $y = x^2$.

x	-3	-2	-1	0	1	2	3
y	9	4	1	0	1	4	9

When $q = 6$, the equation becomes $y = x^2 + 6$.

x	-3	-2	-1	0	1	2	3
y	15	10	7	6	7	10	15

Since the y-coordinates are all 6 greater than those of $y = x^2$, the curve is *translated*, or moved, 6 units up. The y-intercept is 6. The vertex is (0, 6) and the y-axis is still the axis of symmetry.

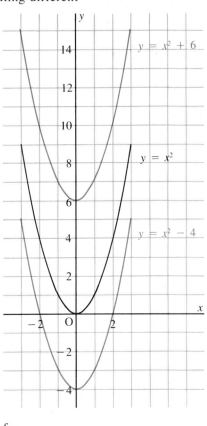

When $q = -4$, the equation becomes $y = x^2 - 4$.

x	-3	-2	-1	0	1	2	3
y	5	0	-3	-4	-3	0	5

The curve is translated 4 units down. The y-intercept is -4, which is the minimum value of y. There are also two x-intercepts, 2 and -2.

Similar results will be found using other values of q.

$y = x^2 + q$ represents a parabola with these properties.
Vertex: (0, q)
Axis of symmetry: y-axis
Direction of opening: up
y-intercept: q
x-intercepts: There are two if $q < 0$.

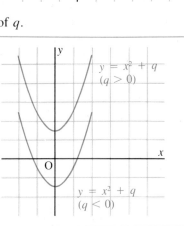

Knowing that $y = x^2 + q$ represents a parabola with the above properties, we can sketch graphs of equations in this form without making tables of values.

Example. Sketch the parabola $y = x^2 - 9$ for $-4 \leqslant x \leqslant 4$.

Solution. The parabola $y = x^2 - 9$ has vertex $(0, -9)$, opens up, and has the y-axis as the axis of symmetry.
When $x = 4$, $y = 4^2 - 9$, or 7
$(4, 7)$ is on the curve and so is $(-4, 7)$.
Knowing the vertex and these two points, we can now sketch the parabola.

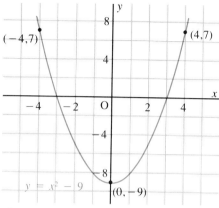

When they exist and if they are integers, the x-intercepts are useful in sketching a parabola. In the *Example*, the x-intercepts can be found by substituting 0 for y.
$0 = x^2 - 9$
$x^2 = 9$
$x = \pm 3$

$(3, 0)$ and $(-3, 0)$ are two additional points on the curve.

EXERCISES 2-3

 a) Make a table of values and graph each parabola on the same grid for $-5 \leqslant x \leqslant 5$.

$y = x^2$	$y = x^2 + 4$	$y = x^2 + 7$
$y = x^2 - 2$	$y = x^2 - 5$	$y = x^2 + 1$

    b) Describe the effect of various values of q on the graph of $y = x^2 + q$.

2. Which graph best represents each equation?
    a) $y = x^2 + 1$ b) $y = x^2 - 4$ c) $y = x^2 - 1$ d) $y = x^2 + 2$
    i)   ii)   iii)   iv)

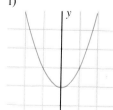 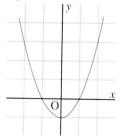 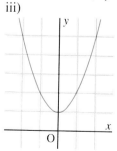 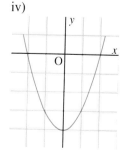

3.) Write an equation that could correspond to each graph.

a)   b)   c)   d)

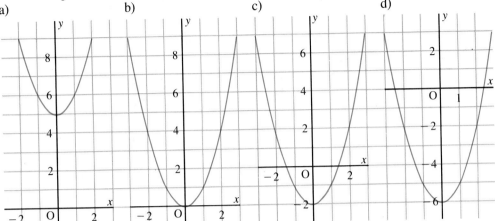

4. For each parabola state:

  i) the direction of opening   ii) the coordinates of the vertex

  iii) the y-intercept   iv) the x-intercepts (if any).

a)   b)   c)   d)

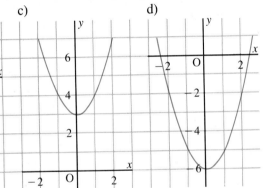

5.) For each parabola state:

  i) the direction of opening   ii) the coordinates of the vertex

  iii) the y-intercept   iv) the x-intercepts (if any).

     a) $y = x^2 + 5$ b) $y = x^2 - 3$ c) $y = x^2 + 2$ d) $y = x^2 + 4$

6.) Sketch each set of graphs on the same grid.

  a) $y = x^2 - 2$ $y = x^2 + 1$ $y = x^2 + 4$

  b) $y = x^2 - 1$ $y = x^2 - 3$ $y = x^2 + 2$

7.) Find the equation of each parabola.

  a) with vertex $(0, 2)$ through $(-3, 11)$

  b) with vertex $(0, -9)$ and x-intercepts ± 3

  c) with vertex $(0, 5)$ through $(2, 9)$

2-4 COMPARING THE GRAPHS OF $y = x^2$ AND $y = (x - p)^2$

In $y = x^2$, if x is replaced by $(x - p)$ we obtain $y = (x - p)^2$. To investigate the effect of this on the graph of the parabola $y = x^2$, we give different values to p and graph the resulting parabolas. When $p = 0$, the equation becomes $y = x^2$ . . . ①

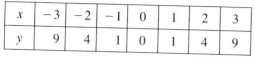

x	-3	-2	-1	0	1	2	3
y	9	4	1	0	1	4	9

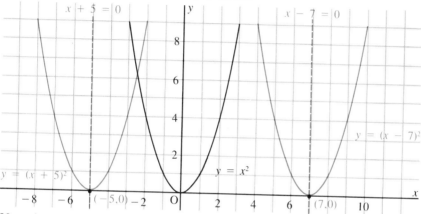

Negative values of p in $y = (x - p)^2$

When $p = -5$, the equation becomes $y = (x + 5)^2$.
For convenience, we choose x-cordinates which give the same y-coordinates as those above. All are 5 *less* than the x-coordinates in ①.

x	-8	-7	-6	-5	-4	-3	-2
y	9	4	1	0	1	4	9

The graph of $y = x^2$ is translated 5 units to the *left*. The vertex is $(-5, 0)$ and the line $x + 5 = 0$ is the axis of symmetry.

Positive values of p in $y = (x - p)^2$

When $p = +7$, the equation becomes $y = (x - 7)^2$.
For convenience, we choose x-coordinates which give the same y-coordinates as those above. All are 7 *greater* than the x-coordinates in ①.

x	4	5	6	7	8	9	10
y	9	4	1	0	1	4	9

The graph of $y = x^2$ is translated 7 units to the *right*. The vertex is $(7, 0)$ and the line $x - 7 = 0$ is the axis of symmetry.

Similar results will be found using other values of p.

$y = (x - p)^2$ represents a parabola with these properties.
Vertex: $(p, 0)$
Axis of symmetry: line $x - p = 0$
Direction of opening: up

For any equation in this form, the sign inside the brackets tells whether the parabola is moved to the left or to the right of the *y*-axis.

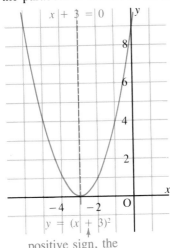

positive sign, the
parabola moved left

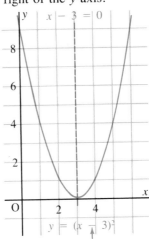

negative sign, the
parabola moved right

We can sketch graphs of equations in this form without using tables of values.

Example.   Graph these parabolas on the same grid.
a) $y = (x - 5)^2$ b) $y = (x + 7)^2$

Solution.   a) The parabola $y = (x - 5)^2$ has vertex (5, 0) and axis of symmetry
$x - 5 = 0$. When $x = 0$, $y = 25$
Thus, one other point on the graph is (0, 25). Another point (10, 25)
is its reflection in the axis of symmetry.
b) The parabola $y = (x + 7)^2$ has vertex $(-7, 0)$ and axis of symmetry
$x + 7 = 0$. When $x = 0$, $y = 49$
Thus, two other points on the graph are (0, 49) and $(-14, 49)$.

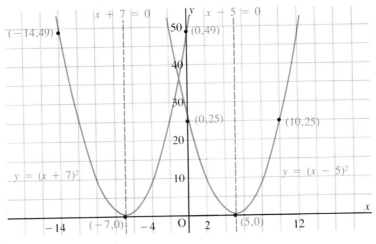

EXERCISES 2-4

Ⓐ

1. Sketch each set of graphs on the same grid.
   a) $y = x^2$ $y = (x - 2)^2$ $y = (x + 4)^2$
   b) $y = x^2$ $y = (x + 3)^2$ $y = (x - 6)^2$
   c) $y = x^2$ $y = (x - 4)^2$ $y = (x + 6)^2$

2. Compare the graphs of $y = x^2$ and $y = (x - p)^2$ when:
   a) $p < 0$ b) $p > 0$.

③ Which graph best represents each equation?
   a) $y = (x - 1)^2$ b) $y = (x + 2)^2$ c) $y = (x + 4)^2$ d) $y = (x - 4)^2$

   i)
   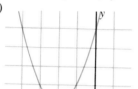

   ii)
   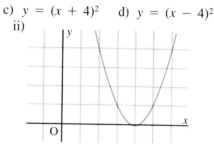

   iii)
   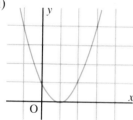

   iv)
   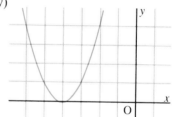

④. Write an equation that could correspond to each graph.
   a)
   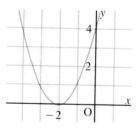

   b)
   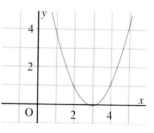

   c)
   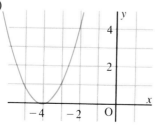

   d)
   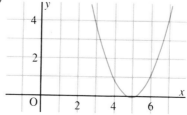

5. For each graph state:
   i) the coordinates of the vertex   ii) the equation of the axis of symmetry
   iii) the direction of opening   iv) the *y*-intercept

a)
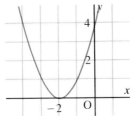

b)
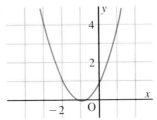

c)
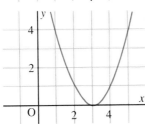

d)
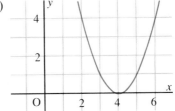

6. State the equation of each parabola in *Exercise 5*.

7. For each parabola state:
   i) the coordinates of the vertex   ii) the equation of the axis of symmetry
   iii) the direction of opening   iv) the *y*-intercept
   a) $y = (x + 3)^2$ b) $y = (x - 8)^2$ c) $y = (x - 2)^2$ d) $y = (x + 4)^2$

8. Sketch the graphs of the parabolas in *Exercise 7*.

9. Sketch the graph of each parabola.
   a) $y = (x - 2)^2$ b) $y = (x + 5)^2$ c) $y = (x - 6)^2$ d) $y = (x + 2)^2$

10. Find the equation of each parabola.
    a) with vertex (4, 0), *y*-intercept 16
    b) with vertex (−3, 0), *y*-intercept 9
    c) with *x*-intercept 7, *y*-intercept 49, axis of symmetry $x - 7 = 0$

Ⓒ
11. Sketch each set of graphs on the same grid.
    a) $y = (x + 4)^2 + 1$ and $y = (x + 4)^2 - 3$
    b) $y = (x - 1)^2 + 2$ and $y = (x - 1)^2 - 2$
    c) $y = x^2 + 6x + 9$ and $y = x^2 + 6x$
    d) $y = (x - 10)^2$ and $y = (10 - x)^2$

 INVESTIGATE

What conditions must be satisfied by *a* and *c* for the parabola $y = ax^2 + c$ to have *x*-intercepts?

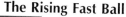

MATHEMATICS AROUND US

The Rising Fast Ball

Some baseball fans believe that pitchers can throw a baseball that rises as it approaches the batter. This appears to contradict common experience that the ball falls because of gravity. However, it has been observed that a ball delivered with backspin experiences an upward lift that acts against gravity. In one study, a computer was programmed to calculate the amount of lift that could be expected when a baseball is pitched with backspin. It was found that, in the absence of gravity, the lifting force due to backspin caused the ball to rise about 15 cm. Thus, the question of whether the ball actually rises depends on how much the ball falls due to gravity on its way to the batter.

The study showed that the rising fast ball is just an illusion. A ball thrown with backspin may appear to rise simply because it does not fall as much as the batter expects it to. You can confirm this by completing the questions below.

QUESTIONS

1. It is about 18.4 m from the pitcher's mound to the batter. A reasonably fast pitch travels at about 150 km/h. Calculate how long it takes the ball to reach the batter at this speed, to the nearest hundredth of a second.

2. Once the ball leaves the pitcher's hand, it begins to fall. The distance s metres that it falls is given by the formula $s = 4.9t^2$, where t is the elapsed time in seconds. Using your answer to *Question 1*, find how far the ball has fallen by the time it reaches the batter. Give your answer to the nearest centimetre.

3. If the ball is thrown with backspin, how far should it fall by the time it reaches the batter?

4. How fast would a pitcher have to throw the ball before it would actually rise on its way to the batter?

THE MATHEMATICAL MIND

The Origin of the Function Concept

The concept of a function originated in the seventeenth century, when scientists and mathematicians became interested in the study of motion.

- Galileo showed that the path of a projectile fired into the air is a parabola.

- The moon's motion was studied because knowledge of its position was used to determine longitude at sea.

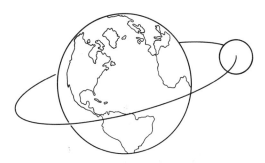

Since moving objects follow a single line or a curve, mathematicians thought that a function was defined by a single equation. For example, this definition was given by James Gregory in 1667.

> A function is a quantity obtained from other quantities by a succession of algebraic operations, or any other operation imaginable.

Leonhard Euler 1707–1783

As late as 1734, Leonhard Euler defined a function as any expression formed in any manner from a variable quantity and constants. He also introduced the $f(x)$ notation.

By 1750, scientists studying vibrating strings had encountered an example of a function that could not be defined by a single equation. This caused a controversy over the question of what a function was. Euler extended the definition to include cases where there were different expressions in different intervals of the domain. For example, Euler would have considered the following expression to be a single function.

$$f(x) = \begin{cases} x + 6, & \text{if } x \le -2 \\ x^2, & \text{if } -2 \le x \le 2 \\ x + 2, & \text{if } x \ge 2 \end{cases}$$

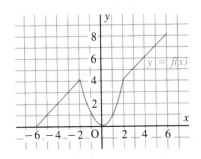

Most mathematicians found this new idea difficult to accept, and the concept of a function given by a single equation dominated mathematics until about 1800.

Joseph Fourier
1768-1830

But the definition of a function was soon to be extended even further. In 1807, Joseph Fourier published a paper about the flow of heat. He used functions whose component parts were not connected. Here is an example of such a function.

$$f(x) = \begin{cases} x + 4, & \text{if } x < -2 \\ x, & \text{if } -2 \le x < 2 \\ x - 4, & \text{if } x \ge 2 \end{cases}$$

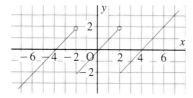

Moreover, Fourier's work implied that a function did not even have to be defined by equations. This led Lejeune Dirichlet to give a new definition of a function in 1837.

> y is a function of x when to each value of x in a given interval there corresponds a unique value of y.

Dirichlet's definition is equivalent to the one given on page 42 of this book. It is a very broad definition because it does not matter whether y depends on x according to one law or more, or whether the dependence can be expressed by equations.

QUESTIONS

1. Graph each function.

   a) $$f(x) = \begin{cases} 2 - x, & x \le -2 \\ x^2, & -2 \le x \le 2 \\ 6 - x, & x \ge 2 \end{cases}$$

   b) $$f(x) = \begin{cases} x + 2, & x < -2 \\ -x, & -2 \le x \le 2 \\ x - 2, & x > 2 \end{cases}$$

   c) $$f(x) = \begin{cases} (x + 4)^2, & x \le -2 \\ x^2, & -2 \le x \le 2 \\ (x - 4)^2, & x \ge 2 \end{cases}$$

2. Write the equations which define this function.

   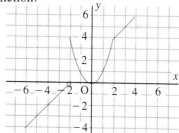

3. Refer to the functions in the examples and exercises of this chapter. Find an example of a function which does not satisfy any of the definitions given above, except the one given by Dirichlet.

4. In 1829 Dirichlet gave an example of a function of x that has one value for all rational values of x and a different value for all irrational values of x. Give an example of such a function.

2-5 COMPARING THE GRAPHS OF $y = x^2$ AND $y = ax^2$

In this section, we investigate the effect on the graph of $y = x^2$ of multiplying x^2 by a constant a to get $y = ax^2$.

Positive values of a

When $a = 1$, the equation becomes $y = x^2$.

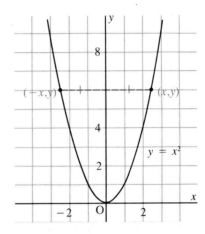

x	y
-3	9
-2	4
-1	1
0	0
1	1
2	4
3	9

The curve is a parabola with the following properties.

Axis of symmetry: The y-axis is the axis of symmetry of the curve. If (x, y) is any point on the curve, then $(-x, y)$ is also on the curve.

Vertex: The point where the axis of symmetry intersects the curve is called the vertex. For this curve the vertex is $(0, 0)$.

Direction of opening: The curve opens up.

Using the same x-coordinates as above, graph a curve of the form $y = ax^2$ for $a > 1$ and another for $a < 1$. Compare the tables of values and graphs with those for $y = x^2$.

When $a = 2$, the equation becomes $y = 2x^2$.

x	-3	-2	-1	0	1	2	3
y	18	8	2	0	2	8	18

Since the y-coordinates are all twice those of $y = x^2$, the curve is expanded vertically.

When $a = \frac{1}{2}$, the equation becomes $y = \frac{1}{2}x^2$.

x	-3	-2	-1	0	1	2	3
y	4.5	2	0.5	0	0.5	2	4.5

Since the y-coordinates are half those of $y = x^2$, the curve is compressed vertically.

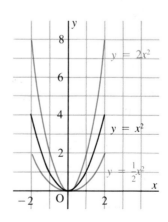

Negative values of *a*

Using the same *x*-coordinates as before, we graph curves of the form $y = ax^2$ for $a < 0$, and compare the tables of values and graphs with those for $y = x^2$.

When $a = -1$, the equation becomes $y = -x^2$.

x	− 3	− 2	− 1	0	1	2	3
y	− 9	− 4	− 1	0	− 1	− 4	− 9

Since the *y*-coordinates are the opposites of those of $y = x^2$, the curve is reflected in the *x*-axis. It opens down.

When $a = -2$, the equation becomes $y = -2x^2$.

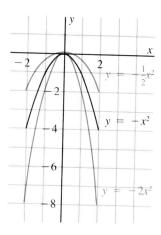

x	− 3	− 2	− 1	0	1	2	3
y	− 18	− 8	− 2	0	− 2	− 8	− 18

The curve $y = x^2$ is reflected in the *x*-axis and expanded vertically.

When $a = -\frac{1}{2}$, the equation becomes $y = -\frac{1}{2}x^2$.

x	− 3	− 2	− 1	0	1	2	3
y	− 4.5	− 2	− 0.5	0	− 0.5	− 2	− 4.5

The curve $y = x^2$ is reflected in the *x*-axis and compressed vertically.

Similar results will be found using other values of *a*, $a \neq 0$.

$y = ax^2$ $(a \neq 0)$ represents a parabola with these properties:

Vertex: (0, 0)

Axis of symmetry: *y*-axis

Direction of opening: up if $a > 0$

down if $a < 0$

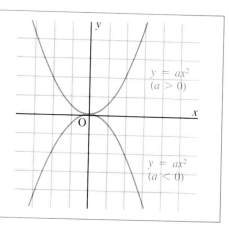

Knowing that $y = ax^2$ represents a parabola with the above properties, we can sketch graphs of equations in this form without making a table of values.

Example 1. Graph these parabolas on the same grid.
  a) $y = 5x^2$ b) $y = -2.5x^2$

Solution.   a) The parabola $y = 5x^2$ opens up.
It has vertex $(0, 0)$ and axis of
symmetry the positive y-axis.
A reasonable graph may be drawn by
finding one other point on the curve.
Substitute 4 for x in the equation.
$y = 5(4)^2$, or 80
The point $(4, 80)$ is on the curve
as is the point $(-4, 80)$ since the
y-axis is the axis of symmetry.
The parabola with vertex $(0, 0)$ and
passing through $(4, 80)$ and $(-4, 80)$
can now be sketched.

  b) The parabola $y = -2.5x^2$ opens
down. It has vertex $(0, 0)$ and axis of
symmetry the negative y-axis.
To find another point on the curve,
substitute 4 for x in the equation.
$y = -2.5(4)^2$, or -40
The parabola passes through $(4, -40)$
and $(-4, -40)$.

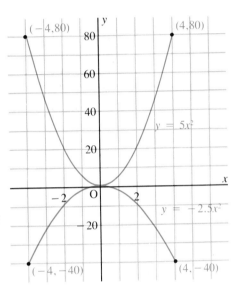

In *Example 1*, the scales on the axes were different. This is often
necessary due to space requirements. While the choice of vertical scale
affects the appearance of the curve, it does not change the vertex, the
axis of symmetry, or the direction of opening.

Example 2. Find the equation of the parabola through $(6, 27)$ which has the y-axis as
its axis of symmetry and $(0, 0)$ as its vertex. Sketch the graph.

Solution.   Let the equation of the parabola be
$y = ax^2$. Since $(6, 27)$ lies on the curve,
its coordinates satisfy the equation.
That is,
$27 = a(6)^2$
$a = \dfrac{3}{4}$

The equation of the parabola is $y = \dfrac{3}{4}x^2$.

The parabola is sketched using the
fact that it passes through $(0, 0)$,
$(6, 27)$, and $(-6, 27)$ since the y-axis
is the axis of symmetry.

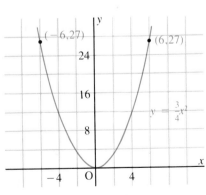

EXERCISES 2-5

1. a) Make a table of values and graph the equations on the same grid for $-5 \leqslant x \leqslant 5$.

   $y = x^2$ $y = 3x^2$ $y = \frac{1}{2}x^2$ $y = -x^2$ $y = -\frac{1}{3}x^2$ $y = -4x^2$

   b) Describe the effect on the graph of $y = ax^2$ as the value of a varies.

2. Which graph best represents each equation?
   a) $y = 5x^2$ b) $y = 0.2x^2$ c) $y = -1.5x^2$ d) $y = -3x^2$
   i)   ii)   iii)   iv)

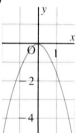
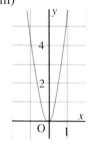
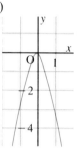

3. Sketch each set of parabolas on the same grid.

   a) $y = x^2$ $y = 3x^2$ $y = \frac{1}{2}x^2$

   b) $y = x^2$ $y = -x^2$ $y = 5x^2$ $y = -3x^2$

   c) $y = 2x^2$ $y = \frac{3}{4}x^2$ $y = -1.5x^2$ $y = -4x^2$

   d) $y = -2x^2$ $y = \frac{1}{4}x^2$ $y = 2.5x^2$ $y = -\frac{1}{2}x^2$

4. Find the equation of the parabola with vertex $(0, 0)$ which passes through each point.
   a) $(3, 18)$ b) $(4, -16)$ c) $(6, -9)$ d) $(2, 24)$

5. Find the equation of the parabola with vertex $(0, 0)$ which passes through each point.

   a) $(2, -10)$ b) $(3, 5)$ c) $\left(\frac{3}{2}, \frac{1}{3}\right)$ d) $(-\sqrt{2}, -6)$

6. The line $3x - y - 3 = 0$ is tangent to a parabola which has vertex $(0, 0)$ and axis of symmetry the y-axis. Find the equation of the parabola.

 INVESTIGATE

If the coordinates of any point are given, is it always possible to find the equation of a parabola through the point with vertex $(0, 0)$ and axis of symmetry the y-axis?

2-6 GRAPHING $y = a(x - p)^2 + q$

In the last three sections we investigated the effect on the graph of $y = x^2$ of the constants a, p, and q in the equations $y = ax^2$, $y = x^2 + q$, and $y = (x - p)^2$. We now investigate the effect on the graph when these three constants are combined in the same equation $y = a(x - p)^2 + q$.

Example 1. Graph.   a) $y = (x - 4)^2 + 3$ b) $y = 2(x - 4)^2 + 3$

Solution.

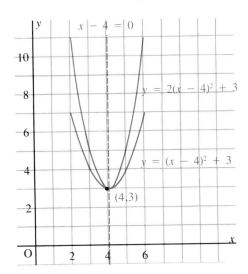

a) $y = (x - 4)^2 + 3$ represents a parabola congruent to $y = x^2$ which has been translated 4 units to the right and 3 units up from the position of $y = x^2$. The vertex is $(4, 3)$ and the line $x - 4 = 0$ is the axis of symmetry.

b) $y = 2(x - 4)^2 + 3$ is similar to the equation in part a). The vertex is $(4, 3)$ and the axis of symmetry is the line $x - 4 = 0$. The only difference is that this parabola is expanded vertically. It is congruent to $y = 2x^2$.

Example 2. Sketch the graph of $y = -\frac{1}{2}(x + 3)^2 + 2$. Show on the graph the coordinates of the vertex, the equation of the axis of symmetry, and the coordinates of two points other than the vertex.

Solution. The coordinates of the vertex are $(-3, 2)$.
The equation of the axis of symmetry is $x + 3 = 0$.
The parabola opens down and is compressed vertically.

It is congruent to $y = -\frac{1}{2}x^2$.

When $x = 0$, $y = -\frac{1}{2}(0 - 3)^2 + 2$,

or -2.5.
$(0, -2.5)$ is a point on the graph.
Since $x + 3 = 0$ is the axis of symmetry, $(-6, -2.5)$ is also on the graph.

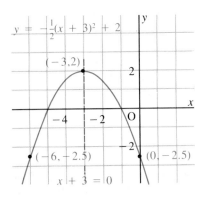

The above examples suggest that in the equation $y = a(x - p)^2 + q$, the constants a, p, and q have the following geometric meaning:

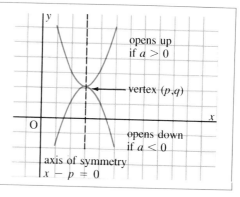

$x - p = 0$ is the axis of symmetry.

$$y = a(x - p)^2 + q$$

Congruent to the parabola $y = ax^2$

Coordinates of the vertex are (p, q)

opens up if $a > 0$

vertex (p,q)

opens down if $a < 0$

axis of symmetry $x - p = 0$

EXERCISES 2-6

Ⓐ

1. Which graph best represents each equation?
   a) $y = (x + 3)^2 + 1$
   b) $y = -2(x + 4)^2 + 3$
   c) $y = \frac{1}{2}(x - 2)^2 - 5$
   d) $y = -(x - 3)^2 + 2$

i)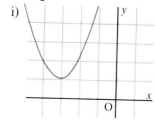

ii)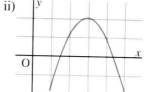

iii)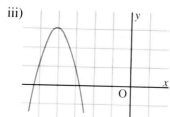

iv)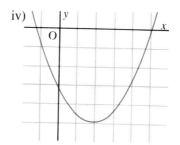

2. Sketch each set of graphs on the same grid.
   a) $y = (x - 5)^2 + 4$ $y = (x - 5)^2 + 2$ $y = (x - 5)^2$
      $y = (x - 5)^2 - 2$ $y = (x - 5)^2 - 4$
   b) $y = (x - 5)^2 + 4$ $y = (x - 3)^2 + 4$ $y = (x - 1)^2 + 4$
      $y = (x + 1)^2 + 4$ $y = (x + 3)^2 + 4$ $y = (x + 5)^2 + 4$
   c) $y = (x - 5)^2 + 4$ $y = 3(x - 5)^2 + 4$ $y = \frac{1}{2}(x - 5)^2 + 4$
      $y = -\frac{1}{2}(x - 5)^2 + 4$ $y = -(x - 5)^2 + 4$ $y = -3(x - 5)^2 + 4$

B

3. For each parabola state:
   - i) the coordinates of the vertex
   - iii) the y-intercept
     - a) $y = (x - 5)^2 + 2$
     - c) $y = -4(x + 1)^2 + 4$
   - ii) the equation of the axis of symmetry
   - iv) the x-intercepts, if any.
     - b) $y = 2(x + 3)^2 - 8$
     - d) $y = \frac{1}{2}(x - 2)^2 - 8$

4. Sketch the graphs of the functions in *Exercise 3*.

5. On a sketch of the graph of each parabola, show:
   - i) the coordinates of the vertex
   - ii) the equation of the axis of symmetry
   - iii) the coordinates of two points on the graph.
     - a) $y = (x + 2)^2 - 5$
     - c) $y = -\frac{1}{2}(x - 4)^2 - 1$
     - e) $y = -2(x - 1)^2 + 3$
     - b) $y = -(x - 3)^2 + 2$
     - d) $y = 2(x + 1)^2 + 4$
     - f) $y = 4(x - 5)^2 - 10$

6. Sketch the graph of each parabola.
   - a) $k = 2(l - 3)^2 - 1$
   - c) $m = \frac{1}{2}(n - 4)^2 - 3$
   - e) $f = -(g + 2.5)^2 + 3$
   - b) $r = -2(t + 3)^2 + 5$
   - d) $p = 3(q - 5)^2 + 1$
   - f) $u = -0.2(v + 2)^2 - 1.5$

7. Write the equation of each parabola.
   - a) with vertex $(4, -1)$, that opens up, and is congruent to $y = 2x^2$
   - b) with vertex $(-2, 3)$, that opens down, and is congruent to $y = \frac{1}{3}x^2$
   - c) with vertex $(-3, 2)$, that opens down, and is congruent to $y = \frac{1}{2}x^2$
   - d) with vertex $(3, -4)$, x-intercepts 1 and 5

8. Write the equation of each parabola.
   - a) with vertex $(3, -1)$, x-intercepts 2 and 4
   - b) with vertex $(-1, 4)$, y-intercept 2
   - c) with vertex $(2, -27)$, y-intercept -15

C

9. Describe what happens to each graph.
   - a) $y = a(x - 4)^2 + 3$ as a varies
   - b) $y = 2(x - p)^2 + 3$ as p varies
   - c) $y = 2(x - 4)^2 + q$ as q varies

10. Find the equation of the parabola, with axis of symmetry the y-axis, which passes through each pair of points.
    - a) $(2, 9)$ and $(3, 14)$
    - b) $(-2, 1)$ and $(4, -5)$

Using Differences to Graph Parabolas

There is a pattern in the table of values for $y = x^2$ which is useful when graphing parabolas.

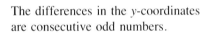

x	y	Differences
0	0	1
1	1	3
2	4	5
3	9	7
4	16	

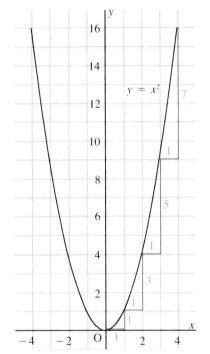

The differences in the y-coordinates are consecutive odd numbers.

    Starting at the vertex, points on the parabola can be found by moving: 1 right and 1 up; then 1 right and 3 up; then 1 right and 5 up; and so on.

    Other points are obtained by reflecting, in the axis of symmetry, those already found, or by repeating the above steps but moving 1 left each time.

    This method can be used for any parabola which is congruent to $y = x^2$, and it can be modified to apply to parabolas congruent to $y = 2x^2$, $y = 3x^2$,

$y = \frac{1}{2}x^2$, and so on.

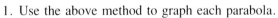

1. Use the above method to graph each parabola.
    a) $y = (x - 3)^2 + 5$ b) $y = (x + 1)^2 - 7$ c) $y = -(x - 2)^2 + 3$

2. Modify the above method to graph each parabola.
    a) $y = 2x^2$ b) $y = 3x^2$

    c) $y = \frac{1}{2}x^2$ d) $y = 2(x - 4)^2 - 6$

    e) $y = 3(x + 2)^2 - 10$ f) $y = -\frac{1}{2}(x + 2)^2 + 5$

USING TECHNOLOGY

Quadratic Functions, Part I

Viewing the Quadratic Function

The vertex of the graph of $y = 2(x - 3)^2 + 4$ is $(3, 4)$ and the graph of this quadratic function opens upward. With this information, we can adjust the viewing window on the graphing calculator so that the graph will include only the origin and the important features of the graph, such as the vertex and the intercepts. In this example, a viewing window of $[-1, 8]$ by $[-1, 25]$ would show these features.

For each quadratic function, determine the smallest viewing window that will display the origin, the vertex, and the intercepts of the graph.

a) $y = -3(x + 1)^2 - 2$ b) $y = \frac{1}{3}(x + 4)^2 - 6$ c) $y = -2(x - 5)^2 - 7$

d) $y = -\frac{3}{4}(x - 6)^2 - 7$ e) $y = (x + 2)^2 + 5$

A Fencing Problem

You have 24 m of fencing to enclose a rectangular-shaped garden. What is the largest area you can enclose with your fence?

Draw a diagram of the situation. In this case, we draw a rectangle with length l and width w. Let the length be represented by x. Since the perimeter is 24 m, then $x + w = 12$. Hence, $w = 12 - x$. The area is $A = lw = x(12 - x)$. To find the maximum value of $x(12 - x)$, enter $Y_1 = X(12 - X)$ on the functions menu of the graphing calculator. Set the viewing window to be $[-1, 12]$ by $[-1, 40]$ and display the graph of Y_1. Use the TRACE feature and position the cursor until you get the maximum value for Y_1. (You may have to adjust the viewing window and magnify portions of the graph).

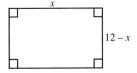

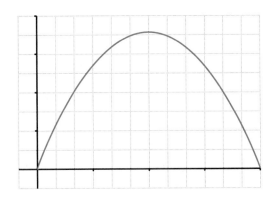

a) What is the maximum value of Y_1?

b) What is the value of X that corresponds to the maximum value of Y_1?

c) Is there always a rectangle of maximum area for any given perimeter? If so, what can be said about it?

The Cost of Cable TV

A cable television company currently serves 500 households and charges $20 per month. A marketing survey indicates that each decrease of $1 in the monthly fee will result in 50 new customers. For a decrease of d dollars per month, the monthly revenue M dollars can be calculated from the formula $M = (500 + 50d)(20 - d)$. If there is no decrease, the revenue is $500 \times \$20$, or $10 000. For a decrease of $2, the revenue is $(500 + 100)(\$20 - \$2)$, or $10 800.
However, for a decrease of $12, the revenue is $(500 + 600) (\$20 - \$12)$, or $8800.

a) Enter the equation for the monthly revenue on the functions menu. What do you think the size of the viewing window should be?

b) Graph the function and use the TRACE feature to determine the monthly fee that will give the highest revenue.

Falling Objects

When a ball is thrown vertically into the air, its height $H(t)$ (in metres) is described by the equation $H(t) = V_0 t - 4.9t^2$, where V_0 is the initial velocity of the ball and t represents the time in seconds. Suppose a ball is thrown from ground level with a velocity of 20 m/s.

a) Write the equation for the height of the ball and enter it on the functions menu.

b) What values of H and t make sense in this situation?

c) Graph the equation in an appropriate viewing window.

d) After how much time will the ball hit the ground?

e) What is the maximum height reached by the ball and when does it occur?

Problems, Anyone?

For each problem, determine two equations which describe the given conditions. Then solve the problem by graphing these equations. Verify your answers algebraically.

1. The length of a rectangle is 7 cm more than its width. The area of the rectangle is 200 cm^2. Find the dimensions of the rectangle.

2. Find two consecutive integers such that four times the first is equal to the square of the second.

An Error in Algebra

One very common mistake in algebra is to conclude that $(x + 4)^2 = x^2 + 16$. Show that this is not true by graphing both sides of the equation separately as $Y_1 = (X + 4)^2$ and $Y_2 = X^2 + 16$.

2-7 GRAPHING $y = ax^2 + bx + c$

In the previous section, we developed a method of sketching the graph of an equation such as $y = 2(x - 3)^2 - 7$ using the geometric meaning of the three constants in the equation. In applications of quadratic functions, however, an equation is more likely to be encountered in the form $y = 2x^2 - 12x + 11$. In this form, the constants used in drawing the graph are not obvious. To obtain these constants, we use the method of *completing the square*.

Example 1. Write $y = 2x^2 - 12x + 11$ in the form $y = a(x - p)^2 + q$, then sketch the graph.

Solution. *Step 1.* Remove 2 as a common factor from the first two terms.
$$y = 2(x^2 - 6x) + 11$$

Step 2. Add and subtract the square of $\frac{1}{2}(-6)$ inside the brackets.
$$y = 2(x^2 - 6x + 9 - 9) + 11$$

Step 3. Remove the last term from the brackets and combine with the constant term.
$$y = 2(x^2 - 6x + 9) - 18 + 11$$
$$= 2(x^2 - 6x + 9) - 7$$

Step 4. Factor the expression in the brackets as a complete square.
$$y = 2(x - 3)^2 - 7$$

By inspection of this equation
The coordinates of the vertex are $(3, -7)$.
The equation of the axis of symmetry
is $x - 3 = 0$.
When $x = 0$, $y = 2(0)^2 - 12(0) + 11$,
or 11
The y-intercept is 11.
Since $x - 3 = 0$ is the axis of symmetry,
$(6, 11)$ is also on the graph.
Knowing the coordinates of the vertex,
the point corresponding to the y-intercept
and its reflection in the axis of symmetry,
we can now sketch the curve.

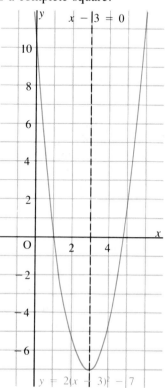

The method of completing the square can be applied to the general form, $f(x) = ax^2 + bx + c$, of the quadratic function to transform it to the standard form $f(x) = a(x - p)^2 + q$.

$$f(x) = ax^2 + bx + c$$
$$= a\left(x^2 + \frac{b}{a}x\right) + c$$
$$= a\left(x^2 + \frac{b}{a}x + \frac{b^2}{4a^2}\right) + c - \frac{b^2}{4a}$$
$$= a\left(x + \frac{b}{2a}\right)^2 + \frac{4ac - b^2}{4a}$$
$$= a\left(x + \frac{b}{2a}\right)^2 + \frac{b^2 - 4ac}{-4a}$$
$$= a\left(x + \frac{b}{2a}\right)^2 + \frac{D}{-4a}, \text{ where } D = b^2 - 4ac$$

For the graph of the function $f(x) = ax^2 + bx + c$

- The coordinates of the vertex are $\left(\dfrac{-b}{2a}, \dfrac{D}{-4a}\right)$, where $D = b^2 - 4ac$.

  Since the vertex is on the parabola, its coordinates satisfy the equation.

  Hence, $\dfrac{D}{-4a} = f\left(\dfrac{-b}{2a}\right)$, and the coordinates of the vertex may be

  written $\left(\dfrac{-b}{2a}, f\left(\dfrac{-b}{2a}\right)\right)$.

- The equation of the axis of symmetry is $x = \dfrac{-b}{2a}$.

Example 2. Sketch the graph of the function $f(x) = x^2 - 4x + 1$.

Solution.   *Step 1.* Find the coordinates (x, y) of the vertex.

$$x = \frac{-b}{2a} \qquad\qquad y = f(2)$$
$$= \frac{-(-4)}{2(1)} \qquad\quad = 2^2 - 4(2) + 1$$
$$= 2 \qquad\qquad\qquad = -3$$

The coordinates of the vertex are $(2, -3)$.

Step 2. The y-intercept is 1. Since the line $x = 2$ is the axis of symmetry, the point $(4, 1)$ is also on the graph.

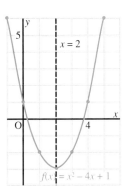

Step 3. Make a table of values and use symmetry to obtain a few other points. Sketch the graph.

x	-1	0	1	2	3	4	5
y	6	1	-2	-3	-2	1	6

Compute these points.   These points are found by symmetry.

To graph $y = ax^2 + bx + c$
- Complete the square and write the equation in the form $y = a(x - p)^2 + q$, or use $x = \dfrac{-b}{2a}$ to locate the vertex.
- Draw the axis of symmetry $x - p = 0$.
- Draw a curve through these three points.
  —the vertex (p, q)
  —the point $(0, c)$ corresponding to the y-intercept
  —the reflection image of $(0, c)$ in the axis of symmetry
- Use symmetry to obtain the coordinates of other points.

EXERCISES 2-7

1. Write each equation in the form $y = a(x - p)^2 + q$. Then sketch each graph.
   a) $y = x^2 - 6x + 8$ b) $y = x^2 + 10x + 14$ c) $y = 2x^2 + 4x + 7$
   d) $y = -2x^2 + 4x + 5$ e) $y = 3x^2 - 24x + 40$ f) $y = -5x^2 - 20x - 30$

2. Sketch each parabola showing:
   i) the coordinates of the vertex   ii) the equation of the axis of symmetry
   iii) the coordinates of two other points on the graph.
   a) $y = x^2 - 6x + 10$ b) $y = 2x^2 + 8x + 7$
   c) $m = -4n^2 - 24n - 20$ d) $u = -2v^2 - 16v - 35$
   e) $y = \frac{1}{2}x^2 - 2x + 7$ f) $r = 4t^2 + 12t - 5$
   g) $k = -2j^2 + 14j - 12$ h) $y = 3x^2 - 4x - 6$

3. Sketch each parabola showing:
   i) the y-intercept   ii) the coordinates of the vertex
   iii) the coordinates of two other points on the graph.
   a) $y = 2x^2 - 5x - 3$ b) $y = 2x^2 - 9x - 18$ c) $y = 0.4x^2 + 2x + 2.5$

4. The x-intercepts of $y = ax^2 + bx + c$ are given by $x = \dfrac{-b \pm \sqrt{b^2 - 4ac}}{2a}$. Show that the x-coordinate of the vertex is the mean of the two x-intercepts.

2-8 MAXIMUM AND MINIMUM VALUES OF A QUADRATIC FUNCTION

When a quadratic function is graphed, the vertex is important because it is either the highest or lowest point on the curve. Consider these examples.

The parabola $y = 2(x - 3)^2 + 4$ has vertex (3, 4) and opens up.

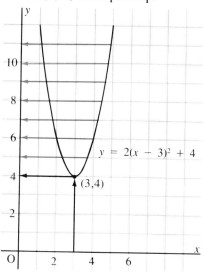

The parabola $y = -2(x - 3)^2 + 4$ has vertex (3, 4) and opens down.

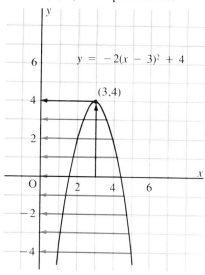

The graph shows that the values of y for points on the curve are never less than 4. That is, the function
$f(x) = 2(x - 3)^2 + 4$
has a *minimum* value of 4 which occurs when $x = 3$.

The graph shows that the values of y for points on the curve are never greater than 4. That is, the function
$f(x) = -2(x - 3)^2 + 4$
has a *maximum* value of 4 which occurs when $x = 3$.

These characteristics of a quadratic function can be obtained from its equation without drawing its graph.

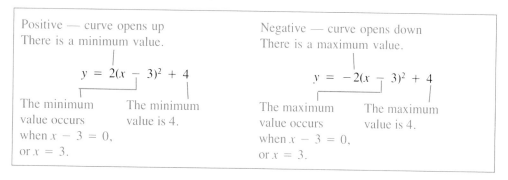

Positive — curve opens up
There is a minimum value.

$$y = 2(x - 3)^2 + 4$$

The minimum value occurs when $x - 3 = 0$, or $x = 3$.

The minimum value is 4.

Negative — curve opens down
There is a maximum value.

$$y = -2(x - 3)^2 + 4$$

The maximum value occurs when $x - 3 = 0$, or $x = 3$.

The maximum value is 4.

As the maximum or minimum value of a quadratic function is the y-coordinate of the vertex, it is given by $f\left(\dfrac{-b}{2a}\right) = \dfrac{D}{-4a}$.

When the maximum or minimum value has been computed, the range of a quadratic function is easily determined. The range of $f(x) = ax^2 + bx + c$ is the unbounded interval

$$\left[\dfrac{D}{-4a}, +\infty\right) \quad \text{if } a > 0$$

or $\left(-\infty, \dfrac{D}{-4a}\right]$ if $a < 0$.

Example 1. Find the maximum or minimum value of $f(x) = 2x^2 - 4x + 5$.

Solution.   Comparing $f(x) = 2x^2 - 4x + 5$ with the general function $f(x) = ax^2 + bx + c$, $a = 2 > 0$, so the function has a minimum value.

$$\text{Minimum value of } f = \dfrac{D}{-4a}$$
$$= \dfrac{b^2 - 4ac}{-4a}$$
$$= \dfrac{(-4)^2 - 4(2)(5)}{-4(2)}$$
$$= 3$$

The minimum value of f is 3.

An alternative solution to *Example 1* would be to find the coordinates (x, y) of the vertex.

$$x = \dfrac{-b}{2a} \qquad\quad y = f(1)$$
$$= \dfrac{-(-4)}{2(2)} \qquad = 2(1)^2 - 4(1) + 5$$
$$= 1 \qquad\qquad = 3$$

Hence, the minimum value is 3, which occurs at $x = 1$.

Example 2. Find the domain and range of $g(x) = 6x - 2x^2$.

Solution.   The domain of g is $\mathbb{R}$.
Comparing $g(x) = -2x^2 + 6x$ with the general function $f(x) = ax^2 + bx + c$, $a = -2 < 0$, so the function has a maximum value.

$$\text{Maximum value of } g = \dfrac{D}{-4a}$$
$$= \dfrac{6^2 - 4(-2)(0)}{-4(-2)}$$
$$= 4.5$$

The range of g is the interval $-\infty, 4.5]$.

Many applications of quadratic functions involve finding the maximum or minimum value.

Example 3. Supermarket cashiers try to memorize current sale prices while they work. A survey showed that, on average, the percent P of prices memorized after t hours is given approximately by the function $P(t) = -40t^2 + 120t$.

a) What is the greatest percent of prices memorized?

b) How long does it take to memorize them?

Solution. Find the coordinates $(t, P(t))$ of the vertex.

$$t = \frac{-b}{2a}$$

$$= \frac{-120}{2(-40)}$$

$$= 1.5$$

$$P(1.5) = -40(1.5)^2 + 120(1.5)$$

$$= -90 + 180$$

$$= 90$$

a) The greatest percent of prices memorized is 90%.

b) It takes 1.5 h to memorize 90% of the prices.

EXERCISES 2-8

1) Using the word maximum or minimum, and data from each graph, complete this sentence: "The ... value of y is ... when $x =$ ..."

a)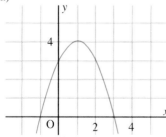

b)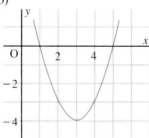

c)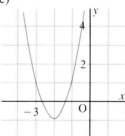

d)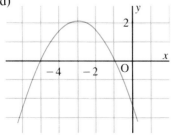

e)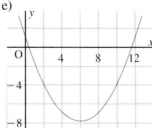

f)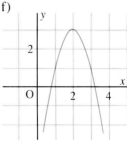

2. For each parabola, state:

   i) the maximum or minimum value of y ii) the value of x where it occurs.

     a) $y = (x - 3)^2 + 5$ b) $y = 2(x + 1)^2 - 3$ c) $y = -2(x - 1)^2 + 4$

     d) $y = -(x + 2)^2 - 6$ e) $y = 0.5x^2 - 9$ f) $y = 7 - 2x^2$

     g) $f(x) = x^2 - 6x + 7$ h) $g(x) = 2x^2 - 8x + 15$ i) $k(x) = -2x^2 + 5x$

(B)

3. Find the domain and range of each function.

     a) $m(x) = 3x^2 - 6x + 5$ b) $q(t) = 40t - 5t^2$ c) $r(x) = \frac{1}{2}x^2 - 3x + 4$

4. Linda owns a jeans store. Her monthly profit $P(x)$ dollars on the sale of x pairs of jeans is given by the equation $P(x) = 50x - \frac{1}{5}x^2$. How many pairs of jeans must Linda sell each month to maximize her profit?

5. A manufacturer of compact disc players has found that the cost in dollars of manufacturing x units per day is given by the cost function $C(x) = 0.25x^2 - 16x + 500$. How many units should be manufactured each day to minimize the cost?

6. Andrea owns and operates her own jewellery store. By studying her past records, she has found that, on the average, if she sells x articles of jewellery in one week, then her weekly profit $P(x)$ dollars can be calculated using the equation $P(x) = 100x - \frac{5}{3}x^2$. What is Andrea's maximum weekly profit?

7. A submarine is engaged in a practice dive. Its dive is defined by the function $d(t) = 4t^2 - 64t$, where $d(t)$ represents the depth in metres and t is the elapsed time in minutes from the start of the dive.

   a) What is the greatest depth reached by the submarine during its dive, and after how many minutes is this depth reached?

   b) Graph this function. State its domain and range.

8. The net income I, in thousands of dollars, from an office building s storeys high is given by $I(s) = -40s^2 + 4000s - 1000$. What is the maximum income?

9. The rate of fuel consumption of an aircraft, f litres per hour, is given approximately by the function defined by $f(v) = 0.01v^2 - 5v + 1000$, where v is the speed in kilometres per hour.

   a) At what speed is the rate of fuel consumption a minimum?

   b) What is the minimum fuel consumption?

10. On a forward somersault dive, Greg's height h metres above the water is given approximately by $h = -5t^2 + 6t + 3$, where t is the time in seconds after he leaves the board.

    a) Find Greg's maximum height above the water.

    b) How long does it take him to reach the maximum height?

    c) How long is it before he enters the water?

    d) How high is the board above the water?

11. The power P watts supplied to a circuit by a 9 V (volt) battery is given by the formula $P = 9I - 0.5I^2$, where I is the current in amperes.

    a) For what value of the current will the power be a maximum?

    b) What is the maximum power?

12. A ball is thrown into the air from the balcony of an apartment building and falls to the ground. The height h metres of the ball relative to the ground t seconds after being thrown is given by $h = -5t^2 + 10t + 35$.

    a) Find the maximum height of the ball above the ground.

    b) How long does it take the ball to reach the maximum height?

    c) After how many seconds does the ball hit the ground?

    d) How high is the balcony above the ground?

    e) What would be the equation if heights were measured relative to the balcony rather than to the ground?

Ⓒ

13. A projectile is launched from a platform, and its height h metres is given as a function of the elapsed time t seconds by $h = -4.9t^2 + 180t + 2$. Draw a graph showing h as a function of t, and use it to estimate:

    a) the maximum height of the projectile

    b) the time required for the projectile to reach its maximum height

    c) the time required for the projectile to reach the ground.

14. If $f(x) = ax^2 + bx + c$ has a minimum value 0, what conditions must be satisfied by a, b, and c?

 INVESTIGATE

Graph the parabola and the line on the same grid.

$y = x^2 - 4x + 3$ $y = -4x + 3$

Compare the graphs. Is there any geometric relation between the parabola and the line?

Determine if the relation holds for other parabolas.

Write a report of your findings.

An Analysis of Quadratic Functions

An analysis of a quadratic function, such as $y = -\frac{1}{2}x^2 + 4x - 5$, involves a combination of many algebraic and geometric skills.

$y = -\frac{1}{2}x^2 + 4x - 5$ common factors

$\quad = -\frac{1}{2}(x^2 - 8x) - 5$ completing the square

$\quad = -\frac{1}{2}(x^2 - 8x + 16 - 16) - 5$

$\quad = -\frac{1}{2}(x - 4)^2 + 3$

The parabola opens down and
is congruent to $y = \frac{1}{2}x^2$.   congruence

The maximum value of y is 3   maximum and
and occurs when $x = 4$.   minimum values

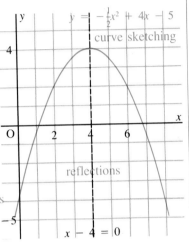

Intercepts   finding intercepts

Let $x = 0$.

$y = -\frac{1}{2}(0)^2 + 4(0) - 5$

$\quad = -5$

The y-intercept is -5.

Let $y = 0$.

$0 = -\frac{1}{2}x^2 + 4x - 5$

$x^2 - 8x + 10 = 0$

$x = \dfrac{-b \pm \sqrt{b^2 - 4ac}}{2a}$

$x = \dfrac{8 \pm \sqrt{24}}{2}$

$\quad = 4 \pm \sqrt{6}$

equation of a
vertical line

solving quadratic
equations

working with radicals

   To analyze a quadratic function in the above manner means to determine all the following information about the function.
- the coordinates of the vertex
- the equation of the axis of symmetry
- the direction of opening
- a congruent parabola
- a sketch of the function
- the y-intercept
- the x-intercepts, if any
- the maximum or minimum value of y
- the value of x for which the maximum or minimum value occurs.

   1. Analyze each parabola.

   a) $y = x^2 - 6x + 5$ b) $y = -\frac{1}{2}x^2 + 5x - 9$ c) $f(x) = 2x^2 - 5x - 12$

2-9 APPLICATIONS OF QUADRATIC FUNCTIONS

In many problems involving the maximum or minimum of a function, the function is not given; it has to be found from the data. Note the steps involved in the solutions of the following examples.

Example 1. Two numbers have a difference of 10. What are the numbers if their product is a minimum?

Solution.   *Step 1.* Identify the quantity to be maximized or minimized.
The quantity to be minimized is the product P of two numbers.

Step 2. Write the algebraic expression for this quantity.
Let the two numbers be x and y. Then, $P = xy$

Step 3. The expression must contain only one variable. If it contains more, use other information to write it in terms of one variable.
Since the numbers have a difference of 10, $x - y = 10$, where x is the greater number.
Solve for y. $y = x - 10$
Substitute $x - 10$ for y in $P = xy$.
$P = x(x - 10)$
$\quad = x^2 - 10x$

Step 4. The expression in Step 3 is a quadratic function. Rearrange it by completing the square.
$P = x^2 - 10x$
$\quad = x^2 - 10x + 25 - 25$
$\quad = (x - 5)^2 - 25$

Step 5. Determine the maximum or minimum value of the function and the value of the variable for which it occurs.
The minimum value of P is -25 which occurs when $x = 5$.

Step 6. Answer the question in the statement of the problem.
Since $x = 5$ and $x - y = 10$, $y = -5$
The two numbers are 5 and -5.

Example 2. A rectangular lot is bounded on one side by a river and on the other three sides by a total of 80 m of fencing. Find the dimensions of the largest possible lot.

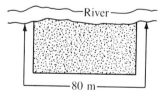

Solution.   *Step 1.* The quantity to be maximized is the area of the lot.
Step 2. Let x metres be the width of the lot and y metres the length.
Then, if A is the area, $A = xy$.

Step 3. Since the total length of fencing is 80 m,
$$2x + y = 80$$
or, $\quad y = 80 - 2x$
Substitute $80 - 2x$ for y in $A = xy$.
$$A = x(80 - 2x)$$
$$= -2x^2 + 80x$$
Step 4. $A = -2(x^2 - 40x)$
$$= -2(x^2 - 40x + 400 - 400)$$
$$= -2(x^2 - 40x + 400) + 800$$
$$= -2(x - 20)^2 + 800$$
Step 5. The maximum value of A is 800 and occurs when $x = 20$.
Step 6. Since $x = 20$ and $2x + y = 80$, $y = 40$
The dimensions of the largest possible rectangular lot are 40 m by 20 m.

Example 3. The cost of a ticket to a hockey arena seating 800 people is $3. At this price every ticket is sold. A survey indicates that if the price is increased, attendance will fall by 100 for every dollar of increase. What ticket price results in the greatest revenue? What is the greatest revenue?

Solution. *Step 1.* The quantity to be maximized is the total revenue R dollars from the tickets to be sold.

Step 2. Let x dollars be the increase in ticket price. Then,
$$R = (\text{cost per ticket})(\text{number of tickets sold})$$
$$= (3 + x)(800 - 100x)$$
$$= -100x^2 + 500x + 2400$$

Step 3. The expression already contains only one variable.

Step 4. $R = -100(x^2 - 5x) + 2400$
$$= -100\left(x^2 - 5x + \frac{25}{4} - \frac{25}{4}\right) + 2400$$
$$= -100\left(x^2 - 5x + \frac{25}{4}\right) + 625 + 2400$$
$$= -100\left(x - \frac{5}{2}\right)^2 + 3025$$

Step 5. The maximum value of R is 3025 and occurs when $x = \frac{5}{2}$, or 2.5.

Step 6. Since an increase in price of $2.50 per ticket results in the greatest revenue, the ticket price should become $5.50. The greatest revenue is $3025.00.

EXERCISES 2-9

(B)

1. Two numbers have a difference of 8. Find the numbers if their product is a minimum.

2. The sum of two natural numbers is 12. If their product is a maximum, find the numbers.

3. The sum of two numbers is 60. Find the numbers if their product is a maximum.

4. Two numbers have a difference of 20. Find the numbers if the sum of their squares is a minimum.

5. The sum of two numbers is 16. Find the numbers if the sum of their squares is a minimum.

6. The sum of two numbers is 28. Find the numbers if the sum of their squares is a minimum.

7. The sum of a number and three times another number is 18. Find the numbers if their product is a maximum.

8. Two numbers have a difference of 16. Find the numbers if the result of adding their sum and their product is a minimum.

9. A rectangular lot is bordered on one side by a stream and on the other three sides by 600 m of fencing. Find the dimensions of the lot if its area is a maximum.

10. A lifeguard marks off a rectangular swimming area at a beach with 200 m of rope. What is the greatest area of water she can enclose?

11. Eighty metres of fencing are available to enclose a rectangular play area.
    a) What is the maximum area that can be enclosed?
    b) What dimensions produce the maximum area?

12. A rectangular area is enclosed by a fence and divided by another section of fence parallel to two of its sides. If the 600 m of fence used encloses a maximum area, what are the dimensions of the enclosure?

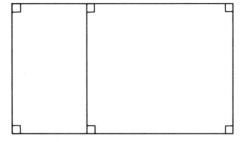

13. A theatre seats 2000 people and charges $10 for a ticket. At this price, all the tickets can be sold. A survey indicates that if the ticket price is increased, the number sold will decrease by 100 for every dollar of increase. What ticket price would result in the greatest revenue?

14. A bus company carries about 20 000 riders per day for a fare of 90¢. A survey indicates that if the fare is decreased, the number of riders will increase by 2000 for every 5¢ of decrease. What ticket price would result in the greatest revenue?

15. A trough is made from a rectangular strip of sheet metal, 50 cm wide, by bending up at right angles a strip *x* centimetres high, along two sides. For what value of *x* is the cross-sectional area a maximum?

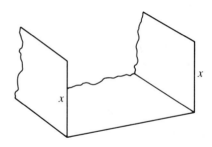

16. What is the maximum area of a triangle having 15 cm as the sum of its base and height?

17. A straight section of railroad track crosses two highways 400 m and 600 m from an intersection. Find the dimensions of the largest rectangular lot that can be laid out in the triangle formed by the railroad and highways.

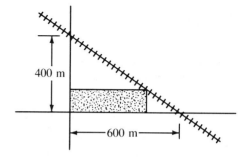

18. A 30 cm piece of wire is cut in two. One piece is bent into the shape of a square, the other piece into the shape of a rectangle with a length-to-width ratio of 2 : 1. What are the lengths of the two pieces if the sum of the areas of the square and rectangle is a minimum?

Ⓒ

19. Find the number which exceeds its square by the greatest possible amount.

20. Find the maximum possible area of a rectangle with a given perimeter.

21. In $\triangle ABC$, $\angle B = 90°$ and AC has a constant length. Prove that the area of $\triangle ABC$ is a maximum when AB = BC.

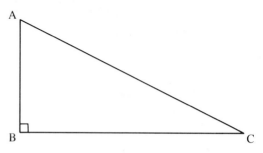

22. Find the minimum distance from $(0, 0)$ to the line $3x + 2y - 12 = 0$.

2-10 INTERVALS OF INCREASE OR DECREASE

The performance of a stock during the month of April can be illustrated graphically. The value of one share of the stock decreased from $3 to $1 during the first 10 days of the month and then increased from $1 to $9 during the remaining 20 days of April.

There are many situations in which we wish to know the intervals on which a function is increasing or decreasing.

A function f is said to be *increasing* on a given interval of its domain if the values of $f(x)$ increase as x increases in the interval. More precisely, if x_1 and x_2 are any numbers in the interval with $x_1 < x_2$, then $f(x_1) < f(x_2)$.

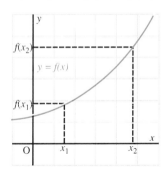

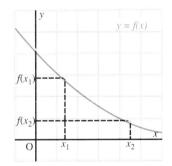

Increasing function—graph rises   Decreasing function—graph falls

A function f is said to be *decreasing* on a given interval of its domain if the values of $f(x)$ decrease as x increases in the interval. That is, if x_1 and x_2 are any numbers in the interval with $x_1 < x_2$, then $f(x_1) > f(x_2)$.

Example 1. Determine the intervals of increase or decrease for the function f whose graph is shown. For which interval is the function constant?

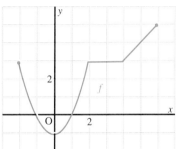

Solution. f is increasing on the intervals $[0,2]$ and $[4,6]$.
f is decreasing on the interval $[-2,0]$.
f is constant on the interval $[2, 4]$.

Example 2. Determine the intervals of increase or decrease for $f(x) = x^2 - 4x + 3$.

Solution.   Sketch the graph and locate the vertex at $(2,-1)$.
The graph of f opens up since $a = 1 > 0$.
f is decreasing on $-\infty, 2]$ and increasing
on $[2, +\infty$.

$f(x) = x^2 - 4x + 3$

The results of *Example 2* show that the vertex of a quadratic function
is the point where the function changes from decreasing to increasing,
or vice versa. Hence, the coordinates of the vertex can be used to
describe the intervals of increase and decrease.

In general, for a quadratic function $f(x) = ax^2 + bx + c$

- If $a > 0$, then f is decreasing on $-\infty, \dfrac{-b}{2a}\right]$ and increasing on $\left[\dfrac{-b}{2a}, +\infty$.

- If $a < 0$, then f is increasing on $-\infty, \dfrac{-b}{2a}\right]$ and decreasing on $\left[\dfrac{-b}{2a}, +\infty$.

EXERCISES 2-10

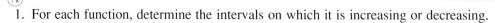

1. For each function, determine the intervals on which it is increasing or decreasing.

a)   b)   c)

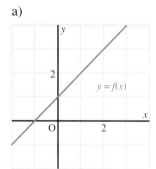   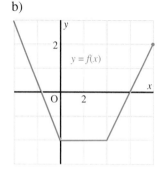   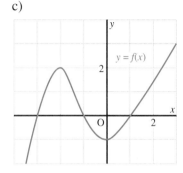

d)

e)

f)

2. For each polynomial function of degree two, determine the intervals on which the function is increasing or decreasing.

a) $f(x) = x^2 - 4x + 7$

b) $g(x) = 8x - 6x^2$

c) $k(x) = 2x^2 - 3x + 5$

d) $m(x) = 9 - 4x - 3x^2$

e) $n(x) = 3x^2 - 2x + 1$

f) $p(x) = -x^2 - 40x + 120$

3. The monthly revenue, in dollars, from the sales of a certain type of calculator is given by $R(x) = 80x - 2x^2$, where x is the selling price in dollars of each calculator. For what interval of prices will the monthly revenue increase?

4. The value of a stock, in dollars, at the end of each month in 1992 varied according to the equation $V(x) = \dfrac{x^2}{4} - 2x + 6$, where x represents the number of months.

a) What was the minimum value of the stock in 1992?

b) For how many months did the stock decrease?

c) For how many months did the stock increase?

5. The number of air conditioners that a department store sells during the summer is given by the function $N(x) = 20 + 24x - x^2, 0 \leqslant x \leqslant 20$, where x is the number of hot days during the summer. For how many hot days will the sale of air conditioners increase?

C

6. The population of a town after t years since 1960 has grown according to the equation $P(t) = 0.06t^2 - 1.2t + 12$, where $P(t)$ is the population in thousands.

a) What was the initial population in 1960?

b) For how many years did the population decrease?

c) In what year did the population reach 30 000?

2-11 ZEROS OF A QUADRATIC FUNCTION

The zeros of a function are the values of the independent variable x for which $f(x) = 0$. That is, the zeros
are the x-coordinates of the points where the graph of
the function crosses the x-axis. For the function f, the
zeros are -2, 0, and 3.

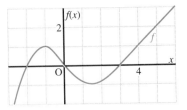

Example 1. Given $f(x) = 2x^2 - 3x - 2$
 a) Find the zeros of f.
 b) Find the elements of the domain that have 3 as their image. Sketch
    the graph.

Solution. a) To find the zeros, set $f(x) = 0$, and
    solve for x in the resulting equation.
$$f(x) = 0$$
$$2x^2 - 3x - 2 = 0$$
$$(2x + 1)(x - 2) = 0$$
$$x = -\frac{1}{2} \text{ or } x = 2$$

The zeros of f are $-\frac{1}{2}$ and 2.

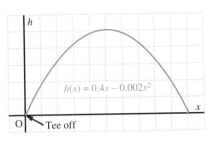

 b) Let $f(x) = 3$
$$2x^2 - 3x - 2 = 3$$
$$2x^2 - 3x - 5 = 0$$
$$(x + 1)(2x - 5) = 0$$
$$x = -1 \text{ or } x = 2.5$$
Thus, there are two elements of the domain, -1 and 2.5, which have
3 as their image.

Example 2. The path of a golf ball follows a parabolic trajectory. The height h metres of
the ball at a distance x metres from tee-
off is given by $h(x) = 0.4x - 0.002x^2$.
How far from the tee-off will the ball hit
the ground?

Solution. When the ball hits the ground, $h(x) = 0$.
$$0.4x - 0.002x^2 = 0$$
Multiply by 1000.
$$400x - 2x^2 = 0$$
$$-2x(x - 200) = 0$$
$$x = 0 \text{ or } x = 200$$
The ball hits the ground 200 m from tee-off.

Example 3. Find the equation of a second-degree polynomial function with vertex $(6,-2)$ and zeros of 2 and 10.

Solution. As the vertex is given, we use the standard form to find the equation of the quadratic function.

$f(x) = a(x - p)^2 + q$, where $p = 6$ and $q = -2$

So, $f(x) = a(x - 6)^2 - 2$

The graph crosses the x-axis at $(2,0)$ and $(10,0)$.

Substitute $x = 2$ and $f(x) = 0$ to find a.

$0 = a(2 - 6)^2 - 2$

$0 = 16a - 2$

$a = \frac{1}{8}$

The second-degree polynomial function has equation

$f(x) = \frac{1}{8}(x - 6)^2 - 2$ in standard form or $f(x) = \frac{1}{8}x^2 - \frac{3}{2}x + \frac{5}{2}$.

In *Example 3*, notice that the x-coordinate of the vertex is the mean of the zeros; that is, $6 = \frac{2 + 10}{2}$. This is true for all second-degree polynomial (that is, quadratic) functions.

Example 4. Sandra dives off a dock, entering the water 2 m from the dock and emerging 10 m from the dock. At a distance of 4 m from the dock, Sandra is 3 m below the surface of the water. Sandra's dive follows a parabolic trajectory. What is the greatest depth reached by Sandra?

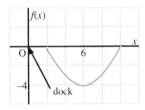

Solution. Since we know the zeros, let the equation of the trajectory be $f(x) = a(x - r)(x - s)$, where r and s are the zeros of f, and x represents the distance from the dock.

Hence, $f(x) = a(x - 2)(x - 10)$.

We know that $(4,-3)$ is a point on the graph of f.

Substitute $x = 4$ and $f(x) = -3$ to find a.

$-3 = a(4 - 2)(4 - 10)$

$-3 = -12a$

$a = \frac{1}{4}$

We can write $f(x) = \frac{1}{4}(x - 2)(x - 10)$.

The greatest depth is the value of $f(x)$ at the vertex.

The x-coordinate of the vertex is $\frac{r + s}{2} = \frac{2 + 10}{2}$, or 6.

Then, $f(6) = \frac{1}{4}(6 - 2)(6 - 10)$

$= -4$

The greatest depth Sandra reaches is 4 m.

EXERCISES 2-11

1. Find the zeros of each function from its graph.

a)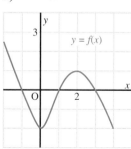

b)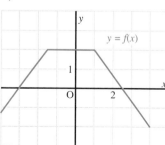

c)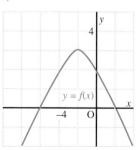

2. Find the zeros of each second-degree polynomial function.

a) $f(x) = x^2 - 2x - 24$ b) $g(x) = -x^2 + 3x + 4$

c) $h(x) = 2x^2 - 16x + 32$ d) $k(x) = 2x^2 - x - 6$

e) $m(x) = 2x^2 - 4x + 1$ f) $n(x) = 2x^2 - 3x + 2$

3. Given $f(x) = 2x^2 - 3x + 2$, find the values of x such that:

a) $f(x) = 2$ b) $f(x) = 7$ c) $f(x) = -1$.

4. Use the given information to find the equation of each quadratic function.

a) with zeros -5 and 3, and vertex $(-1,4)$

b) with zeros 2 and 6, and vertex $(4,-8)$

c) with zeros -1 and 2, and graph passes through the point $(3,-4)$

d) with zeros -2 and 3, and graph has y-intercept 3

e) with zeros 4 and 8, and a maximum value of 20

5. Find the equation of a quadratic function whose vertex is $(1,-3)$ and whose zeros are the same as those of the function $k(x) = -x^2 + 2x + 8$.

6. The height of a flare h metres above the ground is given by $h(t) = -5t^2 + 100t$, where t is the elapsed time in seconds since firing.

a) How long does it take the flare to reach a height of 420 m?

b) When will the flare hit the ground?

7. The power P watts that is consumed by an electrical circuit after t seconds is approximated by the formula $P = 4t^2 + 2t$. How long will it take the power consumption to reach 72 W?

8. A batter hits a long fly ball. Its height h metres after time t seconds is approximated by the function $h(t) = 1 + 6t - 0.2t^2$.

a) Calculate the time required for the ball to reach a height of 41 m.

b) If no fielder catches the ball, how long, to the nearest tenth of a second, will it take to hit the ground?

9. A car dealer estimates that the monthly profit (or loss) $P(x)$, in thousands of dollars, after selling x cars is given by $P(x) = -x^2 + 80x - 1200$.

a) How much money does the dealer lose if no cars are sold?

b) What is the minimum number of cars that must be sold to break even?

c) What is the maximum profit?

10. A football is kicked and it follows a parabolic path. No one catches it and it hits the ground 4 s later. It reaches a maximum height of 25 m. Find the equation of the path of the football.

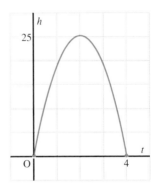

11. When Larry Walker of the Montreal Expos hit his last home run of the season, the trajectory of the ball was a parabola. At a distance of 30 m from home plate, the ball was 27 m high. It hit the ground 120 m from home plate. What was the approximate maximum height reached by the ball? (Locate home plate at the origin. Ignore the height at which the ball was hit.)

12. The trajectory of a rocket is illustrated. If h is the height in metres after time t minutes, find how long, to the nearest tenth of a minute, it will take the rocket to return to earth.

13. Show that if r and s are the zeros of $f(x) = ax^2 + bx + c$, then $f(x) = a(x^2 - Sx + P)$, where S is the sum of the zeros and P is their product.

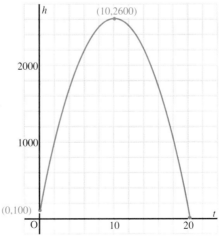

2-12 SOLVING QUADRATIC INEQUALITIES

The quadratic equation $x^2 - 5x + 4 = 0$ can be solved by factoring to obtain $(x - 4)(x - 1) = 0$, and the solutions $x = 1$ and $x = 4$.

This equation can also be solved by graphing the equation $x^2 - 5x + 4 = y$. The solutions are where the graph crosses the x-axis; that is, at $x = 1$ and $x = 4$. Notice that the graph divides the x-axis into three different sets of values for x.

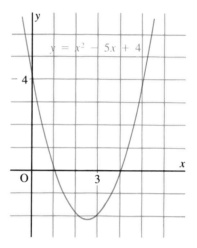

- The values of x that satisfy the equation $x^2 - 5x + 4 = 0$; these are the values of x where the graph crosses the x-axis. The roots of the equation are 1 and 4.
- The values of x that satisfy the inequality $x^2 - 5x + 4 > 0$; these are the values of x where the graph is above the x-axis. The solution of the inequality is $x < 1$ or $x > 4$.
- The values of x that satisfy the inequality $x^2 - 5x + 4 < 0$; these are the values of x where the graph is below the x-axis. The solution of the inequality is $1 < x < 4$.

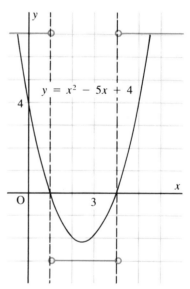

Any quadratic inequality can be solved by graphing. But notice in the above example that the roots of the corresponding equation determine the endpoints of the intervals in the solutions of the inequalities. Hence, a more efficient method of solving a quadratic inequality is to solve the corresponding equation and test values of x in the intervals defined by the roots of the equation.

Example 1.   Solve the inequality $6 - 5x^2 < 13x$.

Solution.   *Step 1*. Solve the equation $6 - 5x^2 = 13x$.

$5x^2 + 13x - 6 = 0$

$(5x - 2)(x + 3) = 0$

Therefore, $x = \frac{2}{5}$ and $x = -3$

The roots are -3 and $\frac{2}{5}$. These divide the x-axis into three intervals: A, B, and C.

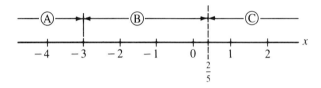

Step 2. Select a value of x in each interval, and substitute it in both sides of the given inequality. If the inequality is satisfied, all values of x in the interval are solutions of the inequality.

A value of x in interval A is -10. Substitute -10 for x.

Left side $= -494$ Right side $= -130$

This value of x satisfies the inequality.

A value of x in interval B is 0. Substitute 0 for x.

Left side $= 6$ Right side $= 0$

This value of x does not satisfy the inequality.

A value of x in interval C is 1. Substitute 1 for x.

Left side $= 1$ Right side $= 13$

This value of x satisfies the inequality.

Step 3. Write the solution of the inequality, or illustrate the solution on a number line.

The solution is $x < -3$ or $x > \frac{2}{5}$.

In the *Example*, the numbers -3 and $\frac{2}{5}$ are not part of the solution. If the inequality had been $6 - 5x^2 \leq 13x$, these numbers would satisfy the inequality, and the solution would be written as $x \leq -3$ or $x \geq \frac{2}{5}$.

Polynomial inequalities of higher degree can be solved in the same way. The initial step of solving the corresponding equation can be carried out by factoring or by using a computer.

Example 2. The graph of a function f is shown at the right. Determine the intervals on which f is positive, and on which f is negative.

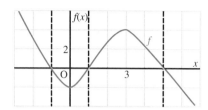

Solution. The zeros of f are -1, 1, and 5.
They divide the x-axis into 4 open intervals.
On each of these intervals, f is positive or negative.
If f is positive on an interval, then its graph lies above the x-axis; that is, $f(x) > 0$ on $-\infty, -1[\cup]1,5[$.
If f is negative on an interval, then its graph lies below the x-axis; that is, $f(x) < 0$ on $]-1, 1[\cup]5, +\infty$.

Example 3. A manufacturer of golf clubs finds that the monthly revenue R dollars, from a particular type of golf club, is given by $R(x) = 64x - x^2$, where x is the number of clubs sold each month. How many clubs must be sold each month for the revenue to be greater than $960?

Solution. We solve the inequality $R(x) > 960$.
First solve the equation $R(x) = 960$.
$$64x - x^2 = 960$$
$$x^2 - 64x + 960 = 0$$
$$(x - 24)(x - 40) = 0$$
$$x = 24 \text{ or } 40$$
Use these zeros to sketch the graph of the associated function $f(x) = R(x) - 960$; that is, $f(x) = -x^2 + 64x - 960$.
From the graph, $f(x) > 0$ for $24 < x < 40$.
This means that the manufacturer must sell between 24 and 40 clubs each month for the revenue to exceed $960.

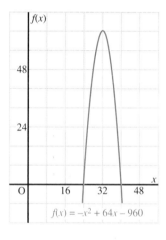

$f(x) = -x^2 + 64x - 960$

EXERCISES 2-12

1. For each function, determine the intervals on which the function is positive or negative.

a)

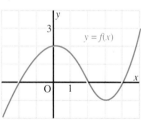

b)

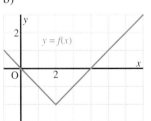

c)

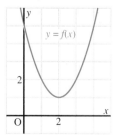

2.) For each quadratic function:
   i) Find the zeros.   ii) Sketch the graph.
   iii) Determine the intervals on which $f(x) > 0$ and $f(x) < 0$.

   a) $f(x) = x^2 - 2x - 15$ b) $f(x) = -x^2 + x + 12$ c) $f(x) = 2x^2 - 5x + 2$

B

3.) Use the method of *Example 1* to solve each inequality.
   a) $(x - 3)(x + 2) > 0$ b) $x^2 - 2x \le 0$ c) $5x < x^2$
   d) $x^2 - 2x \ge 8$ e) $12x - 4 \ge 9x^2$ f) $(x - 1)(x - 4) \le 28$
   g) $2x - 2 - x^2 \ge 0$ h) $6x^2 + 7x < 20$ i) $x^2 - 4x + 5 > 0$

4.) Given $f(x) = x^2 - 4x + 1$, find the values of x such that:
   a) $f(x) > 13$ b) $f(x) \le 1$ c) $f(x) \ge -5$.

5.) A company's profit (or loss), P dollars, varies in an 8-h day according to the
   equation $P(t) = 20t - 4t^2$, where t is the time in hours. Find the values of t such
   that: a) $P(t) > 0$ b) $P(t) < 0$.

6.) During the last 12 months, the monthly balance sheet of a company has followed
   the rule $B(x) = x^2 - 7x + 6$, where x represents the number of months and $B(x)$
   the balance, in thousands of dollars. For how many months was the company in
   the red?

7.) A company manufactures lawn mowers. The monthly net revenue, R dollars, is
   given by $R(x) = -x^2 + 34x - 120$, where x is the number of lawn mowers
   manufactured each month.
   a) What is the maximum number of lawn mowers that the company can
      manufacture before suffering a loss?
   b) How many lawn mowers should the company manufacture monthly to ensure
      a profit?

8.) A corn farmer must plant enough corn so that the harvest will yield a profit. The
   profit as a function of the amount of seed planted is given by
   $P(x) = -x^2 + 12x - 32$, where x is the number of seeds in thousands, and $P(x)$
   the profit in thousands of dollars. How much seed should the farmer plant to
   show a profit?

9.) When a ball is thrown upward, its height h metres is given by
   $h(t) = 1.5 + 19.6t - 4.9t^2$, where t is the time in seconds after the ball is thrown.
   For what length of time is the ball higher than 16.2 m?

C

10. For what values of x does the graph of $y = x^2 - 4x$:
   a) lie above the line $y = 2x - 5$ b) lie below the line $y = x + 14$?

11. Solve each inequality.
   a) $(x + 3)(x - 1)(x - 3) > 0$ b) $-x(x - 2)(x + 5) \le 0$
   c) $x^3 - x < 0$ d) $x^3 - 3x^2 + 2x \ge 0$

Don't Make the Problem Harder

"... there is no right way to approach solving a math problem."

Marilyn Burns

Two numbers have a sum of $\sqrt{7}$ and a difference of $\sqrt{3}$.
What is the product of the two numbers?

Understand the problem
- What are we asked to find?
- Are we asked to find the two numbers?

Think of a strategy
- We could let the numbers be x and y and write two equations.

$$x + y = \sqrt{7}$$
$$x - y = \sqrt{3}$$

- We could solve for x and y, and then multiply the results together.
- This is correct, but it involves unnecessary calculations with square roots.
- Since we do not need to know the values of x and y, a more elegant method might lead directly to the product xy.
- Recall that the sum, difference, and product of two numbers are contained in the formulas for the square of a binomial.
  $$(x + y)^2 = x^2 + 2xy + y^2 \text{ and } (x - y)^2 = x^2 - 2xy + y^2$$
- Do you see how to combine $(x + y)^2$ and $(x - y)^2$ to obtain an expression involving xy?

Carry out the strategy
- Simplify $(x + y)^2 - (x - y)^2$.
- Since we know the values of $x + y$ and $x - y$, we can substitute these in the above expression, and use the result to find the value of xy.

Look back
- Did you get 1 for the product of the two numbers?
- Check that this method is easier than the method of solving the equations.
- Discuss how this problem illustrates the quotation by Marilyn Burns at the top of the page.

PROBLEMS

Ⓑ

1. A farmer offered to cut a log into three pieces for $5.00. How much should he charge to cut the log into six pieces?

2. Find three natural numbers x, y, and z such that $x^1 + y^2 = z^3$.

3. Two numbers have a sum of 5 and a product of 10. Find the sum of their reciprocals.

4. In square ABCD (below left), M and N are the midpoints of AD and BC respectively. If the sides have length x centimetres, find the area of the shaded rhombus.

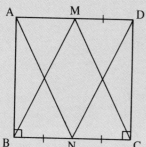   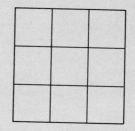

5. Copy the diagram (above right). Write the digits from 1 to 9 in the spaces such that the 3-digit number in the second row is double the 3-digit number in the first row, and the 3-digit number in the third row is triple the 3-digit number in the first row.

6. Solve this system. $29x + 19y = 260$
$19x + 29y = 220$

Ⓒ

7. Two sides of a triangle have length 6 and 8. The length of the third side is an integer.
   a) How many triangles are there satisfying these conditions?
   b) How many of the triangles are isosceles? acute? obtuse?

8. Prove that two unequal numbers, each of which is the square of the other, have a product of 1.

9. Solve this equation. $(x^2 + 3x - 2)(x^2 + 3x - 6) = 32$

10. Solve this equation. $\dfrac{x-a}{b+c+d} + \dfrac{x-b}{a+c+d} + \dfrac{x-c}{a+b+d} + \dfrac{x-d}{a+b+c} = 4$

Ⓓ

11. Prove that for all natural numbers m and n, the expression $\dfrac{(m+1)n + m}{mn + (m-1)}$ is in lowest terms.

Review Exercises

1. Graph each function, and state its domain and range.
   a) $f(x) = -\frac{1}{2}x^2 - 2x + 7$ b) $f(x) = 2x^2 - 12x + 9$

2. In a Test-Your-Strength booth at a fair you strike a pad with a hammer. This projects a weight up a vertical slide. A bell rings if you have hit the pad hard enough. When the pad is struck with just sufficient force to ring the bell, the height h metres of the weight t seconds after the pad is struck is given by $h = 8t - 4.9t^2$.
   a) How high is the weight 0.5 s after the pad is struck?
   b) How high is the bell?

3. Find the equation of each parabola.
   a) with vertex $(-2, 0)$, y-intercept 4
   b) with vertex $(5, 0)$, y-intercept 25
   c) with x-intercept -6, y-intercept 36, and axis of symmetry $x + 6 = 0$

4. Find the equation of the parabola with vertex $(0, 0)$ which passes through each point.
   a) $(2, 16)$ b) $(3, -18)$ c) $(2, 6)$ d) $(-3, 15)$
   e) $\left(\frac{2}{3}, -\frac{2}{3}\right)$ f) $(4, 12)$ g) $\left(-\frac{5}{2}, 5\right)$ h) $\left(\frac{1}{2}, -\frac{1}{2}\right)$

5. Find the equation of each parabola.
   a) with vertex $(-3, 4)$, y-intercept -5
   b) with vertex $(2, -2)$, x-intercepts 1 and 3
   c) with vertex $(4, -4)$, that opens up, and is congruent to $y = \frac{1}{2}x^2$

6. Sketch each parabola showing:
   i) the coordinates of the vertex
   ii) the equation of the axis of symmetry
   iii) the coordinates of two other points on the graph.
   a) $y = x^2 - 6x + 5$ b) $w = 2z^2 - 8z - 5$
   c) $v = \frac{1}{2}t^2 + 10t + 21$ d) $p = -3q^2 + 18q - 20$

7. A producer of synfuel from coal estimates that the cost C dollars per barrel for a production run of x thousand barrels is given by $C = 9x^2 - 180x + 940$. How many thousand barrels should be produced each run to keep the cost per barrel at a minimum? What is the minimum cost per barrel of synfuel?

8. Two numbers have a difference of 24. Find the numbers if the result of adding their sum and their product is a minimum.

9. A bus company carries about 40 000 riders per day for a fare of $1.00. A survey indicates that if the fare is decreased, the number of riders will increase by 2500 for every 5¢ decrease. What fare will result in the greatest revenue?

The speed of a vehicle v kilometres per hour can be estimated from the length d metres of its skid marks. If $v = 12.6\sqrt{d} + 8$, sketch a graph of v as a function of d without making a table of values. (See Section 3-7 *Example 2*.)

3-1 SOLVING EQUATIONS INVOLVING ABSOLUTE VALUE

On the number line, the numbers -4 and 4 are each located 4 units from 0. Each number is said to have an absolute value of 4. We write $|-4| = 4$ and $|4| = 4$.

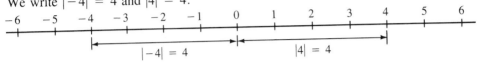

Example 1. Simplify.

a) $|12|$

b) $|-7|$

Solution.

a) The absolute value of a positive number is the number itself.
$|12| = 12$

b) The absolute value of a negative number is the opposite number.
$|-7| = 7$

As *Example 1* indicates, the definition of the absolute value of a number depends on whether the number is positive or negative.

Definition of Absolute Value

If a number is positive or zero, its *absolute value* is the number itself.

If $x \geq 0$, then $|x| = x$

If a number is negative, its *absolute value* is the opposite number.

If $x < 0$, then $|x| = -x$

When this definition is used, both cases must be considered separately.

Example 2. Solve for x. $|x - 2| = 3$

Solution.   *Case 1.* Let $x - 2 \geq 0$

$x \geq 2$

The solution below is valid only if $x \geq 2$.
For these values of x, $|x - 2| = x - 2$

The given equation becomes: $x - 2 = 3$

$x = 5$

Case 2. Let $x - 2 < 0$

$x < 2$

The solution below is valid only if $x < 2$.
For these values of x, $|x - 2| = -(x - 2)$

$= -x + 2$

The given equation becomes: $-x + 2 = 3$

$x = -1$

Therefore, the given equation has two roots, $x = 5$ and $x = -1$.

In some equations, one or both of the roots obtained are not possible values of the variable, and must be rejected.

Example 3. Solve and check. $|x - 3| = 2x$

Solution. *Case 1.* Let $x - 3 \geqslant 0$

$$x \geqslant 3$$

The solution below is valid only if $x \geqslant 3$.
For these values of x, $|x - 3| = x - 3$
The given equation becomes: $x - 3 = 2x$

$$-3 = x$$
$$x = -3$$

This solution is rejected because it is not among the possible values of x.

Case 2. Let $x - 3 < 0$

$$x < 3$$

The solution below is valid only if $x < 3$.
For these values of x, $|x - 3| = -(x - 3)$

$$= -x + 3$$

The given equation becomes: $-x + 3 = 2x$

$$3 = 3x$$
$$x = 1$$

Therefore, the given equation has only one root, $x = 1$.

Check. When $x = 1$, L.S. $= |x - 3|$ R.S. $= 2x$
$$= |1 - 3|$$ $$= 2(1)$$
$$= |-2|$$ $$= 2$$
$$= 2$$

Therefore, $x = 1$ is correct.

In *Example 3*, you can check that the possible root $x = -3$, which was obtained in the first case, does not satisfy the equation $|x - 3| = 2x$.

Occasionally, an equation is encountered that has no roots. This can sometimes be determined by inspection.

Example 4. Solve for x.

a) $|2x + 3| = -5$ b) $|x - 2| + |2x + 6| = 0$

Solution. a) $|2x + 3| = -5$

The expression on the left side is greater than or equal to 0.
Therefore, it is impossible for it to be equal to the right side, -5.
This equation has no roots.

b) $|x - 2| + |2x + 6| = 0$

Each expression on the left side is greater than or equal to 0.
The only way their sum can be zero is for each term to be equal to 0.
But this is impossible, since $|x - 2|$ equals 0 when $x = 2$, and $|2x + 6|$ equals 0 when $x = -3$.
Since there is no value of x which makes both expressions equal 0, the equation has no roots.

EXERCISES 3-1

Ⓐ
1. Solve for x.
   a) $|x| = 5$ b) $|x| = 2$ c) $|x| = 0$ d) $|x| = -4$

Ⓑ
2. Solve for x.
   a) $|x - 2| = 7$ b) $|x + 4| = 3$ c) $|x + 1| = 5$
   d) $0 = |x - 7|$ e) $|3x - 2| = 4$ f) $|x - 4| = -2$
   g) $|1 - x| = 8$ h) $6 = |x - 5|$ i) $|2 - 3x| = 7$

3. Solve for x.
   a) $|x + 1| = 2x$ b) $|x + 4| = x - 1$
   c) $|3 - x| = 4$ d) $3x = |x - 2|$
   e) $x = |2x + 1|$ f) $|4x - 1| = x$

4. Solve for x.
   a) $|x + 3| = 4x$ b) $3x = |2 - x|$ c) $|4 + 3x| = 7x$
   d) $|4x - 1| = 8x$ e) $|10x + 3| = x - 1$ f) $|2 - 5x| = 2 - 3x$

5. Solve for x.
   a) $2|x + 1| = 8$ b) $9 = 3|2 + x|$ c) $2|x - 1| = 5$
   d) $4|4x - 3| = 7x$ e) $\frac{1}{2}|6x + 4| = 2x$ f) $\frac{1}{4}|3 - 2x| = \frac{3}{2}$

6. Solve for x.
   a) $|3x - 4| + |7 - 2x| = 0$ b) $|2x - 8| + |12 - 3x| = 0$
   c) $|2x - 6| = -|x + 4|$ d) $|x - 3| + |3 - x| = 0$

Ⓒ
7. Solve for x.
   a) $|x| = 5|x| - 8$ b) $7|x + 2| = 2|x + 2| + 15$
   c) $|x + 1| + 2 = 3|x + 1|$ d) $|2x - 1| = |2x - 1| + 1$
   e) $|2x + 3| = |2x + 3|$ f) $|5x - 1| = |1 - 5x|$

8. Solve for x.
   a) $|x - 3| + |x - 8| = 17$ b) $|1 - 5x| = |x|$
   c) $|x - 1| + |x - 3| = 6$ d) $|x - 1| + |x - 3| = 2$

9. Solve for x.
   a) $|x + 2| + |2 - x| = 8$ b) $|2x - 1| + |1 - 2x| = 0$
   c) $|2x - 1| - |1 - 2x| = 4$ d) $|2x - 1| - |1 - 2x| = 0$

10. Draw a graph of the function $f(x) = |x - 1| + |x - 4|$ and use it to solve each equation.
    a) $|x - 1| + |x - 4| = 5$
    b) $|x - 1| + |x - 4| = 3$
    c) $|x - 1| + |x - 4| = 1$

3-2 SOLVING INEQUALITIES INVOLVING ABSOLUTE VALUE

To solve inequalities involving absolute value, use the definition of absolute value. The cases where the expression inside the absolute value signs is positive and negative must be considered separately.

Example 1. Solve for x. $|3x - 1| < 5$

Solution.   *Case 1.* Let $3x - 1 \geqslant 0$

$$x \geqslant \frac{1}{3}$$

The solution below is valid only if $x \geqslant \frac{1}{3}$.

For these values of x, $|3x - 1| = 3x - 1$

The given inequality becomes: $3x - 1 < 5$

$$3x < 6$$
$$x < 2$$

Since the only possible values of x are those shown on the number line above, the values of x which satisfy the inequality lie between $\frac{1}{3}$ (including $\frac{1}{3}$) and 2.

$$\frac{1}{3} \leqslant x < 2$$

Case 2. Let $3x - 1 < 0$

$$x < \frac{1}{3}$$

The solution below is valid only if $x < \frac{1}{3}$.

For these values of x, $|3x - 1| = -(3x - 1)$
$$= -3x + 1$$

The given inequality becomes: $-3x + 1 < 5$

$$-3x < 4$$
$$x > -\frac{4}{3}$$

Since the only possible values of x are those shown on the number line above, the values of x which satisfy the inequality lie between $-\frac{4}{3}$ and $\frac{1}{3}$.

$$-\frac{4}{3} < x < \frac{1}{3}$$

Combining the results of Cases 1 and 2, we see that the solution set of the given inequality consists of all real numbers between $-\frac{4}{3}$ and 2.

$$-\frac{4}{3} < x < 2$$

Any inequality involving absolute value expressions can be solved in the same way. In some cases, the solutions obtained are not possible values of *x* and must be rejected.

Example 2.   Solve for *x*. $|x - 2| > 2x$

Solution.   *Case 1*. Let $x - 2 \geqslant 0$

$$x \geqslant 2$$

The solution below is valid only if $x \geqslant 2$.
For these values of *x*, $|x - 2| = x - 2$

The given inequality becomes: $x - 2 > 2x$
$$x - 2x > 2$$
$$-x > 2$$
$$x < -2$$

This result contradicts the initial statement that $x \geqslant 2$. Hence, there is no solution for this case.

Case 2. Let $x - 2 < 0$

$$x < 2$$

The solution below is valid only if $x < 2$.
For these values of *x*, $|x - 2| = -(x - 2)$
$$= -x + 2$$

The given inequality becomes: $-x + 2 > 2x$
$$-3x > -2$$
$$x < \frac{2}{3}$$

Since the only possible values of *x* are those shown on the number line above, the values of *x* which satisfy the inequality are less than $\frac{2}{3}$.

Hence, the solution set of the given inequality consists of all real numbers less than $\frac{2}{3}$.

$x < \frac{2}{3}$

EXERCISES 3-2

Ⓐ

1. Solve.
   a) $|x| < 3$
   b) $|x| > 4$
   c) $|2x| \leqslant 12$
   d) $|x - 2| < 5$
   e) $|5x| \geqslant 8$
   f) $|x + 1| \leqslant 9$

2. Solve.
   a) $|x - 1| \leqslant 4$
   b) $|x + 1| > 7$
   c) $|2x + 1| < 9$
   d) $|3x - 1| < 5$
   e) $|x + 3| \geqslant 10$
   f) $|4x - 1| \geqslant 11$

(B)

3. Solve.
   a) $|x| > x - 2$
   b) $|2x - 5| \leq 7$
   c) $|5x + 2| > 3$
   d) $|3x - 2| < x + 1$
   e) $|7x + 12| \leq -5$
   f) $|x + 1| > 3x$

4. Solve.
   a) $|2x + 1| < 9$
   b) $\left|\frac{1}{2}x + 1\right| \leq 2$
   c) $|4x - 9| > 15$
   d) $|3 - x| < 2x$
   e) $|2 - 3x| < 3x - 4$
   f) $|3x + 2| < 5x + 1$

5. Solve.
   a) $|7x - 3| \geq 11$
   b) $\left|\frac{x - 2}{3}\right| < 1$
   c) $|x + 1| > x - 1$
   d) $|2x + 1| < 3x$
   e) $|6 - 3x| \leq x - 2$
   f) $|5x + 2| < 3x + 1$

(C)

6. Solve.
   a) $|x| + |x - 1| < 5$
   b) $|3x - 1| \leq |2x + 18|$
   c) $|x + 2| - |x| > 4$
   d) $|12x + 5| \leq |5x + 12|$

7. Solve.
   a) $|x + |x|| < 10$
   b) $||x| - 2| > 6$
   c) $\left|\frac{x - 3}{x + 5}\right| < 2$
   d) $\left|\frac{3x - 6}{4x - 8}\right| \geq 1$

8. a) If the area of a rectangle, in square centimetres, is represented by $7x - x^2 - 9$, and its width in centimetres is represented by $x - 2$, find an expression for its length.
   b) Assuming that the length is greater than or equal to the width, for what values of x does the expression found in part a) represent the length of the rectangle?

9. Write an absolute value inequality whose solution set is each given graph.
   a)
   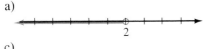
   b)
   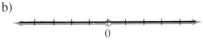
   c)

   d)
   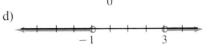

10. Write an absolute value inequality for each solution set.
    a) $x \geq 3$
    b) $0 \leq x \leq 4$
    c) $x < 0$ or $x > 4$
    d) $x \neq 2$

11. Write an absolute value inequality which has:
    a) no solution
    b) every real number as a solution
    c) only one solution.

3-3 THE ABSOLUTE-VALUE FUNCTION

The real function defined by $f(x) = |x|$ is called the *absolute-value function*. Recall that if $x \geqslant 0$, then $|x| = x$ and if $x < 0$, then $|x| = -x$.

We can draw the graph of $f(x) = |x|$ by using this definition.

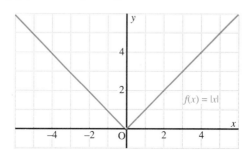

x	$f(x)$
-3	3
-2	2
-1	1
0	0
1	1
2	2
3	3

There are two parts to the V-shaped graph.
If $x \geqslant 0$, the graph is that of $y = x$.
If $x < 0$, the graph is that of $y = -x$.

The main properties of $f(x) = |x|$ are:
—Vertex is (0,0).   —Minimum value is 0.
—Domain is $\mathbb{R}$.   —The function is decreasing on $-\infty, 0]$.
—Range is $[0, +\infty$.   —The function is increasing on $[0, +\infty$.
—The zero is 0.   —The function is positive for all real values of x.

   In *Chapter 2*, we found that when certain changes were made in the equation of the quadratic function $f(x) = x^2$, there were corresponding changes in the position and appearance of the parabola. Similarly, when certain changes are made in the equation $f(x) = |x|$, the appearance and position of the graph changes, but its characteristic shape does not change.

Example 1.   Graph $g(x) = -|x| + 1$. State the main properties of g.

Solution.   To graph the function, follow these steps.
Step 1. Graph $y = |x|$.

Step 2. Reflect $y = |x|$ in the x-axis to obtain the graph of $y = -|x|$.

Step 3. Translate all the points on the graph of $y = -|x|$ one unit up.

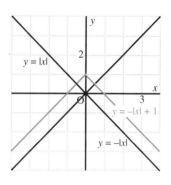

The main properties of g are:

—Vertex is $(0,1)$.

—Domain is $\mathbb{R}$.

—Range is $-\infty, 1]$.

—Zeros are $\{-1,1\}$.

—$g(x) > 0$ for $x \in \,]-1, 1[$

—$g(x) < 0$ for $x \in \,-\infty,-1[\,\cup\,]1, +\infty$

—Maximum value is 1.

—The function is increasing on $-\infty, 0]$.

—The function is decreasing on $[0, +\infty$.

In *Example 1*, the first two steps are useful because they aid in visualizing the graph. These steps can often be omitted.

Example 2. Graph the function $g(x) = |6 - 2x| - 1$.

Solution. Simplify the expression $|6 - 2x|$. Use the fact that

$|ab| = |a| \, |b|, \,\forall a, b \in \mathbb{R}.$

$$
\begin{aligned}
|6 - 2x| &= |-2x + 6| \\
&= |-2(x - 3)| \\
&= |-2| \, |x - 3| \\
&= 2|x - 3|
\end{aligned}
$$

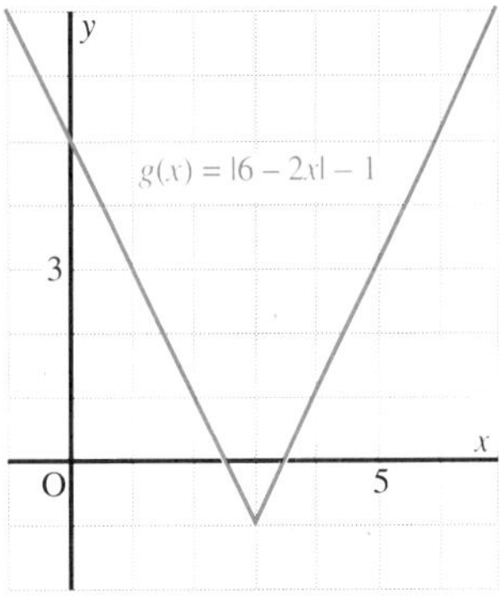

To graph $g(x) = 2|x - 3| - 1$, we note that it is in the form $y = a|x - p| + q$ with $a = 2$, $p = 3$, and $q = -1$. The vertex is $(3,-1)$, the graph opens up since $a > 0$, and the two parts of the graph have slopes equal to $\pm a$; that is, $m = \pm 2$.

$g(x) = |6 - 2x| - 1$

Example 3. Given $f(x) = 3|2x - 1| + 4$, find x when $f(x) = 10$.

Solution. $f(x) = 3|2x - 1| + 4$

We want the values of x for which $f(x) = 10$.

Substitute $f(x) = 10$.

$$3|2x - 1| + 4 = 10$$
$$3|2x - 1| = 6$$
$$|2x - 1| = 2$$
$$2x - 1 = 2 \ \text{ or } \ 2x - 1 = -2$$
$$2x = 3 \qquad\qquad 2x = -1$$
$$x = 1.5 \qquad\qquad x = -0.5$$

When $f(x) = 10$, $x = 1.5$ and -0.5

Example 4. During a chemistry experiment, the temperature T degrees Celsius of a liquid as a function of time t minutes is given by

$$T(t) = -\frac{|t - 30|}{2} + 10, \, 0 \leqslant t \leqslant 60$$

a) Sketch a graph of the function.

b) For how many minutes is the temperature of the liquid at least 0°C?

Solution.   We want the values of t for which $T(t) \geqslant 0$.

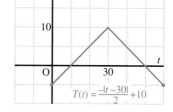

$$-\frac{|t - 30|}{2} + 10 \geqslant 0$$

$$-\frac{|t - 30|}{2} \geqslant -10$$

$$-|t - 30| \geqslant -20$$

$$|t - 30| \leqslant 20$$

$$-20 \leqslant t - 30 \leqslant 20$$

$$10 \leqslant t \leqslant 50$$

The temperature is at least 0°C for 50 min − 10 min = 40 min.

EXERCISES 3-3

Ⓐ

1. Given $f(x) = |x| + 2$ and $g(x) = |2 - x|$, calculate:

   a) $f(-2)$ b) $g(-2)$

   c) $f(-1) - g(5)$ d) $2f(5) - g(-1)$.

2. Graph these functions on the same grid.

   a) $f(x) = |x|$ b) $g(x) = 2|x|$

   c) $h(x) = -|x|$ d) $k(x) = -\frac{1}{2}|x|$

3. Repeat *Exercise 2* for these functions.

   a) $f(x) = |x| - 4$ b) $g(x) = |x - 2|$

   c) $h(x) = -|x| - 1$ d) $k(x) = -|x + 2|$

Ⓑ

4. Graph each function and state its main properties.

   a) $f(x) = |x - 1| + 3$

   b) $g(x) = \frac{1}{3}|x + 1| - 2$

   c) $h(x) = -4|x + 1| + 2$

5. Change each equation into the form $y = a|x - p| + q$, and draw its graph. State the domain and range of each function.

   a) $f(x) = |3x - 6| + 1$

   b) $g(x) = 4 - |2 - x|$

   c) $f(x) = \dfrac{|2 - 4x|}{4} - 3$

6. Find the zeros of each function.

   a) $f(x) = |2 - x| - 5$

   b) $g(x) = \dfrac{1}{3}|2x - 1| + 5$

   c) $k(x) = -2|3 - 2x| + 6$

7. Given $f(x) = |3x - 2| - 1$, find the value(s) of x such that:

   a) $f(x) = 0$ b) $f(x) = 4$

   c) $f(x) = -1$ d) $f(x) = -7$.

8. Given $g(x) = |2x - 1| - 3$, find the intervals for which:

   a) $g(x) > 0$ b) $g(x) \leq 0$

   c) $g(x) \geq 4$ d) $g(x) < -5$.

9. For the function $k(x) = -2|x - 1| + 4$, find the intervals of increase and decrease.

10. a) Find the equation of the absolute-value function whose graph is shown at the right.

    b) What are the zeros of this function?

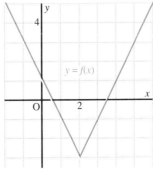

11. On "cheap" Tuesday, a movie theatre sells adult and child tickets at the same price. The revenue, R dollars, is given by $R(x) = 750 - 75|10 - 2x|$, where x dollars is the price of one ticket. Last Tuesday, the revenue collected was $375. What was the "cheap" price charged for a single ticket?

12. During a chemistry experiment, the temperature T degrees Celsius of a liquid as a function of time t minutes is given by $T(t) = 2|t - 25| - 30, 0 \leq t \leq 60$. For how many minutes is the temperature of the liquid at least 0°C?

3-4 THE SQUARE-ROOT FUNCTION

The problem of finding a ship's longitude at sea was so important to exploration and trade in the sixteenth and seventeenth centuries that several countries offered substantial prizes for its solution. The solution that was eventually found required the accurate recording of time using pendulum clocks.

The period T seconds of a pendulum of length l metres is given approximately by the formula $T = 2\sqrt{l}$. This function is an example of a *square-root function*.

l	T
0	0
1	2
2	2.8
3	3.5
4	4.0
5	4.5

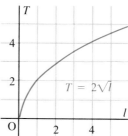

A simple square-root function is $f(x) = \sqrt{x}$. Since there are real values for $\sqrt{x}$ only when $x \geq 0$, the graph has an unusual property: it starts at a fixed point $(0,0)$ and extends in one direction only. The graph is the upper half of the parabola $y^2 = x$.

x	$f(x)$
0	0
1	1
2	1.4
3	1.7
4	2.0
5	2.2

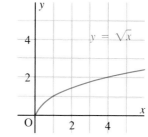

The main properties of $f(x) = \sqrt{x}$ are:
—Domain is $[0, +\infty$.   —Minimum value is 0.
—Range is $[0, +\infty$ —The function is increasing on $[0, +\infty$.
—The zero is 0.   —The function is positive for $x > 0$.

Example 1. Find the domain of $f(x) = \sqrt{4x - 4} - 2$. Draw the graph of this function.

Solution.   The expression $\sqrt{4x - 4}$ has real values only when

$$4x - 4 \geq 0$$
$$4x \geq 4$$
$$x \geq 1$$

Hence, the domain is $[1, +\infty$.
Rewrite the equation of $f(x)$ in the form
$f(x) = a\sqrt{x - p} + q$.

$$f(x) = \sqrt{4x - 4} - 2$$
$$= \sqrt{4(x - 1)} - 2$$
$$= 2\sqrt{x - 1} - 2$$

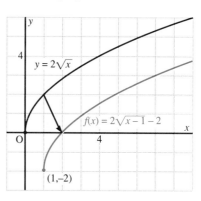

The graph of $f(x)$ can be obtained from the graph of $y = 2\sqrt{x}$ by translating it 1 unit right and 2 units down.

Example 2. Draw the graph of $g(x) = \sqrt{-x}$. State the domain and range of this function.

Solution. The expression $\sqrt{-x}$ has real values only when $-x \geq 0$; that is, for $x \leq 0$. Make a table of values and sketch the graph.

x	$g(x)$
0	0
-1	1
-2	1.4
-3	1.7
-4	2
-5	2.2

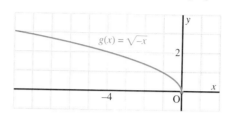

The domain is $\mathbb{R}_-$. The range is $\mathbb{R}_+$.

In *Example 2*, notice that the graph of $g(x) = \sqrt{-x}$ is the reflection in the y-axis of the graph of $f(x) = \sqrt{x}$. The point with coordinates $(-x, y)$ is on the graph of g whenever (x, y) is on the graph of f. In general, the graph of $y = f(-x)$ is the reflection of the graph of $y = f(x)$ in the y-axis.

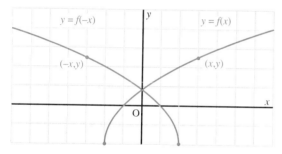

Example 3. Graph $f(x) = \sqrt{1 - x} + 2$. Is the function increasing or decreasing?

Solution. Rewrite $f(x)$ in the form
$$f(x) = a\sqrt{-(x - p)} + q.$$
$$f(x) = \sqrt{1 - x} + 2$$
$$= \sqrt{-x + 1} + 2$$
$$= \sqrt{-(x - 1)} + 2$$

The graph of $f(x)$ can be obtained by translating the graph of $y = \sqrt{-x}$ 1 unit right and 2 units up.

The function is decreasing on $-\infty, 1]$.

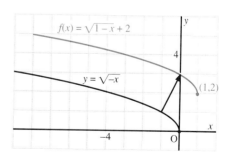

In general, the graph of the square-root function defined by
$f(x) = a\sqrt{bx + c} + d$ is a semiparabola with vertex $\left(-\dfrac{c}{b}, d\right)$.

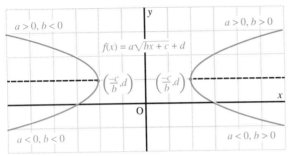

The domain is $-\infty, \dfrac{-c}{b}$, or $\dfrac{-c}{b}, +\infty$. The range is $-\infty, d]$ or $[d, +\infty$.

EXERCISES 3-4

(A)

1. Graph these functions on the same grid.

   a) $f(x) = \sqrt{x}$

   b) $g(x) = 2\sqrt{x}$

   c) $h(x) = \dfrac{1}{2}\sqrt{x}$

   d) $k(x) = -\sqrt{x}$

   e) $p(x) = -3\sqrt{x}$

   f) $q(x) = -\dfrac{1}{4}\sqrt{x}$

2. Repeat *Exercise 1* for these graphs.

   a) $f(x) = \sqrt{-x}$

   b) $g(x) = 3\sqrt{-x}$

   c) $h(x) = 0.2\sqrt{-x}$

   d) $k(x) = -\sqrt{-x}$

   e) $p(x) = -\dfrac{5}{2}\sqrt{-x}$

   f) $q(x) = -0.5\sqrt{-x}$

3. Graph each function and state its main properties.

   a) $f(x) = 2\sqrt{x} - 1$

   b) $g(x) = -\sqrt{x + 1} + 2$

   c) $h(x) = -\sqrt{2 - x} + 1$

4. Find the domain of each function.

   a) $f(x) = 4\sqrt{3x - 1}$

   b) $g(x) = 2\sqrt{2x + 3} + 1$

   c) $h(x) = \dfrac{1}{5}\sqrt{4 - 2x} + 3$

5. Graph each function and state its main properties.

   a) $f(x) = \sqrt{2x + 5} - 3$

   b) $g(x) = -\dfrac{1}{4}\sqrt{4x - 8} - 1$

Ⓑ

6. Find the zero of each function.

   a) $f(x) = 2\sqrt{2x - 1} - 4$ b) $g(x) = \frac{1}{4}\sqrt{4 - 5x} - 2$

7. Given $f(x) = \sqrt{2x - 1} + 3$, for what value of x is:
   a) $f(x) = 6$ b) $f(x) = -5$?

8. On what interval is $g(x) = \frac{1}{2}\sqrt{2 - x} + 1$ increasing or decreasing?

9. For which interval is the function $h(x) = -2\sqrt{x + 1} + 4$ positive?

10. Find the equation of the square-root function whose graph is shown here.

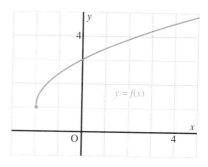

11. In shallow water, the velocity of a wave v metres per second is a function of the depth d metres of the water. $v(d) = 3.1\sqrt{d}$
    a) Graph the function for $d \in [0,10]$.
    b) What is the velocity of a wave in water 12 m deep?
    c) The velocity of a wave is 50 km/h. How deep is the water?

    Give the answers to 1 decimal place.

12. Since 1980, the population of a town has grown according to the formula $P(t) = 6 + 2\sqrt{t}$, where $P(t)$ is the population in thousands and t is the elapsed time since 1980.
    a) Graph this function for $t \in [0,20]$.
    b) What was the population in 1988?
    c) In what year will the population reach 14 000?

PROBLEM SOLVING

Arithmetic and Geometric Means

"Students are accustomed to encountering mathematics in its finished form. Problem solving is mathematics in the making."

Peggy A. House

For any two positive numbers x and y, we define the arithmetic mean and the geometric mean as follows.

Arithmetic mean: $\dfrac{x + y}{2}$ *Geometric mean:* $\sqrt{xy}$

Prove that the geometric mean is always less than or equal to the arithmetic mean. When are the two means equal?

Understand the problem
- Try some numerical examples. Choose any two positive numbers x and y, and calculate their arithmetic mean and geometric mean.
- Is the geometric mean less than or equal to the arithmetic mean? Under what conditions are they equal?
- Does this prove that the geometric mean will always be less than or equal to the arithmetic mean?

Think of a strategy
- We are required to prove that $\sqrt{xy} \leqslant \dfrac{x + y}{2}$.
- What formula in algebra involves both the sum of two variables, $x + y$, and their product, xy?

Carry out the strategy
- Start with the formula for the square of a binomial, $(x + y)^2$, and try to rearrange the terms to prove that $\sqrt{xy} \leqslant \dfrac{x + y}{2}$.
- You will also need the formula for $(x - y)^2$.
- Under what conditions does $\sqrt{xy} = \dfrac{x + y}{2}$?

Look back
- Could we prove that $\sqrt{xy} \leqslant \dfrac{x + y}{2}$ by squaring both sides and simplifying?
- A rectangle has length x and width y. How long is each side of a square if it has: the same perimeter as the rectangle? the same area as the rectangle?

PROBLEMS

Ⓑ

1. Prove that the inequality on the facing page is equivalent to this inequality.

$$\left(\frac{x + y}{2}\right)^2 \leq \frac{x^2 + y^2}{2}$$

2. Sketch some examples of quadrilaterals in which the diagonals bisect each other. What kind of quadrilaterals are they? Prove your prediction.

3. The arithmetic mean and the geometric mean of the roots of a quadratic equation are p and q respectively. Determine the equation.

4. A cube has edges of length n. The faces of the cube are all painted, then it is cut into n^3 smaller cubes.
   a) How many of the smaller cubes have:
      i) no faces painted
      ii) exactly one face painted
      iii) exactly two faces painted
      iv) exactly three faces painted
   b) Use the results of part a) to factor the expression $n^3 - 8$.

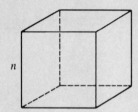

n

Ⓒ

5. a) Prove that $x_1y_1 + x_2y_2 \leq \sqrt{x_1^2 + x_2^2} \sqrt{y_1^2 + y_2^2}$.
   b) Under what conditions does the equality hold?

6. If x, y, and z are any three positive numbers, prove that $(x + y)(y + z)(z + x) \geq 8xyz$. Under what conditions does the equality hold?

7. a) Given the three numbers 1, 2, and -3, show that if these three numbers are used as the coefficients of a quadratic equation, in any order, the equation has rational roots.
   b) State a general result suggested by part a) and prove it.

8. If $x + y = 1$, prove that $\left(1 + \frac{1}{x}\right)\left(1 + \frac{1}{y}\right) \geq 9$.

Ⓓ

9. Triangle ABC has sides of length a, b, and c. Prove that $\triangle$ABC is equilateral if, and only if, $(a + b + c)^2 = 3(ab + bc + ac)$.

3-5 THE INVERSE-VARIATION FUNCTION

When money is invested at an annual interest rate of $r\%$, the approximate number of years n it takes to double is given by $n = \dfrac{72}{r}$.

r	n
5	14.4
7.5	9.6
10	7.2
12.5	5.8
15	4.8

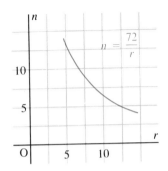

This is an example of an *inverse-variation function*, since the number of years n is *inversely proportional* to the interest rate r percent.

A simple inverse-variation function is $f(x) = \dfrac{1}{x}$. We can graph $f(x) = \dfrac{1}{x}$ by using a table of values.

x	y
-4	-0.25
-2	-0.5
-1	-1
-0.5	-2
-0.25	-4
0.25	4
0.5	2
1	1
2	0.5
4	0.25

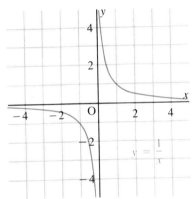

There is no point on the graph for $x = 0$ because $\dfrac{1}{x}$ is not defined when $x = 0$. The branches of the curve draw closer to the axes without ever touching them. The axes are said to be *asymptotes* of the graph.

The curve is called a *hyperbola*. It has two separate branches corresponding to positive and negative values of x. In most applications, the variables are positive and the graph consists of only the branch of the hyperbola located in the first quadrant.

Since the reciprocal of x is $\dfrac{1}{x}$, provided that $x \neq 0$, the function $f(x) = \dfrac{1}{x}$ is referred to as the *reciprocal* of the function $g(x) = x$.

Other examples of inverse-variation functions, or reciprocal functions, are:

$$f(x) = \frac{2}{x} \qquad g(x) = -\frac{4}{x} \qquad h(x) = \frac{3}{2x}$$

The general inverse-variation function is defined by $f(x) = \frac{k}{x}$, $x \neq 0$. In this equation, k is a nonzero constant called the *constant of proportionality*.

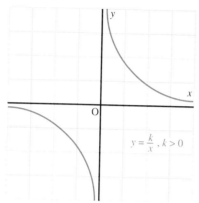

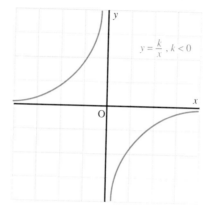

The main properties of $y = \frac{k}{x}$, $x \neq 0$, $k > 0$ are:

—Domain is $\mathbb{R}^*$.   —When $k > 0$, the function is decreasing on $\mathbb{R}^*$.
—Range is $\mathbb{R}^*$.   —When $k < 0$, the function is increasing on $\mathbb{R}^*$.
              —Asymptotes are $y = 0$ (x-axis) and $x = 0$ (y-axis).

Example 1. If f is an inverse-variation function and $f(-2) = 8$, find the equation of f.

Solution. The general equation is $f(x) = \frac{k}{x}$.

$(-2, 8)$ is on the graph of f since $f(-2) = 8$.
Substitute $x = -2$ and $f(-2) = 8$.

$$8 = \frac{k}{-2}$$
$$k = -16$$

The equation is $f(x) = \frac{-16}{x}$.

Example 2. The demand D for a certain product is inversely proportional to its selling price p dollars. If 200 items of the product are sold at \$6 each, how many items will be sold if the price is reduced to \$4?

Solution. The general equation is $D = \dfrac{k}{p}$.

Substitute $D = 200$ and $p = 6$.

$$200 = \frac{k}{6}$$

$$k = 1200$$

The equation is $D = \dfrac{1200}{p}$.

Substitute $p = 4$.

$$D = \frac{1200}{4}$$

$$= 300$$

Hence, 300 items will be sold at \$4 each.

EXERCISES 3-5

(A)

1. Given $f(x) = -\dfrac{2}{3x}$, state which of the following points lie on the graph of this function.

   a) $\left(2, -\dfrac{1}{3}\right)$ b) $(0, 0)$ c) $\left(-\dfrac{1}{9}, 6\right)$ d) $\left(\dfrac{1}{2}, -\dfrac{4}{3}\right)$

2. Graph these functions on the same grid.

   a) $y = \dfrac{1}{x}$ b) $y = \dfrac{2}{x}$ c) $y = \dfrac{1}{2x}$

3. Repeat *Exercise 2* for these functions.

   a) $y = -\dfrac{1}{x}$ b) $y = -\dfrac{2}{x}$ c) $y = -\dfrac{1}{2x}$

(B)

4. Graph each function and state its main properties.

    a) $f(x) = \dfrac{3}{x}$

    b) $g(x) = -\dfrac{4}{x}$

    c) $h(x) = \dfrac{3}{2x}$

5. The graph of an inverse-variation function passes through the point $\left(\dfrac{1}{3}, -4\right)$. Find the equation of this function.

6. Find the equation of each hyperbola.

    a)

    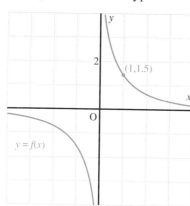

    b)

    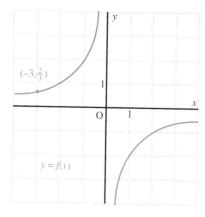

7. The demand for a clock radio is inversely proportional to its price. During a certain week, a store sold 12 clock radios at the regular selling price of $50. The following week, the store offered a discount of 40% on the selling price of each clock radio. How many did the store sell during that week?

8. In a closed electrical circuit, the current I amperes is inversely proportional to the resistance R ohms. An ammeter in the circuit registers 1.8 A when the resistance is measured at 200 Ω.

    a) What is the current when the resistance in the circuit is 240 Ω?

    b) What is the resistance if an electric drill requiring 3 A of current is placed in the circuit?

MATHEMATICS AROUND US

Inverse Variation

Police often identify speeders on a highway by measuring, from the air, the time it takes a car to cover a marked portion of the road. The table shows how the speed of a car is related to the time it takes to travel 0.5 km.

Time t (s)	Speed v (km/h)
20	90
40	45
60	30
80	22.5
100	18

The table shows that when t is doubled, v is divided by 2; when t is tripled, v is divided by 3, and so on. That is, the product of v and t is constant. We say that v *varies inversely* as t, and write $vt = k$, or $v = \dfrac{k}{t}$, where k is a constant. From the table, we can verify that $vt = 1800$ for all values of v and t.

If we plot the data, the resulting curve is part of a *rectangular hyperbola*. The equation of this hyperbola is $vt = 1800$.

The graph shows only one branch of the hyperbola. Another branch, corresponding to negative values of v and t, could be plotted in the third quadrant, but this would not be appropriate for distances and speeds, which are positive.

We can use the equation or the graph to find the speed of the car for times other than those given in the table. For example, if the time is measured as 23 s, then the speed of the car is found by substituting 23 for v in $vt = 1800$. Solving for v, we find $v \doteq 78$. Hence, a car which takes 23 s to complete the marked portion of the road is travelling at about 78 km/h.

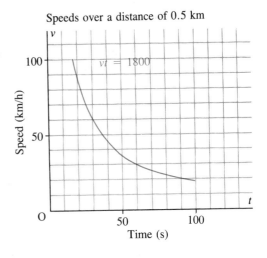

Speeds over a distance of 0.5 km

$vt = 1800$

Speed (km/h)

Time (s)

QUESTIONS

1. Make a table of values and sketch the rectangular hyperbola represented by each equation on the same grid. Show both branches of each hyperbola.
   a) $xy = 24$ b) $xy = 12$ c) $xy = 6$ d) $xy = 1$

2. If y varies inversely as x, find the equation relating x and y, then copy and complete the tables.

   a)

x	4	8	12	16	24
y	12				

   b)

x	10	12	15	20	30
y	6				

3. y varies inversely as x and when $x = 9$, $y = 4$.
   a) Find an equation relating x and y.
   b) Find: i) y when $x = 12$ ii) x when $y = 2$.
   c) Graph the relation between x and y.

4. The time it takes to complete a bike-a-thon course varies inversely as the cyclist's average speed. At an average speed of 15 km/h it takes 3.2 h to complete the course.
   a) How long does it take to complete the course at: i) 12 km/h   ii) 20 km/h?
   b) If the course is completed in 2 h, what is the average speed?
   c) Graph the relation between the time to complete the course and the average speed.

5. The number of hours required to construct a motion-picture set varies inversely as the number of workers. If the set can be constructed in 3 days by 20 workers, how many days would 12 workers require?

6. The number of years required for an investment to double varies inversely as the interest rate. At 8% per annum compound interest, an investment will double in about 9 years. Find an equation expressing the time n years for an investment to double as a function of the interest rate r percent.

7. Each rectangle in a set of rectangles has an area of 360 cm².
   a) Graph the relation between the length and the width of the rectangles.
   b) Graph the relation between the length and the perimeter.
   c) Does the length vary inversely as: i) the width   ii) the perimeter?

8. The intensity of illumination of a screen varies inversely as the square of its distance from a projector. When the distance is 4 m, the intensity is 10 units.
   a) Find an equation relating the intensity I units to the distance d metres.
   b) If a graph of the relation between I and d were drawn, explain why the curve would not be a rectangular hyperbola.
   c) Explain how a graph of the relation could be drawn such that the curve would be a rectangular hyperbola.

3-6 THE GREATEST INTEGER FUNCTION

A company that designs posters and calendars charges its clients a postage and handling fee when it delivers material to them by mail. The company uses the following table to calculate the fee.

POSTAGE AND HANDLING	
Orders up to $20.00	$2.00
$20.00 to $40.00	$4.00
$40.00 to $60.00	$6.00
Over $60.00	$8.00

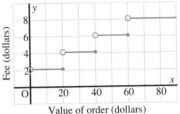

The graph shows the fee charged as a function of the value of the order. It is a series of steps and, hence, is called a *step function*.

There is a special step function called the *greatest integer function*. This function is defined by $f(x) = [x], x \in \mathbb{R}$, where the symbol $[x]$ denotes the greatest integer less than or equal to x. This means, for example:

$[5] = 5, \qquad [2.6] = 2, \qquad [0.6] = 0, \qquad [-1.6] = -2, \qquad [-\pi] = -4$

Using a table of values, we can draw the graph of $f(x) = [x]$.

x	$y = [x]$
$-2 \leqslant x < -1$	-2
$-1 \leqslant x < 0$	-1
$0 \leqslant x < 1$	0
$1 \leqslant x < 2$	1
$2 \leqslant x < 3$	2

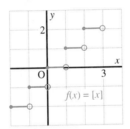

The graph is an infinite number of horizontal steps, each of length 1 unit. The vertical distance between adjacent steps is also 1 unit. Each step is closed on the left and open on the right. The domain of the function is the set of real numbers $\mathbb{R}$, and the range is the set of integers $\mathbb{Z}$.

Example 1. Graph $g(x) = 2[x]$. State the domain and range of the function.

Solution. The graph of $g(x) = 2[x]$ can be obtained from the graph of $f(x) = [x]$ by doubling each of its y-values. Each step has length 1 unit, but the vertical distance separating two adjacent steps is 2 units.
The domain is $\mathbb{R}$.
The range is $\{y = 2k, k \in \mathbb{Z}\}$ or $\{\ldots -4, -2, 0, 2, 4, \ldots \}$.

Example 2. Graph $h(x) = [x - 1] + 2$. State the domain and range of the function.

Solution. To graph $h(x) = [x - 1] + 2$, translate each step of the graph of $f(x) = [x]$ 1 unit right and 2 units up.
The length of each step is 1 unit and the vertical distance between adjacent steps is 1 unit.
The domain is $\mathbb{R}$.
The range is $\mathbb{Z}$.

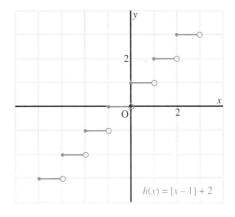

$h(x) = [x - 1] + 2$

Example 3. Graph $k(x) = [-x]$. State the domain and range of the function.

Solution. The graph of $k(x) = [-x]$ is a reflection of the graph of $f(x) = [x]$ in the y-axis.
Each step is open on the left and closed on the right.
The length of each step is 1 unit and the vertical distance between adjacent steps is 1 unit.
The domain is $\mathbb{R}$.
The range is $\mathbb{Z}$.

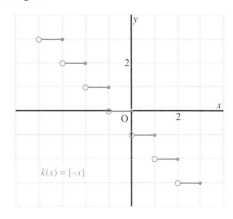

$k(x) = [-x]$

Example 4. Graph $f(x) = [2x]$ and $g(x) = \left[\dfrac{1}{2}x\right]$.

Solution. Make a table of values for each graph.
For $f(x) = [2x]$, since we are doubling the values of x, we begin with values of x differing by half a unit.

x	$2x$	$y = [2x]$
$-1.5 \leq x < -1.0$	$-3.0 \leq x < -2.0$	-3
$-1.0 \leq x < -0.5$	$-2.0 \leq x < -1.0$	-2
$-0.5 \leq x < 0$	$-1.0 \leq x < 0$	-1
$0 \leq x < 0.5$	$0 \leq x < 1.0$	0
$0.5 \leq x < 1.0$	$1.0 \leq x < 2.0$	1
$1.0 \leq x < 1.5$	$2.0 \leq x < 3.0$	2

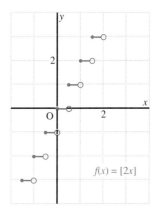

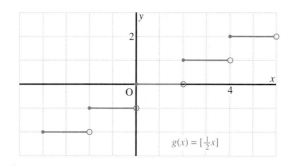

For $g(x) = \left[\dfrac{1}{2}x\right]$, since we are halving the values of x, we begin with values of x differing by 2.

x	$\dfrac{1}{2}x$	$y = \left[\dfrac{1}{2}x\right]$
$-6.0 \leqslant x < -4.0$	$-3.0 \leqslant x < -2.0$	-3
$-4.0 \leqslant x < -2.0$	$-2.0 \leqslant x < -1.0$	-2
$-2.0 \leqslant x < 0$	$-1.0 \leqslant x < 0$	-1
$0 \leqslant x < 2.0$	$0 \leqslant x < 1.0$	0
$2.0 \leqslant x < 4.0$	$1.0 \leqslant x < 2.0$	1
$4.0 \leqslant x < 6.0$	$2.0 \leqslant x < 3.0$	2

Compare each graph in *Example 4* with the graph of $f(x) = [x]$.
The graph of $f(x) = [2x]$ is a *horizontal compression* of the graph of $f(x) = [x]$. We say that $f(x) = [2x]$ is the image of $f(x) = [x]$ after a horizontal compression of factor $\dfrac{1}{2}$.

The graph of $g(x) = \left[\dfrac{1}{2}x\right]$ is a *horizontal expansion* of the graph of $f(x) = [x]$. We say that $g(x) = \left[\dfrac{1}{2}x\right]$ is the image of $f(x) = [x]$ after a horizontal expansion of factor 2.

In general, the graph of $y = f(kx)$ is the image of $y = f(x)$ after a horizontal expansion or compression of factor $\dfrac{1}{k}$.

If $0 < k < 1$, then there has been a horizontal expansion.
If $k > 1$, then there has been a horizontal compression.

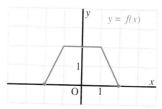
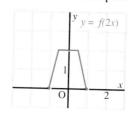
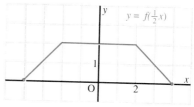

In summary, the function $f(x) = a[bx]$, $a \neq 0$, $b \neq 0$, has these properties:

- The length of each step is $\dfrac{1}{|b|}$ units.
- The distance between adjacent steps is $|a|$ units.
- If $b > 0$, the steps are closed on the left and open on the right; and if $b < 0$, the steps are open on the left and closed on the right.

Example 5. Graph the function $g(x) = 2\left[\dfrac{x}{2} - 1\right] + 1$.

Solution. Write the function $g(x) = 2\left[\dfrac{x}{2} - 1\right] + 1$

in the form $g(x) = a\left[b\left(x + \dfrac{c}{b}\right)\right] + d$;

that is, $g(x) = 2\left[\dfrac{1}{2}(x - 2)\right] + 1$.

First graph $f(x) = \left[\dfrac{1}{2}x\right]$.

Then graph $h(x) = 2\left[\dfrac{1}{2}x\right]$.

Finally, translate the graph

of $h(x) = 2\left[\dfrac{1}{2}x\right]$ 2 units right

and 1 unit up.

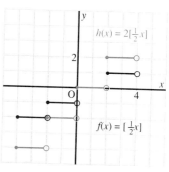

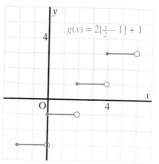

The results of *Example 5* illustrate, in general, that the graph of $g(x) = a[bx + c] + d$ can be obtained from the graph of $f(x) = a[bx]$ by the translation $T\left(-\dfrac{c}{b}, d\right)$ since $a[bx + c] + d = a\left[b\left(x + \dfrac{c}{b}\right)\right] + d$.

EXERCISES 3-6

Ⓐ

1. If $f(x) = [x]$ and $g(x) = [-2x]$, calculate each value.
   a) $f(\pi)$ b) $g(3)$ c) $f(2\sqrt{3})$ d) $g(-1.5)$
   e) $f(-4.5)$ f) $g(\sqrt{2})$ g) $g(-4.6)$ h) $f(-2.6) - g(4)$

2. If $f(x) = [x - 1]$ and $g(x) = \frac{1}{2}[x] + 1$, calculate each value.
   a) $f(-2.1)$ b) $g(4.2)$ c) $f(\pi + 1)$ d) $g(-\pi)$
   e) $f\left(-\frac{1}{2}\right)$ f) $g(\sqrt{2})$ g) $f\left(-\frac{5}{3}\right)$ h) $f\left(-\frac{9}{2}\right) + g\left(\frac{7}{2}\right)$

Ⓑ

3. Graph each function. State its domain and range.
   a) $f(x) = 3[x]$ b) $g(x) = [3x]$ c) $h(x) = -[x]$ d) $k(x) = -[-x]$

4. For each function, determine:
   i) the length of each step and the vertical distance between adjacent steps
   ii) if the steps are closed on the left or on the right
   iii) its domain and range, then graph it.
   a) $f(x) = 2[x] + 1$ b) $f(x) = [x + 1] - 2$ c) $f(x) = -\frac{1}{2}[x - 1] + 1$

   d) $f(x) = [-2x] - 1$ e) $f(x) = -2[-x] - 1$ f) $f(x) = 4\left[\frac{1}{3}x + 1\right] - 2$

5. The cost C dollars for delivering packages in a certain town is given by
   $C(x) = \left[\frac{x}{2}\right] + 3, x > 0$, where x represents the mass of the package in kilograms.
   a) What is the cost of delivering a package with each mass?
      i) 2.5 kg   ii) 12 kg   iii) 17.8 kg
   b) Graph this function for $x \in \,]0, 10[$.

6. A cab driver computes her fares according to the equation $F(d) = 0.50[d] + 2.50$,
   where $F(d)$ is the fare charged in dollars and d is the distance travelled in
   kilometres.
   a) Graph this function for $0 \leqslant d < 10$.
   b) What is the range of the function for $d \in [0, 10[$?
   c) What is the fare for a trip of 20.5 km?

Ⓒ

7. The daily charge to park a car in a municipal parking lot is $1.00 for the first
   hour and $2.00 for each additional hour or portion of an hour.
   a) How much does it cost to park a car for each time interval?
      i) 1 h 30 min   ii) 2 h 45 min   iii) 4 h
   b) Graph this function for a time interval of 8 h of parking.
   c) Find the equation that describes this function.

3-7 GRAPHING $y = af(x - p) + q$

In previous sections, we investigated the effects of the constants a, p, and q on the graphs of such functions as $y = a|x|$, $y = [x] + q$, and $y = \sqrt{x - p}$. We now consider the combined effects of these constants on the graph of a function such as $y = 2|x - 4| + 3$. The numbers in the equation indicate how to obtain its graph from the graph of $y = |x|$.

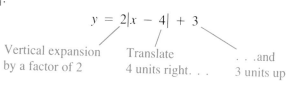

$$y = 2|x - 4| + 3$$

Vertical expansion   Translate   . . .and
by a factor of 2   4 units right. . .   3 units up

To graph the function, follow these steps.

Step 1. Graph $y = |x|$.

Step 2. Graph $y = 2|x|$.

Step 3. Translate all points on the graph in Step 2, 4 units to the right and 3 units up.

The first two steps are useful because they aid in visualizing the appearance of the graph. They can often be omitted, as Example 1 shows.

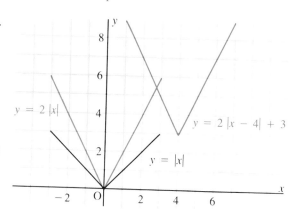

Example 1. Graph. $y = -\frac{1}{2}\sqrt{x + 1} + 2$

Solution.   The numbers in the equation indicate how the graph is obtained from the graph of the square-root function $y = \sqrt{x}$.

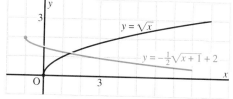

$$y = -\frac{1}{2}\sqrt{x + 1} + 2$$

Reflect in   Translate   . . . and
x-axis.   1 unit left . . .   2 units up
Vertical
compression by
a factor of $\frac{1}{2}$

Example 2. The speed of a vehicle v kilometres per hour can be estimated from the length d metres of its skid marks. If $v = 12.6\sqrt{d} + 8$, where $5 \leq d \leq 60$, sketch a graph of v as a function of d without making a table of values.

Solution. The numbers in the equation indicate how the graph is obtained from the graph of the square-root function $v = \sqrt{d}$.

$$v = 12.6\sqrt{d} + 8$$

Vertical expansion   Translate
by a factor of 12.6   8 units up

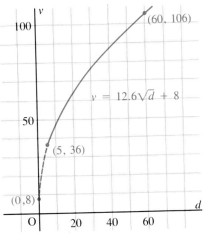

The v-coordinates of the endpoints of the graph can be found with a calculator and serve to determine the scales for the axes. A third point $(0,8)$, the maximum speed at which the vehicle leaves no skid marks, enables an approximation of the graph to be drawn.

The diagram below illustrates how the graph of the function defined by $y = af(x - p) + q$ is determined by the graph of $y = f(x)$ and the values of the constants a, p, and q.

Transformations of Functions

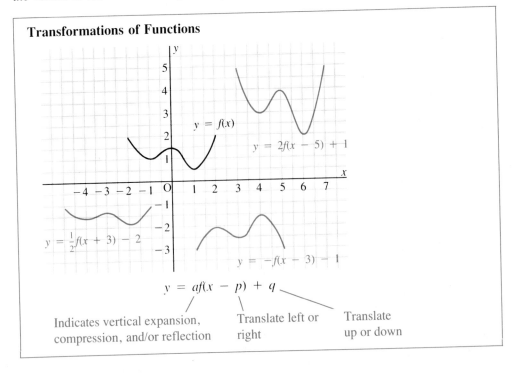

$$y = af(x - p) + q$$

Indicates vertical expansion,   Translate left or   Translate
compression, and/or reflection   right   up or down

EXERCISES 3-7

(A)

1. Which graph best represents each function?

i) $f(x) = 2\sqrt{x - 2} + 2$ ii) $f(x) = \dfrac{-2}{x}$ iii) $f(x) = -\dfrac{1}{2}|x - 1| - 2$

a)

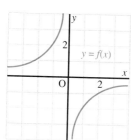

b)

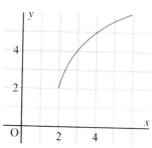

c)

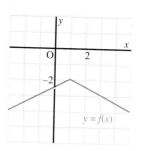

2. Sketch each pair of graphs on the same grid without making a table of values.

a) $y = 2|x + 4| - 3$ $y = \dfrac{1}{2}|x + 4| - 3$

b) $y = 2[x] + 4$ $y = \dfrac{1}{2}[x] + 4$

(B)

3. Which of the four functions best represents each graph?

i) $f(x) = 2|x + 3| - 1$ ii) $f(x) = -|x - 2| + 4$ iii) $f(x) = \dfrac{-1}{2x}$ iv) $f(x) = \dfrac{-3}{x}$

a)

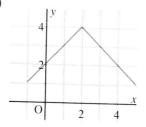

b)

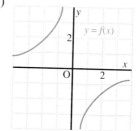

4. Sketch each pair of graphs on the same grid without making a table of values.

a) $y = 3\sqrt{x + 5} - 1$ $y = -\sqrt{x - 2} + 3$

b) $y = \dfrac{1}{2}|x + 2| - 4$ $y = -|x + 2| + 4$

5. Sketch the graph of each function. State its domain and range.

a) $f(x) = \dfrac{1}{2}|x - 6| + 1$

b) $f(x) = -|x + 3| - 2$

c) $f(x) = 2\sqrt{x + 1} - 3$

d) $f(x) = -2\sqrt{1 - x} + 3$

e) $f(x) = -2[-x] + 1$

f) $f(x) = -1.5[x - 2] + 1$

6. The graph of a function $y = f(x)$ is shown. Sketch each pair of graphs on the same grid.
   a) $y = f(x)$ and $y = f(x - 2) + 4$
   b) $y = f(x)$ and $y = 3f(x + 1)$
   c) $y = f(x)$ and $y = \frac{1}{2}f(x + 3) - 2$
   d) $y = f(x)$ and $y = -f(x - 2) - 1$

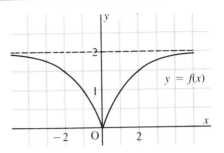

INVESTIGATE

Classifying Functions

In earlier work, certain functions were classified as linear and others as quadratic. There are other ways that functions can be classified.

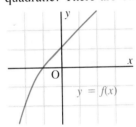

Increasing

As x increases
$f(x)$ increases

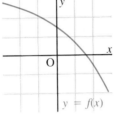

Decreasing

As x increases
$f(x)$ decreases

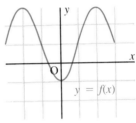

Periodic

There is a repeating pattern in the graph.

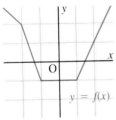

Piecewise Linear

The graph has parts all of which are linear.

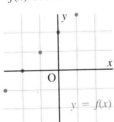

Discrete

The graph consists of separate points.

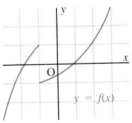

Discontinuous

The graph cannot be drawn without lifting the pencil.

Refer to the functions in the examples and exercises of Chapters 1, 2, and 3.

1. Find at least one function of each kind illustrated above.

2. Find an example of a function which has none of the above properties.

MATHEMATICS AROUND US

Other Kinds of Functions

There are many other kinds of functions in addition to those described
in this chapter. A few of these are illustrated here.

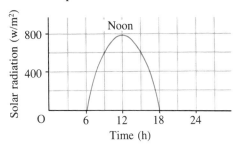

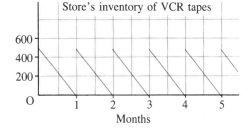

1. This graph shows the daily pattern of
   solar radiation on a clear day in the
   spring or fall, when the sun rises at
   6 A.M. and sets at 6 P.M.
   a) How would the graph differ if it
      were drawn for:
      i) a day in the summer
      ii) a day in the winter?
   b) Draw a similar graph in which the
      horizontal axis represents three con-
      secutive days.

2. At the end of each month a store buys
   500 VCR tapes to replace those sold
   during the month. How would the graph
   showing the store's inventory differ if:
   a) the 500 tapes bought each month
      were sold out after the first 3 weeks
      of the next month
   b) the store sold only 400 tapes each
      month?

- Most of the babies born this year can
  expect to live at least 75 years. A few
  should survive to age 100 or more.

- A corn plant matures in about 100 days to
  a mass of about 80 g. Growth is most
  rapid in the second and third months.

- Wind speed usually increases rapidly with height in the first few
  metres above the ground. Above 20 m or so, the speed is about
  5 m/s, and changes little for the next few hundred metres.

3. Graphs illustrating the three situations described above are shown below.
   a) Identify the graph which corresponds to each situation.
   b) Draw each graph, including appropriate scales and titles on the axes.
   c) In what ways do all three graphs differ from the graphs above?
      i)   ii)   iii)

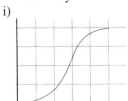

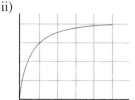

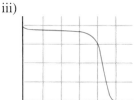

USING TECHNOLOGY

Special Functions

Solving Absolute-Value Equations Graphically
To solve $|x - 2| = 3$ graphically, we rewrite the
equation as $|x - 2| - 3 = 0$. Enter $Y_1 = |X - 2| - 3$
on the functions menu of your graphing calculator.
Graph this equation in the viewing window of $[-3, 7]$
by $[-5, 5]$. Use the TRACE feature to confirm that the
graph crosses the x-axis at $x = -1$ and $x = 5$.
    A second method of solution would be to define
$Y_1 = |X - 2|$ and $Y_2 = 3$. Graph these two functions
together in the same viewing window. With the
TRACE feature, confirm that the horizontal line
$Y_2 = 3$ intersects Y_1 at $x = -1$ and $x = 5$.

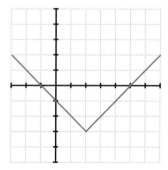

    To solve $|x - 2| < 3$, we display the graph of
$Y_1 = |X - 2| - 3$. We see that the graph lies below
the x-axis between the x-coordinates of -1 and 5; that
is, $Y_1 < 0$ in the interval $]-1, 5[$.
    Similarly, upon graphing $Y_1 = |X - 2|$ and
$Y_2 = 3$, we observe that $Y_1 < Y_2$ in the interval
$]-1, 5[$.

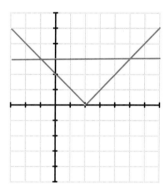

a) Solve each equation and inequality graphically. Verify your answers algebraically.

   i) $|x + 3| = 5$ ii) $|x + 5| = x + 1$ iii) $2|x + 4| - 5 = 0$

   iv) $|3 - x| < 8$ v) $|x - 5| > 3$ vi) $|2x - 6| \leq 20$

Explorations I
a) Enter $Y_1 = |X + 2|$ and $Y_2 = |X|$ in the functions menu and display the graphs
   of Y_1 and Y_2 on the same screen.

b) From the graphs, determine the values of x for which $|x + 2| < |x|$.

c) Explain your answer using the definition of absolute value.

Explorations II
a) Is the graph of $Y_1 = \sqrt{X^2}$ the same as the graph of $Y_2 = X$? Explain your answer in
   writing.

b) Verify your answer by displaying the graphs of Y_1 and Y_2.

c) Find another function that has the same graph as $Y_1 = \sqrt{X^2}$.

Viewing the Greatest Integer Function

Enter $Y_1 = [X]$ on the functions menu. Display the graph in a viewing window of $[-5, 5]$ by $[-5, 5]$.

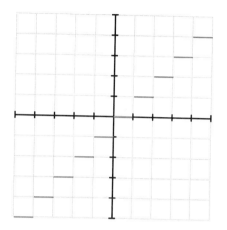

a) Using the TRACE feature, position the cursor to evaluate each expression.

   i) $[4.5]$ ii) $[-2.1]$

   iii) $[2.1]$ iv) $[-0.1]$

   v) $[3]$ vi) $[-3]$

b) Use the TRACE feature to observe the changing values of Y as X changes from $+3$ to -3 and back to $+3$.

Transforming the Greatest Integer Function

a) Explain why each pair of equations below may or may not be equivalent for all values of x. Verify your reasoning by displaying the graphs of each pair of equations.

   i) $Y_1 = [X - 3]$ $Y_2 = [X] - 3$
   ii) $Y_1 = 2[X]$ $Y_2 = [2X]$
   iii) $Y_1 = [X + 1]$ $Y_2 = [X] + 1$

Bike Rentals

a) Peter rents his bike for $4 an hour or each part of an hour. Define a function Y_1 which represents this situation and display its graph on your graphing calculator. Define your viewing window so that it includes only reasonable values of X and Y. From the graph, find the cost of renting Peter's bike for 2 h 20 min and 4 h 40 min. Verify your answers numerically.

b) To rent David's bike, it would cost you $7 plus $2 per hour or each part of an hour. Define a function Y_2 to represent this situation. Use the graph of Y_2 to find the cost of renting David's bike for 2 h 20 min and 4 h 40 min. Verify your answers numerically.

c) If you were to rent a bike and had to choose one of the two rates above, which would you choose?

3-8 APPLICATIONS OF SPECIAL FUNCTIONS

In the previous sections, we studied four special functions:
- the absolute-value function, $f(x) = a|x - p| + q$
- the square-root function, $f(x) = a\sqrt{x - p} + q$
- the inverse-variation function, $f(x) = \dfrac{k}{x}$
- the greatest integer function, $f(x) = a[bx + c] + d$

We shall now consider these functions in a variety of applications.

EXERCISES 3-8

A

1. Classify each function as absolute-value, square-root, inverse-variation, or greatest integer.

   a) The period T seconds of a pendulum of length l metres is $T = 2\pi\sqrt{\dfrac{l}{9.8}}$.

   b) The length l of a rectangle of fixed area that varies inversely as the width w

   c) The age A, in years, at a person's most recent birthday as a function of the total time t years that has elapsed since the person's birth

   d) The volume of water V litres in a swimming pool as a function of time t hours as the pool is emptied and then refilled at a constant rate

2. A teacher decides to adjust the marks of the students who failed a test. Which of these functions would transform a mark of 58 to 60?

   a) $r(x) = \dfrac{1}{2}|x - 50| + x$

   b) $s(x) = 6\sqrt{x} + 10$

   c) $t(x) = \dfrac{3200}{x}$

   d) $v(x) = \left[\dfrac{x + 4}{3}\right] + 40$

B

3. In the last two years, the market value of a stock has varied according to the equation $V(t) = \dfrac{1}{3}|t - 6| + 4$, where V dollars represents the value of one share and t is the elapsed time in months.

   a) Graph this function for $t \in [0,24]$.

   b)   i) What was the initial value of each share?

        ii) What is each share worth now?

   c)   i) For how many months did the stock decrease?

        ii) What was the minimum value attained by each share of the stock?

4. When a parachutist jumps from an airplane, the time t seconds that it takes the parachutist to travel d metres in free fall is given by $t = \sqrt{\dfrac{d}{4.9}}$. How long does it take for a jump resulting in a free fall of 250 m? Give the answers to the nearest tenth of a second.

5. Boyle's law states that the pressure P kilopascals of a confined gas at constant temperature varies inversely as the volume V litres of the gas. The volume of a particular gas is 20 L at a pressure of 180 kPa. What is the volume of the same gas at 250 kPa?

6. To mail a parcel within certain distances in Canada costs $0.85 for the first 100 g (or portion thereof) and 0.50¢ more for each additional 100 g (or portion thereof). If m is the mass in grams of a parcel, and C is the cost in dollars of mailing it, draw the graph of $C(m)$ for $0 < m \leqslant 500$.

7. On a warm winter day, the temperature between 6 A.M. and midnight varied according to the equation $T(t) = -\dfrac{5}{4}|t - 8| + 7.5$, where T is the temperature in degrees Celsius and t is the elapsed time in hours since 6 A.M.
   a) i) What was the maximum temperature reached on that day?
      ii) What time did it occur?
   b) For how many hours was the temperature above 0°C?

8. The period T seconds of a simple pendulum with length l metres is given by $T = 2\pi\sqrt{\dfrac{l}{9.8}}$.
   a) A small ball swings freely from a string 75 cm long. Find its period to the nearest hundredth of a second.
   b) What is the length of a pendulum with a period of 2.46 s?

9. The approximate number of years n required for an investment to double varies inversely as the interest rate r percent. At 12% compound interest, an investment will double in about 6 years.
   a) How many years does it take an investment to double at:
      i) 6%   ii) 8%   iii) 10.5%?
   b) At what interest rate will an investment double in 4 years?

10. Kelly made a long distance telephone call to her friend Susanna. The cost of the phone call is $1.00 for the first minute (or fraction thereof) and $0.50 for each additional minute (or fraction thereof).

    a) Draw a graph of the cost, C dollars, as a function of the time, t minutes, for $0 < t \le 5$.

    b) Kelly talked to Susanna for half an hour. What was the cost of the phone call?

11. From a height h metres above the Earth's surface, the unobstructed distance d kilometres that one can see to the horizon is given by $d = 3.57\sqrt{h}$. Find the distance to the horizon from the top of the CN Tower, in Toronto, which is 553 m tall. Give the answer to the nearest kilometre.

12. Each spring, Mrs. Potter empties most of the water from her swimming pool and then refills it with clean water. The quantity of water Q thousands of litres after time t hours from the start of this operation is given by $Q(t) = 5|t - 4| + 10$.

    a) How much water was in the pool at the start?

    b) What is the minimum amount of water left in the pool before Mrs. Potter starts to refill it?

    c) The capacity of the pool is 50 000 L. How long does it take to refill it?

    d) What is the domain and range of this function?

13. Michael has planted a small spruce tree on his front lawn. He estimates that the yearly growth of the tree is given by the equation $G(n) = 1.5\sqrt{n + 4} - 2$, where G represents the height in metres and n is the number of years elapsed since the tree was transplanted.

    a) Graph this function for $n \in [0,12]$.

    b) What was the height of the spruce at transplantation?

    c) What will be the height of the tree 20 years after transplantation? Give the answer to the nearest tenth of a metre.

14. Michelle sells parts for printing machines. She is paid a basic salary each week plus a bonus of $50 for each $500 worth of sales she brings in. This situation can be represented by the function $S(x) = 200 + 50 \left[\dfrac{x}{500} \right]$, where x represents the weekly sales and $S(x)$ represents the total pay for the week.

    a) What is Michelle's basic weekly salary?

    b) How much did Michelle earn for a week in which her sales were $3200?

    c) Draw the graph of this function for sales less than $5000.

    d) Michelle wants to earn $1000 for the coming week. What is the minimum total of sales that she must achieve?

15. The length of time t minutes required to cook food in a pressure cooker varies inversely as the pressure setting P kilopascals of the cooker. A roast cooks in 55 min when the pressure is set at 125 kPa. How long will it take to cook the same roast at 200 kPa? Give the answer to the nearest second.

16. The formula $v(T) = 330 \sqrt{1 + \dfrac{T}{273}}$ expresses the velocity of sound v metres per second as a function of the air temperature T degrees Celsius.

   a) What is the velocity of sound in air with a temperature of 5°C? Give the answer to the nearest whole number.

   b) What is the air temperature if the speed of sound is 337 m/s? Give the answer to 1 decimal place.

17. What is the area of the triangle formed by the intersection of the graph of $f(x) = \dfrac{-|x - 4|}{2} + 3$ with the x-axis?

18. An insurance company offers its workers life insurance with an annual premium based on a function defined by $P(a) = \left[\dfrac{a - 15}{10}\right]$. In this equation, P represents the annual premium in dollars per $1000 of life insurance purchased and a represents the age of the insured person in years. What is the difference between the annual premium for a 25-year-old worker and that for a 50-year-old worker for a life insurance policy of $100 000?

19. Andrea borrowed $30 000 to buy a new car. The amount A dollars that she repaid after t years is given by $A(t) = 30\,000 - 10\,000\sqrt{10 - t}$. How long did it take Andrea to repay half her loan?

20. A train derailment caused an acid spill in a nearby lake. After a few days, chemists decided to add lime to the water daily to neutralize the acid. The pH of the water was described by the function $p(d) = \dfrac{|d - 9|}{3} + 3$, where p represents the pH of the lake and d represents the number of days elapsed since the derailment.

   a) Graph this function.

   b) What was the pH of the lake at the time of the spill?

   c) After how many days did the chemists decide to add lime?

   d) After how many days did the pH return to its level before the spill?

   e) For how many days was the pH below 4?

Review Exercises

1. a) Using a table of values, graph each function.

    i) $y = -2|x|$ ii) $y = -\frac{1}{2}\sqrt{-x}$ iii) $y = \frac{1}{4x}$ iv) $y = [0.2x]$

  b) State the domain and range of each function in part a).

2. Which function best represents each graph?

    i) $f(x) = -2|x - 1| + 2$ ii) $f(x) = 2\sqrt{x + 1} - 3$

    iii) $f(x) = \frac{1}{2x}$ iv) $f(x) = 1.5[x + 1] - 1$

a)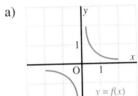

b)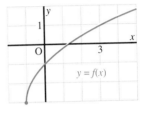

c)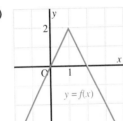

d)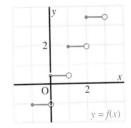

3. Without making tables of values, sketch each set of graphs on the same grid.
    a) $y = |x|$ $y = |x - 2|$ $y = |x + 2|$
    b) $y = [x]$ $y = [x - 2]$ $y = [x + 2]$

4. Without making tables of values, sketch each set of graphs on the same grid.

    a) $y = \frac{1}{x}$ $y = \frac{2}{x}$ $y = -\frac{2}{x}$ b) $y = |x|$ $y = 3|x|$ $y = -3|x|$

5. Without making tables of values, sketch each set of graphs on the same grid.

    a) $y = |2x|$ $y = -|2x|$ $y = |-2x|$

    b) $y = \sqrt{\frac{1}{2}x}$ $y = -\sqrt{\frac{1}{2}x}$ $y = \sqrt{-\frac{1}{2}x}$

6. Graph each function. State its domain and range.
    a) $f(x) = -2|2x - 1| + 2$ b) $g(x) = 2\sqrt{x - 1} + 3$

    c) $h(x) = \frac{-5}{x}$ d) $k(x) = 2.5\left[\frac{1}{2}x + 1\right] + 1$

1. Simplify.

   a) $3\sqrt{12} + 4\sqrt{27} - \sqrt{75}$

   b) $\sqrt{32} - 2\sqrt{24} - 4\sqrt{18}$

   c) $2\sqrt{5}(3\sqrt{7} + 8\sqrt{12})$

   d) $(4\sqrt{3} - 2\sqrt{5})(4\sqrt{3} + 2\sqrt{5})$

2. Simplify.

   a) $\dfrac{33\sqrt{6}}{3\sqrt{24}}$

   b) $\dfrac{12}{5\sqrt{7}}$

   c) $\dfrac{8\sqrt{2} - 6}{\sqrt{2}}$

   d) $\dfrac{6\sqrt{5} + \sqrt{8}}{\sqrt{5}}$

3. Solve and check.

   a) $6(x + 1) - 12x = 3 - 4(2x - 1)$

   b) $\dfrac{2x - 4}{5} - \dfrac{x - 3}{4} = \dfrac{5 - 3x}{8}$

   c) $3x^2 - x - 14 = 0$

   d) $2x^2 + 4x - 7 = 0$

   e) $5x^2 + 8x + 3 = 0$

   f) $\dfrac{4}{x - 1} - \dfrac{5}{x + 2} = \dfrac{3}{x}$

4. Determine the nature of the roots of each equation.

   a) $4x^2 + 20x + 25 = 0$ b) $2x^2 - 5x + 2 = 0$ c) $3x^2 - 4x + 8 = 0$

5. Write a quadratic equation given the roots $\dfrac{3}{4}$ and -2.

6. For what values of k does:

   a) $3x^2 - kx + 2 = 0$ have equal roots

   b) $2x^2 - 5x - k = 0$ have no real roots?

7. Solve.

   a) $\sqrt{5x + 4} = 7$

   b) $\sqrt{2x - 3} + 3 = x$

   c) $\sqrt{x + 5} + x = 7$

   d) $2x + 2\sqrt{x} = 5$

8. Solve.

   a) $2x^2 - 5x + 4 = 0$

   b) $4x^3 - 3x^2 + 2x = 0$

   c) $x^3 - 7x - 6 = 0$

   d) $2x^3 - 3x^2 - 8x + 12 = 0$

   e) $(x^2 - 4x + 5)(x^2 - 4x + 2) = -2$

   f) $\dfrac{4}{x + 1} - \dfrac{12}{x + 3} = \dfrac{-5}{x + 2}$

9. If $g(x) = x^2 + 2x - 24$, for what values of x is:

   a) $g(x) = 0$ b) $g(x) = -9$ c) $g(x) = 11$?

10. Sketch each set of graphs on the same axes.

   a) $y = x^2$ $y = x^2 + 4$ $y = x^2 - 3$

   b) $y = x^2$ $y = 3x^2$ $y = \frac{1}{2}x^2$ $y = -x^2$

   c) $y = x^2$ $y = (x - 1)^2$ $y = (x + 3)^2$

   d) $y = x^2$ $y = 2(x + 1)^2 + 3$ $y = \frac{1}{2}(x - 2)^2 - 4$ $y = -(x - 3)^2 + 5$

11. For each parabola, state:

   i) the coordinates of the vertex   ii) the equation of the axis of symmetry

   iii) the direction of opening   iv) the y-intercept.

   a) $y = 3(x + 7)^2$

   b) $y = -2(x - 3)^2 + 4$

   c) $y = -\left(x - \frac{1}{2}\right)^2 - \frac{3}{4}$

   d) $y = \frac{1}{2}(x + 6)^2 - 3$

12. Find the equation of each parabola.

   a) with vertex $(0, 0)$, through $(2, 7)$

   b) with vertex $(-1, 4)$, and y-intercept 16

   c) with vertex $(-3, -2)$, that opens down, and is congruent to $y = 3x^2$

   d) with y-intercept 10, x-intercept 2, and axis of symmetry $x - 3 = 0$

13. A rectangular piece of land, bounded on one side by a hedge, is to be fenced on its other three sides. What is the maximum area that can be enclosed by 200 m of fencing?

14. Solve, if possible.

   a) $|2x - 1| = 7$

   b) $|x + 5| - x + 2 = 3$

   c) $x + 2|x + 1| = 8$

   d) $|3x + 2| = 2x - 4$

15. Find the zeros of each function.

   a) $f(x) = |3x - 2| - 1$

   b) $g(x) = |2x - 1| - 3$

   c) $g(x) = -\frac{1}{4}\sqrt{4x - 8} + 1$

   d) $f(x) = 2\sqrt{2x + 3} - 1$

16. State the domain and range of each function.

   a) $k(x) = -2|3 - 2x| + 6$

   b) $f(x) = \sqrt{2x + 5} - 3$

   c) $y = -\frac{1}{2x}$

   d) $g(x) = \left[\frac{1}{2}x\right]$

4 Quadratic Relations

Some bridges have curved arches like this one. If the type of arch is known, and if the height and the width at its base are known, how can the height be determined at any other point under the arch? (See Section 4-10 *Example 1*.)

4-1 LOCUS

To make this photograph, a point source of
light was mounted on a wheel. A camera
recorded the light at split-second intervals as
the wheel rolled along a flat surface. The
path traced out by the light is an example of
a locus. Another example of a locus is the
path traced out by a pencil point when
compasses are used to construct a circle.

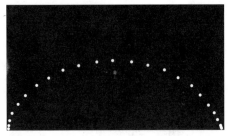

A *locus* is the path traced out by a point which moves according
to a given condition. If the given condition is simple enough, we can find
an equation which represents the path.

Example 1. A point moves such that it is always 3 units from the point A(2, 0).
  a) Identify the locus.
  b) Find the equation of the locus.

Solution. a) The locus is a circle with centre (2, 0)
  and radius 3.
  b) Let P(x, y) be any point on the locus.
  Then,
  $$AP = 3$$
  $$\sqrt{(x - 2)^2 + (y - 0)^2} = 3$$
  Square both sides.
  $$(x - 2)^2 + y^2 = 9$$
  The equation of the locus is
  $$(x - 2)^2 + y^2 = 9,$$
  or $x^2 + y^2 - 4x - 5 = 0$

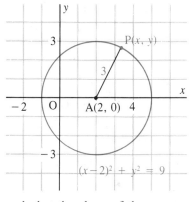

Example 2. Let N be the point (1, −2). A point P moves such that the slope of the
segment NP is always $\frac{3}{4}$.

  a) Identify the locus.
  b) Find the equation of the locus.

Solution. a) The locus is a straight line with slope
  $\frac{3}{4}$, passing through N(1, −2).
  b) Let P(x, y) be any point on the locus.
  Then, since the slope of NP is $\frac{3}{4}$,
  $$\frac{y + 2}{x - 1} = \frac{3}{4}$$
  $$3x - 3 = 4y + 8$$
  $$3x - 4y - 11 = 0$$
  The equation of the locus is
  $$3x - 4y - 11 = 0$$

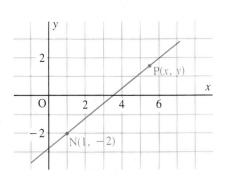

In *Examples 1* and *2* we could identify the locus before we found its equation. If the given condition is more complicated, it may not be possible to do this.

Example 3. A point P moves such that it is always the same distance from the point F(5, 1) as it is from the line defined by $y = -1$.
a) Find the equation of the locus.
b) Identify the locus and sketch its graph.
c) Find the value of y_1 if T(11, y_1) is on the graph.

Solution. a) Let P(x, y) be any point on the locus.
Then according to the given condition,
$$PF = PN$$
$$\sqrt{(x - 5)^2 + (y - 1)^2} = y + 1$$
Square both sides.
$$(x - 5)^2 + (y - 1)^2 = (y + 1)^2$$
$$x^2 - 10x + 25 + y^2 - 2y + 1 = y^2 + 2y + 1$$
$$4y = x^2 - 10x + 25$$
$$y = \frac{1}{4}(x - 5)^2$$

b) The locus is a parabola with vertex (5, 0), and axis of symmetry $x = 5$. The parabola opens up, and is congruent to the parabola defined by $y = \frac{1}{4}x^2$.

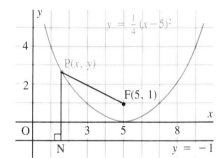

c) Substitute 11 for x and y_1 for y in the equation.
$$y = \frac{1}{4}(x - 5)^2$$
$$y_1 = \frac{1}{4}(11 - 5)^2$$
$$= 9$$
Hence, if T(11, y_1) is on the graph, $y_1 = 9$.

In the above examples we used the following fundamental properties of a locus.

Properties of a Locus
- The coordinates of every point on a locus satisfy the equation of the locus.
- Every point whose coordinates satisfy the equation of a locus is on the locus.

EXERCISES 4-1

Ⓐ

1. Describe each graph as a locus.

a)
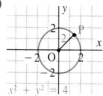
$x^2 + y^2 = 4$

b)
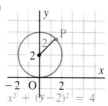
$x^2 + (y - 2)^2 = 4$

c)
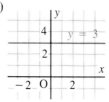
$y = 3$

d)
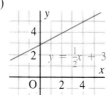
$y = \frac{1}{2}x + 3$

e)
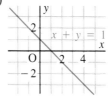
$x + y = 1$

f)
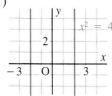
$x^2 = 4$

2. Describe the graph of each equation as a locus.
   a) $y = -5$ b) $x = -2$ c) $x^2 + y^2 = 49$
   d) $y = x + 2$ e) $(x - 1)^2 + (y + 4)^2 = 16$ f) $(x - 1)^2 + y^2 = 1$

Ⓑ

3. A point P moves such that it is always 6 units from the point B(0,3).
   a) Identify the locus.
   b) Find the equation of the locus.

4. A point P moves such that it is always 5 units from the point C($-1,2$).
   a) Find the equation of the locus.
   b) Identify the locus and sketch its graph.
   c) Find the value of y_1 if A(3,y_1) is on the graph.

5. Find the equation of the locus of P. Identify the locus and sketch its graph.

   a) The slope of the line through P and M(3, -1) is $\frac{2}{3}$.

   b) P is equidistant from the point F(0,1) and the line defined by $y = -1$.
   c) P is equidistant from the point F(3, -1) and the line defined by $y = 1$.

6. A point P moves such that it is always equidistant from the point G(2,5) and the line defined by $y = 3$.
   a) Find the equation of the locus.
   b) Identify the locus and sketch its graph.
   c) Find the value of y_1 if B($-4,y_1$) is on the graph.

7. Find the equation of the locus of P. Identify the locus and sketch its graph.
   a) P is always the same distance from A($-2,3$) as it is from B(8, -1).
   b) P is always twice as far from A(8,0) as it is from B(2,0).
   c) The slope of the line through P and A(2,1) is equal to the slope of the line through P and B($-1,4$).

8. A point P moves such that the slope of the line through P and S(2,0) is always 2 greater than the slope of the line through P and T(-2,0).
   a) Find the equation of the locus.
   b) Identify the locus and sketch its graph.
   c) Find the value of x_1 if M(x_1,16) is on the graph.

9. A point P moves such that the product of the slopes of the line segments joining P to Q(-5,0) and to R(5,0) is -1.
   a) Find the equation of the locus.
   b) Identify the locus and sketch its graph.
   c) Find the value of y_1 if the point D(2,y_1) lies on the graph.

10. Perpendicular lines are drawn through A(4,0) and B(-4,0).
    a) Find the equation of the locus of the point of intersection of these lines.
    b) Identify the locus and draw its graph.

Ⓒ

11. A line segment 10 units long has its endpoints on the x- and y-axes. Find the equation of the locus of its midpoint, and sketch its graph.

12. Find the equation of the locus of P. Sketch the graph of the locus.
    a) P is 3 units from the x-axis.
    b) The product of the distances from P to the x- and y-axes is 6.
    c) The sum of the distances from P to the x- and y-axes is 5.
    d) The difference of the distances from P to the x- and y-axes is 3.
    e) P is equidistant from the x- and y-axes.
    f) P is always twice as far from the x-axis as it is from the point V(0,3).

13. Find the equation of the locus of a point P which moves such that the slope of the line segment joining P to A(-3,0) is half the slope of the line segment joining P to B(3,0). Identify the locus and sketch its graph.

14. Find the equation of the locus of P.
    a) The sum of the distances from P to A(2,0) and B(-2,0) is 8.
    b) The difference of the distances from P to C(4,0) and D(-4,0) is 2.

15. In △ABC, ∠C $= 90°$ and C is the point (5,3). If A is on the x-axis and B is on the y-axis, find the equation of the locus of the midpoint of AB.

INVESTIGATE

A circle can be defined as the locus of a point which moves such that its distance to a given point is constant. By examining the examples and exercises of this section:
a) list some other possible definitions of a circle
b) list some possible definitions of: a straight line; a parabola.

4-2 INTRODUCTION TO QUADRATIC RELATIONS

The ancient Greeks defined a cone as the surface generated when a line is rotated about a fixed point P on the line. Notice that the cone has two symmetric parts on either side of P.

The curves that result when a plane intersects a cone are called *conic sections*, or *conics*. The Greeks discovered many properties of conics, but they were not interested in practical applications. In the seventeenth century, Isaac Newton proved that the orbit of a body revolving around another in accordance with the law of gravitation is a conic.

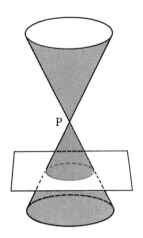

When a plane intersects a cone, the angle of inclination of the plane with respect to the cone determines the shape of the curve that results.

The Circle

In the drawing above, the plane is parallel to the base of the cone. In this case the curve of intersection is a *circle*. Hence, a circle is a conic.

The orbits of satellites and planets are nearly circular. The spectacular photographs we see of a total solar eclipse are caused by the fact that both the sun and the moon appear to us as circular discs of about the same size.

Although the conics are defined as sections of a cone, they also occur as the graphs of certain equations in x and y.

Example 1. Graph the relation $x^2 + y^2 = 16$.

Solution. We could use a table of values to draw the graph. A more efficient method is to observe that the equation expresses the condition that the distance from a point $P(x,y)$ to $O(0,0)$ be 4 units. Hence, the graph is a circle, with centre $(0,0)$ and radius 4.

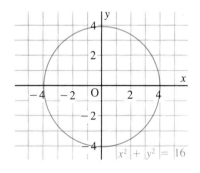

$x^2 + y^2 = 16$

The Ellipse

If the intersecting plane is inclined to the base of the cone as shown, an *ellipse* results. As the angle of the intersecting plane increases, the shape of the ellipse changes from circular to long and elongated.

Satellites, planets, and some comets travel in elliptical orbits. Halley's comet, which returns to the sun approximately every 76 years, has a very long elliptical orbit.

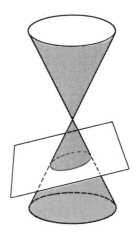

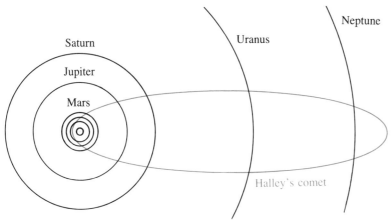

Saturn

Jupiter

Mars

Uranus

Neptune

Halley's comet

Example 2. Graph the relation $4x^2 + 9y^2 = 36$ using a table of values.

Solution. To prepare a table of values, we first solve the equation for y.

$$4x^2 + 9y^2 = 36$$
$$9y^2 = 36 - 4x^2$$
$$y = \frac{\pm\sqrt{36 - 4x^2}}{3}$$

x	y
0	± 2.00
0.5	± 1.97
1.0	± 1.89
1.5	± 1.73
2.0	± 1.49
2.5	± 1.11
3.0	0

x	y
0	± 2.00
-0.5	± 1.97
-1.0	± 1.89
-1.5	± 1.73
-2.0	± 1.49
-2.5	± 1.11
-3.0	0

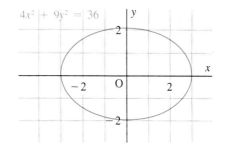

The Parabola

In this diagram, the intersecting plane is parallel to the line AB on the cone. The resulting curve is a *parabola*. Hence, a parabola is a conic.

Parabolas have many applications in astronomy. The mirrors in some telescopes have surfaces whose cross sections are parabolas. Many comets have orbits which extend far beyond the outermost planets. In the vicinity of the sun, these orbits are nearly parabolic. A parabolic shape is sometimes formed by the coma and dust tail of a comet.

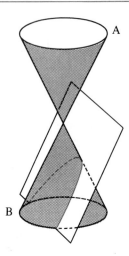

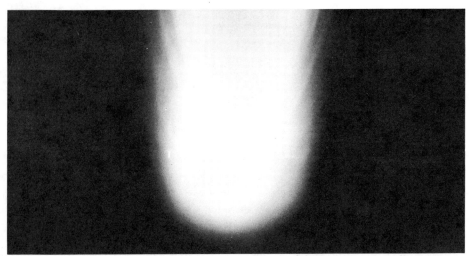

Example 3. Graph the relation $x^2 - 4y = 0$.

Solution. We could use a table of values to draw the graph. A more efficient method is to solve the equation for y and use our knowledge of the transformations of functions.

$$x^2 - 4y = 0$$

$$y = \frac{1}{4}x^2$$

The graph is a parabola with vertex $(0,0)$, axis of symmetry the y-axis, and opens up. It is a vertical compression of the parabola $y = x^2$.

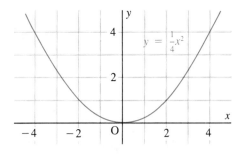

The Hyperbola

If the plane intersects the cone as shown, the resulting curve is called a *hyperbola*. Note that a hyperbola intersects both parts of the cone. Hence, a hyperbola has two distinct parts, or branches.

Some comets travel along paths which are slightly hyperbolic. As a result, they only appear once near the sun, and do not return. If a star passes another star, each is deflected along a hyperbolic path by the other. Another example of a hyperbolic path is provided by the Voyager 2 space probe which was launched to the outer planets in August, 1977. The diagram shows Voyager's path as it passed by Uranus in January, 1986.

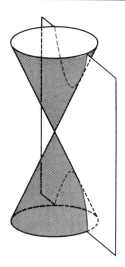

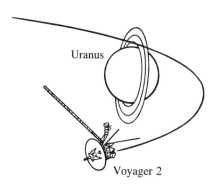

Example 4.   Graph the relation $x^2 - y^2 = 4$ using a table of values.

Solution.   To prepare a table of values, we first solve the equation for y.

$$x^2 - y^2 = 4$$
$$y^2 = x^2 - 4$$
$$y = \pm\sqrt{x^2 - 4}$$

x	y
2	0
3	± 2.24
4	± 3.46
5	± 4.58
6	± 5.66

x	y
-2	0
-3	± 2.24
-4	± 3.46
-5	± 4.58
-6	± 5.66

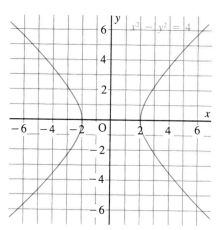

Each equation in the above examples has terms of the second degree in x or y. Any relation whose defining equation contains terms of the second degree, but no terms of higher degree, is called a *quadratic relation*.

These are quadratic relations.

$x^2 + 9y^2 = 18$
$2x^2 + xy - 2x = 14$

These are not quadratic relations.

$y = x^3$
$x^2 + 2xy^2 + 3y = 6$

In this chapter we will develop techniques for graphing certain quadratic relations without making tables of values.

EXERCISES 4-2

Ⓐ

1. Which of these are quadratic relations?
   a) $x^2 - y^2 = 9$
   b) $2x^3 + y^3 = 24$
   c) $3x^2 + 2y^2 = 12$
   d) $x^2 + 3x^2y = 6$
   e) $x^2 - 2y^2 + x - y = 7$
   f) $xy = 12$

Ⓑ

2. Graph each relation and identify the curve.
   a) $x^2 + y^2 = 9$
   b) $4x^2 + y^2 = 16$
   c) $4x^2 - y^2 = 16$
   d) $y = \dfrac{x^2}{8}$
   e) $4x^2 + 25y^2 = 100$
   f) $4x^2 - 25y^2 = 100$

3. a) Graph each relation.
      i) $x^2 + y^2 = 0$
      ii) $x^2 - y^2 = 0$
      iii) $(x - y)^2 = 0$
   b) Explain how the graphs of the relations in part a) could result when a plane intersects a cone.

4. A jet breaking the sound barrier creates a shock wave which has the shape of a cone. Describe the shape of the shock wave on the ground if the jet is:
   a) flying parallel to the ground
   b) gaining altitude
   c) losing altitude.

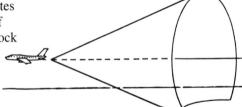

 INVESTIGATE

Models of the Conics

You can make models of the conics using styrofoam cones, which can be obtained from a craft store. Cut some styrofoam cones with a fine-toothed saw to create a circle, an ellipse, a parabola, and a hyperbola. Paint the surfaces.

Can you make four cuts in one cone to show a circle, an ellipse, a parabola, and a hyperbola?

4-3 THE CIRCLE

Many farms in western North America use an automated centre-pivot irrigation system. A long pipe sprays water as it rotates about the centre. Distinctive circular traces are left by the wheels, and, since the end of the pipe is always the same distance from the centre, the area watered forms a circle.

A circle is the locus of a point which moves such that it is always the same distance from a fixed point called the *centre*. This distance is called the *radius*. We can find the equation of any circle with centre $C(h, k)$ and radius r. Let $P(x, y)$ be any point on the circle. Then

$$CP = r$$
$$\sqrt{(x - h)^2 + (y - k)^2} = r$$

Square both sides.

$$(x - h)^2 + (y - k)^2 = r^2$$

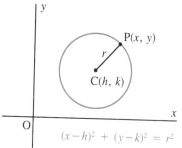

This is the *standard equation* of a circle with centre (h, k) and radius r.

Standard Equation of a Circle

The equation of a circle with centre (h, k) and radius r is

$$(x - h)^2 + (y - k)^2 = r^2.$$

If the centre is $(0, 0)$, the equation is

$$x^2 + y^2 = r^2.$$

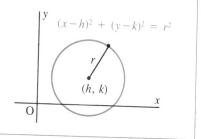

Example 1. A circle has centre $(2, -1)$ and radius 5 units.
a) Write the equation of the circle.
b) If $(4, y_1)$ is on the circle, find the value of y_1 to two decimal places.

Solution.
a) The equation of the circle is
$$(x - 2)^2 + (y + 1)^2 = 25$$
b) Substitute 4 for x and y_1 for y.
$$(4 - 2)^2 + (y_1 + 1)^2 = 25$$
$$4 + y_1{}^2 + 2y_1 + 1 = 25$$
$$y_1{}^2 + 2y_1 - 20 = 0$$
$$y_1 = \frac{-2 \pm \sqrt{84}}{2}$$
$$= -1 \pm \sqrt{21}$$
$$\doteq 3.58 \text{ or } -5.58$$

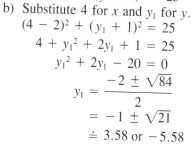

In *Example 1* we can expand the left side of the equation of the circle.

$$(x - 2)^2 + (y + 1)^2 = 25$$
$$x^2 - 4x + 4 + y^2 + 2y + 1 = 25$$
$$x^2 + y^2 - 4x + 2y - 20 = 0$$

The form in which this equation is written is called the *general form* of the equation. When the equation of a circle is written in general form, the radius and the coordinates of the centre cannot be seen in the equation. But we can determine the radius and the coordinates of the centre using the method of *completing the square*.

Example 2. A circle has the equation $x^2 + y^2 - 6x + 14y + 10 = 0$. Determine the radius and the coordinates of the centre.

Solution. We collect the terms containing x, and the terms containing y and then use the method of completing the square.

$$x^2 + y^2 - 6x + 14y + 10 = 0$$
$$x^2 - 6x + y^2 + 14y + 10 = 0$$

Add the squares of $\frac{1}{2}(-6)$ and $\frac{1}{2}(14)$ to both sides.

$$(x^2 - 6x + 9) + (y^2 + 14y + 49) + 10 = 9 + 49$$
$$(x - 3)^2 + (y + 7)^2 = 48$$

The radius is $\sqrt{48}$, or $4\sqrt{3}$, and the centre is $(3, -7)$.

The general equation of a circle is usually written as $x^2 + y^2 + 2Gx + 2Fy + C = 0$. We can use the method of *Example 2* to find expressions for its centre and radius.

$$x^2 + y^2 + 2Gx + 2Fy + C = 0$$
$$x^2 + 2Gx + y^2 + 2Fy + C = 0$$

Complete each square.

$$x^2 + 2Gx + G^2 + y^2 + 2Fy + F^2 + C = G^2 + F^2$$
$$(x + G)^2 + (y + F)^2 = G^2 + F^2 - C$$

This equation represents a circle with centre $(-G, -F)$ and radius $\sqrt{G^2 + F^2 - C}$, provided that $G^2 + F^2 - C \geqslant 0$.

General Equation of a Circle
- The equation $x^2 + y^2 + 2Gx + 2Fy + C = 0$ represents a circle, provided that $G^2 + F^2 - C \geqslant 0$.
- The coordinates of the centre are $(-G, -F)$.
- The radius is $\sqrt{G^2 + F^2 - C}$.

Observe that in the general equation of a circle the quadratic terms are $x^2 + y^2$.

Example 3. Which equations represent circles? Find the coordinates of the centre, and the radius, of each circle.

a) $x^2 + y^2 + 8x - 12y + 42 = 0$
b) $2x^2 + 2y^2 - 12x + 9y + 27 = 0$
c) $x^2 + 2y^2 + 6x - 10y - 3 = 0$
d) $x^2 - y^2 - 4x + 7y = 0$
e) $x^2 + y^2 - 2x + 3y + 4 = 0$

Solution. The equations in parts c) and d) do not represent circles because they cannot be written in a form in which the quadratic terms are $x^2 + y^2$.

a) $x^2 + y^2 + 8x - 12y + 42 = 0$

For this equation, $G = \frac{1}{2}(8) \qquad F = \frac{1}{2}(-12) \qquad C = 42$

$$= 4 \qquad\qquad = -6$$

$$G^2 + F^2 - C = 4^2 + (-6)^2 - 42$$
$$= 10$$

The equation represents a circle with radius $\sqrt{10}$ and centre $(-4, 6)$.

b) $2x^2 + 2y^2 - 12x + 9y + 27 = 0$

Divide both sides by 2 to write the equation in general form.

$$x^2 + y^2 - 6x + \frac{9}{2}y + \frac{27}{2} = 0$$

For this equation, $G = \frac{1}{2}(-6) \qquad F = \frac{1}{2}\left(\frac{9}{2}\right) \qquad C = \frac{27}{2}$

$$= -3 \qquad\qquad = \frac{9}{4}$$

$$G^2 + F^2 - C = (-3)^2 + \left(\frac{9}{4}\right)^2 - \frac{27}{2}$$

$$= 9 + \frac{81}{16} - \frac{27}{2}$$

$$= \frac{9}{16}$$

The equation represents a circle with radius $\sqrt{\frac{9}{16}}$, or $\frac{3}{4}$, and centre $\left(3, -\frac{9}{4}\right)$.

e) $x^2 + y^2 - 2x + 3y + 4 = 0$

For this equation, $G = \frac{1}{2}(-2) \qquad F = \frac{1}{2}(3) \qquad C = 4$

$$= -1 \qquad\qquad = \frac{3}{2}$$

$$G^2 + F^2 - C = (-1)^2 + \left(\frac{3}{2}\right)^2 - 4$$

$$= -0.75$$

Since this expression is negative, the given equation does not represent a circle.

EXERCISES 4-3

Ⓐ

1. Determine if each point is on the circle defined by $x^2 + y^2 = 85$.
   a) $(9, -2)$ b) $(-5, 8)$ c) $(-7, -6)$ d) $(4, 8)$

2. State the radius and the coordinates of the centre of the circle defined by each equation.
   a) $x^2 + y^2 = 64$
   b) $x^2 + y^2 = 12$
   c) $(x - 3)^2 + (y + 4)^2 = 81$
   d) $(x + 2)^2 + (y - 1)^2 = 5$
   e) $(x + 4)^2 + y^2 = 15$
   f) $x^2 + (y - 6)^2 = 48$

3. Write the equation of the circle with each given centre and radius.
   a) $(0, 0), 3$ b) $(0, 0), 7$ c) $(5, 3), 4$ d) $(-2, 6), 5$

   e) $(4, 0), 6$ f) $(0, -3), 9$ g) $(0, 0), \sqrt{5}$ h) $(3, -5), \sqrt{10}$

4. Convert each equation to general form.
   a) $(x - 3)^2 + (y + 2)^2 = 25$
   b) $(x - 1)^2 + (y - 6)^2 = 30$
   c) $(x + 4)^2 + (y - 2)^2 = 11$
   d) $(x + 5)^2 + y^2 = 25$

5. Convert each equation to standard form.
   a) $x^2 + y^2 - 4x + 10y + 13 = 0$ b) $x^2 + y^2 + 8x - 6y - 25 = 0$

Ⓑ

6. Sketch the circles defined by these equations on the same grid.
   a) $x^2 + y^2 = 9$
   b) $(x - 4)^2 + y^2 = 9$
   c) $x^2 + (y - 5)^2 = 9$
   d) $(x - 4)^2 + (y - 5)^2 = 9$

7. A circle has centre $(0, 0)$ and radius 6 units.
   a) Find the equation of the circle.
   b) Find the value of y_1 if $(4, y_1)$ is on the circle.

8. A circle has centre $(3, 2)$ and radius 5 units.
   a) Find the value of x_1 if $(x_1, 3)$ is on the circle.
   b) Find the value of y_1 if $(2, y_1)$ is on the circle.

9. Which equations represent circles? Find the radius, and the coordinates of the centre of each circle.
   a) $x^2 + y^2 - 10x + 4y + 20 = 0$
   b) $x^2 + y^2 - 6x - 2y - 15 = 0$
   c) $x^2 + y^2 + 6x - 2y + 12 = 0$
   d) $x^2 + y^2 + x + y - 4 = 0$
   e) $2x^2 + 2y^2 - 4x + 3y - 5 = 0$
   f) $3x^2 + 3y^2 + 5x - 9y + 40 = 0$

10. Sketch the circle represented by each equation.
    a) $x^2 + y^2 - 6x + 5 = 0$
    b) $x^2 + y^2 + 2y - 8 = 0$
    c) $x^2 + y^2 - 2x - 6y = 0$
    d) $x^2 + y^2 + 6x - 4y + 9 = 0$
    e) $x^2 + y^2 - 6x + 10y + 25 = 0$
    f) $x^2 + y^2 + 8x + 8y + 16 = 0$

11. Under what condition(s) does the equation $x^2 + y^2 + 2Gx + 2Fy + C = 0$ represent a circle:
    a) with centre on: i) the x-axis   ii) the y-axis   iii) both axes
    b) which passes through the origin
    c) which is tangent to: i) the x-axis   ii) the y-axis   iii) both axes.

12. Suggest why the coefficients of x and y in the general equation of a circle contain the factor 2.

13. A point P moves such that it is always twice as far from A(6, 0) as it is from the origin.
    a) Find the equation of the locus.
    b) Identify the locus and sketch its graph.
    c) Verify from the graph that points on the graph are twice as far from A as they are from the origin.

14. Determine the equation of the circle defined by the given conditions.
    a) The centre is C(3, −2), and R(−1, 1) is a point on the circle.
    b) The endpoints of a diameter are M(5, 1) and N(−3, 3).
    c) The circle passes through A(2, 2) and B(5, 3), and the centre is on the line defined by $y = x + 1$.

15. The three circles shown have the same centre, and the middle circle has a radius of 1. If the colored region has the same area as the shaded region, what is the relation between x and y?

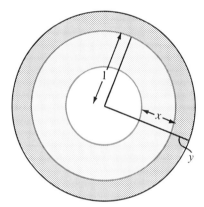

16. Determine if the circles defined by each pair of equations intersect.
    a) $x^2 + y^2 - 8x - 4y + 12 = 0$; $x^2 + y^2 + 4x - 12y + 22 = 0$
    b) $x^2 + y^2 - 6x + 2y + 5 = 0$; $x^2 + y^2 - 2x + 4y - 27 = 0$
    c) $x^2 + y^2 - 10x + 2y + 17 = 0$; $x^2 + y^2 + 6x + 14y + 9 = 0$
    d) $x^2 + y^2 - 4x - 6y + 9 = 0$; $x^2 + y^2 - 2x - 4y - 8 = 0$

17. Given the circles defined by $x^2 + y^2 + 2G_1x + 2F_1y + C_1 = 0$ and $x^2 + y^2 + 2G_2x + 2F_2y + C_2 = 0$, what conditions must be satisfied by G_1, F_1, C_1, G_2, F_2, and C_2 if the circles intersect?

18. Determine the equation of the circle which passes through the points J(−3, 2), K(4, 1), and L(6, 5).

19. A circle has x-intercepts 0 and a, and y-intercepts 0 and b. Determine the equation of the circle.

20. Two points $A_1(a_1, 0)$ and $A_2(a_2, 0)$ are given on the x-axis, and two points $B_1(0, b_1)$ and $B_2(0, b_2)$ are given on the y-axis. What condition(s) must be satisfied by a_1, a_2, b_1, and b_2 if a circle passes through all four points?

4-4 TANGENTS TO A CIRCLE

For any straight line and any circle, one of the following occurs:

There are two points
of intersection.

There is one point
of intersection.

There is no point
of intersection.

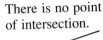

The line is called
a *secant*.

The line is called
a *tangent*.

A wheel standing on level ground illustrates a
tangent to a circle. The centre of the wheel is directly
above the point where the wheel touches the ground.
That is, the angle formed by the radius to this point
and the ground is 90°.

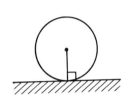

Tangent property of a circle
The angle between the tangent to a circle and the radius it touches is 90°.

Length of a Tangent

The tangent property can be used to calculate the length of the tangent
to a circle from any point outside it.

Example 1. Find the length of the tangent from point
P(5, 7) to the circle $x^2 + y^2 = 10$.

Solution. Let the tangent from P intersect the circle
at T. Since PT is perpendicular to OT, by
the Pythagorean Theorem:
$OP^2 = OT^2 + PT^2$
$OP = \sqrt{5^2 + 7^2}$, or $\sqrt{74}$, and OT $= \sqrt{10}$
Substitute these values.
$74 = 10 + PT^2$
$PT^2 = 64$
$PT = 8$
The tangent from P(5, 7) to the circle is
8 units long.

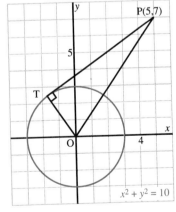

In *Example 1*, note that it was not necessary to find the coordinates of
the point of tangency to find the length of the tangent.

Equation of a Tangent

The tangent property can also be used to find the equation of the tangent at any point on a given circle.

Example 2. A(3, 4) is a point on the circle $x^2 + y^2 = 25$. Find the equation of the tangent at A.

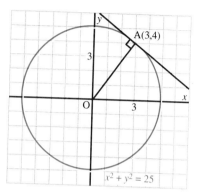

Solution. Slope of radius OA $= \dfrac{4 - 0}{3 - 0}$

$$= \dfrac{4}{3}$$

Since the tangent is perpendicular to OA, the slope of the tangent is $-\dfrac{3}{4}$.

Since the tangent passes through $(3, 4)$, its equation is:

$$y - 4 = -\dfrac{3}{4}(x - 3)$$
$$4y - 16 = -3x + 9$$
$$3x + 4y - 25 = 0$$

EXERCISES 4-4

(A)

1. Find the length of each tangent PQ.

   a)

   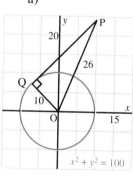

   b)

   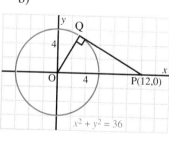

   c)

   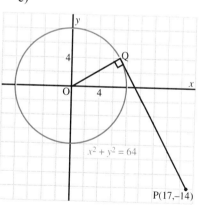

2. a) Graph the circle $x^2 + y^2 = 25$.

   b) Find the length of the tangents to the circle from each point.

   i) $(11, -2)$ ii) $(8, 6)$ iii) $(3, 8)$

3. Find the length of the tangents from $(8, 3)$ to each circle.

   a) $x^2 + y^2 = 9$ b) $x^2 + y^2 = 36$ c) $x^2 + y^2 = 65$

4. The equation of a circle and a point on it are given. Find the equation of the tangent at that point.

a) $x^2 + y^2 = 25$,　(4, 3)

b) $x^2 + y^2 = 100$,　(6, −8)

c) $x^2 + y^2 = 5$,　(1, 2)

d) $x^2 + y^2 = 13$,　(−3, −2)

(B)

5. a) Graph the circle $(x − 2)^2 + (y − 3)^2 = 25$.

b) Find the length of the tangents to the circle from each point.

　　i) (5, −3)　　　　　ii) (−1, −6)　　　　　iii) (−6, 2)

6. Find the length of the tangents to the circle from each point.

a) $(x − 4)^2 + (y + 3)^2 = 25$,　(7, 4)

b) $(x + 4)^2 + (y − 1)^2 = 36$,　(6, 3)

c) $(x − 3)^2 + (y + 5)^2 = 12$,　(−4, 1)

d) $(x + 5)^2 + (y + 2)^2 = 48$,　(−3, 8)

7. The tangent from (8, −1) to the circle $x^2 + y^2 = r^2$ has length 4. Find the value of r.

8. P is a point on the line $x = 4$ such that the tangent from P to the circle $x^2 + y^2 = 4$ has length 6. Find the possible coordinates of P, and illustrate graphically.

9. The equation of a circle, and a point on it are given. Find the equation of the tangent at that point.

a) $x^2 + y^2 = 10$,　(−1, 3)

b) $x^2 + y^2 = 16$,　(0, −4)

c) $x^2 + y^2 = 4$,　$(\sqrt{2}, \sqrt{2})$

d) $x^2 + y^2 = 11$,　$(3, −\sqrt{2})$

10. The three lines given pass through (2, −3) on the circle $x^2 + y^2 = 13$. Which line is the tangent at (2, −3)?

$3x + 2y = 0$,　　　　$3x − 2y − 12 = 0$,　　　　$2x − 3y − 13 = 0$

11. A diameter of the circle $x^2 + y^2 = 29$ has one endpoint (5, 2). Find the equations of the tangents at both endpoints.

12. In the diagram, A(−5, 0) and B(4, 3) are points on the circle $x^2 + y^2 = 25$.

a) Show that point P(7, 4) lies on line AB.

b) Find the length of tangent PT.

c) Show that $PT^2 = PA \times PB$.

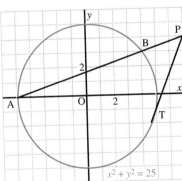

13. A go-kart race track starts on a straightaway which is tangent to the main circular track at F (below left). The starting point is S(0, 10). The circular part of the track has radius 60 m and centre C(70, 60).

a) Find the length of the straightaway section.

b) Find the length of the race if karts start at S, make 10 circuits, and finish at F. Give the answers to 1 decimal place.

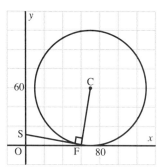 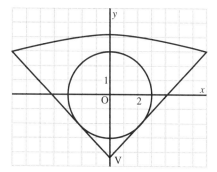

14. A steel ball radius 3 cm is dropped into a right circular cone (above right). The vertex of the cone is at V(0, −4.6). What is the length of the section of the cone from the point of tangency with the ball to the vertex? Give the answer to 1 decimal place.

15. A heavy circular disk is rolled up a linear inclined plane (below left). When the disk reaches a point (0.6, 1.4) on the line, the point of contact of the disk is diametrically opposite, and touching, an overhanging branch at (3, 3).

a) What is the equation of the circle of the disk when it has reached this position?

b) What is the equation of the line that represents the inclined plane?

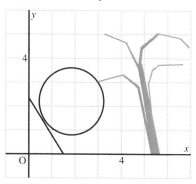 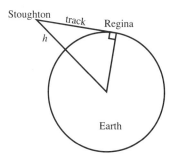

16. One of the world's longest straight stretches of railway track runs 140 km between Regina and Stoughton, Saskatchewan (above right). As the diagram shows, the track is not perfectly straight because of the curvature of the Earth. If the track were perfectly straight, its end at Stoughton would be a certain distance, h, above the town. Estimate the value of h assuming that the radius of the Earth is approximately 6370 km. Give the answer to the nearest tenth of a kilometre.

17. The diagram (below left) shows a round ball floating, partly submerged, in the sea ($y = 0$). The ball has centre C(0, 5) and radius 13 cm. A stick is tangent to the circle at sea level. Find two equations which represent the position of the stick.

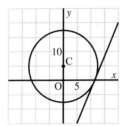
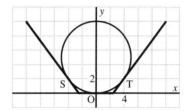

18. A ball bearing is in a moulding whose cross section is a trapezoid (above right). The ball bearing is tangent to the moulding at points S(−4, 2), O(0, 0), and T(4, 2).

a) What is the equation of the circular cross section of the ball bearing?

b) How deep must the moulding be so that the bearing fits inside, and its top is level with the top of the moulding?

Ⓒ

19. A child's teeter-totter is balanced on a circular log, radius 15 cm, which rests on the ground. When the left end of the beam is on the ground, its equation is $7x - 24y = 0$.

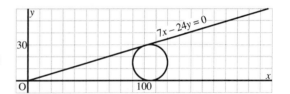

a) Find the equation of the circular log.

b) How long is the beam of the teeter-totter?

20. A box, whose cross section is a right triangle with sides $y = -4$, $x = 4$, and $y = x + b$, $b > 0$, encloses and is tangent to the circle $x^2 + y^2 = 16$.

a) Find the value of b.

b) Find the point of tangency of the circle with the hypotenuse.

c) Find the perimeter of the cross section of the box.

21. a) Derive a formula for the length of the tangent from the point (x_1, y_1) to the circle with equation $(x - h)^2 + (y - k)^2 = r^2$.

b) Use the formula to find the length of the tangent to the circle $(x - 3)^2 + (y - 2)^2 = 25$ from each point.

   i) $(8, 9)$ ii) $(-4, 2)$ iii) $(0, 6)$ iv) $(0, 0)$

c) What is the geometric significance of the answers to part b) iii) and iv)?

22. Find the equation of the tangent at the point (x_1, y_1) on the circle $x^2 + y^2 = r^2$.

23. P is any point on $x^2 + y^2 = 29$. Find the length of the tangent from P to the circle $x^2 + y^2 = 13$.

4-5 THE PARABOLA: VERTEX (0,0)

When major league baseball games are televised, a parabolic reflector microphone is often used to pick up the voices of the players and umpires. A cross section of the microphone has the shape of a parabola. Another example from baseball is the parabolic path of the ball when it is hit or thrown.

A parabola is defined as follows.

> A *parabola* is the locus of a point P which moves such that it is always the same distance from a fixed point F and a fixed line *d*.
>
> The point F is called the *focus* of the parabola.
>
> The line *d* is called the *directrix*. The point V, halfway between F and *d* is the *vertex*. The line through F perpendicular to the directrix is the *axis*.

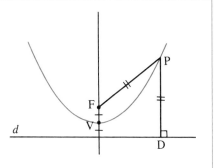

We can use the defining property to develop the equation of a parabola. The equation depends on the positions of the focus and the directrix.

For example, suppose the vertex is the origin and the focus in on the *x*-axis. Then the focus is F(p, 0) and the directrix is the line $x = -p$. Let P(x, y) be any point on the parabola. Then, if D is the point $(-p, y)$,

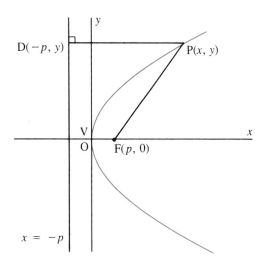

$$PF = PD$$
$$\sqrt{(x - p)^2 + y^2} = \sqrt{(x + p)^2}$$

Square both sides.

$$(x - p)^2 + y^2 = (x + p)^2$$
$$x^2 - 2px + p^2 + y^2 = x^2 + 2px + p^2$$
$$y^2 = 4px$$

This is the *standard equation* of a parabola with vertex (0, 0) and focus F(p, 0) on the *x*-axis. Similarly, the standard equation of a parabola with vertex (0, 0) and focus F(0, p) on the *y*-axis is $x^2 = 4py$.

In these equations, p may be positive or negative.

Standard Equations of a Parabola with Vertex (0, 0)

The equation of a parabola with vertex (0, 0) and focus on the x-axis is $y^2 = 4px$.

The equation of a parabola with vertex (0, 0) and focus on the y-axis is $x^2 = 4py$.

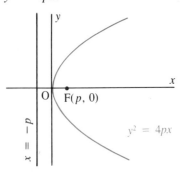

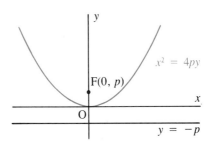

Coordinates of focus: $(p, 0)$
Equation of directrix: $x = -p$
If $p > 0$, the parabola opens right.
If $p < 0$, the parabola opens left.

Coordinates of focus: $(0, p)$
Equation of directrix: $y = -p$
If $p > 0$, the parabola opens up.
If $p < 0$, the parabola opens down.

Example 1. A parabola has the equation $y^2 = -6x$. Sketch the parabola, showing the coordinates of the focus and the equation of the directrix.

Solution. Compare the given equation $y^2 = -6x$
with the standard equation $y^2 = 4px$.

Hence $4p = -6$

$$p = -\frac{3}{2}, \text{ or } -1.5$$

The coordinates of the focus are $(-1.5, 0)$, and the equation of the directrix is $x = 1.5$.

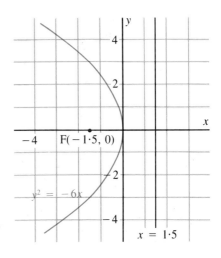

Example 2. A parabola has vertex (0, 0) and focus on the y-axis.
a) Find the equation of the parabola if it passes through the point A(4, 12).
b) Find the value of y_1 if B(3, y_1) is on the parabola.

Solution.   a) Let the equation of the
parabola be $x^2 = 4py$.
Since A(4, 12) is a point
on the parabola, its coordinates satisfy the equation.
Substitute 4 for x and 12
for y in $x^2 = 4py$.

$x^2 = 4py$

$4^2 = 4p(12)$

$p = \dfrac{1}{3}$

The equation of the parabola is

$x^2 = \dfrac{4}{3}y$

or $y = \dfrac{3}{4}x^2$

b) Substitute 3 for x and y_1 for y in $y = \dfrac{3}{4}x^2$.

$y_1 = \dfrac{3}{4}(3)^2$

$= \dfrac{27}{4}$

Hence, if B(3, y_1) is on the parabola, $y_1 = \dfrac{27}{4}$.

EXERCISES 4-5

Ⓐ

1. Determine if each point is on the parabola defined by $y = 3x^2$.
   a) $(-1, 3)$ b) $(3, 9)$ c) $(-2, -12)$ d) $(-2, 12)$.

2. State the coordinates of the focus and the equation of the directrix of the parabola
   defined by each equation.
   a) $y^2 = 4x$ b) $y^2 = 12x$ c) $y^2 = -6x$ d) $x^2 = 8y$
   e) $x^2 = -2y$ f) $x^2 = 3y$ g) $y^2 = -9x$ h) $x^2 = -5y$

Ⓑ

3. Sketch the parabola defined by each equation, showing the coordinates of the focus
   and the equation of the directrix.
   a) $y^2 = 8x$ b) $y^2 = -3x$ c) $x^2 = 4y$ d) $x^2 = -10y$

4. A parabola has vertex $(0, 0)$ and focus on a coordinate axis. Write the equation of
   the parabola if:
   a) the focus is: i) $(4, 0)$ ii) $(-6, 0)$ iii) $(0, 3)$
   b) the directrix is the line defined by $y = 8$.

5. A parabola has vertex $(0, 0)$ and focus on the y-axis. Find the equation of the
   parabola if it passes through each point.
   a) $(2, 8)$ b) $(4, 6)$ c) $(-4, 10)$ d) $(4, -2)$

6. A parabola has vertex (0, 0) and focus on the *x*-axis. Find the equation of the parabola if it passes through each point.
   a) (20, 8)   b) (12, 10)   c) (5, −6)   d) (3, 7)

7. A parabola has vertex (0, 0) and focus on the *y*-axis.
   a) Find the equation of the parabola if it passes through each point.
      i) (8, 8)   ii) (5, 5)   iii) (−3, −3)   iv) (−7, −7)
   b) What conclusion can you make about the equation of a parabola if it passes through a point whose *x*- and *y*-coordinates are equal?

8. The focus of a parabola is F(5, 0) and the directrix is the line $x = -5$. Use the definition of a parabola to derive the equation of this parabola.

9. Use the definition to derive the equation of a parabola with focus F(0, p) on the *y*-axis and directrix the line $y = -p$.

10. A rectangle has a perimeter of 50 cm, and a length of *x* centimetres.
    a) Write the area *A* square centimetres as a function of the length.
    b) Draw a graph of the function in part a).

11. Use the definition of a parabola to prove that a parabola is symmetric about its axis. That is, if P_1 is any point on a parabola, and if the axis is the perpendicular bisector of P_1P_2, then P_2 is also on the parabola.

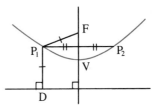

12. A line passing through the focus of a parabola, and perpendicular to the axis intersects the parabola at L and R. Prove that the length of LR is four times the distance between the focus and the vertex.

©

13. In the second diagram on page 161, find the coordinates of P if △PFD is:
    a) an equilateral triangle   b) a right triangle.

 INVESTIGATE

Parabolas and Pythagorean triples

Three natural numbers, such as 5, 12, and 13, which satisfy the equation $a^2 + b^2 = c^2$ are called *Pythagorean Triples.*

1. a) Sketch the graph of the parabola defined by $y^2 = 4px$. Locate points on the parabola whose *x*-coordinates are p, $4p$, $9p$, $16p$, . . .
   b) Let P be any of the points in part a). Let N be the point on the *x*-axis with the same *x*-coordinate as P. Prove that the lengths of the sides of △PNF are Pythagorean triples. (Assume p is a natural number.)

2. Use the result of *Question 1* to find formulas for some Pythagorean triples.

MATHEMATICS AROUND US

Reflector Property of the Parabola

We have all seen dish antennas for receiving TV signals from satellites. These antennas have parabolic cross sections. When the antenna is aimed at a satellite, the signals entering the antenna are reflected to the receiver, which is placed at the focus of the antenna.

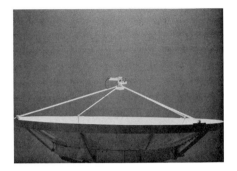

Every parabola has a *focus*, which is a particular point on the axis of symmetry. The position of the focus can be defined as follows.

For any parabola, the *focus* is the point on the axis of symmetry which is half as far from the vertex as it is from the parabola, measured along a line perpendicular to the axis of symmetry. For example, in the diagram, FV = p, and FL = $2p$. That is, F is half as far from V as from L. Hence, F is the focus of the parabola. Every parabola has one and only one focus.

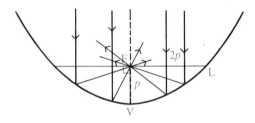

You can illustrate the reflector property of the parabola by completing the questions below.

QUESTIONS

1. a) Use a table of values to construct an accurate graph of the parabola defined by $y = \frac{1}{8}x^2$ for values of x between -8 and 8.

   b) Mark the point F(0,2) on the graph. Verify that F satisfies the above definition of the focus.

2. a) Mark any point P on the parabola you constructed in *Question 1*. Join PF, and draw a line PM parallel to the axis of symmetry. By estimation, draw a tangent to the parabola at P. Verify that PF and PM form equal angles with the tangent.

   b) Repeat part a) for other points P on the parabola.

3. Use the above definition of the focus to prove that the coordinates of the focus of the parabola defined by $y = ax^2$ are $\left(0, \frac{1}{4a}\right)$.

USING TECHNOLOGY

Quadratic Functions, Part II

Sketching Parabolas

a) Using the function $y = x^2$ as a reference, sketch the graph of each function without your graphing calculator. Each sketch should include the vertex, y-intercept, and two other points. Confirm your sketches by graphing these curves on your graphing calculator.

i) $y = -4x^2$ ii) $y = 2x^2 + 3$ iii) $y = -2(x - 1)^2$

iv) $y = 3(x + 2)^2 - 4$ v) $y = -(x - 2)^2 + 5$ vi) $y = -\dfrac{1}{2}(x + 3)^2 - 4$

Explorations I

a) With your graphing calculator, verify graphically that $Y_1 = X^2$ and $Y_2 = \sqrt{X}$ intersect in two points. What are the two solutions of $x^2 = \sqrt{x}$?

b) From your understanding of transformations and by graphing, verify that $x^2 + 1 = \sqrt{x}$ has no solution.

c) Using the TRACE and magnification features of your graphing calculator, find the value of a for which $ax^2 + 1 = a\sqrt{x}$ has only one solution. In other words, for which value of a will the graphs of $Y_1 = aX^2 + 1$ and $Y_2 = a\sqrt{X}$ touch at one point?

d) What is the value of x for the point of tangency in part c)?

The Price of Travel

The distance k kilometres that an automobile can travel on 4 L of gasoline is a function of its speed v kilometres per hour.

For speeds between 25 km/h and 105 km/h, $k = -\dfrac{1}{80}v^2 + \dfrac{3}{2}v$. Display the graph of this function on your graphing calculator. Use the TRACE feature to find the most economical speed for a trip.

Explorations II

a) Will the graph of every quadratic function have an x-intercept? Explain.

b) Will the graph of every quadratic function have a y-intercept? Explain.

c) The zeros of a quadratic function are -3 and 5. Write the equation of this function and check it by graphing. Is there only one equation?

d) The zeros of a quadratic function are -3 and 5 and the y-intercept is 2. How many equations of the function are there under these conditions? Explain.

Making a Box

Equal squares of side 6 cm are cut from the corners of a square piece of cardboard. An open box is formed by folding up the sides.

The volume of the box is 1944 cm³. What were the dimensions of the original piece of cardboard?

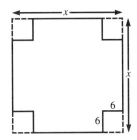

Let the original piece of cardboard have side length x centimetres. Then, the length and width of the box are each $(x - 12)$ centimetres and the height is 6 cm. Hence, the volume is $6(x - 12)^2$ cm³.

Enter $Y_1 = 6(X - 12)^2$ on your graphing calculator and display the graph in a viewing window of $[-10, 40]$ by $[-10, 2000]$.

a) Use the TRACE and magnification features to locate the value of X for which Y equals 1944.

b) Find 2 values of X for which the value of Y is 384. Are both values valid lengths for the side of the square? Explain.

The Biggest Box

Equal squares of side x centimetres are cut from the corners of a square piece of metal of side 10 cm. The sides are folded to form a metal box with no top.

a) What are the measures of the length, width, and height of the box?

b) Write an expression for the volume V of the box in terms of x.

c) What is the side length of the largest square that can be cut from each corner of the box?

d) Will the volume of the box be the same regardless of the size of the square that is removed from each corner? Explain your answer with several examples.

e) Enter the equation of the volume of the box in the functions menu. Display the graph in a viewing window of $[-2, 8]$ by $[-10, 100]$. Find 3 values of X for which Y equals 50 cm³. Are all 3 values valid for this situation? Explain.

f) What size square should be cut from each corner to obtain the largest possible volume?

4-6 THE PARABOLA: VERTEX (h,k)

We can use the definition of a parabola to find the equation of a parabola
with any vertex V(h, k). We let p represent the distance from the vertex
to the focus and to the directrix.

If the axis of symmetry is horizontal,
the coordinates of the focus are F($h + p$, k)
and the equation of the directrix is
$x = h - p$.

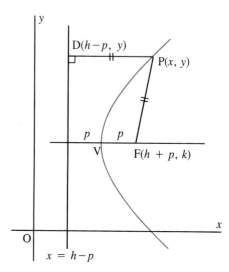

Let P(x, y) be any point on the parabola.
Then, if D is the point ($h - p$, y),

$$PF = PD$$
$$\sqrt{(x - h - p)^2 + (y - k)^2} = \sqrt{(x - h + p)^2}$$

Square both sides.

$$(x - h - p)^2 + (y - k)^2 = (x - h + p)^2$$
$$x^2 + h^2 + p^2 - 2hx - 2px + 2hp + (y - k)^2 = x^2 + h^2 + p^2 - 2hx + 2px - 2hp$$
$$(y - k)^2 = 4p(x - h)$$

This is the standard equation of a parabola with vertex (h, k) and a
horizontal axis of symmetry. Similarly, the standard equation of a parabola
with vertex (h, k) and a vertical axis of symmetry is $(x - h)^2 = 4p(y - k)$.

Standard Equations of a Parabola with Vertex (h, k)

Horizontal axis of symmetry: Vertical axis of symmetry:

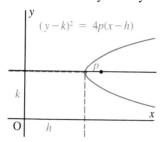

$(y - k)^2 = 4p(x - h)$

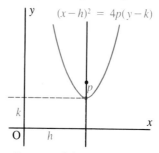

$(x - h)^2 = 4p(y - k)$

Coordinates of focus: ($h + p$, k)   Coordinates of focus: (h, $k + p$)
Equation of directrix: $x = h - p$ Equation of directrix: $y = k - p$
Equation of axis: $y - k = 0$ Equation of axis: $x - h = 0$
Opening: right if $p > 0$, left if $p < 0$ Opening: up if $p > 0$, down if $p < 0$

Example.   Sketch the parabola defined by each equation. Show the vertex and the focus, and the equations of the directrix and the axis.

a) $(y + 3)^2 = -8(x - 4)$ b) $(x + 1)^2 = 6(y - 2)$

Solution.   a) Compare $(y + 3)^2 = -8(x - 4)$
with the standard equation
$(y - k)^2 = 4p(x - h)$.
Hence, $4p = -8$ $h = 4$
$\qquad p = -2$ $k = -3$
Vertex: V$(4, -3)$
Axis: $y = -3$
Since the parabola opens to the left,
the coordinates of the focus are
F$(4 - 2, -3)$ or F$(2, -3)$, and the
equation of the directrix is
$x = 4 - (-2)$, or $x = 6$.

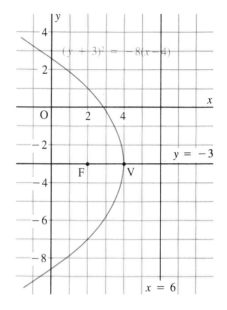

b) Compare $(x + 1)^2 = 6(y - 2)$ with
the standard equation
$(x - h)^2 = 4p(y - k)$.
Hence, $4p = 6$ $h = -1$
$\qquad p = 1.5$ $k = 2$
Vertex: V$(-1, 2)$
Axis: $x = -1$
Since the parabola opens up,
the coordinates of the focus are
F$(-1, 2 + 1.5)$, or F$(-1, 3.5)$,
and the equation of the directrix is
$y = 2 - 1.5$, or $y = 0.5$.

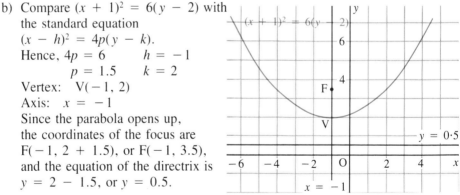

In the equations of the *Example*, the binomial squares may be
expanded, and the equations written in *general form*. For example, in
general form the equation $(y + 3)^2 = -8(x - 4)$ becomes
$$y^2 + 6y + 9 = -8x + 32$$
$$y^2 + 8x + 6y - 23 = 0$$
In general form the coordinates of the vertex cannot be seen in the
equation.

EXERCISES 4-6

Ⓐ

1. State the coordinates of the vertex, the equation of the axis, and the direction of opening of the parabola defined by each equation.
   a) $(y - 2)^2 = 4(x - 3)$
   b) $(y + 1)^2 = -8(x - 2)$
   c) $(x + 1)^2 = 4(y + 5)$
   d) $(x - 4)^2 = -12(y - 1)$
   e) $(y - 3)^2 = 8x$
   f) $x^2 = 16(y - 2)$

2. Convert each equation to general form.
   a) $(y + 3)^2 = 2(x - 1)$
   b) $(y - 1)^2 = -(x + 3)$
   c) $(x + 5)^2 = -4(y - 2)$
   d) $(x - 2)^2 = 3y$

3. Convert each equation to standard form.
   a) $x^2 - 2x - 3y - 8 = 0$
   b) $x^2 + 6x + 5y - 1 = 0$
   c) $y^2 - 4x + 4y + 24 = 0$
   d) $y^2 + 3x - 2y + 7 = 0$

Ⓑ

4. Sketch the parabola defined by each equation. Show the coordinates of the vertex and the focus, and the equations of the axis and the directrix on your sketch.
   a) $(y + 2)^2 = 4(x - 1)$
   b) $(y - 3)^2 = -2(x + 4)$
   c) $(x - 3)^2 = 2(y + 2)$
   d) $x^2 = -3(y - 1)$
   e) $y^2 = -8(x - 2)$
   f) $x^2 = 4(y + 1)$

5. Determine the equation of the parabola defined by the given conditions.
   a) The vertex is V(1, 2) and the focus is F(3, 2).
   b) The vertex is V(−1, 3) and the equation of the directrix is $x - 2 = 0$.
   c) The focus is F(2, 0) and the equation of the directrix is $y + 6 = 0$.

6. A point P moves such that it is always the same distance from the point F(3, 0) as it is from the line defined by $x - 1 = 0$.
   a) Find the equation of the locus.
   b) Identify the locus and sketch its graph.
   c) Verify from the graph that points on the graph are equidistant from F(3, 0) and the line defined by $x - 1 = 0$.

7. A point P moves such that it is always equidistant from the point F(−1, 2) and the line defined by $y - 6 = 0$. Find the equation of the locus.

Ⓒ

8. A point P moves such that it is always 2 units farther from the line defined by $x + 4 = 0$ than it is from the point F(4, 0). Find the equation of the locus of P.

9. Investigate whether the locus of a point, which moves such that the difference of its distances from a fixed point and a fixed line is constant, is a parabola.

10. What condition(s) must be satisfied by p, h, and k, if each equation represents a parabola whose focus is the origin?
   a) $(y - k)^2 = 4p(x - h)$
   b) $(x - h)^2 = 4p(y - k)$

4-7 THE ELLIPSE

A spotlight is often used in skating shows. The light rays form a cone of light which illuminates an elliptical region on the ice.

An ellipse also results when a cylindrical tube is cut at an angle. In machinery, elliptical gears are sometimes used to provide a powerful stroke followed by a quick return.

An ellipse may be defined as follows.

An *ellipse* is the locus of a point P which moves such that the sum of its distances from two fixed points F_1 and F_2 is constant.
F_1 and F_2 are called the *foci* of the ellipse.
PF_1 and PF_2 are called *focal radii*.

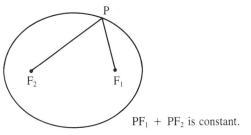

$PF_1 + PF_2$ is constant.

Let the line F_1F_2 intersect the ellipse at A_1 and A_2. Let the perpendicular bisector of F_1F_2 intersect the ellipse at B_1 and B_2.

- A_1 and A_2 are called the *vertices*.
- Line segment A_1A_2 is called the *major axis*; its length is represented by $2a$.
- Line segment B_1B_2 is called the *minor axis*; its length is represented by $2b$.
- Since A_1A_2 is longer than B_1B_2, $a > b > 0$.
- A_1A_2 and B_1B_2 intersect at the *centre*, O.
- OA_1 is called the *semi-major axis*, and has length a.
- OB_1 is called the *semi-minor axis*, and has length b.
- The distance from the centre to either focus is represented by c.
- Both the major axis and the minor axis are lines of symmetry of the ellipse.

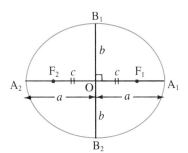

Properties of the Ellipse

According to the definition, $PF_1 + PF_2$ is constant for all positions of P on the ellipse. In particular, P could be at A_1 or at B_1.

Suppose P is at A_1. $PF_1 + PF_2 = A_1F_1 + A_1F_2$
$$= A_2F_2 + A_1F_2 \quad \text{(by symmetry)}$$
$$= A_1A_2, \text{ or } 2a.$$

Hence, for all positions of P on the ellipse, $PF_1 + PF_2$ is equal to the length of the major axis.

Suppose P is at B_1. $PF_1 + PF_2 = B_1F_1 + B_1F_2$
$$= 2B_1F_1 \quad \text{(by symmetry)}$$
$$= 2a$$

Hence, $B_1F_1 = a$. That is, the distance from the endpoints of the minor axis to either focus is equal to the length of the semi-major axis.
Since $\triangle OB_1F_1$ is a right triangle,
$B_1F_1{}^2 = OB_1{}^2 + OF_1{}^2$
$\quad a^2 = b^2 + c^2$

Focal Radii Property	**Pythagorean Property**
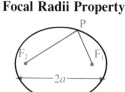	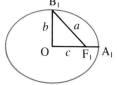
$PF_1 + PF_2 = 2a$	$a^2 = b^2 + c^2$

The Equation of an Ellipse

We can use the defining property to find the equation of any ellipse.

Example 1.   The foci of an ellipse are $F_1(3, 0)$ and $F_2(-3, 0)$, and the sum of the focal radii is 10 units. Find the equation of the ellipse.

Solution.   Let $P(x, y)$ be any point on the ellipse. Since the sum of the focal radii is 10 units,

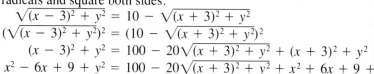

$$PF_1 + PF_2 = 10$$
$$\sqrt{(x - 3)^2 + y^2} + \sqrt{(x + 3)^2 + y^2} = 10$$

Isolate one of the radicals and square both sides.
$$\sqrt{(x - 3)^2 + y^2} = 10 - \sqrt{(x + 3)^2 + y^2}$$
$$(\sqrt{(x - 3)^2 + y^2})^2 = (10 - \sqrt{(x + 3)^2 + y^2})^2$$
$$(x - 3)^2 + y^2 = 100 - 20\sqrt{(x + 3)^2 + y^2} + (x + 3)^2 + y^2$$
$$x^2 - 6x + 9 + y^2 = 100 - 20\sqrt{(x + 3)^2 + y^2} + x^2 + 6x + 9 +$$

Isolate the radical and square both sides again.
$$20\sqrt{(x + 3)^2 + y^2} = 100 + 12x$$
$$5\sqrt{(x + 3)^2 + y^2} = 25 + 3x$$
$$25(x^2 + 6x + 9 + y^2) = 625 + 150x + 9x^2$$

This equation simplifies to
$$16x^2 + 25y^2 = 400$$
or
$$\frac{x^2}{25} + \frac{y^2}{16} = 1$$

Hence, the equation of the ellipse is $\dfrac{x^2}{25} + \dfrac{y^2}{16} = 1$.

We can use the method of *Example 1* to derive the standard equation of an ellipse with centre $(0, 0)$ and foci on the x-axis.

Let the coordinates of the foci be $F_1(c, 0)$ and $F_2(-c, 0)$.

Let $P(x, y)$ be any point on the ellipse.

Then, by the focal radii property, the sum of the focal radii is $2a$.

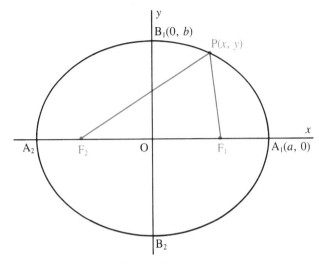

$$PF_1 + PF_2 = 2a$$
$$\sqrt{(x - c)^2 + y^2} + \sqrt{(x + c)^2 + y^2} = 2a$$

Isolate one of the radicals and square both sides.

$$\sqrt{(x - c)^2 + y^2} = 2a - \sqrt{(x + c)^2 + y^2}$$
$$(\sqrt{(x - c)^2 + y^2})^2 = (2a - \sqrt{(x + c)^2 + y^2})^2$$
$$(x - c)^2 + y^2 = 4a^2 - 4a\sqrt{(x + c)^2 + y^2} + (x + c)^2 + y^2$$
$$x^2 - 2cx + c^2 + y^2 = 4a^2 - 4a\sqrt{(x + c)^2 + y^2} + x^2 + 2cx + c^2 + y^2$$

Isolate the radical and square both sides again.

$$4a\sqrt{(x + c)^2 + y^2} = 4a^2 + 4cx$$
$$a\sqrt{(x + c)^2 + y^2} = a^2 + cx$$
$$a^2(x^2 + 2cx + c^2 + y^2) = a^4 + 2a^2cx + c^2x^2$$

This equation may be written as

$$(a^2 - c^2)x^2 + a^2y^2 = a^2(a^2 - c^2)$$

By the Pythagorean property, $a^2 - c^2 = b^2$. Hence, the equation becomes

$$b^2x^2 + a^2y^2 = a^2b^2$$

or
$$\frac{x^2}{a^2} + \frac{y^2}{b^2} = 1$$

This is the *standard equation* of an ellipse with centre $(0, 0)$ and foci on the x-axis. Similarly, the standard equation of an ellipse with centre $(0, 0)$ and foci on the y-axis is $\dfrac{x^2}{b^2} + \dfrac{y^2}{a^2} = 1$.

Standard Equations of an Ellipse with Centre (0, 0)

The equation of an ellipse with centre (0, 0) and major axis on the x-axis is $\dfrac{x^2}{a^2} + \dfrac{y^2}{b^2} = 1$, where $a > b$.

The equation of an ellipse with centre (0, 0) and major axis on the y-axis is $\dfrac{x^2}{b^2} + \dfrac{y^2}{a^2} = 1$, where $a > b$

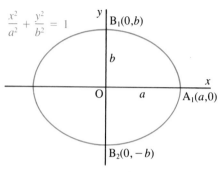

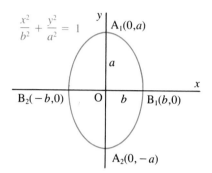

Length of major axis: $2a$
Length of minor axis: $2b$
Vertices: $(a, 0)$ and $(-a, 0)$
Foci: $(c, 0)$ and $(-c, 0)$
where $c^2 = a^2 - b^2$

Length of major axis: $2a$
Length of minor axis: $2b$
Vertices: $(0, a)$ and $(0, -a)$
Foci: $(0, c)$ and $(0, -c)$
where $c^2 = a^2 - b^2$

We can always tell whether the major axis is on the x-axis or the y-axis from the standard equation. If the larger denominator occurs in the term containing x, the major axis is on the x-axis; if it occurs in the term containing y, the major axis is on the y-axis.

Example 2.   Given the equation $4x^2 + 25y^2 = 100$

      a) Show that this equation represents an ellipse. Determine the lengths of the major and minor axes, the coordinates of the vertices, and the coordinates of the foci.

      b) Graph the ellipse.

Solution.   a) Since the standard equation has 1 on the right side, we divide both sides of the equation by 100.

$$\dfrac{4x^2}{100} + \dfrac{25y^2}{100} = 1$$

$$\dfrac{x^2}{25} + \dfrac{y^2}{4} = 1$$

b)

Hence, the equation represents an ellipse.

For this equation, $a = 5$ and $b = 2$
The major axis has length $2a$, or 10.
The minor axis has length $2b$, or 4.

Since the larger denominator occurs under x^2, the major axis lies on the x-axis. The coordinates of the vertices are $(5, 0)$ and $(-5, 0)$.
$$c^2 = a^2 - b^2$$
$$= 25 - 4$$
$$= 21$$
$$c = \sqrt{21}$$
The coordinates of the foci are $(\sqrt{21}, 0)$ and $(-\sqrt{21}, 0)$.

EXERCISES 4-7

1. Determine if each point is on the ellipse defined by $x^2 + 4y^2 = 20$.
   a) $(4, 1)$ b) $(-2, 2)$ c) $(0, -5)$ d) $(0, \sqrt{5})$

2. State the coordinates of the vertices, the coordinates of the foci, and the lengths of the major and minor axes of the ellipse defined by each equation.
   a) $\dfrac{x^2}{16} + \dfrac{y^2}{9} = 1$ b) $\dfrac{x^2}{36} + \dfrac{y^2}{25} = 1$ c) $\dfrac{x^2}{4} + \dfrac{y^2}{9} = 1$
   d) $\dfrac{x^2}{16} + \dfrac{y^2}{49} = 1$ e) $\dfrac{x^2}{64} + \dfrac{y^2}{16} = 1$ f) $\dfrac{x^2}{9} + \dfrac{y^2}{25} = 1$

(B)

3. An ellipse has centre $(0, 0)$ and major axis on the x-axis. Write the equation of the ellipse if:
   a) $a = 5$ and $b = 3$
   b) $a = 8$ and $b = 6$
   c) $b = 4$ and $c = 2$
   d) the x-intercepts are ± 7 and the y-intercepts are ± 3
   e) the minor axis has length 6, and the sum of the focal radii is 10
   f) one vertex is $A_1(6, 0)$ and one focus is $F_1(4, 0)$.

4. For each ellipse whose equation is given below
   i) Write the standard equation.
   ii) Determine the lengths of the major and minor axes, the coordinates of the vertices, and the coordinates of the foci.
   iii) Graph the ellipse.
      a) $4x^2 + 9y^2 = 36$ b) $x^2 + 4y^2 = 16$ c) $16x^2 + 9y^2 = 144$
      d) $25x^2 + 16y^2 = 400$ e) $9x^2 + y^2 = 9$ f) $2x^2 + 3y^2 = 6$

5. The foci of an ellipse are $F_1(2, 0)$ and $F_2(-2, 0)$, and the sum of the focal radii is 6 units. Use the definition of an ellipse to derive the equation of this ellipse.

6. Use the definition to derive the equation of an ellipse with sum of focal radii $2a$ and foci $F_1(0, c)$ and $F_2(0, -c)$ on the y-axis.

7. An ellipse has centre $(0, 0)$ and one vertex $A(10, 0)$.
   a) Find the equation of the ellipse if it passes through $R(6, 4)$.
   b) Find the value of x_1 if $S(x_1, 3)$ is on the ellipse.
   c) Find the value of y_1 if $T(5, y_1)$ is on the ellipse.

8. Is a circle an ellipse? Justify your answer.

9. A point P moves such that it is always twice as far from the line $x = 8$ as it is from the point $(2, 0)$.
   a) Find the equation of the locus.
   b) Identify the locus and sketch its graph.
   c) Verify from the graph that points on the graph are twice as far from the line $x = 8$ as they are from the point $(2, 0)$.

10. On page 171, O was defined to be the midpoint of F_1F_2. Use the definition of an ellipse to prove that O is also the midpoint of A_1A_2.

11. Use the definition of an ellipse to prove that an ellipse is symmetric about the minor axis. That is, if P_1 is any point on the ellipse, and if B_1B_2 is the perpendicular bisector of P_1P_2, then P_2 is also on the ellipse.

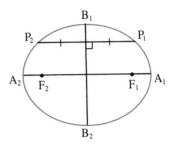

12. Use the definition of an ellipse to prove that an ellipse is symmetric about its major axis.

Ⓒ

13. Describe how the graph of the ellipse $\dfrac{x^2}{a^2} + \dfrac{y^2}{b^2} = 1$ changes if:

   a) b is kept constant and a varies
   b) a is kept constant and b varies.

14. Given the equation $Ax^2 + By^2 + C = 0$, what conditions must be satisfied by A, B, and C if this equation represents an ellipse with foci on:
   a) the x-axis
   b) the y-axis?

15. Draw a diagram to represent the ellipse defined by $\dfrac{x^2}{a^2} + \dfrac{y^2}{b^2} = 1$. Let P be any point on this ellipse.
   a) On the same diagram, draw the circle defined by $x^2 + y^2 = a^2$. Draw a vertical line through P to intersect this circle at Q and the x-axis at R. Prove that
   $$\frac{PR}{QR} = \frac{b}{a}.$$
   b) On the same diagram, draw the circle defined by $x^2 + y^2 = b^2$. Draw a horizontal line through P to intersect this circle at S and the y-axis at T. Prove that
   $$\frac{PT}{ST} = \frac{a}{b}.$$

MATHEMATICS AROUND US

Reflector Property of the Ellipse

In the Capitol at Washington, D.C., there is a room known as the whispering gallery. In this room there are two points a considerable distance apart, where a whisper at one point can be heard at the other point. The room has an elliptical cross section. When someone standing at one of the points whispers, the curved walls reflect the sound waves and focus them at the other point, where the whisper can be clearly heard.

Every ellipse has two *foci*, which are particular points on the major axis. The positions of the foci can be defined as follows.

For any ellipse, let the centre be O, and let A_1 and A_2 be the vertices. Let the *semi-major axis* OA_1 have length a. Let B_1 and B_2 be the points at the ends of the minor axis. Then, the *foci* are the points F_1 and F_2 on A_1A_2 such that $B_1F_1 = a$ and $B_1F_2 = a$.

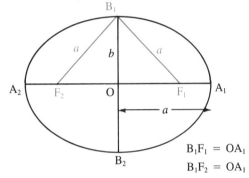

$$B_1F_1 = OA_1$$
$$B_1F_2 = OA_1$$

You can illustrate the reflector property of the ellipse by completing the questions below.

QUESTIONS

1. a) Use a table of values to construct an accurate graph of the ellipse defined by $\dfrac{x^2}{100} + \dfrac{y^2}{64} = 1$.

   b) Mark the points $F_1(6,0)$ and $F_2(-6,0)$ on the graph. Verify that F_1 and F_2 satisfy the above definition of the foci.

2. a) Mark any point P on the ellipse you constructed in *Question 1*. Join PF_1 and PF_2. By estimation, draw a tangent to the ellipse at P. Verify that PF_1 and PF_2 form equal angles with the tangent.

   b) Repeat part a) for other points P on the ellipse.

3. Use the above definition of the foci to find expressions for the coordinates of the foci of the ellipse defined by $\dfrac{x^2}{a^2} + \dfrac{y^2}{b^2} = 1$.

PROBLEM SOLVING

All Parabolas Have the Same Shape

"When I use a word," Humpty Dumpty said in a rather scornful tone, "it means just what I choose it to mean — neither more nor less."

Lewis Carroll

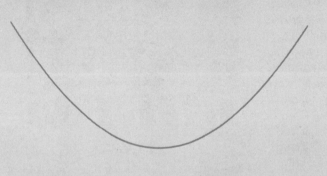

Prove that all parabolas have the same shape.

Understand the problem
- Do these parabolas look like they have the same shape?
- What does "have the same shape" mean?

The diagrams below suggest a general definition for "same shape".

All circles have the same shape.

All squares have the same shape.

Similar triangles have the same shape.

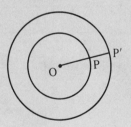 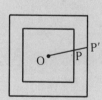 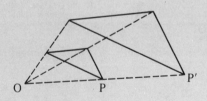

$$\frac{OP'}{OP} = k$$

$$\frac{OP'}{OP} = k$$

$$\frac{OP'}{OP} = k$$

Two curves C and C' have the *same shape* if there is a point O such that $\frac{OP'}{OP} = k$ for every point P on C and a corresponding point P' on C', where O, P, and P' are collinear and k is a constant.

Think of a strategy

● If it is true that all parabolas have the same shape, then we should be able to prove this using the defining property of a parabola. Since the defining property involves the focus, the point O is probably the focus.

● Draw two parabolas with the same focus, O.

● Draw a line through O to intersect the parabolas at P and Q. We must prove that $\dfrac{OQ}{OP}$ is constant.

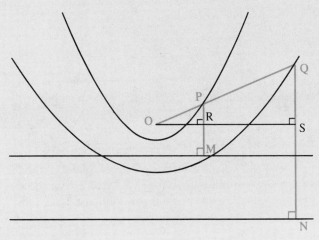

Carry out the strategy

● Drop perpendiculars PM and QN to the corresponding directrices. Then, according to the defining property of a parabola, OP = PM and OQ = QN.

● The proof will probably involve △OPR and △OQS. What properties do these triangles have?

● Since OQ = QN = QS + SN and OP = PM = PR + RM, we may write $\dfrac{OQ}{OP} = \dfrac{QS + SN}{PR + RM}$. Use this equation, and the fact that

△OPR ~ △OQS to prove that $\dfrac{OQ}{OP} = \dfrac{SN}{RM}$.

● Explain why this proves that $\dfrac{OQ}{OP}$ is a constant.

Look back

● Do the parabolas on page 178 have the same shape? Do they look like they have the same shape? Explain this apparent inconsistency.

PROLEMS

1. If this pattern is cut out and folded to make a polyhedron, how many edges will it have? How many vertices will it have?

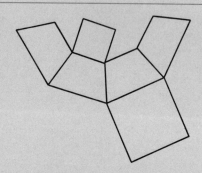

2. An airplane leaves Calgary in the evening and arrives in London, England early the next morning. During the flight passengers see a sunset and a sunrise. Explain why both are seen on the left side of the plane.

3. A parallelogram is defined as a quadrilateral with both pairs of opposite sides parallel. We can define a "perpendicularogram" as a quadrilateral with both pairs of opposite sides perpendicular.
   a) Sketch an example of a perpendicularogram.
   b) State a property of one of the angles of a perpendicularogram.

4. To promote sales, a store offers to reduce the price of articles by the amount of the provincial sales tax, 6%. Customers then pay 6% sales tax on the reduced amount. What percent reduction on the final price do customers pay as a result?

5. In $\triangle ABC$, points D and E are located on AB and AC such that DE $\parallel$ BC. If DE bisects the area of $\triangle ABC$, and if BC has length x, express the length of DE as a function of x.

6. Any chord of an ellipse which passes through the centre is called a *diameter*. Let P be any point on the ellipse $b^2x^2 + a^2y^2 = a^2b^2$.
   a) Prove that the product of the slopes of the segments joining P to the endpoints of any diameter is constant.
   b) Discuss how the result in part a) is a generalization of the theorem in geometry that the angle in a semicircle is a right angle.

7. In a semicircle, three connected chords have lengths 1, 2, and 3 respectively. Calculate the radius of the semicircle.

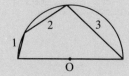

4-8 THE HYPERBOLA: FOCI ON *x*-AXIS

The *Saddledome* was built for the figure
skating and hockey events of the 1988
Olympic Winter Games in Calgary, and it
is used by the Calgary Flames hockey team.
Horizontal cross-sections of its saddle-
shaped roof are hyperbolas; when viewed
from the side the roof outlines a parabola.
The roof is an example of a geometrical
surface called a hyperbolic paraboloid.

A hyperbola may be defined as follows.

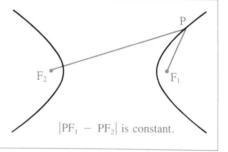

A *hyperbola* is the locus of a point P which
moves such that the difference of its distances from two fixed points F_1 and F_2 is
constant. F_1 and F_2 are called the *foci* of the
hyperbola. PF_1 and PF_2 are called the *focal
radii*.

$|PF_1 - PF_2|$ is constant.

Let the line F_1F_2 intersect the hyperbola at A_1 and A_2, and construct the
perpendicular bisector of F_1F_2.
- A_1 and A_2 are called the *vertices*.
- Line segment A_1A_2 is called the *transverse
  axis*; its length is represented by $2a$.
- The midpoint of F_1F_2 is the *centre* O.
- OA_1 is called the *semi-transverse axis*,
  and has length a.
- The distance from the centre to either focus
  is represented by c, where $c > a > 0$.
- Both the transverse axis and its perpendicular bisector are lines of
  symmetry of the hyperbola.

Focal Radii Property

According to the definition, $|PF_1 - PF_2|$ is constant for all positions of
P on the hyperbola. In particular, P could be at A_1.

Suppose P is at A_1.
$$\begin{aligned}|PF_1 - PF_2| &= |A_1F_1 - A_1F_2| \\ &= |A_2F_2 - A_1F_2| \quad \text{(by symmetry)} \\ &= A_1A_2 \\ &= 2a\end{aligned}$$

Hence, for all positions of P on the hyperbola, $|PF_1 - PF_2|$ is equal to
the length of the transverse axis.

The Equation of a Hyperbola

We can use the defining property to find the equation of any hyperbola.

Example 1.   The foci of a hyperbola are $F_1(5, 0)$ and $F_2(-5, 0)$, and the difference of the focal radii is 8 units. Find the equation of the hyperbola.

Solution.

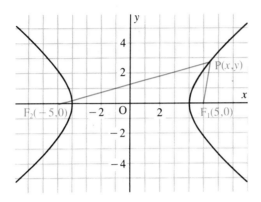

Let $P(x, y)$ be any point on the hyperbola. Since the difference of the focal radii is 8 units,

$$PF_1 - PF_2 = \pm 8$$
$$\sqrt{(x - 5)^2 + y^2} - \sqrt{(x + 5)^2 + y^2} = \pm 8$$

Isolate one of the radicals and square both sides.

$$\sqrt{(x - 5)^2 + y^2} = \pm 8 + \sqrt{(x + 5)^2 + y^2}$$
$$(\sqrt{(x - 5)^2 + y^2})^2 = (\pm 8 + \sqrt{(x + 5)^2 + y^2})^2$$
$$(x - 5)^2 + y^2 = 64 \pm 16\sqrt{(x + 5)^2 + y^2} + (x + 5)^2 + y^2$$
$$x^2 - 10x + 25 + y^2 = 64 \pm 16\sqrt{(x + 5)^2 + y^2} + x^2 + 10x + 25 + y^2$$

Isolate the radical and square both sides again.

$$-20x - 64 = \pm 16\sqrt{(x + 5)^2 + y^2}$$
$$-5x - 16 = \pm 4\sqrt{(x + 5)^2 + y^2}$$
$$25x^2 + 160x + 256 = 16(x^2 + 10x + 25 + y^2)$$

This equation simplifies to

$$9x^2 - 16y^2 = 144$$

or $$\frac{x^2}{16} - \frac{y^2}{9} = 1$$

Hence, the equation of the hyperbola is $\dfrac{x^2}{16} - \dfrac{y^2}{9} = 1$.

In *Example 1* we can find the x-intercepts of the hyperbola by substituting 0 for y to obtain $\frac{x^2}{16} = 1$, or $x = \pm 4$. These x-intercepts correspond to the vertices $A_1(4, 0)$ and $A_2(-4, 0)$. The graph shows that there are no y-intercepts. This is also shown by the equation; if we substitute 0 for x, we obtain $-\frac{y^2}{9} = 1$, or $y^2 = -9$, which has no real solution.

Nevertheless, it is useful to consider the term $\frac{y^2}{9}$ without the negative sign, and to identify two points $B_1(0, 3)$ and $B_2(0, -3)$ on the y-axis. These points are not on the hyperbola, but they are related to it, as explained below.

The diagram shows the graph of *Example 1* with a rectangle centred at the origin. The points A_1, A_2, B_1, and B_2 are the midpoints of the sides of this rectangle. We see that the hyperbola lies between the lines containing its diagonals. As $|x|$ increases, the hyperbola comes closer to these lines. We can see why by solving the equation of the hyperbola for y.

$$\frac{x^2}{16} - \frac{y^2}{9} = 1$$

$$\frac{y^2}{9} = \frac{x^2}{16} - 1$$

$$\frac{y^2}{9} = \frac{x^2 - 16}{16}$$

$$y = \pm\frac{3}{4}\sqrt{x^2 - 16}$$

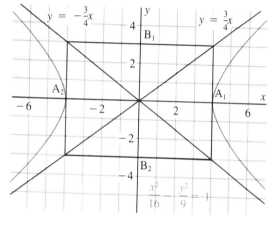

If $|x|$ is large, then x^2 is very large compared with 16. Hence,

$$y \doteq \pm\frac{3}{4}\sqrt{x^2}$$

$$\doteq \pm\frac{3}{4}x$$

The lines defined by $y = \frac{3}{4}x$ and $y = -\frac{3}{4}x$ are called the *asymptotes* of the hyperbola. The line segment B_1B_2 is called the *conjugate axis*.

We can use the method of *Example 1* to derive the standard equation of a hyperbola with centre $(0, 0)$ and foci on the x-axis. Let the coordinates of the foci be $F_1(c, 0)$ and $F_2(-c, 0)$. Let $P(x, y)$ be any point on the hyperbola. Then, by the focal radii property, the difference of the focal radii is $2a$.

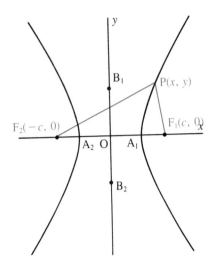

$$PF_1 - PF_2 = \pm 2a$$
$$\sqrt{(x - c)^2 + y^2} - \sqrt{(x + c)^2 + y^2} = \pm 2a$$

Isolate one of the radicals and square both sides.

$$\sqrt{(x - c)^2 + y^2} = \pm 2a + \sqrt{(x + c)^2 + y^2}$$
$$(\sqrt{(x - c)^2 + y^2})^2 = (\pm 2a + \sqrt{(x + c)^2 + y^2})^2$$
$$(x - c)^2 + y^2 = 4a^2 \pm 4a\sqrt{(x + c)^2 + y^2} + (x + c)^2 + y^2$$
$$x^2 - 2cx + c^2 + y^2 = 4a^2 \pm 4a\sqrt{(x + c)^2 + y^2} + x^2 + 2cx + c^2 + y^2$$

Isolate the radical and square both sides again.

$$-4a^2 - 4cx = \pm 4a\sqrt{(x + c)^2 + y^2}$$
$$-a^2 - cx = \pm a\sqrt{(x + c)^2 + y^2}$$
$$a^4 + 2a^2cx + c^2x^2 = a^2(x^2 + 2cx + c^2 + y^2)$$

This equation may be written as

$$(c^2 - a^2)x^2 - a^2y^2 = a^2(c^2 - a^2)$$

To simplify this equation, we *define* $b^2 = c^2 - a^2$.
Hence, the equation becomes

$$b^2x^2 - a^2y^2 = a^2b^2$$

or $$\frac{x^2}{a^2} - \frac{y^2}{b^2} = 1$$

This is the standard equation of a hyperbola with centre $(0, 0)$ and foci on the x-axis.

Since we defined $b^2 = c^2 - a^2$, we can identify points $B_1(0, b)$ and $B_2(0, -b)$ on the y-axis, which are the endpoints of the conjugate axis. And, as we saw in the above example, we can use the points A_1, A_2, B_1, and B_2 to draw a rectangle centred at $(0, 0)$ whose diagonals are the asymptotes of the hyperbola. Observe that for the hyperbola there is no restriction that a be greater than b as there was for the ellipse.

Hence, every equation of the form $\dfrac{x^2}{a^2} - \dfrac{y^2}{b^2} = 1$ represents a hyperbola
with foci on the *x*-axis for all positive values of *a* and *b*.

**Standard Equation of a Hyperbola with Centre (0, 0) and Foci on
the *x*-axis**
The equation of a hyperbola
with centre (0, 0) and
foci on the *x*-axis
is $\dfrac{x^2}{a^2} - \dfrac{y^2}{b^2} = 1$.

Length of transverse axis: $2a$
Length of conjugate axis: $2b$
Vertices: $(a, 0)$ and $(-a, 0)$
Foci: $(c, 0)$ and $(-c, 0)$
      where $c^2 = a^2 + b^2$

Asymptotes: $y = \dfrac{b}{a}x$ and $y = -\dfrac{b}{a}x$

Example 2.   Given the equation $9x^2 - 16y^2 = 144$
a) Show that this equation represents a hyperbola. Determine the lengths
   of the transverse and conjugate axes, the coordinates of the vertices,
   and the coordinates of the foci.
b) Write the equations of the asymptotes.
c) Graph the hyperbola.

Solution.   a) The standard equation has 1 on the right side. Hence, we divide both
       sides of the equation by 144.
$$\frac{9x^2}{144} - \frac{16y^2}{144} = 1$$
$$\frac{x^2}{16} - \frac{y^2}{9} = 1$$

Hence, the equation represents a hyperbola.
For this equation, $a = 4$ and $b = 3$
Length of transverse axis: $2a = 8$
Length of conjugate axis: $2b = 6$
Vertices: $(4, 0)$ and $(-4, 0)$

$$c^2 = a^2 + b^2$$
$$= 16 + 9$$
$$= 25$$
$$c = 5$$

Foci: (5, 0) and (−5, 0)

b) The equations of the asymptotes are $y = \frac{3}{4}x$ and $y = -\frac{3}{4}x$.

c) To graph the hyperbola, locate the vertices and draw a rectangle centred at the origin, with length 8 units and width 6 units. Next, draw the asymptotes, which are the diagonals of this rectangle. Then sketch the hyperbola.

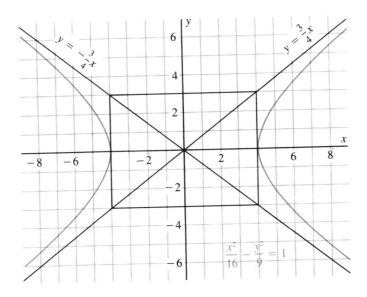

Example 3.   The LORAN (LOng RAnge Navigation) system of navigation is based on the definition of a hyperbola. Equipment on a ship determines the difference of the distances to two transmitters on shore by measuring the time difference for simultaneous signals to reach the ship from the transmitters. If the transmitters are 300 km apart and the ship is 200 km farther from one transmitter than the other, determine an equation of the hyperbola on which the ship is located.

Solution. Use a system of coordinates in which the transmitters have coordinates $F_1(150, 0)$ and $F_2(-150, 0)$. Let $S(x, y)$ represent the position of the ship. Then S is on a hyperbola with foci F_1 and F_2. For this hyperbola,

$c = 150$ and $2a = 200$

$\qquad a = 100$

$b^2 = c^2 - a^2$

$\quad = 22\,500 - 10\,000$

$\quad = 12\,500$

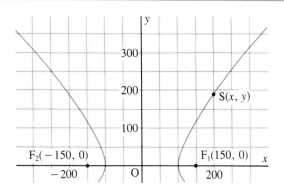

The equation of the hyperbola is $\dfrac{x^2}{a^2} - \dfrac{y^2}{b^2} = 1$

$$\frac{x^2}{10\,000} - \frac{y^2}{12\,500} = 1$$

$$\text{or} \quad 5x^2 - 4y^2 = 50\,000$$

In *Example 3*, if a second pair of transmitters is used, a second hyperbola on which the ship is located can be determined. Then the position of the ship can be found since it is on both hyperbolas.

EXERCISES 4-8

Ⓐ

1. Determine if each point is on the hyperbola defined by $3x^2 - 2y^2 = 10$.
   a) $(-2, 1)$　　　b) $(5, 6)$　　　c) $(6, -7)$　　　d) $(0, \sqrt{5})$

2. State the coordinates of the vertices, the coordinates of the foci, and the lengths of the transverse and conjugate axes of the hyperbola defined by each equation.
   a) $\dfrac{x^2}{4} - \dfrac{y^2}{16} = 1$　　　b) $\dfrac{x^2}{25} - \dfrac{y^2}{9} = 1$　　　c) $\dfrac{x^2}{81} - \dfrac{y^2}{49} = 1$

Ⓑ

3. A hyperbola has centre $(0, 0)$ and transverse axis on the x-axis. Write the equation of the hyperbola if:
   a) $a = 6$ and $b = 3$
   b) $a = 3$ and $b = 2$
   c) $b = 4$ and $c = 6$
   d) the conjugate axis has length 14, and the difference of the focal radii is 10
   e) one vertex is $A_1(2, 0)$ and one focus is $F_1(3, 0)$
   f) one x-intercept is 7 and one asymptote is defined by $y = -x$.

4. For each hyperbola whose equation is given below
   i) Write the standard equation.
   ii) Find the lengths of the transverse and conjugate axes, the coordinates of the vertices and foci, and the equations of the asymptotes.
   iii) Graph the hyperbola.

   a) $9x^2 - 4y^2 = 36$ b) $x^2 - 9y^2 = 36$ c) $25x^2 - 9y^2 = 225$
   d) $4x^2 - y^2 = 16$ e) $x^2 - 3y^2 = 12$ f) $4x^2 - 5y^2 = 20$

5. The foci of a hyperbola are $F_1(6, 0)$ and $F_2(-6, 0)$, and the difference of the focal radii is 4 units. Use the definition of a hyperbola to derive the equation of this hyperbola.

6. A hyperbola has centre $(0, 0)$ and one vertex $A(\sqrt{6}, 0)$.
   a) Find the equation of the hyperbola if it passes through $J(9, 5)$.
   b) Find the value of x_1 if $K(x_1, 2)$ is on the hyperbola.
   c) Find the value of y_1 if $L(3, y_1)$ is on the hyperbola.

7. A *rectangular hyperbola* is one whose transverse axis and conjugate axis have the same length.
   a) Write the equation of a rectangular hyperbola with vertices $A_1(3, 0)$ and $A_2(-3, 0)$.
   b) For the hyperbola in part a), determine the coordinates of the foci and the equations of the asymptotes.

8. A point P moves such that it is always twice as far from the point $(4, 0)$ as it is from the line $x = 1$.
   a) Find the equation of the locus.
   b) Identify the locus and sketch its graph.
   c) Verify from the graph that points on the graph are twice as far from the point $(4, 0)$ as they are from the line $x = 1$.

9. On page 181, O was defined to be the midpoint of F_1F_2. Use the definition of a hyperbola to prove that O is also the midpoint of A_1A_2.

10. Use the definition of a hyperbola to prove that a hyperbola is symmetric about:
    a) the conjugate axis   b) the transverse axis.

11. Prove that the length of the perpendicular from a focus of a hyperbola to an asymptote is equal to the length of the semi-conjugate axis.

Ⓒ

12. Describe how the graph of the hyperbola defined by $\dfrac{x^2}{a^2} - \dfrac{y^2}{b^2} = 1$ changes if:

    a) b is kept constant and a varies   b) a is kept constant and b varies.

13. Since the ellipse defined by $\dfrac{x^2}{b^2} + \dfrac{y^2}{a^2} = 1$ has its foci on the y-axis, one might

    think that the hyperbola defined by $\dfrac{x^2}{b^2} - \dfrac{y^2}{a^2} = 1$ has its foci on the y-axis.
    Investigate whether this is true.

MATHEMATICS AROUND US

Reflector Property of the Hyperbola

Like the parabola and the ellipse, the hyperbola also has a reflector property. This property is sometimes employed in the design of telescopes. The *Space Telescope*, for example, contains two hyperboloidal mirrors. Light striking the primary mirror is reflected to the secondary mirror, where it is reflected back through a hole in the centre of the primary mirror to a focus behind the primary mirror.

Every hyperbola has two *foci*, which are particular points on the axis of symmetry containing the transverse axis. The positions of the foci can be defined as follows.

For any hyperbola, let the centre be O, and let A_1 and A_2 be the vertices. Let the *semi-transverse axis* OA_1 have length a. Let B_1 and B_2 be the points at the ends of the conjugate axis. Then, the *foci* are the points F_1 and F_2 on the line A_1A_2 such that $OF_1 = OF_2 = A_1B_1$.

You can illustrate the reflector property of the hyperbola by completing the questions below.

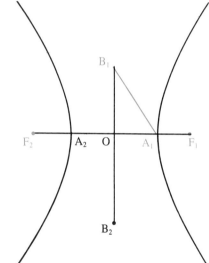

QUESTIONS

1. a) Use a table of values to construct an accurate graph of the hyperbola defined by $\dfrac{x^2}{36} - \dfrac{y^2}{64} = 1$.

   b) Mark the points $F_1(10,0)$ and $F_2(-10,0)$ on the graph. Verify that F_1 and F_2 satisfy the above definition of the foci.

2. a) Mark any point P on the hyperbola you constructed in *Question 1*. Join PF_1 and PF_2. By estimation, draw a tangent to the hyperbola at P. Verify that PF_1 and PF_2 form equal angles with the tangent.

   b) Repeat part a) for other points P on the hyperbola.

3. Use the above definition of the foci to find expressions for the coordinates of the foci of the hyperbola defined by $\dfrac{x^2}{a^2} - \dfrac{y^2}{b^2} = 1$.

4-9 THE HYPERBOLA: FOCI ON *y*-AXIS

In the preceding section we found that the equation $\frac{x^2}{a^2} - \frac{y^2}{b^2} = 1$
represents a hyperbola with centre (0, 0) and foci ($\pm c$, 0) on the
x-axis, where $c^2 = a^2 + b^2$. To obtain the equation of a hyperbola
with foci on the *y*-axis, we interchange *x* and *y* in the equation above.
This has the effect of reversing the coordinates of the points which satisfy the equation. Hence, the graph of the hyperbola is reflected in the
line defined by $y = x$.

If we interchange *x* and *y* in the equation above, we obtain

$$\frac{y^2}{a^2} - \frac{x^2}{b^2} = 1$$

or $$\frac{x^2}{b^2} - \frac{y^2}{a^2} = -1$$

Hence, this equation represents a hyperbola with centre (0, 0) and foci
(0, $\pm c$) on the *y*-axis, where $c^2 = a^2 + b^2$. This equation can also
be obtained using the locus definition of a hyperbola; the derivation is
left to the exercises.

**Standard Equation of a Hyperbola with Centre (0, 0) and Foci
on the *y*-axis**

The equation of a hyperbola
with centre (0, 0) and
foci on the *y*-axis is

$$\frac{x^2}{b^2} - \frac{y^2}{a^2} = -1.$$

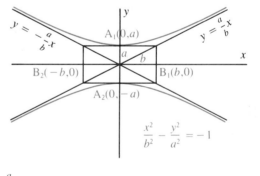

Length of transverse axis: $2a$
Length of conjugate axis: $2b$
Vertices: (0, a) and (0, $-a$)
Foci: (0, c) and (0, $-c$)
        where $c^2 = a^2 + b^2$

Asymptotes: $y = \frac{a}{b}x$ and $y = -\frac{a}{b}x$

We can always tell whether the transverse axis of the hyperbola is
on the *x*-axis or the *y*-axis from the standard equation. If there is a 1
on the right side, the transverse axis is on the *x*-axis; if there is a -1
on the right side, the transverse axis is on the *y*-axis. In either case, the
value of *a* occurs in the term on the left side that has the same sign
as the term on the right side.

Example. Given the hyperbola defined by $x^2 - 2y^2 = -8$
a) Determine the lengths of the transverse and conjugate axes, the coordinates of the vertices and the coordinates of the foci.
b) Graph the hyperbola.

Solution. a) Divide both sides of the equation by 8.

$$\frac{x^2}{8} - \frac{y^2}{4} = -1$$

For this equation, $a^2 = 4$ and $b^2 = 8$

$$a = 2 \qquad b = 2\sqrt{2}$$

Length of transverse axis: $2a = 4$
Length of conjugate axis: $2b = 4\sqrt{2}$
Vertices: $(0, 2)$ and $(0, -2)$

$$c^2 = a^2 + b^2$$
$$= 4 + 8$$
$$= 12$$
$$c = \sqrt{12}, \text{ or } 2\sqrt{3}$$

Foci: $(0, 2\sqrt{3})$ and $(0, -2\sqrt{3})$

b) To graph the hyperbola, locate the vertices and draw a rectangle, centred at the origin, with length $4\sqrt{2}$ units and width 4 units. Draw the diagonals, and extend them to form the asymptotes. Then sketch the hyperbola.

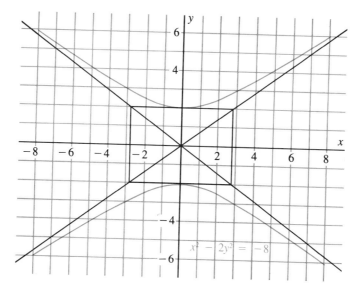

EXERCISES 4-9

Ⓐ

1. Determine if each point is on the hyperbola defined by $7x^2 - 3y^2 = -20$.
   a) $(-1, 3)$ b) $(2, -4)$ c) $(5, 8)$ d) $(-7, -11)$

2. State the coordinates of the vertices, the coordinates of the foci, and the lengths of the transverse and conjugate axes of the hyperbola defined by each equation.

   a) $\dfrac{x^2}{16} - \dfrac{y^2}{9} = -1$ b) $\dfrac{x^2}{4} - \dfrac{y^2}{25} = -1$ c) $\dfrac{x^2}{64} - \dfrac{y^2}{36} = -1$

Ⓑ

3. A hyperbola has centre $(0, 0)$ and transverse axis on the y-axis. Write the equation of the hyperbola if:
   a) $a = 3$ and $b = 4$
   b) $a = 7$ and $c = 8$
   c) $b = 3$ and $c = 6$
   d) the transverse axis has length 10 and one focus is $F_1(0, 4\sqrt{2})$
   e) one focus is $(0, 2\sqrt{5})$ and one asymptote is defined by $y = 2x$.

4. For each hyperbola whose equation is given below
   i) Write the standard equation.
   ii) Find the lengths of the transverse and conjugate axes, the coordinates of the vertices and foci, and the equations of the asymptotes.
   iii) Graph the hyperbola.
      a) $4x^2 - 9y^2 = -36$ b) $x^2 - 4y^2 = -16$ c) $16x^2 - 25y^2 = -400$
      d) $4x^2 - y^2 = -100$ e) $x^2 - 2y^2 = -50$ f) $3x^2 - 4y^2 = -24$

5. The foci of a hyperbola are $F_1(0, 3)$ and $F_2(0, -3)$, and the difference of the focal radii is 2 units. Use the definition of a hyperbola to derive the equation of this hyperbola.

6. Use the definition to derive the equation of a hyperbola with difference of focal radii $2a$ and foci $F_1(0, c)$ and $F_2(0, -c)$ on the y-axis.

Ⓒ

7. Describe how the graph of the hyperbola defined by $\dfrac{x^2}{b^2} - \dfrac{y^2}{a^2} = -1$ changes if:

   a) b is kept constant and a varies   b) a is kept constant and b varies.

8. Given the equation $Ax^2 + By^2 + C = 0$, what conditions must be satisfied by A, B, and C if this equation represents a hyperbola with transverse axis on the y-axis?

9. Two hyperbolas are called *conjugate hyperbolas* if the transverse axis of one is the conjugate axis of the other.
   a) Give an example of the equations of two conjugate hyperbolas.
   b) If the equation of a hyperbola is given in standard form, how can you find the equation of the conjugate hyperbola?

MATHEMATICS AROUND US

The Shadow of a Sphere

This photograph suggests that the shadow of a sphere is an ellipse. Since the sun is so far away that we can assume its rays are parallel, the rays of light intercepted by the sphere form a cylinder. Hence, we can prove that the shadow of a sphere in sunlight is an ellipse if we can prove that the curve formed when a plane intersects a cylinder is an ellipse.

QUESTIONS

1. A plane intersects a cylinder, forming a closed curve. Two spheres, each of which is tangent to the plane, are inscribed in the cylinder. Let F_1 and F_2 be the points of contact of the spheres and the plane. Let Q_1 and Q_2 be points of contact of the spheres and the cylinder. Let P be any point on the curve. Prove that the curve is an ellipse by showing that $PF_1 + PF_2$ is constant.

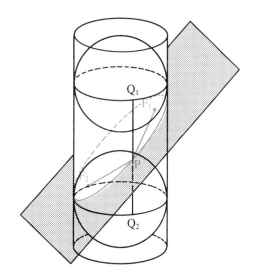

2. Obtain a large ball, such as a basketball, and set it on a level surface in direct sunlight, preferably in the late afternoon when it will cast a long shadow.
   a) Measure the lengths of the major and minor axes of the elliptical shadow as accurately as you can.
   b) Determine the positions of the foci of the ellipse.
   c) Use the result of part a) to determine the angle of elevation of the sun at the time the measurements were taken.

4-10 APPLICATIONS OF QUADRATIC RELATIONS

Quadratic relations have many applications in astronomy, and in construction and design. The problems are usually solved by using the given data to determine an equation of a conic in standard form, and then using the equation to determine some unknown quantity.

Example 1. A bridge over a river is supported by a parabolic arch which is 40 m wide at water level. The maximum height of the arch is 16 m.
a) Write an equation to represent the arch.
b) How high is the arch at a point 10 m from the centre?

Solution.   a) Use a coordinate system as shown.

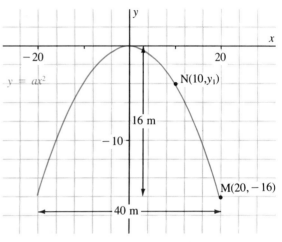

Let the equation of the arch be $y = ax^2$. From the given information, and the diagram, the point $M(20, -16)$ is on the parabola. Hence, these coordinates satisfy the equation. Substitute 20 for x and -16 for y in $y = ax^2$.

$$-16 = a(20)^2$$
$$-16 = 400a$$
$$a = -\frac{16}{400}$$
$$= -0.04$$

The equation of the parabola is $y = -0.04x^2$.

b) Let $N(10, y_1)$ represent a point on the arch which is 10 m from the centre. Then these coordinates satisfy the equation. Substitute 10 for x and y_1 for y in $y = -0.04x^2$.

$$y_1 = -0.04(10)^2$$
$$= -4$$

A point 10 m from the centre is 4 m below the highest point, and therefore 12 m above the water level. Hence, the arch is 12 m high at a point 10 m from the centre.

In *Example 1* we used the standard form of the equation of a parabola given in the previous section, $y = ax^2$. We could also have used the standard form, $x^2 = 4py$. Both forms are equivalent, because they are derived from the equation $y = x^2$ by multiplying one side of the equation by a constant.

Example 1 was solved using the fundamental property of a locus. That is, the coordinates of every point on the graph of a relation satisfy its equation; and, every point whose coordinates satisfy the equation of a relation is on its graph.

Example 2. The arch of a bridge has the shape of a rectangular hyperbola. The base is 120 m wide, and the vertex is 30 m above the base.
 a) Find an equation of the hyperbola.
 b) Find the height of the arch at a point 25 m from the centre.

Solution. a) Let the equation of the hyperbola be $x^2 - y^2 = -a^2$. The coordinates of vertex A_2 are $(0, -a)$. Let P be a point 60 m to the right of A_2 and 30 m below A_2. Hence, the coordinates of P are $(60, -a - 30)$. Since P is on the hyperbola, its coordinates satisfy the equation. Substitute 60 for x and $-a - 30$ for y in $x^2 - y^2 = -a^2$.

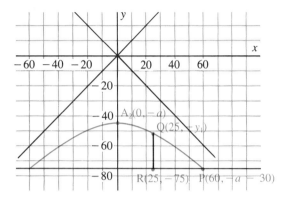

$$3600 - (-a - 30)^2 = -a^2$$
$$3600 - (a^2 + 60a + 900) = -a^2$$
$$a = \frac{2700}{60}$$
$$= 45$$

Hence, the equation of the hyperbola is $x^2 - y^2 = -45^2$, or $x^2 - y^2 = -2025$.

 b) Let $Q(25, -y_1)$ represent a point on the arch 25 m from the centre. Then these coordinates satisfy the equation. Substitute 25 for x and $-y_1$ for y.

$$x^2 - y^2 = -2025$$
$$625 - y_1^2 = -2025$$
$$y_1^2 = 2650$$
$$y_1 = \sqrt{2650}$$
$$\doteq 51.5$$

The coordinates of Q are $(25, -51.5)$. From part a), the coordinates of P are $(60, -75)$. Hence, the coordinates of R are $(25, -75)$, and the length of segment QR is $75 - 51.5$, or 23.5. Hence, the arch is 23.5 m high at a point which is 25 m from the centre.

EXERCISES 4-10

B

1) The cables of a suspension bridge hang in a curve which approximates a parabola. The road bed passes through the vertex. If the supporting towers are 720 m apart and 60 m high, find:
a) an equation of the parabola
b) the height of the cables at a point 30 m from the vertex.

2. A stone thrown horizontally from a bridge 25 m above a river splashes in the water 40 m from the base of the bridge. If the stone falls in a parabolic path, find its equation relative to the position from which it was thrown.

3. The supporting structure for the roof of a curling rink has parabolic arches anchored at ground level. If the arches are 15.3 m high, and span 70 m, find:
a) an equation of the parabola
b) the height of the arches at a point 10 m from the centre.

4. A pool has the shape of an ellipse. The major axis has length 10 m and the minor axis has length 6 m.
a) Write an equation of the ellipse.
b) Find the width of the pool at a point on the major axis which is 2 m from the centre.

5. A retractable dome on a sports stadium has the shape of an ellipse. Its height is 125 m and it spans 300 m.
a) Write an equation of the ellipse.
b) Calculate the height of the dome at a point on the major axis which is 20 m from the centre.

6. A tunnel is built under a river for a road 12 m wide with a 2 m sidewalk on either side. The top of the tunnel is semi-elliptical. A local bylaw stipulates that there must be a clearance of at least 3.6 m at all points on the road. If the smallest possible ellipse is used, find the clearance at the centre of the road.

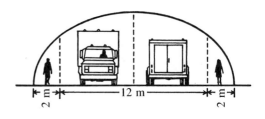

7. A bridge over a river is supported by a hyperbolic arch which is 200 m wide at the base. The maximum height of the arch is 50 m. How high is the arch at a point 30 m from the centre?

C

8. The orbit of a satellite is an ellipse with the centre of the Earth on its major axis. One satellite has an orbit with major axis 15 540 km and minor axis 15 490 km. The centre of the orbit is 600 km from the centre of the Earth. The radius of the Earth is 6370 km. Calculate the height of the satellite at:
a) its lowest point (the *perigee*)   b) its highest point (the *apogee*).

4-11 QUADRATIC INEQUALITIES IN TWO VARIABLES

The graph shows the circle defined by the equation $(x - 2)^2 + (y - 3)^2 = 25$. The circle divides the plane into *three* regions.

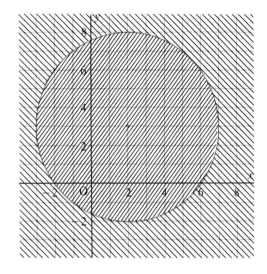

- *Region 1* contains all the points *on* the circle. These points have coordinates which satisfy the given equation. For example, the point $(-1, 7)$ is on the circle. It satisfies the equation, as shown below.

$$\begin{aligned} \text{Left side} &= (x - 2)^2 + (y - 3)^2 \\ &= (-1 - 2)^2 + (7 - 3)^2 \\ &= 9 + 16 \\ &= 25 \\ &= \text{Right side} \end{aligned}$$

For points on the circle,
$(x - 2)^2 + (y - 3)^2 = 25$

- *Region 2* contains all points *inside* the circle. If the coordinates of a point inside the circle are substituted into the left side of the equation, the result is *less than* the right side. For example, the point $(4, 2)$ is inside the circle. Substitute into the equation.

$$\begin{aligned} \text{Left side} &= (x - 2)^2 + (y - 3)^2 \\ &= (4 - 2)^2 + (2 - 3)^2 \\ &= 4 + 1 \\ &= 5 \text{ which is less than 25, the right side} \end{aligned}$$

For points inside the circle, $(x - 2)^2 + (y - 3)^2 < 25$

- *Region 3* contains all points *outside* the circle. If the coordinates of a point outside the circle are substituted into the left side of the equation, the result is *greater than* the right side. For example, the point $(8, -2)$ is outside the circle. Substitute into the equation.

$$\begin{aligned} \text{Left side} &= (x - 2)^2 + (y - 3)^2 \\ &= (8 - 2)^2 + (-2 - 3)^2 \\ &= 36 + 25 \\ &= 61 \text{ which is greater than 25, the right side} \end{aligned}$$

For points outside the circle, $(x - 2)^2 + (y - 3)^2 > 25$

To graph an inequality, follow these steps.

Step 1. Graph the corresponding equation.

Step 2. Select a point whose coordinates satisfy the inequality.

Step 3. Plot that point on the grid and shade in the region that contains it.

Example 1. Graph the inequality $(x + 2)^2 + (y + 1)^2 < 9$.

Solution.   The corresponding equation is
$(x + 2)^2 + (y + 1)^2 = 9$.
This is a circle, centre $(-2, -1)$
and radius 3.
A point which satisfies the
inequality is $(0, 0)$, since
$(0 + 2)^2 + (0 + 1)^2 < 9$.
Since the point $(0, 0)$ lies
inside the circle, that region
is shaded.

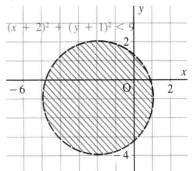

In *Example 1*, the circle is drawn as a broken curve because the
symbol $<$ indicates that the curve is not part of the inequality.

Example 2. Graph the inequality $y \geq (x + 4)^2 - 2$. Write the domain and range of
this relation.

Solution.   The corresponding equation is
$y = (x + 4)^2 - 2$. This is a
parabola which opens up, with
vertex $(-4, -2)$ and axis of
symmetry $x = -4$.
A point which satisfies the
inequality is $(-4, 0)$, since
$0 > (-4 + 4)^2 - 2$.
Since the point $(-4, 0)$ lies
inside the parabola, shade
this region.

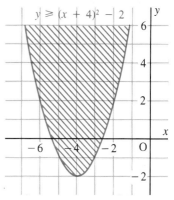

The shaded area of the graph is the solution set of the inequality. The
parabola will continue indefinitely; hence the domain is $\mathbb{R}$.
The minimum value of y is -2; hence the range is $\{y \mid y \geq -2, y \in \mathbb{R}\}$.
This can be written in interval notation as $[-2, +\infty$.

In *Example 2*, the parabola is drawn as a solid curve, because the
symbol $\geq$ indicates that the curve is part of the inequality.

EXERCISES 4-11

1. State the coordinates of a point which satisfies each inequality.
    a) $(x - 1)^2 + y^2 \leq 16$ b) $(x + 3)^2 + (y - 7)^2 > 81$
    c) $y \leq (x + 2)^2 - 5$ d) $(x + 4)^2 + (y + 1)^2 < 36$
    e) $y > (x - 3)^2 + 1$ f) $(x - 2)^2 + (y + 6)^2 \geq 100$

2. State the coordinates of a point which satisfies each inequality, and whether this point is inside or outside the region enclosed by the broken curve.

a)

$(x - 2)^2 + (y - 1)^2 < 1$

b)

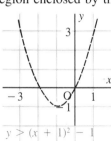

$y > (x + 1)^2 - 1$

c)

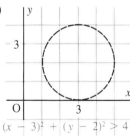

$(x - 3)^2 + (y - 2)^2 > 4$

3. Write an inequality that represents each shaded region.

a)

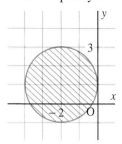

b)

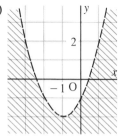

c)

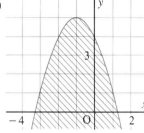

B

4. Write an inequality that represents each shaded region.

a)

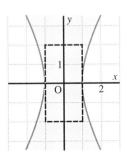

b)

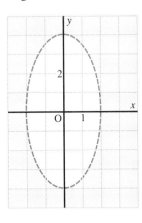

c)

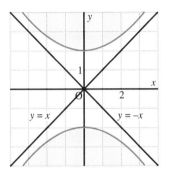

d)

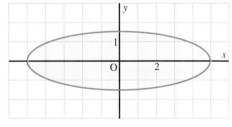

5. Graph each inequality.

   a) $(x + 1)^2 + (y + 1)^2 < 16$
   b) $(x - 5)^2 + (y - 2)^2 \leqslant 36$
   c) $y < (x - 3)^2 + 4$
   d) $(x + 1)^2 + (y - 4)^2 \geqslant 25$
   e) $y \geqslant (x + 3)^2 - 4$
   f) $(x - 6)^2 + (y + 4)^2 \leqslant 64$

6. Graph each inequality.

   a) $x^2 + \left(\dfrac{y}{2}\right)^2 < 4$
   b) $\left(\dfrac{x}{3}\right)^2 + y^2 \geqslant 9$
   c) $(2x)^2 + y^2 > 36$
   d) $x^2 + \left(\dfrac{2y}{3}\right)^2 \leqslant 16$
   e) $\left(\dfrac{x}{3}\right)^2 - \left(\dfrac{y}{2}\right)^2 < 16$
   f) $(3x)^2 - \left(\dfrac{y}{2}\right)^2 \geqslant 36$

7. Give the domain and range of the region associated with each inequality.

   a) $(y - 2)^2 \leqslant 4(x - 4)$
   b) $(x - 3)^2 + (y - 4)^2 < 16$
   c) $y^2 + 4x + 4y + 24 > 0$
   d) $4x^2 - 9y^2 \leqslant 36$
   e) $x^2 + 4x < y$
   f) $x^2 - \left(\dfrac{y}{3}\right)^2 \geqslant 9$

8. Automatic water sprinklers have been installed in a park (below left). Each sprinkler covers a circular region 3 m in radius.

   a) Write the relation which represents the area watered by each sprinkler.

   b) Park seats are located at $(5, 5)$, $(2, -2)$, and $(7, 0)$. Which seats will get wet when the sprinklers start?

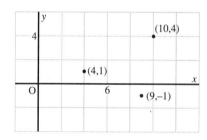

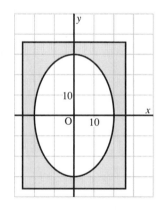

9. A town has installed an elliptical skating rink in a park (above right). The length of the major axis is 60 m and of the minor axis is 40 m. The park is rectangular and allows a clearance of at least 6 m all around the rink. Give the equation of the part of the park *not* covered by the rink, including the restrictions on domain and range.

10. A goat is tethered to 2 posts, which are 6 m apart, by a rope of length 10 m. The rope passes through a ring on the collar of the goat, so that the rope can slide. Write the inequality which represents the region in which the goat can feed. (Consider that the origin is midway between the posts.)

11. The cross section of a tunnel, which is being excavated, is in the shape of a parabola (below left). The height is 4.5 m and the width at the base is 12 m. Find the relation which represents the cross section of the excavated region.

©

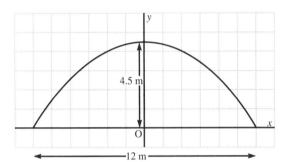

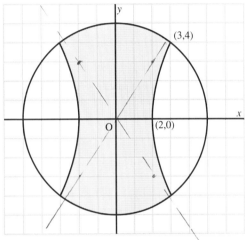

12. The diagram (above right) shows the steering wheel of a toy car. The outer rim is circular with radius 5 cm. The shaded inner section is a region whose outline is a hyperbola with one vertex at $(2, 0)$. One of the points of intersection of the hyperbola and circle is $(3, 4)$.

a) Find the relation which represents the shaded region.

b) Find the domain and range of this relation.

13. Graph the region defined by each pair of inequalities.

a) $(x - 2)^2 + (y + 4)^2 < 36$ and $(x - 2)^2 + (y + 4)^2 > 9$

b) $(x + 3)^2 + (y - 1)^2 \geq 16$ and $(x - 1)^2 + (y - 2)^2 < 9$

c) $(x - 1)^2 + y^2 > 25$ and $(x - 1)^2 + \left(\dfrac{y}{2}\right)^2 < 25$

d) $(x + 4)^2 + (y - 2)^2 > 4$ and $y > (x + 4)^2 - 3$

e) $y > (x - 1)^2 - 3$ and $\left(\dfrac{2x}{3}\right)^2 + (y - 1)^2 \geq 4$

f) $y > (x - 3)^2 - 2$ and $y < -(x - 2)^2 + 4$

Review Exercises

1. Find the equation of the locus of a point P which moves according to each condition. Identify the locus and sketch its graph.
   a) P is always 3 units from $Q(-2,1)$.
   b) The slope of the segment from P to $S(5,-3)$ is $-\frac{3}{4}$.
   c) P is the same distance from $F(3,2)$ as it is from the line $y = -2$.
   d) P is the same distance from $A(2,-5)$ as it is from $B(-6,1)$.

2. Graph each relation and identify the curve.
   a) $\dfrac{x^2}{16} + \dfrac{y^2}{9} = 1$ b) $x^2 = 4y$ c) $x^2 + y^2 = 25$
   d) $x^2 - y^2 = 9$ e) $4x^2 + 4y^2 = 49$ f) $9x^2 - 16y^2 = -144$

3. Determine if the given point is on the given conic. Identify the conic.
   a) $(-2,-20);\ y = 5x^2$ b) $(-4,7);\ x^2 + y^2 = 65$
   c) $(-7,2);\ \dfrac{x^2}{25} - \dfrac{y^2}{4} = 1$ d) $(2,-\sqrt{2});\ 4x^2 + 9y^2 = 36$

4. Find the coordinates of the centre, and the radius of each circle.
   a) $4x^2 + 4y^2 = 25$ b) $x^2 + y^2 - 4x + 6y - 12 = 0$

5. Find the equation of a parabola with vertex $(0,0)$ and axis of symmetry the y-axis if it passes through: a) $(4,2)$ b) $(-4,-24)$.

6. An ellipse has centre $(0,0)$ and major axis on the y-axis. Write the equation of the ellipse if:
   a) the x- and y-intercepts are ± 3 and ± 5 respectively
   b) the major axis is 12 units and the minor axis is 6 units.

7. Find the equation of the hyperbola, centre $(0,0)$, conjugate axis on the y-axis, and:
   a) vertices at $(\pm 4,0)$, and an asymptote defined by $y = 2x$
   b) a transverse axis of 8 units, and a conjugate axis of 14 units.

8. A stone thrown horizontally from a bridge 25 m above the river splashes in the water 40 m from the base of the bridge. If the stone falls in a parabolic path, find its equation.

9. One of the supports in a retractable roof of a sports complex is semi-elliptical. If it is 25 m high and spans 60 m, find its equation.

10. The base of a bridge arch is 80 m wide and 25 m high. Find its equation if the arch is in the shape of a rectangular hyperbola.

5 Exponential and Logarithmic Functions

In 1947 an investor bought Van Gogh's painting *Irises* for $84 000. In 1987 she sold it for $49 million. What annual rate of interest corresponds to an investment of $84 000 which grows to $49 million in 40 years? (See Section 5-12 *Example 2*.)

5-1 THE LAWS OF EXPONENTS

By counting the bacteria in a culture, scientists can learn how bacteria grow under controlled conditions. The growth of a certain bacteria is shown in the table. The number of bacteria doubles every hour, over several hours. The number of bacteria N is an exponential function of the time t hours. We can represent this function by the equation

$N(t) = 1000(2)^t$ . . . ①

with the graph shown below.

Time t hours	Number of bacteria N
−3	125
−2	250
−1	500
0	1 000
1	2 000
2	4 000
3	8 000
4	16 000

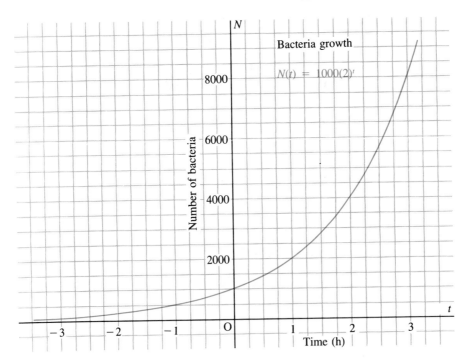

We can use the following definitions to approximate the number of bacteria at any time.

Definition of Integral and Rational Exponents

$a^0 = 1$ where $a \neq 0$ $a^{-n} = \dfrac{1}{a^n}$ where $n \in \mathbb{N}$, $a \neq 0$

$a^{\frac{m}{n}} = (\sqrt[n]{a})^m$ and $a^{-\frac{m}{n}} = \dfrac{1}{a^{\frac{m}{n}}} = \dfrac{1}{(\sqrt[n]{a})^m}$ where $m, n \in \mathbb{N}$, $a > 0$

Example 1.   How many bacteria are in the culture when:

a) $t = 0$ h   b) $t = -2$ h   c) $t = \frac{1}{2}$ h   d) $t = 1$ h 40 min?

Solution.   Substitute each value of t into equation ①.

a) $N(0) = 1000(2)^0$
   $= 1000(1)$
   $= 1000$

b) $N(-2) = 1000(2)^{-2}$
   $= 1000\left(\frac{1}{2^2}\right)$
   $= 250$

c) $N\left(\frac{1}{2}\right) = 1000(2)^{\frac{1}{2}}$
   $= 1000\sqrt{2}$
   $\doteq 1414$

d) 1 h 40 min $= 1\frac{2}{3}$ h, or $\frac{5}{3}$ h

   $N\left(\frac{5}{3}\right) = 1000(2)^{\frac{5}{3}}$
   $= 1000(\sqrt[3]{2})^5$
   $\doteq 3175$

Example 2.   Evaluate each expression without using a calculator.

a) $(0.75)^{-2}$ b) $9^{1.5}$ c) $8^{-\frac{2}{3}}$

Solution.   a) $(0.75)^{-2} = \left(\frac{3}{4}\right)^{-2}$

   $= \dfrac{1}{\left(\dfrac{3}{4}\right)^2}$

   $= \dfrac{16}{9}$

b) $9^{1.5} = 9^{\frac{3}{2}}$
   $= (\sqrt{9})^3$
   $= 27$

c) $8^{-\frac{2}{3}} = \dfrac{1}{8^{\frac{2}{3}}}$

   $= \dfrac{1}{(\sqrt[3]{8})^2}$

   $= \dfrac{1}{4}$

The definition of a positive integral exponent, as indicating repeated multiplication, leads to the five exponent laws shown below. It can be shown that the definitions of integral and rational exponents are consistent with these laws. In fact, the definition of an exponent and the laws of exponents can even be extended to include irrational exponents such as π and $\sqrt{2}$.

Laws of Exponents for Real Exponents
If m and n are any real numbers, then

1. $a^m \times a^n = a^{m+n}$

2. $\dfrac{a^m}{a^n} = a^{m-n}$ $(a \neq 0)$

3. $(a^m)^n = a^{mn}$

4. $(ab)^n = a^n b^n$

5. $\left(\dfrac{a}{b}\right)^n = \dfrac{a^n}{b^n}$ $(b \neq 0)$

The laws of exponents are useful for simplifying expressions involving exponents.

Example 3. Simplify each expression.

a) $\dfrac{a^2b^{-1}}{a^{-3}b}$
b) $\left(\dfrac{a^{\frac{1}{2}}}{b^{-2}}\right)^{\frac{2}{3}}$
c) $\left(\dfrac{x}{y^2}\right)^{\frac{1}{2}}(xy^2)^{-\frac{1}{2}}$

Solution.

a) $\dfrac{a^2b^{-1}}{a^{-3}b} = a^{2-(-3)}b^{-1-1}$

$= a^5b^{-2}$, or $\dfrac{a^5}{b^2}$

b) $\left(\dfrac{a^{\frac{1}{2}}}{b^{-2}}\right)^{\frac{2}{3}} = (a^{\frac{1}{2}}b^2)^{\frac{2}{3}}$

$= a^{\frac{1}{3}}b^{\frac{4}{3}}$

c) $\left(\dfrac{x}{y^2}\right)^{\frac{1}{2}}(xy^2)^{-\frac{1}{2}} = (xy^{-2})^{\frac{1}{2}}(xy^2)^{-\frac{1}{2}}$

$= x^{\frac{1}{2}}y^{-1}x^{-\frac{1}{2}}y^{-1}$

$= x^0y^{-2}$

$= \dfrac{1}{y^2}$

Example 4. If $x = 4$ and $y = \dfrac{1}{9}$, evaluate this expression. $(x^2y^{-\frac{1}{2}})^{-2}(x^{-3}y)^{-\frac{1}{2}}$

Solution. Simplify the expression before substituting.

$(x^2y^{-\frac{1}{2}})^{-2}(x^{-3}y)^{-\frac{1}{2}} = (x^{-4}y^1)(x^{\frac{3}{2}}y^{-\frac{1}{2}})$

$= x^{-\frac{5}{2}}y^{\frac{1}{2}}$

Substitute. $= 4^{-\frac{5}{2}}\left(\dfrac{1}{9}\right)^{\frac{1}{2}}$

$= \dfrac{1}{(\sqrt{4})^5}\left(\dfrac{1}{3}\right)$

$= \left(\dfrac{1}{32}\right)\left(\dfrac{1}{3}\right)$

$= \dfrac{1}{96}$

Example 5. a) Evaluate $3.2^{2.57}$ to the nearest thousandth.
b) Explain the meaning of the result.

Solution. a) Using the $\boxed{y^x}$ key on a calculator, we obtain
$3.2^{2.57} \doteq 19.872$

b) To explain the meaning of the result, write the exponent 2.57 in fractional form.

$2.57 = \dfrac{257}{100}$

Hence, $3.2^{2.57} = 3.2^{\frac{257}{100}}$

$= (\sqrt[100]{3.2})^{257}$

Hence, $(\sqrt[100]{3.2})^{257} \doteq 19.872$

EXERCISES 5-1

1. Evaluate.

a) 7^0 b) 5^{-1} c) $\left(\dfrac{2}{5}\right)^3$ d) 2^{-3} e) 4^{-2} f) $\left(\dfrac{4}{9}\right)^0$

g) $\left(\dfrac{1}{2}\right)^{-2}$ h) $\left(\dfrac{3}{2}\right)^{-4}$ i) 8^{-2} j) $\left(\dfrac{5}{3}\right)^{-2}$ k) 3^4 l) $\left(\dfrac{3}{4}\right)^{-3}$

2. Evaluate.

a) $27^{\frac{1}{3}}$ b) 3^{-2} c) $(0.4)^{-1}$ d) $25^{\frac{1}{2}}$ e) $(0.008)^{-\frac{1}{3}}$ f) $16^{-\frac{1}{4}}$

g) 10^{-3} h) $64^{\frac{1}{6}}$ i) $\left(\dfrac{25}{49}\right)^{-\frac{1}{2}}$ j) $81^{-\frac{1}{2}}$ k) $(0.125)^{-\frac{1}{3}}$ l) $32^{\frac{1}{5}}$

3. Evaluate.

a) $36^{-\frac{3}{2}}$ b) $27^{\frac{2}{3}}$ c) $(0.125)^{-\frac{2}{3}}$ d) $16^{-\frac{5}{4}}$ e) $9^{-\frac{5}{2}}$ f) $(2.25)^{\frac{3}{2}}$

g) $(0.6)^{-3}$ h) $100^{-\frac{3}{2}}$ i) $\left(\dfrac{8}{125}\right)^{\frac{2}{3}}$ j) $(0.36)^{-\frac{3}{2}}$ k) $64^{\frac{5}{6}}$ l) $81^{-\frac{3}{4}}$

4. Evaluate.

a) $4^{2.5}$ b) $25^{-1.5}$ c) $81^{-1.25}$ d) $400^{1.5}$

e) $32^{0.6}$ f) $\left(\dfrac{1}{16}\right)^{-0.75}$ g) $\left(\dfrac{27}{49}\right)^0$ h) $(6.25)^{-2.5}$

i) $(0.0625)^{-\frac{1}{4}}$ j) $\left(\dfrac{32}{243}\right)^{0.8}$ k) $\left(\dfrac{9}{4}\right)^{-1.5}$ l) $(5.25)^0$

5. Evaluate to the nearest thousandth.

a) $2.1^{1.6}$ b) $3.7^{2.14}$ c) $7.4^{0.85}$ d) $16^{0.75}$ e) $4.5^{3.19}$ f) $1.9^{1.9}$

g) $1.4^{-2.2}$ h) $2.8^{-1.7}$ i) $4.65^{2.75}$ j) $0.52^{-3.61}$ k) $3.82^{-1.44}$ l) $1.75^{-0.64}$

6. Simplify.

a) $m^2 \times m^{-8}$ b) $\dfrac{x^{-4}}{x^{-9}}$ c) $-15a^{-3} \times 3a^{10}$

d) $\dfrac{42s^4}{-3s^{-11}}$ e) $-3m^4 \times 12m^{-6} \times \dfrac{1}{4}m^7$ f) $\dfrac{(16n^{-2})(12n^{-3})}{15n^{-6}}$

7. Simplify.

a) $x^{\frac{2}{3}} \times x^{-\frac{5}{3}}$ b) $\dfrac{s^{-\frac{3}{4}}}{s^{-\frac{1}{2}}}$ c) $\dfrac{-12m^{-\frac{8}{5}}}{4m^{\frac{2}{5}}}$

d) $\dfrac{18a^{\frac{2}{5}}}{-6a^{-\frac{1}{5}}}$ e) $n^{\frac{3}{4}} \times n^{-\frac{3}{5}} \times n^{\frac{2}{3}}$ f) $\dfrac{-5x^{-\frac{1}{2}} \times 8x^{-\frac{3}{4}}}{10x^{-2}}$

B

8. Simplify.

a) $3^2 - 16^{\frac{1}{2}}$

b) $2^5 - 5^2$

c) $3^{-2} + 2^{-3}$

d) $2^{-4} - 4^{-2}$

e) $3^3 - \left(\frac{1}{2}\right)^{-4}$

f) $12^0 - 4^{-\frac{1}{2}}$

g) $(8^{\frac{2}{3}})(16^{\frac{3}{2}})$

h) $4^{\frac{1}{2}} + \left(\frac{1}{2}\right)^4$

i) $\left(\frac{4}{9}\right)^{-\frac{3}{2}} \div \left(\frac{16}{25}\right)^{-\frac{1}{2}}$

9. A colony of insects doubles in size every 6 days. If there are now 2000 insects in the colony, how many

a) will there be in: i) 12 days   ii) 21 days   iii) 3 days;

b) were there: i) 6 days ago   ii) 3 days ago   iii) 10 days ago?

10. During the twentieth century, the population of Canada has been growing at the rate of approximately 1.85% per annum. The population in 1981 was 24.3 million.

a) Write an equation representing the population P million as a function of the time t years relative to 1981.

b) Use this equation to approximate the population in 1971.

11. In 1940, a large computer could perform about 100 operations per second. Since then, the speed of computers has multiplied 10-fold about every 7 years.

a) Express the number of operations per second N as an exponential function of the time t years since 1940.

b) About how many operations per second could computers perform in 1986?

12. Simplify.

a) $\dfrac{-28a^2b^{-5}}{4a^{-7}b^3}$

b) $4m^{-3}n^9 \times 5m^{-4}n^{-6}$

c) $\dfrac{12x^{-2}y^4 \times 15x^7y^{-11}}{20x^{-4}y^5}$

d) $\dfrac{6a^3b^{-7}c^0 \times 18a^{-5}b^2}{-9a^{-5}b^{-1}c^4}$

e) $\dfrac{(14m^{-3}n)(-15m^4n^{-2})}{-21mn^{-5}}$

f) $\dfrac{(24x^3z^{-4})(-35x^{-7}z^3)}{(-8x^5z^0)(-14x^{-5}z^{-6})}$

13. Simplify.

a) $\dfrac{-12a^{-\frac{1}{3}}b}{3a^{-\frac{1}{3}}b^{\frac{2}{3}}}$

b) $\dfrac{-25m^{\frac{3}{4}}n^{-\frac{1}{2}}}{-10m^{-\frac{1}{4}}n^{\frac{1}{3}}}$

c) $\left(\dfrac{x^{\frac{2}{3}}}{y^{-\frac{1}{2}}}\right)^{\frac{6}{5}}$

d) $\left(\dfrac{a^2}{b^{\frac{1}{3}}}\right)^{\frac{3}{4}}(a^2b^{-1})^{-3}$

e) $\left(\dfrac{m^{\frac{3}{4}}n^{\frac{4}{3}}}{m^2}\right)^{\frac{2}{3}}$

f) $\dfrac{(a^{-5}b^3)^{\frac{1}{2}}}{a^{-\frac{2}{3}}b^{-\frac{1}{2}}}$

14. Simplify.

a) $\dfrac{-21m^{\frac{5}{6}}n^{-\frac{1}{3}}}{7m^{\frac{1}{2}}n^{\frac{1}{6}}}$

b) $-7a^{\frac{2}{3}}b^{-\frac{1}{2}} \times 6a^{-\frac{1}{2}}b^{\frac{2}{3}}$

c) $\dfrac{-8x^{-\frac{4}{3}}y^{\frac{1}{2}} \times 6x^{-\frac{3}{4}}y^{-\frac{2}{3}}}{24x^{-\frac{5}{6}}y^{-\frac{1}{6}}}$

d) $\dfrac{(9a^{-\frac{1}{3}}b^{-\frac{4}{5}}c^{-\frac{4}{5}})(-4a^{-\frac{1}{2}}b^{\frac{3}{5}}c^0)}{-18a^{\frac{1}{6}}b^{-\frac{1}{2}}c^{-\frac{1}{3}}}$

e) $\dfrac{(13a^{-\frac{3}{4}}c^{-\frac{1}{2}})(-6a^{-\frac{1}{2}}c^{-\frac{3}{2}})}{(-21c^{\frac{1}{4}})(-39a^{-\frac{3}{2}}c^{\frac{3}{4}})}$

f) $\dfrac{(25x^{\frac{1}{4}}z^{\frac{1}{2}})(-16x^{-\frac{3}{4}}z^{\frac{3}{2}})}{(-6x^{-\frac{1}{4}}z^{-\frac{1}{2}})(-15x^{\frac{3}{2}}z^{\frac{3}{4}})}$

15. If $a = \dfrac{1}{8}$ and $b = 4$, evaluate each expression.

a) $a^{-1}b^{\frac{1}{2}}$ b) $(a^{-2}b^{\frac{1}{2}})(a^{\frac{1}{3}}b^{\frac{3}{2}})^{-1}$ c) $(a^{\frac{4}{3}}b^{-\frac{3}{2}})^3(a^{-2}b^{\frac{5}{2}})$ d) $(a^{\frac{2}{3}}b^{-2})^2(a^{-\frac{2}{3}}b^{-1})^{-3}$

16. If $x = \dfrac{4}{9}$ and $y = 27$, evaluate each expression.

a) $-x^2y^{\frac{2}{3}}$ b) $(3x^{-1}y^{\frac{1}{3}})(-4x^{\frac{3}{2}})^{-2}$ c) $\dfrac{6x^{-\frac{3}{2}}y^{-\frac{2}{3}}}{16x^{-\frac{5}{2}}y^{-\frac{4}{3}}}$ d) $\dfrac{-16x^{-\frac{5}{2}}y^{\frac{4}{3}}}{-9x^{-\frac{1}{2}}y^{-\frac{1}{3}}}$

17. If $x = 2a^4$, $y = a^3$, and $z = \dfrac{1}{2}a^2$, write each expression as an exponential function of a.

a) $(xyz)^{\frac{1}{2}}$ b) $xy^{-2}z^{-1}$ c) $(3x^2yz)^3$

18. If $p = 3x$, $q = \dfrac{2}{3}x^2$, and $r = x^5$, write each expression as an exponential function of x.

a) p^2qr b) $p^{-1}q^2r^{-3}$ c) $(9p^{-2}q^2r^{-1})^{-1}$

19. Simplify.

a) $\dfrac{(x^{2a})(x^{-5a})}{x^{-3a}}$ b) $\dfrac{(s^{2n})(s^{-n})}{(s^{-3n})(s^{-4n})}$ c) $\dfrac{(a^{x-1})(a^{x+1})}{a^{2x-1}}$

d) $\dfrac{(m^{-ac})(m^{-ab})}{m^{-bc}}$ e) $\dfrac{(x^{-3})^a(x^a)^2}{x^{a-2}}$ f) $\dfrac{(a^{2x-y})(a^{x-y})}{(3a^{x+y})^2}$

g) $\dfrac{(x^{\frac{a}{4}})(x^{-\frac{a}{3}})}{x^{\frac{a}{12}}}$ h) $\dfrac{(m^{-\frac{n}{2}})(n^{-\frac{m}{4}})}{(m^{\frac{n}{3}})(n^{\frac{m}{2}})}$ i) $\dfrac{(a^{-\frac{x}{2}})^3(a^{-\frac{x}{3}})^4}{(a^{\frac{x}{4}})^2}$

Ⓒ

20. Use your calculator to evaluate to the nearest thousandth.

a) 3^π b) π^π c) $10^{\sqrt{2}}$ d) $(\sqrt{2})^{\sqrt{3}}$

e) $4^{-\pi}$ f) $7^{-\sqrt{2}}$ g) $2^{\sqrt{\pi}}$ h) $2^{\sqrt{2}} + 2^{-\sqrt{2}}$

21. a) Evaluate each power.

i) 2^2 ii) $(0.5)^2$ iii) 2^{-2} iv) $(0.5)^{-2}$

v) $4^{\frac{1}{2}}$ vi) $(0.25)^{\frac{1}{2}}$ vii) $4^{-\frac{1}{2}}$ viii) $(0.25)^{-\frac{1}{2}}$

b) Using the results of part a) as a guide, make a conjecture about how you can tell, given the values of x and y ($y > 0$), if:

i) $y^x > 1$ ii) $0 < y^x < 1$.

22. Write as a single power.

a) $3(5)^{\frac{1}{3}} + 2(5)^{\frac{1}{3}}$ b) $(2^x)^2 + 2^{2x}$ c) $3(4)^x + 2^{2x}$

MATHEMATICS AROUND US

Measuring Air Pollution

The pollution generated by automobiles and industry in heavily populated areas occasionally becomes a danger to health. It is therefore important to have a measure of the amount of air pollution so that appropriate action can be taken before serious health problems develop.

In Ontario, an Air Pollution Index (API) is determined for certain areas of the province. This index depends on two quantities which are constantly being monitored:

CoH — the coefficient of haze, a measure of the suspended particles in the air;

SO_2 — the concentration of sulphur dioxide in parts per million.

Here is how the API is measured for three areas of Ontario.

Toronto: $0.2[30.5 \text{ CoH} + 126.0 \text{ SO}_2]^{1.35}$

Hamilton: $2.5[13.9 \text{ CoH} + 104.5 \text{ SO}_2]^{0.8}$

Sudbury: $1.84[11.0 \text{ CoH} + 161.0 \text{ SO}_2]^{0.87}$

To interpret the API, the following guide is used.

Acceptable range	Warning range	Sources of pollution may be ordered to curtail operations.	Sources of pollution will be ordered to curtail operations.
0	32	50	100

QUESTIONS

1. Calculate the API for each town.
   a) Toronto:
      i)   CoH 0.42, SO_2 0.13
      ii) CoH 1.3, SO_2 0.24
   b) Hamilton:
      i)   CoH 1.84, SO_2 0.24
      ii) CoH 2.2, SO_2 0.18
   c) Sudbury:
      i)   CoH 0.92, SO_2 0.36
      ii) CoH 1.6, SO_2 0.40

2. In Toronto, the highest API occurred at about the time of the Grey Cup game in 1962. Visibility on the playing field was so poor that it was necessary to complete the game on the following day. At the time, the values of CoH and SO_2 were about 2.7 and 0.44 respectively. Calculate the API for these values.

3. Suggest why there is a different formula for calculating the API for each city.

5-2 SOLVING EQUATIONS INVOLVING EXPONENTS

The exponent laws may be used to solve equations involving exponents.

Example 1. Solve. a) $x^{\frac{3}{4}} = 8$ b) $2y^{\frac{2}{3}} = 18$

Solution.   a) $x^{\frac{3}{4}} = 8$

To simplify the left side of the equation, raise it to the power $\frac{4}{3}$.
Do the same to the right side.
$$(x^{\frac{3}{4}})^{\frac{4}{3}} = 8^{\frac{4}{3}}$$
$$x = (\sqrt[3]{8})^4$$
$$= 16$$

b) $2y^{\frac{2}{3}} = 18$

Divide both sides by 2.
$$y^{\frac{2}{3}} = 9$$

Raise both sides to the power $\frac{3}{2}$.
$$(y^{\frac{2}{3}})^{\frac{3}{2}} = 9^{\frac{3}{2}}$$
$$y = (\sqrt[2]{9})^3$$
$$= 27$$

Often, the variable may appear as the exponent in an equation. For example, in a ladies-singles tennis tournament there are 64 entries. If each competitor plays until she loses, the number of rounds, n, required is found by solving the equation $2^n = 64$.
To solve the equation, express 64 as a power of 2.
$$2^n = 2^6$$
Since the bases are the same, the exponents are equal.
$$n = 6$$
Six rounds of tennis must be played in the competition.

An equation such as $2^n = 64$ is called an *exponential equation*, since the unknown is the exponent or in the exponent. Other exponential equations are:
$$5^x = 625 \qquad 16^{3n-2} = 2.$$
Such equations can be solved by expressing both sides as powers of the same base.

Example 2. Solve. $3^x = 81$

Solution. Write 81 as a power of 3. $3^x = 3^4$
When the powers are equal and the bases are the same, the exponents are equal.
Therefore, $x = 4$

Example 3. Solve.

    a) $2^{x+3} = 16$ b) $9^{x-1} = 27$

Solution.   a) Write 16 as a power of 2. $2^{x+3} = 2^4$

           Since the bases are the same, the exponents are equal.

           $x + 3 = 4$

               $x = 1$

          b) Write both sides as powers of 3.

           L.S. $= 9^{x-1}$ R.S. $= 3^3$

                $= (3^2)^{x-1}$

                $= 3^{2x-2}$

           The equation becomes $3^{2x-2} = 3^3$

           Since the bases are the same, the exponents are equal.

           $2x - 2 = 3$

               $2x = 5$

                $x = 2.5$

Example 4. The number of insects in a colony doubles every month. If there are now 250 insects, about how long will it take for the colony to grow to 8000?

Solution.   Let n be the required number of months.

          Then, $250 \times 2^n = 8000$

$$2^n = \frac{8000}{250}$$

$$= 32$$

$$n = 5$$

          In 5 months, the colony will number 8000 insects.

Example 5. How long does it take money invested at 12% compounded annually to double in value?

Solution.   Let n denote the number of years for a sum of money to double.

          The value of \$1 after n years is $\$1(1.12)^n$.

          The condition that the money doubles in n years is $(1.12)^n = 2$

          We solve the equation by systematic trial, trying various values of n.

n	5	6	7
$(1.12)^n$	1.762	1.974	2.211

          Since $1.974 \doteq 2$, then $(1.12)^6 \doteq 2$, and $n \doteq 6$

          Money invested at 12% compounded annually doubles in value in approximately 6 years.

EXERCISES 5-2

(A)

1. Solve.

    a) $x^{\frac{1}{2}} = 7$ b) $x^{\frac{1}{3}} = 4$ c) $x^{\frac{1}{4}} = 2$ d) $x^{\frac{2}{3}} = 4$

    e) $x^{\frac{3}{4}} = 27$ f) $x^{\frac{3}{2}} = 125$ g) $x^{\frac{5}{3}} = 32$ h) $2x^{\frac{4}{5}} = 162$

2. Solve.
a) $2^x = 32$ b) $10^x = 100\ 000$ c) $3^x = 81$
d) $5^x = 625$ e) $(-2)^x = -128$ f) $4^x = 64$
g) $9^x = 729$ h) $20^x = 8000$ i) $7^x = 2401$

3. Solve.
a) $2^{x+1} = 4$ b) $2^{x-1} = 8$ c) $3^{x-5} = 9$
d) $5^{x+3} = 25$ e) $10^{x+1} = 1000$ f) $4^{x+2} = 16$

4. Solve.
a) $7^x = 1$ b) $6^x = \dfrac{1}{36}$ c) $5^x = 5$ d) $10^x = 0.01$

5. How long does it take money invested at 9% compounded annually to double in value?

6. How long will it take $1000 to triple if it is invested at 12% compounded annually?

7. Solve.
a) $2^{2x+1} = 8$ b) $3^{2-x} = 9$ c) $5^{3x-2} = 25$
d) $9^{x+1} = 1$ e) $4^x = 32$ f) $9^x = 27$
g) $8^{x+2} = 16$ h) $9^{1-2x} = 81$ i) $16^{x-1} = 64$

8. Solve.
a) $3 \times 2^x = 12$ b) $5 \times 2^x = 40$ c) $10 \times 3^x = 270$
d) $10 \times 2^x = 640$ e) $6 \times 3^x = 162$ f) $4 \times 5^x = 500$
g) $3 \times 6^x = 108$ h) $4 \times 7^x = 4$ i) $2 \times 4^x = 1$

9. The number of ants in a nest doubles every month. If there are now 600 ants, about how long will it take for their number to grow to 9600?

10. If the salt content of Lake Ontario continues to increase at the rate given in the news item:
a) write an expression for the salt concentration after n years
b) in about how many years will the lake have the same salt concentration as the Dead Sea?

SALT HARMS ENVIRONMENT

TORONTO. Salt spread on roads in winter is finding its way into Lake Ontario and causing the lake's salt content to double every five years. The present level is about 25 parts per million. There is, however, no immediate danger of the lake becoming another Dead Sea which has a salt content of 10 000 parts per million.

11. Solve and check.
a) $4^x + 4^{x+1} = 40$ b) $3^x - 3^{x-1} = \dfrac{2}{27}$ c) $5 \times 2^x - 3 \times 2^{x-1} = 224$

12. Solve by systematic trial. Give the answers to 2 decimal places.
a) $x^x = 2$ b) $2^x + x = 10$ c) $2^x + x^2 = 12$

5-3 INTRODUCTION TO EXPONENTIAL FUNCTIONS

Exponents were originally introduced into mathematics as a shorthand for repeated multiplication. Repeated multiplication occurs frequently in applications involving growth and decay.

Compound Interest

Compound interest provides a simple example of *exponential growth*. Suppose you make a long-term investment of $500 at a fixed interest rate of 8% per annum compounded annually. We can calculate the value of your investment at the end of each year.
Value in dollars of the investment after
year 1: $500(1.08) = 540$
year 2: $500(1.08)(1.08) = 500(1.08)^2$, or 583.20
year 3: $500(1.08)(1.08)(1.08) = 500(1.08)^3$, or 629.86

.   .

.   .

.   .

year n: $500(1.08)^n$

Hence, the value of an investment A dollars can be expressed as a function of the number of years n by this equation.
$$A = 500(1.08)^n$$
In this equation, n is a natural number since it indicates how many factors of 1.08 there are in the expression. Using values of n from 1 to 25, we obtain values of A and draw the graph shown. The fact that we can draw a smooth curve through the plotted points on the graph suggests that an expression such as $(1.08)^n$ can be defined for values of n that are not natural numbers. We will see how to do this in the next section.

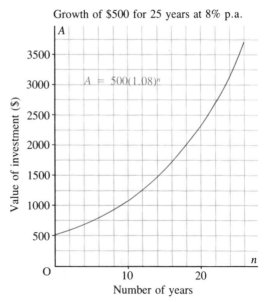

Growth of $500 for 25 years at 8% p.a.

$A = 500(1.08)^n$

Value of investment ($)

Number of years

Growth of Populations

In 1987 the world population reached 5 billion, and was increasing at the rate of approximately 1.6% per year. If we assume that this rate of growth is maintained, we can write an equation expressing the predicted population P billion as a function of the number of years n since 1987.
$$P \doteq 5(1.016)^n$$

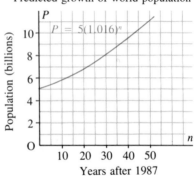

Predicted growth of world population

$P = 5(1.016)^n$

Population (billions)

Years after 1987

The graph on the facing page shows this equation plotted for values of n from 0 to 50 corresponding to the years from 1987 to 2037. In this equation, n is also a natural number, but since the graph represents as many as 50 values of n, the graph is drawn as a smooth curve.

A Bouncing Ball

A bouncing ball provides a simple example of *exponential decay*. In this picture, on each bounce the ball rises to 70% of the height from which it fell. Suppose that the ball originally fell from a height of 2.00 m. We can calculate the height to which the ball rises on each successive bounce.

Height in metres of the ball after

bounce 1: $2.00(0.7) = 1.4$

bounce 2: $2.00(0.7)(0.7) = 2.0(0.7)^2$, or 0.98

bounce 3: $2.00(0.7)(0.7)(0.7) = 2.0(0.7)^3$, or 0.69

. . . .

. . . .

. . . .

bounce n: $2.00(0.7)^n$

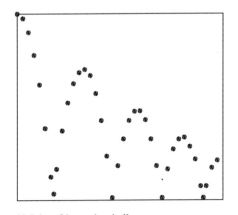

Height of bouncing ball

Hence, the height h metres can be expressed as a function of the number of bounces n by this equation.

$$h = 2.00(0.7)^n$$

The graph shows the values of n for $0 \leq n \leq 10$. Since it is not meaningful to have a fractional number of bounces, the points are not joined by a smooth curve.

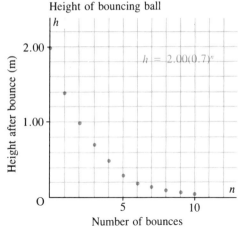

Number of bounces

Light Penetration Under Water

For every metre a diver descends below the surface, the light intensity is reduced by 2.5%. Hence, the percent P of surface light present can be expressed as a function of the depth d metres by this equation.

$$P = 100(1 - 0.025)^d$$
$$\text{or} \quad P = 100(0.975)^d$$

The graph shows P as a function of d for $0 \leq d \leq 100$. Although d is understood to represent a natural number in the expression above, we have drawn a smooth curve to indicate light intensity at all depths to 100 m, including those depths that are not whole numbers of metres.

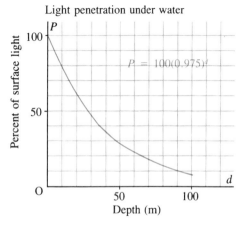

Light penetration under water

Depth (m)

In each of the above equations, the variable in the expression on the right side appears in an exponent. Functions whose defining equation have this property are called exponential functions.

> An *exponential function* has an equation which can be written in the form $f(x) = ca^x$, where c and a are constants, and $a > 0$.

Note the following properties of the variable x, and the constants a and c.
- In this section, x is understood to represent a natural number, since it represents the number of times the constant a occurs as a factor. This restriction will be removed in the next section.
- Since all the applications of exponential functions are ones in which the base is positive, we will assume that $a > 0$.
- The constant c is any real number, though in most applications we shall encounter this number is usually positive also.

In the following example an exponential function is defined by a statement describing how variables are related.

Example. In favorable breeding conditions, a colony of insects can multiply 10-fold every 3 weeks. If there are now 500 insects in the colony, express the number of insects N as a function of the elapsed time w weeks.

Solution. "Multiply 10-fold every 3 weeks" means that every time 3 weeks elapse, there are 10 times as many insects as before.
Number of insects after:
3 weeks: $500(10)$
6 weeks: $500(10)^2$ Each exponent is $\frac{1}{3}$ of
9 weeks: $500(10)^3$ the number of weeks.

$\cdot$ $\cdot$

$\cdot$ $\cdot$

$\cdot$ $\cdot$

w weeks: $500(10)^{\frac{w}{3}}$
Hence, $N(w) = 500(10)^{\frac{w}{3}}$

EXERCISES 5-3
Note: Exercises 1 to 8 refer to the above examples.

Ⓑ

1. Use the graph on page 214 to estimate how many years it takes, at 8%, for the original investment:
   a) to double in value   b) to triple in value.

2. Describe how the graph would differ if:
   a) the interest rate were
      i) greater than 8%   ii) less than 8%;
   b) the original investment were
      i) greater than $500   ii) less than $500.

3. Use the graph on page 214 to estimate the number of years required for the population of the world to double.

4. Describe how the population graph would differ for a country such as:
   a) Mexico which has a growth rate of approximately 3.5%
   b) Japan which has a growth rate of approximately 1.1%.

5. Use the graph on page 215 to estimate how many bounces are needed before the ball bounces to only 10% of the original height from which it was dropped.

6. Describe how both the graph and the equation on page 215 would differ for a ball which is:
   a) more resilient, and bounces higher than the one shown
   b) less resilient, and does not bounce as high as the one shown.

7. Use the graph on page 215 to estimate the depth where the light intensity in only 50% of that at the surface.

8. The depth to which light penetrates under water depends on the color of the light. The graph was drawn for yellow light. How would the graph differ for:
   a) red light which penetrates about 20% as far as yellow light
   b) blue light which penetrates about 4 times as far as yellow light?

9. At current growth rates, the population of Mexico is doubling about every 20 years. The population in 1985 was 80 million. Write an expression for the population P million as an exponential function of the time n years since 1985.

10. There are now 300 insects in a colony. The population of the colony doubles every 5 days. Express the population P of the colony as an exponential function of the elapsed time d days.

11. Several layers of glass are stacked together, as shown. Each layer reduces the light passing through it by 5%. Write an expression for the percent P of light that passes through n panes of glass.

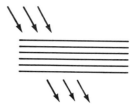

C

12. Most cars have a plastic container which holds fluid for cleaning the windshield. Throughout the winter, a motorist used 100% pure solvent in the container. One day in the spring, when the container was half full of solvent, she topped up the container with water. From then on throughout the summer, whenever the container was half full, she topped it up with water. Write an equation that expresses the concentration C of the solvent in the container as an exponential function of the number of times n it was topped up with water.

MATHEMATICS AROUND US

The Loudness of Sounds

The range of sounds detectable by the human ear is enormous. A rock group can be *10 trillion* times as loud as a leaf rustling in a breeze. The loudness of sounds is measured in units called *decibels* (dB).

> Every increase of 10 dB corresponds to a 10-fold increase in loudness.

For example, the increase from the hum of a refrigerator to an air conditioner is 20 dB. This is 2 increases of 10 dB, so the increase in loudness is $(10)^2$, or 100. Hence, an air conditioner is 100 times as loud as a refrigerator.

QUESTIONS

1. a) How many times as loud as conversational speech is a chain saw?
   b) How many times as loud as a quiet whisper is a chain saw?

2. Let L_1 and L_2 represent the loudnesses of sounds of S_1 decibels and S_2 decibels respectively. Show that
$$\frac{L_2}{L_1} = 10^{0.1(S_2 - S_1)}$$
   Use this equation in the questions below.

3. How many times as loud as:
   a) an air conditioner is a heavy truck
   b) a refrigerator hum is average street traffic
   c) average street traffic is a jet at 100 m?

4. It was once reported that the loudness level of a heavy snore is 69 dB. How many times is this as loud as:
   a) conversational speech
   b) a quiet whisper?

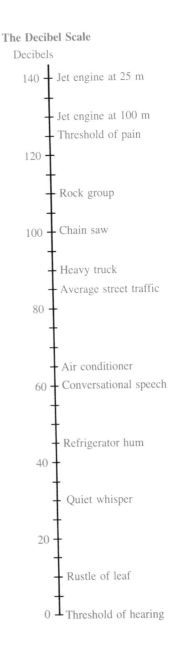

The Decibel Scale

Decibels

140 — Jet engine at 25 m

— Jet engine at 100 m
— Threshold of pain

120 —

— Rock group

100 — Chain saw

— Heavy truck
— Average street traffic

80 —

— Air conditioner

60 — Conversational speech

— Refrigerator hum

40 —

— Quiet whisper

20 —

— Rustle of leaf

0 — Threshold of hearing

Composers use these symbols to indicate the levels of loudness for playing their music.

pp   pianissimo (very soft)
p   piano (soft)
mp   mezzopiano (moderately soft)
mf   mezzoforte (moderately loud)
f   forte (loud)
ff   fortissimo (very loud)

But do performers actually play in such a way that the differences between six levels of loudness can be detected? It has been determined that, during a performance, the level of loudness must change by at least 5 dB before most people can detect it. Several musicians were asked to play their instruments at each of the six loudness levels indicated above. The difference in loudness between the softest notes and the loudest notes was measured. These are the results.

Bassoon 10 dB   Flute 20 dB   Trumpet 36 dB   Clarinet 45 dB

5. a) For which instruments could the six loudness levels have been detected?
   b) At how many levels of loudness could each instrument have been played?

6. The use of earplugs can reduce the noise level by as much as 25 dB. How many times less intense would a sound be if earplugs were worn?

7. In a noise reduction study, the noise caused by a train was compared at two locations A and B. It was found that the forest reduced high frequency sounds by as much as 20 dB, but low frequency sounds were reduced by 4 dB or less. By what factor did the forest reduce:
   a) high frequency sounds   b) low frequency sounds?

8. A person's hearing can be permanently damaged by listening to very loud sounds for prolonged periods of time. An 8 h exposure to a 90 dB sound is considered acceptable. For every 5 dB increase in loudness, the acceptable exposure time is reduced by one-half.
   a) Derive an equation expressing the acceptable exposure time *t* hours as an exponential function of the loudness level *d* decibels.
   b) What is the acceptable exposure time for:
      i) a rock group playing at 100 dB?   ii) a jet engine at 130 dB? 140 dB?

Relating Addition and Multiplication

"One cannot escape the feeling that these mathematical formulas have an independent existence and an intelligence of their own, that they are wiser than we are, wiser even than their discoverers, that we get more out of them than was originally put into them."

Heinrich Hertz

Find a function $f(x)$ such that $f(x + 2) = 9f(x)$ for all values of x.

Understand the problem
- What does $f(x + 2)$ mean?
- What does $9f(x)$ mean?

Think of a strategy
- The left side involves addition, and the right side involves multiplication. What kinds of functions relate addition and multiplication?
- The numbers in the given equation are 2 and 9. What kind of natural number is 9? How might this be related to the 2?
- What kind of function might $f(x)$ be?

Carry out the strategy
- The function $f(x)$ might be an exponential function.
- Let $f(x) = a^x$, where x is a constant to be determined.
- If $f(x) = a^x$, then what does $f(x + 2)$ equal? What does $9f(x)$ equal?
- Since $f(x + 2) = 9f(x)$, can you find the value of a?
- What is the function $f(x)$?

Look back
- For the function $f(x)$ you found, check that $f(x + 2) = 9f(x)$.
- Is the function $f(x)$ unique?
- Write similar relations involving $f(x + 3)$, $f(x + 4)$, ..., $f(x + n)$.
- Find a function $f(x)$ such that $f(x + n) = kf(x)$ for all values of x.

PROBLEMS

Ⓑ

1. Triangle ABC is an equilateral triangle with sides 6 cm long. Calculate the area of the shaded square, to the nearest hundredth of a square centimetre.

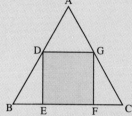

2. The natural number 64 is both a perfect square (since $64 = 8^2$) and a perfect cube (since $64 = 4^3$).
   a) Find other natural numbers which are both perfect squares and perfect cubes.
   b) Find a natural number which is a perfect square, a perfect cube, and a perfect fourth power.

3. Three cylindrical logs with radius 10 cm are piled as shown. Determine the distance from the top of the pile to the ground.

4. Find the equations of the lines which are parallel to the line $3x - 4y + 12 = 0$, and 2 units from it.

Ⓒ

5. Determine if it is possible to find two prime numbers p and q such that $pq + 1$ is a perfect square. If it is possible, find out as much as you can about primes that have this property.

6. The double factorial symbol !! is defined as follows.
   $$n!! = n(n - 2)(n - 4) \ldots 5 \times 3 \times 1 \text{ if } n \text{ is odd}$$
   $$n(n - 2)(n - 4) \ldots 6 \times 4 \times 2 \text{ if } n \text{ is even}$$
   a) Simplify $n!!(n - 1)!!$ b) Prove that $(2n)!! = 2^n(n!)$
   c) Find a similar expression for $(2n - 1)!!$

7. The ellipse $b^2x^2 + a^2y^2 = a^2b^2$ is inscribed in the circle $x^2 + y^2 = a^2$. $P(x_1, y_1)$ is any point on the circle, forming an angle θ with the major axis. If P' is the corresponding point on the ellipse, determine the ratio $\dfrac{OP'}{OP}$ in terms of a, b, and θ.

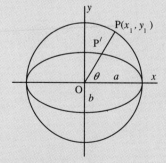

Ⓓ

8. Prove that it is impossible to fill a rectangular box completely with cubes no two of which are congruent.

5-4 GRAPHING EXPONENTIAL FUNCTIONS

Some of the properties of exponential functions that we have studied
can be illustrated on a graph. For example, we can graph the function
$f(x) = 2^x$ using a table of values.

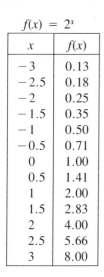

$f(x) = 2^x$

x	$f(x)$
-3	0.13
-2.5	0.18
-2	0.25
-1.5	0.35
-1	0.50
-0.5	0.71
0	1.00
0.5	1.41
1	2.00
1.5	2.83
2	4.00
2.5	5.66
3	8.00

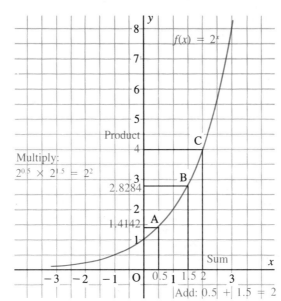

We can use the graph to illustrate the following properties of the function $f(x) = 2^x$.

Vertical intercept

$f(0) = 2^0$
$= 1$

The vertical intercept is 1.

Horizontal intercept

Let $f(x) = 0$.
Then $2^x = 0$
This equation has no real solution since
$2^x > 0$ for all real values of x. Hence,
there is no horizontal intercept.

Domain

Since we can define 2^x for all real values
of x, the domain is the set of all real
numbers.

Range

Since there is a value of x for all positive
real values of 2^x, the range is the set of
all positive real numbers.

Law of Exponents

Select any two points on the curve, such as A(0.5, $2^{0.5}$) and B(1.5, $2^{1.5}$).
Add their x-coordinates.   *Multiply* their y-coordinates.
$0.5 + 1.5 = 2$ $(2^{0.5})(2^{1.5}) = 2^2$
The results are the coordinates of another point C(2, 2^2) on the graph.
Is this true for any two points on the graph?
      We can graph other exponential functions using tables of values,
but it is more efficient to sketch the graphs by considering how they
are related to the graph of $f(x) = 2^x$, which we have already drawn.

Example 1. Sketch these functions on the same grid.

  a) $f(x) = 2^x$ b) $g(x) = 1.5^x$ c) $h(x) = 1^x$ d) $k(x) = 0.5^x$

Solution. All four graphs pass through the point (0,1).

a) The graph of $f(x) = 2^x$ is shown.

b) If $x > 0$, then $1.5^x < 2^x$. Hence, in the first quadrant, the graph of $g(x) = 1.5^x$ lies below that of $f(x) = 2^x$. To judge how far below, use a test point. Substitute $x = 2$ into 1.5^x to get 2.25. Hence, the point (2, 2.25) lies on the graph.

Conversely, if $x < 0$, then $1.5^x > 2^x$. Hence, in the second quadrant, the graph of $g(x) = 1.5^x$ lies above that of $f(x) = 2^x$. To judge how far above, use a test point. Substitute $x = -2$ into 1.5^x to get approximately 0.44. Hence, (−2, 0.44) lies on the graph.

c) Since $1^x = 1$ for all values of x, the graph of $h(x) = 1^x$ is a horizontal line 1 unit above the x-axis.

d) If $x > 0$, 0.5^x is less than 1. Also, as x increases, 0.5^x becomes closer and closer to 0. If $x < 0$, 0.5^x becomes larger and larger, without limit.

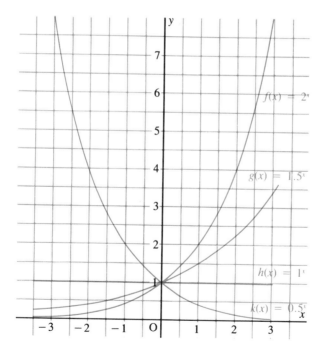

In *Example 1*, notice that the graphs of $f(x) = 2^x$ and $g(x) = 1.5^x$ are increasing for all real values of x. The graph of $k(x) = 0.5^x$ is decreasing for all real values of x. As $x \to -\infty$, 2^x and 1.5^x both approach 0. As $x \to +\infty$, 0.5^x approaches 0. The graphs of the three functions draw closer to the x-axis without ever touching it. The x-axis is said to be an *asymptote* of the graphs of these three functions.

Example 1 illustrates properties of the graph of the exponential function $f(x) = a^x$.

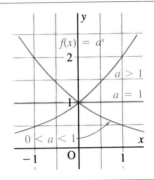

Properties of the graph of the function $f(x) = a^x$
Vertical intercept: 1
Horizontal intercept: none
Domain: all real numbers
Range: all positive real numbers
Asymptote: x-axis $(y = 0)$
Increasing: $\forall x \in \mathbb{R}\,;\, a > 1$
Decreasing: $\forall x \in \mathbb{R}\,;\, 0 < a < 1$

Example 2. Draw the graph of $g(x) = 2^{x-1} + 2$. State the properties of this function.

Solution.   The graph of $g(x) = 2^{x-1} + 2$ can be obtained from the graph of $f(x) = 2^x$ by a translation t(1,2) defined by the transformation $T(x, y) = (x + 1, y + 2)$.

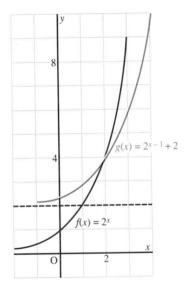

The properties of $g(x) = 2^{x-1} + 2$ are:
—Vertical intercept is 2.5.
—There is no horizontal intercept.
—Domain is $\mathbb{R}$.
—Range is $]2, +\infty$.
—Asymptote is $y = 2$.
—The function is increasing on $\forall x \in \mathbb{R}$.

EXERCISES 5-4

1. Identify the graph which best represents each function.

a) $f(x) = 3^x$ b) $g(x) = 10^x$ c) $h(x) = \left(\dfrac{3}{4}\right)^x$ d) $k(x) = \left(\dfrac{1}{4}\right)^x$

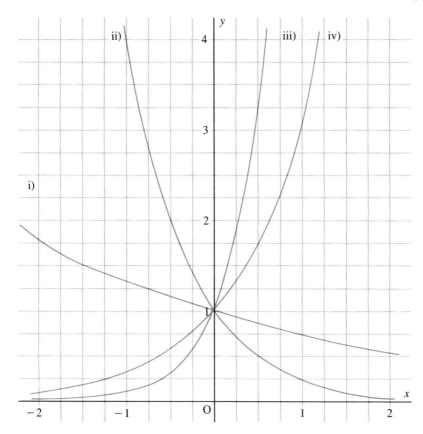

2. Describe how the graph of $f(x) = a^x$ varies as a varies.

B

3. a) Make tables of values and graph these functions on the same grid.

$$f_1(x) = 3^x \text{ for } -2 \leq x \leq 2 \qquad f_2(x) = \left(\dfrac{1}{3}\right)^x \text{ for } -2 \leq x \leq 2$$

b) On the same grid as in part a), sketch the graph of each function.

$$f_1(x) = 4^x \qquad g_1(x) = 2^x \qquad f_2(x) = \left(\dfrac{1}{2}\right)^x \qquad g_2(x) = \left(\dfrac{1}{4}\right)^x$$

4. Draw the graphs of these functions on the same grid.

$$f_1(x) = 2^x \qquad g_1(x) = 5^x \qquad h_1(x) = 10^x$$
$$f_2(x) = \left(\dfrac{1}{2}\right)^x \qquad g_2(x) = \left(\dfrac{1}{5}\right)^x \qquad h_2(x) = \left(\dfrac{1}{10}\right)^x$$

5. The graph of an exponential function $f(x) = a^x$ passes through each point. Find the value of the base a.

a) A(3,216)   b) B(5,32)   c) C(3,512)   d) D(4,256)

e) E(−2,64)   f) $F\left(-3, \frac{1}{216}\right)$ g) G(3,343)   h) $H\left(\frac{1}{3}, 3\right)$

6. Graph these functions on the same grid. Write the properties of each function.

a) $y = 2^x$ b) $y = 2^{0.5x}$ c) $y = 2^{2x}$ d) $y = -2^x$ e) $y = 2^{-x}$

7. Repeat *Exercise 6* for these functions.

a) $y = 2^x$ b) $y = 2^x + 1$ c) $y = 2^x - 1$ d) $y = 2^{x+1}$ e) $y = 2^{x-1}$

8. Graph each function. State the domain, the range, and the equation of the asymptote.

a) $f(x) = 3(2^x)$ b) $g(x) = 3^{x-1} + 2$ c) $h(x) = 0.5^{x+1} - 2$

9. The equation of an exponential function is given. Find the equation of its image under the given translation t, and graph both functions on the same grid.

a) $f(x) = 4^x$; t(2, −1)   b) $g(x) = 0.2^x$; t(0, 2)   c) $h(x) = 3^x$; t(−1, 4)

10. For each function, state:

   i) the equation of the asymptote   ii) the domain
   iii) the range   iv) whether the function is decreasing or increasing.

   a) $f(x) = 3^{x+2} - 5$ b) $g(x) = \left(\frac{1}{2}\right)^{x-1} + 3$ c) $h(x) = 4^{x+5} - 2$

Ⓒ

11. If $a > 0$, for what values of a and x is each statement true?

a) $a^x = 1$ b) $a^x > 1$ c) $0 < a^x < 1$

12. Prove that if $f(x) = a^x$, then $f(x)f(y) = f(x + y)$.

 **INVESTIGATE**

The ⬚log key on a Calculator

Find out what the ⬚log key on your calculator does. Try a wide variety of numbers such as those below. Look for patterns in the results.

- Numbers selected at random, for example, 3, 65, 239, 4772
- Powers of 10; for example, 10, 100, 1000, 10 000, 1, 0.1, 0.01, 0.001
- Multiples of 10; for example, 20, 200, 2000, 30, 300, 3000
- Zero and negative numbers; for example, 0, −2, −3, −10

Write a report of your findings.

THE MATHEMATICAL MIND

Doubling the Cube

It is said that around 427 B.C. in ancient Greece, a plague was responsible for the death of more than a quarter of the Athenian population. A special delegation was sent to the oracle of Apollo at Delos to inquire how the plague should be averted. The oracle instructed that they must double the size of Apollo's cubical altar. The Athenians thought that they could do this by doubling each dimension of the altar, but in doing so, they were not able to curb the plague. Since each dimension was doubled, they had in fact multiplied the volume of the altar by $2 \times 2 \times 2$, or 8.

According to the legend, this faulty mathematics on the part of the Athenians led the Greek geometers to study the problem of doubling the volume of a given cube while keeping its cubic shape. The first progress in the solution of this problem was given by Hippocrates. He reduced the problem to that of constructing lengths x and y such that $\dfrac{r}{x} = \dfrac{x}{y} = \dfrac{y}{2r}$, where r is the given length of an edge of the cubical altar. From these equations he deduced that $x^3 = 2r^3$. Hence, x is the edge length of a cube having twice the volume of the cube with edge length r.

For 2000 years mathematicians tried to construct a segment of length x using straightedge and compasses, but none succeeded. This construction was proved to be impossible by the mathematicians of the nineteenth century.

QUESTIONS

1. a) Show that $x^3 = 2r^3$ can be deduced from the equations $\dfrac{r}{x} = \dfrac{x}{y} = \dfrac{y}{2r}$.

   b) Solve the equation for x.

   c) Find a similar equation for y, and solve it.

2. In his attempt to solve the problem of doubling the cube, Plato used this diagram. Show that if the figure were constructed such that $DE = r$ and $CE = 2r$, then BE would be the segment whose length is the edge length of the cubical altar to be constructed.

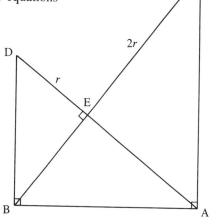

MATHEMATICS AROUND US

Carbon Dating

In 1950 the Nobel Prize in chemistry went to Dr. W.F. Libby who had developed a method of dating organic matter, known as *carbon dating*. All living matter contains traces of radioactive carbon-14. When an organism dies, the carbon-14 decays with a halflife of about 5760 years. Hence, the age of an ancient specimen can be determined by measuring the radioactivity of the carbon-14 it contains, and comparing it with that of living matter. The table shows the percent remaining at various times after an organism dies.

Time		Percent remaining P
Halflives n	Years t	
0	0	100
1	5 760	50
2	11 520	25
3	17 280	12.5
4	23 040	6.25
5	28 800	3.125

The percent P remaining after n halflives have elapsed is expressed as a function of n by the equation $P = 100(0.5)^n$. Since $t = 5760n$, we can write this equation in terms of t.

$$P = 100(0.5)^{\frac{t}{5760}}$$

We can use this equation to approximate the age of a specimen if we know the radioactivity of its carbon-14 relative to living matter.

QUESTIONS

1. The Dead Sea Scrolls are about 2000 years old. What percent radioactivity should be expected from a sample taken from the Dead Sea Scrolls?

2. Charred remains found in Lascaux Cave in France are about 15.3% radioactive. About how old might the famous paintings in this cave be?

3. Determine the approximate age of each specimen, given its radioactivity relative to living matter.
   a) charred bread found at Pompeii   79.6%
   b) wood in First Dynasty tombs   68.9%
   c) charcoal found at Stonehenge   62.0%
   d) specimen from the end of the last ice age   24.0%
   e) skin of a Siberian mammoth   2.2%

4. Illustrate the above results on a graph.

5-5 COMMON LOGARITHMS

In *Exercises 5-3* we encountered problems such as these.

In how many years will an investment of $500 double in value at 8% per annum compounded annually?

At what depth under water is the light level 50% of the light level at the surface?

The answer to this question is the solution of this equation.

$$1000 = 500(1.08)^n$$

or $(1.08)^n = 2$

The answer to this question is the solution of this equation.

$$50 = 100(0.975)^d$$

or $(0.975)^d = 0.5$

In these equations the variable appears in an exponent. Such equations are called *exponential equations*, and they can be solved to any degree of accuracy by systematic trial. However, exponential equations occur so frequently in applications that mathematicians have developed a more direct method of solution. This method involves logarithms. After defining a logarithm and introducing some of its properties, we will show how the above equations can be solved using logarithms.

In the preceding investigation you may have discovered that the $\boxed{\log}$ key of a calculator gives exponents for powers of 10.

Using a calculator: log 100 = 2
2 is the exponent that 100 has when it is expressed as a power of 10.
Since $100 = 10^2$
we write log 100 = 2

Using a calculator: log 0.001 = −3
−3 is the exponent that 0.001 has when it is expressed as a power of 10.
Since $0.001 = 10^{-3}$
we write log 0.001 = −3

These logarithms are called *common logarithms* since they are the exponents of numbers written as powers with base 10. In a later section we will study logarithms with bases other than 10.

Definition of a Logarithm
- log x is the exponent that x would have if it were written as a power with base 10.
- log $x = y$ means that $x = 10^y$.

Since $10^y > 0$ for all real values of y, then $x > 0$. Hence, log x is defined as a real number only when $x > 0$.

Example 1. Use the definition of a logarithm to evaluate each expression.
   a) log 100 000   b) log 0.01   c) log $\sqrt{10}$ d) log 1

Solution.
   a) Since $100\ 000 = 10^5$, then log 100 000 = 5
   b) Since $0.01 = 10^{-2}$, then log 0.01 = −2
   c) Since $\sqrt{10} = 10^{0.5}$, then log $\sqrt{10}$ = 0.5
   d) Since $1 = 10^0$, then log 1 = 0

The answers in *Example 1* can be checked with a calculator.

We can use the $\boxed{\log}$ key of a calculator to find approximations to the logarithm of any positive number. Hence, we can write any positive number as a power of 10.

Example 2. Use your calculator to evaluate each logarithm. Then write the result in exponential form.

a) log 7   b) log 500   c) log 0.4

Solution.   a) log 7 $\doteq$ 0.845 098
                    This means that $10^{0.845098} \doteq 7$
                 b) log 500 $\doteq$ 2.698 97
                    This means that $10^{2.69897} \doteq 500$
                 c) log 0.4 $\doteq$ $-0.397\ 94$
                    This means that $10^{-0.39794} \doteq 0.4$

The results in *Example 2* can be checked using the $\boxed{10^x}$ or $\boxed{y^x}$ keys.

Since log x is defined as a real number only when $x > 0$, you will get an error message if you attempt to find the logarithm of 0, or of a negative number.

log 0 $= y$ means $10^y = 0$, which is   log $(-2) = y$ means $10^y = -2$, which
impossible.   is impossible.

Example 3. Simplify each expression.

a) log 10^x b) $10^{\log x}$

Solution.   a) log 10^x is the exponent that 10^x would have if it were written as a power of 10. But, 10^x *is* written as a power of 10, and has exponent x. Hence, log $10^x = x$
                 b) $10^{\log x}$ is 10 raised to the exponent that x would have if x were written as a power of 10. Hence, $10^{\log x} = x$

Example 3 shows that taking a common logarithm of a number and raising the number to a power of 10 are inverse operations, just as squaring a number and taking the square root of the number are inverse operations. If your calculator has a $\boxed{10^x}$ key, you can illustrate this by using the $\boxed{10^x}$ and $\boxed{\log}$ keys in succession in either order. For example, log $\left(10^{4.5}\right) = 4.5$ and $10^{\log 4.5} = 4.5$

Summary
- A logarithm is an exponent.
- log $x = y$ means that $x = 10^y$, $x > 0$.
- log x is defined only when $x > 0$.
- log $10^x = x$ and $10^{\log x} = x$

EXERCISES 5-5

(A)

1. Use the definition to evaluate each logarithm.
   a) $\log 100$
   b) $\log 1000$
   c) $\log 1\,000\,000$
   d) $\log 10$
   e) $\log 0.1$
   f) $\log 0.001$
   g) $\log 1$
   h) $\log \sqrt[3]{10}$
   i) $\log 10^5$
   j) $\log 10^{\frac{1}{5}}$
   k) $\log 10^{\frac{2}{3}}$
   l) $\log 10^n$

2. Use your calculator to evaluate each logarithm to 4 decimal places. Then write each result in exponential form, and check it with the calculator.
   a) $\log 5$
   b) $\log 18$
   c) $\log 62.4$
   d) $\log 4877$
   e) $\log 0.25$
   f) $\log 0.8$
   g) $\log 0.02$
   h) $\log 0.006$

3. In 1987, the Canadian astronomer Ian Shelton discovered a supernova, or exploding star, from an observatory in Chile. State the common logarithm of each number.
   a) The supernova was more than 100 000 light years, or 10^{20} m, from the Earth.
   b) At its brightest, a supernova is about 10^9 times as bright as a star like the sun.
   c) Throughout recorded history only about 10 supernovas have been visible to the unaided eye.

4. On a single optical disk, an amount of data equivalent to all the text appearing in 15 years of daily newspapers can be recorded. State the common logarithm of each number.
   a) More than 10^{12} bytes of data are recorded on each disk.
   b) To avoid errors, a laser beam is focused within 10^{-7} m of dead centre for each pit on the surface of the disk.
   c) The error rate for a typical disk is 10^{-12}.

(B)

5. Write in exponential form.
   a) $\log 10\,000 = 4$
   b) $\log 10 = 1$
   c) $\log 0.01 = -2$

6. Write in logarithmic form.
   a) $10^3 = 1000$
   b) $10^0 = 1$
   c) $10^{-3} = 0.001$

7. One centillion is defined as the 100th power of 1 000 000. What is the common logarithm of one centillion?

8. Solve each equation.
   a) $\log x = 2$
   b) $\log x = 5$
   c) $\log x = -3$
   d) $\log x = 0$
   e) $\log x = 1$
   f) $\log (\log x) = 1$

9. Simplify each expression.
   a) $\log 10^4$
   b) $\log 10^5$
   c) $\log 10^{-3}$
   d) $10^{\log 100}$
   e) $10^{\log 20}$
   f) $10^{\log 0.2}$

10. a) Use your calculator to evaluate each logarithm.
    i) $\log 2$
    ii) $\log 20$
    iii) $\log 200$
    iv) $\log 2000$
    v) $\log 0.2$
    vi) $\log 0.02$
    vii) $\log 0.002$
    viii) $\log 0.0002$
    b) Account for the pattern in the results.

5-6 THE LAWS OF LOGARITHMS (BASE 10)

A logarithm is an exponent. Hence, it should be possible to write the laws of exponents in logarithmic form.

Consider an example of the law of exponents for multiplication, such as $10^2 \times 10^3 = 10^5$. Since $\log 10^2 = 2$, $\log 10^3 = 3$, and $\log 10^5 = 5$, we can write this equation as:

$\log 10^2 + \log 10^3 = \log 10^5$

or $\qquad \log 10^5 = \log 10^2 + \log 10^3$

This example suggests that a possible law of logarithms for multiplication might be $\log xy = \log x + \log y$. This equation states that the exponent that xy would have if it were expressed as a power of 10 is equal to the sum of the exponents that x and y would have if they were expressed as powers of 10.

Theorem   Law of Logarithms for Multiplication (Base 10)

If x and y are any positive real numbers, then $\log xy = \log x + \log y$

Given: Two real numbers x and y
Required to Prove: $\log xy = \log x + \log y$
Proof: Let $\log x = M$ and $\log y = N$
$$x = 10^M \qquad y = 10^N$$
Hence, $xy = (10^M)(10^N)$
$$= 10^{M+N}$$
Therefore, $\log xy = \log (10^{M+N})$
$$= M + N$$
$$= \log x + \log y$$

Corollary   Law of Logarithms for Division (Base 10)

If x and y are any positive real numbers, then $\log \left(\dfrac{x}{y} \right) = \log x - \log y$

Example 1.   Write $\log 6$ as:
   a) a sum of two logarithms   b) a difference of two logarithms.

Solution.   a) Since $6 = 2 \times 3$, then by the law of logarithms for multiplication,
   $\log 6 = \log 2 + \log 3$
   b) Since $6 = 12 \div 2$, then by the law of logarithms for division,
   $\log 6 = \log 12 - \log 2$

In *Example 1*, $\log 6$ can be expressed as a sum or a difference of logarithms in infinitely many other ways, such as:

$\log 6 = \log 1.5 + \log 4 \qquad \log 6 = \log 18 - \log 3$
$\log 6 = \log 10 + \log 0.6 \qquad \log 6 = \log 60 - \log 10$

Check these results with your calculator.

Example 2. Write each expression as a single logarithm.

a) log 5 + log 4 b) log 21 − log 3

Solution. a) log 5 + log 4 = log (5 × 4) b) log 21 − log 3 = log $\left(\frac{21}{3}\right)$

= log 20

= log 7

Example 3. Given that log 5 ≐ 0.698 97, find an approximation for each logarithm.

a) log 50 b) log 500 c) log 0.5 d) log 0.05

Solution. a) log 50 = log 10 + log 5 b) log 500 = log 100 + log 5

≐ 1 + 0.698 97 ≐ 2 + 0.698 97

≐ 1.698 97 ≐ 2.698 97

c) log 0.5 = log 5 − log 10 d) log 0.05 = log 5 − log 100

≐ 0.698 97 − 1 ≐ 0.698 97 − 2

≐ −0.301 03 ≐ −1.301 03

Check the results of *Examples 2* and *3* with your calculator.

The law of logarithms for products may be applied when the factors are equal. For example, if $x = y$, then the law:

log xy = log x + log y may be written

log $(x)(x)$ = log x + log x

or log (x^2) = 2 log x

This example suggests that a possible law of logarithms for powers might be log (x^n) = n log x. This equation states that the exponent that x^n would have if it were expressed as a power of 10 is n times the exponent that x would have if it were expressed as a power of 10.

Theorem **Law of Logarithms for Powers (Base 10)**

If x and n are real numbers, and $x > 0$, then log (x^n) = n log x

---

Given: Two real numbers x and n, where $x > 0$

Required to Prove: log (x^n) = n log x

Proof: Let log x = M

$x = 10^M$

Hence, $x^n = (10^M)^n$

= 10^{nM}

Therefore, log (x^n) = log (10^{nM})

= nM

= n log x

Corollary **Law of Logarithms for Roots (Base 10)**

If x and n are real numbers, and $x > 0$, then log $\sqrt[n]{x}$ = $\dfrac{1}{n}$ log x

---

Example 4. a) Write log 125 as a product of a whole number and a logarithm.
  b) Write 4 log 3 as a single logarithm.

Solution. a) Since $125 = 5^3$, then $\log 125 = \log (5^3)$
$$= 3 \log 5$$
  b) $4 \log 3 = \log (3^4)$, or log 81

Example 5. Given that $\log 2 \doteq 0.301\ 03$, find an approximation for each logarithm.
  a) log 8   b) $\log \sqrt[3]{2}$

Solution. a) $\log 8 = \log (2^3)$
$$= 3 \log 2$$
$$\doteq 3(0.301\ 03)$$
$$\doteq 0.903\ 09$$

  b) $\log \sqrt[3]{2} = \log (2^{\frac{1}{3}})$
$$= \frac{1}{3} \log 2$$
$$\doteq \frac{1}{3}(0.301\ 03)$$
$$\doteq 0.100\ 34$$

Check the results of *Examples 4* and *5* with your calculator.

Laws of Logarithms (Base 10)

- Multiplication $\quad \log xy = \log x + \log y \qquad x, y > 0$
- Division $\qquad\quad \log \left(\frac{x}{y}\right) = \log x - \log y \qquad x, y > 0$
- Powers $\qquad\quad \log (x^n) = n \log x \qquad\qquad x > 0$
- Roots $\qquad\qquad \log \sqrt[n]{x} = \frac{1}{n} \log x \qquad\qquad x > 0$

These laws are the laws of exponents (with base 10) restated in logarithmic form.

Example 6. Write in terms of log a and log b.

  a) $\log (100ab^2)$ b) $\log \left(\frac{a^2}{\sqrt{b}}\right)$

Solution. a) $\log (100ab^2) = \log 100 + \log a + \log (b^2)$
$$= 2 + \log a + 2 \log b$$

  b) $\log \left(\frac{a^2}{\sqrt{b}}\right) = \log (a^2) - \log (\sqrt{b})$
$$= 2 \log a - \frac{1}{2} \log b$$

Example 7. Write as a single logarithm.

  a) $\log a + \log b - \log c$ b) $\log a + 3 \log b - \frac{1}{2} \log c$

Solution. a) $\log a + \log b - \log c = \log ab - \log c$
$$= \log \left(\frac{ab}{c}\right)$$

  b) $\log a + 3 \log b - \frac{1}{2} \log c = \log a + \log (b^3) - \log \sqrt{c}$
$$= \log \left(\frac{ab^3}{\sqrt{c}}\right)$$

An important application of the laws of logarithms is to the problem of expressing any positive number as a power of any other positive number (except 1).

Example 8.   Express 19 as a power of 2 and check with a calculator.

Solution.   Let $19 = 2^x$

Take the logarithm of each side.

$$\log 19 = \log (2^x)$$
$$\log 19 = x \log 2$$

Hence, $x = \dfrac{\log 19}{\log 2}$

$$\doteq 4.247\ 927\ 5$$

Therefore, $19 \doteq 2^{4.2479275}$

To check, use the $\boxed{y^x}$ key on your calculator.

EXERCISES 5-6

(A)

1. Write as a single logarithm, and check with your calculator.
   a) $\log 6 + \log 7$ b) $\log 24 - \log 6$ c) $\log 3 + \log 8$
   d) $\log 35 - \log 5$ e) $\log 12 + \log 7$ f) $\log 1 - \log 2$
   g) $\log 5 + \log 8 - \log 4$ h) $\log 6 + \log 3 + \log 5$
   i) $\log 12 - \log 4 + \log 7$ j) $\log 7 + \log 8 - \log 2$

2. Write as a sum of logarithms, and check with your calculator.
   a) $\log 10$ b) $\log 21$ c) $\log 28$ d) $\log 36$
   e) $\log 9$ f) $\log 44$ g) $\log 57$ h) $\log 121$

3. Write as a difference of logarithms, and check with your calculator.
   a) $\log 5$ b) $\log 8$ c) $\log 12$ d) $\log 13$
   e) $\log 10$ f) $\log 21$ g) $\log 17$ h) $\log 40$

4. Write as a product of a whole number and a logarithm, and check with your calculator.
   a) $\log 9$ b) $\log 25$ c) $\log 8$ d) $\log 27$
   e) $\log 1000$ f) $\log 32$ g) $\log 343$ h) $\log 128$

5. Write as a single logarithm, and check with your calculator.
   a) $2 \log 6$ b) $3 \log 4$ c) $2 \log 9$ d) $2 \log 7$
   e) $5 \log 3$ f) $4 \log 2$ g) $3 \log 6$ h) $5 \log 10$

(B)

6. Given $\log 3 \doteq 0.477\ 12$, find an approximation for each logarithm.
   a) $\log 30$ b) $\log 3000$ c) $\log 0.3$ d) $\log 0.003$
   e) $\log 9$ f) $\log 81$ g) $\log \sqrt{3}$ h) $\log \sqrt[5]{3}$

7. Given that $\log 5 \doteq 0.698\ 97$, find an approximation for each logarithm.
   a) $\log 625$ b) $\log \sqrt[3]{5}$ c) $\log 0.2$ d) $\log 0.04$

8. If $\log 70 \doteq 1.8451$, find an approximation for each logarithm.
    a) $\log 7$
    b) $\log 700$
    c) $\log 0.07$
    d) $\log 0.7$
    e) $\log 700\ 000$
    f) $\log 0.007$

9. Write in terms of $\log a$ and $\log b$.
    a) $\log (1000ab)$
    b) $\log (a^2b)$
    c) $\log (a\sqrt{b})$
    d) $\log \left(\dfrac{a}{b^2}\right)$
    e) $\log \left(\dfrac{\sqrt{a}}{b}\right)$
    f) $\log \left(\dfrac{\sqrt[3]{a}}{b^2}\right)$

10. Write each expression in terms of $\log x$.
    a) $\log (10x^2)$ b) $\log \sqrt{x}$ c) $\log \sqrt{10x}$ d) $\log \sqrt{10}x$ e) $\log 10\sqrt{x}$

11. Write as a single logarithm.
    a) $\log x + \log y - \log z$
    b) $\log m - (\log n + \log p)$
    c) $\log a + \log b - \log c - \log d$
    d) $\log a + \log (a + b) - \log (a - b)$

12. Write as a single logarithm.
    a) $2 \log a + 5 \log b$
    b) $3 \log x + \dfrac{1}{2} \log y$
    c) $2 \log m + \log n - 5 \log p$
    d) $\dfrac{1}{2} \log x - 2 \log y - \log z$
    e) $3 \log a + \dfrac{1}{2} \log b - \dfrac{5}{4} \log c$
    f) $10 \log a - 3 \log b + \dfrac{1}{2} \log c - \log d$

13. Write as a single logarithm. For what values of the variable is each expression not defined?
    a) $\log (x + 3) - \log (x - 1)$
    b) $\log (2x - 7) - \log (x + 3)$
    c) $-\log (a - 2) + \log (a + 2)$
    d) $\log (8a + 15) - \log (2a + 3)$

14. If $\log 2 = x$ and $\log 3 = y$, write each logarithm as an expression in x and y.
    a) $\log 6$
    b) $\log 1.5$
    c) $\log 60$
    d) $\log 12$
    e) $\log 18$
    f) $\log 36$
    g) $\log 3.6$
    h) $\log \left(\dfrac{1}{6}\right)$

15. Express.
    a) 7 as a power of 3
    b) 5 as a power of 2
    c) 29 as a power of 2
    d) 77 as a power of 8
    e) 3 as a power of 0.5
    f) 0.45 as a power of 6

16. Solve to the nearest thousandth.
    a) $2^x = 11$
    b) $3^x = 17$
    c) $6^x = 5$
    d) $5^{x-1} = 9$
    e) $2^{x+3} = 6$
    f) $5^{1+x} = 2^{1-x}$

17. Solve.
    a) $3^x = 2$
    b) $4^x = 5$
    c) $7^{-x} = 3$
    d) $3^{1-x} = 5$
    e) $\left(\dfrac{1}{8}\right)^x = 25$
    f) $5^{3x} = 41$

18. x and y are two positive numbers. How are $\log x$ and $\log y$ related if:

 a) $y = 10x$
 b) $y = \dfrac{1}{x}$
 c) $y = x^2$

 d) $y = \sqrt{x}$
 e) $y = 10\sqrt{x}$
 f) $y = \sqrt{10x}$?

Ⓒ

19. Prove each identity, and state the value(s) of x for which the identity is true.
 a) $\log (x - 1) + \log (x - 2) = \log (x^2 - 3x + 2)$
 b) $\log x + \log (x + 3) = \log (x^2 + 3x)$
 c) $\log (x - 5) + \log (x + 5) = \log (x^2 - 25)$

20. Solve and check.
 a) $\log (x + 2) + \log (x - 1) = 1$
 b) $\log (3x + 2) + \log (x - 1) = 2$
 c) $2 \log (x - 1) = 2 + \log 100$

21. Express y as a function of x. What is the domain?
 a) $\log 3 + \log y = \log (x + 2) - \log x$
 b) $\log y - 2 + \log x - \log (x + 1) = 0$
 c) $\log 4y = x + \log 4$

22. The table shows some large prime numbers that were discovered using computers. How many digits does each prime number have?

	Prime Number	Year	Computer
a)	$2^{11213} - 1$	1963	ILLIAC-II
b)	$2^{21701} - 1$	1978	CDC-CYBER-174
c)	$2^{132049} - 1$	1983	CRAY-1
d)	$2^{216091} - 1$	1985	CRAY-1

23. In 1938, the physicist Sir Arthur Eddington calculated that the number of particles in the universe is 33×2^{259}. He called this number the *cosmical number*.
 a) Write the cosmical number in scientific notation.
 b) How many digits are there in this number?

24. If n is a natural number, find the least value of n such that:
 a) $1.1^n > 10^9$
 b) $1.01^n > 10^9$
 c) $1.001^n > 10^9$
 d) 1.001^n exceeds the capacity of your calculator's display.

25. Let N be any positive number, no matter how large. Prove that no matter how small the positive number x is, it is always possible to find a value of n such that $(1 + x)^n > N$.

MATHEMATICS AROUND US

Orders of Magnitude

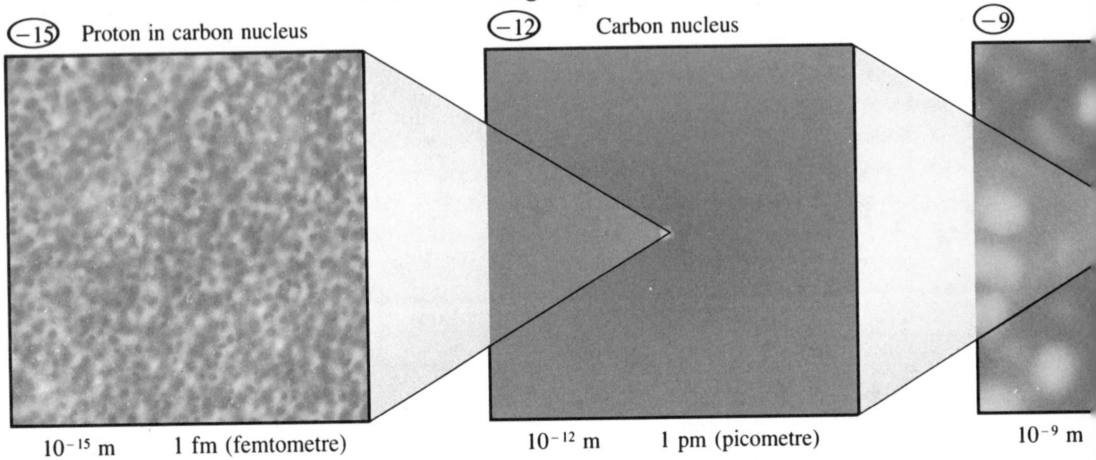

(-15) Proton in carbon nucleus   (-12)   Carbon nucleus   (-9)

10^{-15} m   1 fm (femtometre) 10^{-12} m   1 pm (picometre) 10^{-9} m

Scientists have always wanted to extend our range of observation of the world around us, from the microscopic scale to the astronomic scale. What might we see if we could take an imaginary journey along a straight line beginning at the nucleus of an atom and ending at the farthermost reaches of outer space?

The first illustration shows part of the nucleus of a carbon atom. As we get farther and farther away, greater and greater distances are brought into view. The steps we take in this journey are not regular steps, but rather, each step is 1000 times as great as the previous one.

Hence, the dimensions of each illustration represent a distance 1000 times as long as the one before it. And, each illustration shows a 1000× enlargement of a small portion at the center of the next one. Although it can be seen in only the first illustration, the nucleus of the carbon atom where we started the journey is at the center of all of them.

The journey covers four pages in this book. Study the illustrations on all four pages before you begin the questions.

QUESTIONS

1. Notice the circled number in the upper left corner of each illustration.
   a) How is this number related to the distance represented by the illustration?
   b) As you move from one illustration to the next, compare the change in the circled number with the change in the distance represented by the illustration.

2. A factor of 10 is called one *order of magnitude*. Hence, a factor of 100, or 10×10, represents two orders of magnitude. How many orders of magnitude are represented by the change from:
   a) any illustration to the next
   b) the first illustration to the last?

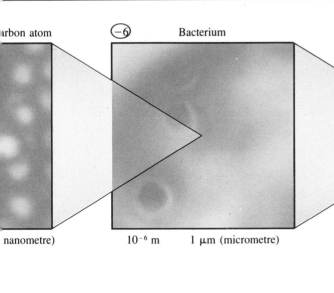

arbon atom

-6   Bacterium

nanometre) 10^{-6} m   1 μm (micrometre)

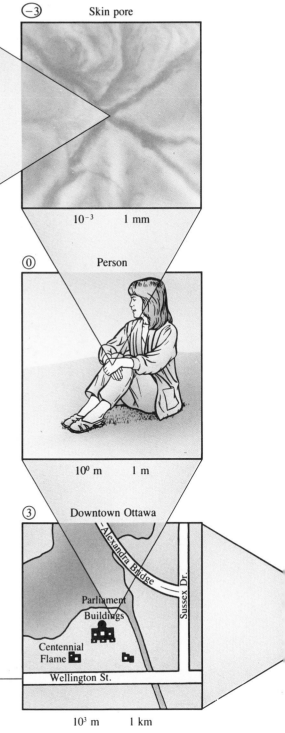

-3   Skin pore

10^{-3} 1 mm

⓪   Person

10^0 m   1 m

③   Downtown Ottawa

Alexandra Bridge

Sussex Dr.

Parliament Buildings

Centennial Flame

Wellington St.

10^3 m   1 km

3. Two common units of length are the Ångstrom unit (used for measuring atoms) and the fermi (used for measuring nuclear particles).

1 Ångstrom unit	10^{-10} m
1 fermi	10^{-15} m

a) How many orders of magnitude is the Ångstrom unit greater than the fermi?

b) Name two other units of length that differ by the same order of magnitude.

4. The double-helix strands of a DNA molecule are approximately 2×10^{-9} m apart. If the twisted molecule were stretched out, its length would be 7 orders of magnitude greater. How long is the molecule?

5. What common interval of time is approximately 4 orders of magnitude longer than one minute?

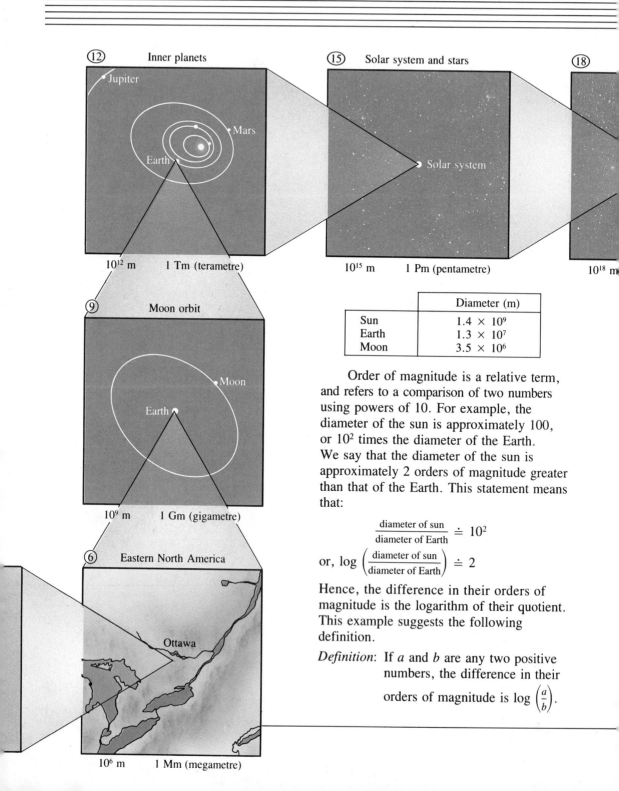

⑫ Inner planets

Jupiter
Mars
Earth

10^{12} m   1 Tm (terametre)

⑮ Solar system and stars

Solar system

10^{15} m   1 Pm (pentametre)

⑱

10^{18} m

⑨ Moon orbit

Moon
Earth

10^9 m   1 Gm (gigametre)

⑥ Eastern North America

Ottawa

10^6 m   1 Mm (megametre)

	Diameter (m)
Sun	1.4×10^9
Earth	1.3×10^7
Moon	3.5×10^6

Order of magnitude is a relative term, and refers to a comparison of two numbers using powers of 10. For example, the diameter of the sun is approximately 100, or 10^2 times the diameter of the Earth. We say that the diameter of the sun is approximately 2 orders of magnitude greater than that of the Earth. This statement means that:

$$\frac{\text{diameter of sun}}{\text{diameter of Earth}} \doteq 10^2$$

or, $\log \left(\dfrac{\text{diameter of sun}}{\text{diameter of Earth}} \right) \doteq 2$

Hence, the difference in their orders of magnitude is the logarithm of their quotient. This example suggests the following definition.

Definition: If *a* and *b* are any two positive numbers, the difference in their orders of magnitude is $\log \left(\dfrac{a}{b} \right)$.

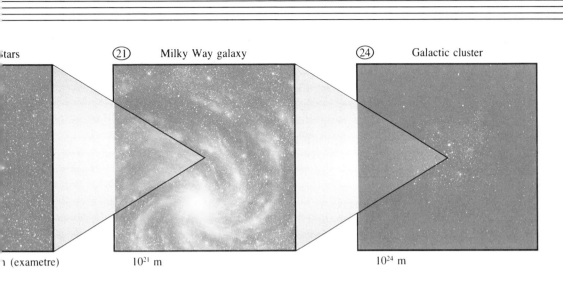

tars   ㉑   Milky Way galaxy   ㉔   Galactic cluster

1 (exametre) 10^{21} m 10^{24} m

6. Show that the diameter of the sun is approximately 2.6 orders of magnitude greater than that of the moon.

7. Two common units of length are the astronomical unit (used for measuring planetary distances) and the light year (used for measuring stellar and galactic distances).

1 astronomical unit	1.5×10^{11} m
1 light year	9.5×10^{15} m

How many orders of magnitude is the light year greater than the astronomical unit?

8. The planets Neptune and Pluto are approximately 5×10^{12} m from the Earth. How many orders of magnitude greater than this are these distances?
   a) The nearest star, Proxima Centauri, 4×10^{18} m from Earth
   b) The centre of the Milky Way Galaxy, 6.7×10^{20} m from Earth
   c) A chain of galaxies 7×10^{24} m from Earth

9. In 1989, the space probe *Voyager II* photographed the planet Neptune, about 5×10^{12} m from the Earth. The *Space Telescope* was designed to examine objects 13.4 orders of magnitude farther. How far away is that?

10. The limit of the known universe is about 2.3 orders of magnitude greater than the distance represented by the last illustration above. How many metres is this?

11. Now that we have finished our journey from the nucleus of the carbon atom to outer space, suppose we reverse our direction and take the return trip back to the nucleus of the carbon atom where we started. What percent of the remaining distance would we cover from one illustration to the next?

5-7 INTRODUCTION TO LOGARITHMIC FUNCTIONS

Many examples of exponential functions were given in the previous sections of this chapter. Associated with each of these functions there is a corresponding function whose equation we can obtain by solving for the variable in the exponent.

Growth of Populations

In 1987 the world population reached 5 billion. At the time, the population was increasing at the rate of approximately 1.6% per year. If the rate of growth remains constant, then the population P billion is expressed as an exponential function of the number of years n relative to 1987 by this equation.

$$P = 5(1.016)^n \ldots \text{①}$$

Suppose we ask in how many years will the population reach P billion? We express the number of years n as a function of P by solving equation ① for n. Hence, we take the logarithm of each side.

$$\log P = \log 5 + n \log 1.016$$

Solve for n.

$$n \log 1.016 = \log P - \log 5$$

$$n = \frac{\log \left(\frac{P}{5} \right)}{\log 1.016}$$

The coefficient of the expression on the right side is $\frac{1}{\log 1.016}$, or about 145.

Hence, the equation for n becomes

$$n \doteq 145 \log \left(\frac{P}{5} \right) \ldots \text{②}$$

Equation ② expresses the number of years n as a logarithmic function of the population P. The graph shows the values of n for $3 \leq P \leq 10$. Compare this graph with the one on page 214.

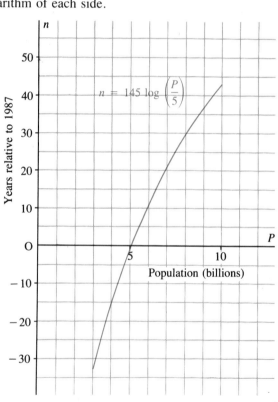

In this example, notice that n is not defined if P is 0, or if P is negative. This is reasonable, since the population P must be a positive number. Hence, the domain of the function is the set of positive integers.

Light Penetration Under Water

For every metre a diver descends below the surface, the light intensity is reduced by 2.5%. The percent P of surface light present is expressed as an exponential function of the depth d metres by this equation.

$$P = 100(0.975)^d \ldots \text{①}$$

Suppose we ask at what depth is the light intensity $P\%$? We express d as a function of P by solving equation ① for d. Take the logarithm of each side.

$$\log P = \log 100 + d \log 0.975$$

Solve for d.

$$d = \frac{\log\left(\frac{P}{100}\right)}{\log 0.975}$$

$$d \doteq -90.9 \log\left(\frac{P}{100}\right) \ldots \text{②}$$

Equation ② expresses the depth d metres as a logarithmic function of the light intensity P. The graph shows the values of d for $0 < P \leqslant 100$. Compare this graph with the one on page 215.

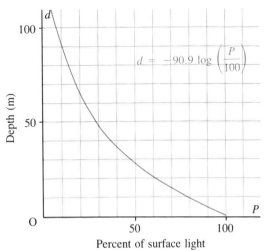

In the final equations of the above examples, the expression on the right side involves the logarithm of the variable. Functions whose defining equation have this property are called logarithmic functions.

> A *logarithmic function* has an equation which can be written in the form $f(x) = k \log x$, where k is a constant, and $x > 0$.

Example.   Given the exponential function $f(x) = 10^x$
    a) Determine the inverse function $f^{-1}(x)$.
    b) Graph $f(x)$ and $f^{-1}(x)$ on the same grid.

Solution.   a) Recall that to obtain the inverse of a function from its equation, we interchange x and y in the equation and solve for y. Hence, to find the inverse of $f(x) = 10^x$:
    Step 1. Let $y = 10^x$, then interchange x and y. $x = 10^y$
    Step 2. Solve for y. $y = \log x$
    Hence, the inverse of the exponential function $f(x) = 10^x$ is the logarithmic function $f^{-1}(x) = \log x$.

b) We graph $f(x) = 10^x$ using a table of values. Recall that we can graph the inverse by reflecting the graph of $y = 10^x$ in the line $y = x$. This is equivalent to interchanging the ordered pairs in the table of values for $y = f(x)$.

$f(x) = 10^x$

x	y
-2	0.01
-1.5	0.03
-1	0.10
-0.5	0.32
-0.2	0.63
0	1.00
0.1	1.26
0.2	1.58
0.3	2.00

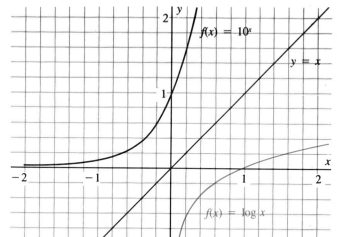

Recall that in *Section 5-5* we observed that taking a common logarithm of a number and raising the number to a power of 10 are inverse operations. This is consistent with the above *Example*, which shows that the logarithmic function $y = \log x$ can be defined as the inverse of the exponential function $y = 10^x$.

EXERCISES 5-7

Ⓐ

1. Solve each equation for x, thus expressing x as a logarithmic function of y.
   a) $y = 5(2)^x$
   b) $y = 1.3(10)^x$
   c) $y = 8.2(1.03)^x$
   d) $y = 6.4\left(\frac{1}{2}\right)^x$
   e) $y = 3.5(2.7)^x$
   f) $y = 2.75\left(\frac{2}{3}\right)^x$

Ⓑ

2. An investment of $500 at 8% per annum compounded annually grows to A dollars in n years. In *Section 5-3*, page 214, we showed that an equation expressing the amount A dollars as an exponential function of the time n years is $A = 500(1.08)^n$.
   a) Solve this equation for n, thus expressing n as a logarithmic function of A.
   b) Calculate the value of n for each value of A and interpret the result.
      i) $A = 1250$ ii) $A = 350$

c) Graph the function in part a) for $0 < A \leqslant 1250$. Compare your graph with the one on page 214.

d) State the domain and range of the function.

3. A ball is dropped from a height of 2.00 m. On each bounce the ball rises to 70% of the height from which it fell. In *Section 5-3*, page 215, we showed that an equation expressing the bounce height h metres as an exponential function of the number of bounces n is $h = 2.00(0.7)^n$.

a) Solve this equation for n, thus expressing n as a logarithmic function of h.

b) Calculate the value of n for each value of h and interpret the result.

    i) 0.7 m   ii) 0.12 m

c) Graph the function in part a) for $0 < h \leqslant 2.00$. Compare your graph with the one on page 215.

d) What is the range of the function?

4. a) The population of the town of Elmira was 6800 in 1987. If the population is growing at the rate of 1.8% per annum, write an equation expressing the population P as a function of n, the number of years relative to 1987.

b) Solve this equation for n.

c) Find the value of n if P is: i) 9200   ii) 5500.

d) Graph the functions in parts a) and b). How are these functions related?

5. On bright sunny days, the amount of bromine in a municipal swimming pool decreases by 10% each hour. If there was 145 g of bromine in the pool at noon on a sunny day, when would the pool contain: a) 102 g   b) 85 g   c) 200 g?

6. Given the exponential function $f(x) = 3^x$, graph $y = f(x)$ and $y = f^{-1}(x)$ on the same grid.

7. Graph each function and its inverse on the same grid.

  a) $f(x) = 2^x$ b) $g(x) = \left(\dfrac{2}{3}\right)^x$

INVESTIGATE

At the beginning of this section, the equation $n \doteq 145 \log\left(\dfrac{P}{5}\right)$ was derived to represent the number of years for the world population to grow to P billion, assuming a constant growth rate of 1.6% per year. Notice that the coefficient 145 is the reciprocal of the logarithm of the base of the corresponding exponential function; that is, $\dfrac{1}{\log 1.016} \doteq 145$. This suggests that the form of the equation of the logarithmic function will be simpler if the base of the corresponding exponential function is 10, for then that coefficient will be 1, since $\log 10 = 1$.

    Investigate whether this is true by first changing the base of the corresponding exponential function, $P = 5(1.016)^n$, to base 10, and then solving for n to obtain the corresponding logarithmic function.

5-8 DEFINING AND GRAPHING LOGARITHMIC FUNCTIONS

In the *Example* of the preceding section we saw that the logarithmic function $y = \log x$ can be defined as the inverse of the exponential function $y = 10^x$. This suggests that other logarithmic functions can be defined as inverses of exponential functions with bases other than 10. In fact, for each choice of base for the exponential function $g(x) = a^x$, $a > 0$, there is an associated logarithmic function. Hence, we define the function $f(x) = \log_a x$, $a > 0$, as follows.

> The logarithmic function $f(x) = \log_a x$ ($a > 0$, $a \neq 1$) is the inverse of the exponential function $g(x) = a^x$.

We say, "$f(x)$ equals log to the base a of x".

Recall that we can graph the inverse of any function by reflecting its graph in the line $y = x$. This is equivalent to interchanging the ordered pairs in the table of values of the function. For example, the graph below shows the function $g(x) = 2^x$ and its inverse $g^{-1}(x) = \log_2 x$. Compare this graph with the one on page 244.

$g(x) = 2^x$

x	y
-3	0.13
-2	0.25
-1	0.50
-0.5	0.71
0	1.00
0.5	1.41
1	2.00
1.5	2.83
2	4.00

$g^{-1}(x) = \log_2 x$

x	y
0.13	-3
0.25	-2
0.50	-1
0.71	-0.5
1.00	0
1.41	0.5
2.00	1
2.83	1.5
4.00	2

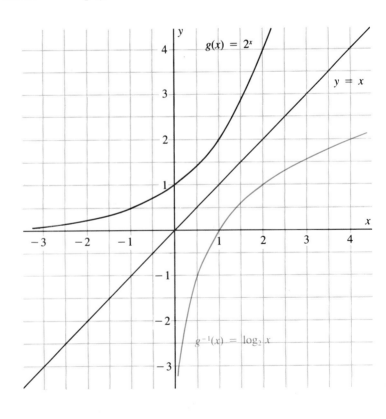

The graph illustrates the following properties of the function $g^{-1}(x) = \log_2 x$. These properties are consequences of the corresponding properties of $y = 2^x$.

Vertical intercept

There is no vertical intercept since the function $g(x) = 2^x$ has no horizontal intercept.

Horizontal intercept

The horizontal intercept is 1, since the vertical intercept of $g(x) = 2^x$ is 1. Hence, $\log_2 1 = 0$

Domain

The domain of $g^{-1}(x) = \log_2 x$ is the set of positive real numbers, since this is the range of $g(x) = 2^x$.

Range

The range of $g^{-1}(x) = \log_2 x$ is the set of all real numbers, since this is the domain of $g(x) = 2^x$.

If any exponential function is given, we can sketch its graph. The graph of the inverse function is then the graph of the corresponding logarithmic function.

Example 1.   a) Sketch the graph of the exponential function $f(x) = \left(\frac{1}{3}\right)^x$.

b) Sketch the graph of the inverse of the function in part a) on the same grid.

c) Write the equation of the inverse function.

Solution.   a) $f(x) = \left(\frac{1}{3}\right)^x$

When x is very large and positive, $f(x)$ is very small and positive.
$f(0) = 1$
When x is negative and has a large absolute value, $f(x)$ is very large.

b) Reflect $y = \left(\frac{1}{3}\right)^x$ in the line $y = x$. The image is $y = \log_{\frac{1}{3}} x$.

c) The equation of the inverse function is $f^{-1}(x) = \log_{\frac{1}{3}} x$.

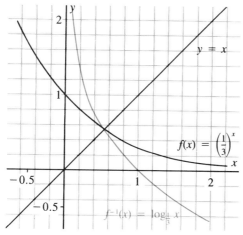

The graphs in the above examples illustrate properties of the logarithmic function $f(x) = \log_a x$.

Properties of the graph of the function $f(x) = \log_a x$

Vertical intercept: none
Horizontal intercept: 1
Domain: all positive real numbers
Range: all real numbers
Asymptote: y-axis ($x = 0$)
Increasing: $\forall x \in \mathbb{R}_+^*; a > 1$
Decreasing: $\forall x \in \mathbb{R}_+^*; 0 < a < 1$

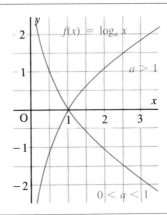

Example 2. Graph $g(x) = \log_2 (2x - 1)$. State the properties of this function.

Solution.   For $g(x) = \log_2 (2x - 1)$ to be defined,
$$2x - 1 > 0$$
$$x > 0.5$$
Make a table of values.

x	$\dfrac{5}{8}$	$\dfrac{3}{4}$	1	1.5	2.5	4.5
y	-2	-1	0	1	2	3

The properties of $g(x) = \log_2 (2x - 1)$ are:
—There is no vertical intercept.
—Horizontal intercept is 1.
—Domain is $]0.5, +\infty$.
—Range is $\mathbb{R}$.
—Asymptote is $x = 0.5$.
—The function is increasing on $]0.5, +\infty$.

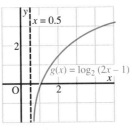

Example 3. The graph of a logarithmic function $f(x) = \log_a x$ passes through the point P(4,−2). Find the base of this function.

Solution. $f(x) = \log_a x$
Since $(4,−2)$ lies on the graph, its coordinates satisfy the equation.
$$-2 = \log_a 4$$
Solve for a.
$$a^{-2} = 4$$
$$a = 4^{-\frac{1}{2}}$$
$$= \frac{1}{\sqrt{4}}$$
$$= \frac{1}{2}$$
The base of the function is 0.5.

EXERCISES 5-8

(A)

1. Write the inverse of each exponential function. State the properties of the function and its inverse.

   a) $f(x) = 10^x$ b) $g(x) = (0.4)^x$ c) $h(x) = \left(\frac{3}{2}\right)^x$ d) $k(x) = \left(\frac{1}{5}\right)^x$

2. Repeat *Exercise 1* for these logarithmic functions.

   a) $f(x) = \log x$ b) $g(x) = \log_{\frac{1}{2}} x$ c) $h(x) = \log_{\frac{5}{4}} x$ d) $k(x) = \log_{\frac{2}{3}} x$

(B)

3. Copy each graph and sketch the graph of the inverse of the given function on the same grid. Then write the equation of the inverse function.

a)

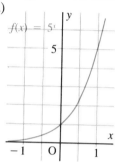

b)

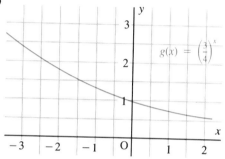

4. a) Sketch the graph of the exponential function $f(x) = 3^x$.
   b) Sketch the graph of the inverse of the function in part a) on the same grid.
   c) Write the equation of the inverse function.

5. Repeat *Exercise 4*, starting with the function $g(x) = \left(\frac{1}{2}\right)^x$.

6. Graph each function and state its properties.

   a) $f(x) = \log_4 x$ b) $g(x) = \log_2 (x + 1)$ c) $h(x) = \log_{\frac{1}{2}} x - 1$

7. The graph of a logarithmic function $f(x) = \log_a x$ passes through each point. Find the value of the base.

   a) $A(4, 2)$ b) $B(9, -2)$ c) $C\left(27, -\frac{3}{2}\right)$ d) $D\left(6, \frac{1}{2}\right)$ e) $E\left(\sqrt{5}, -\frac{1}{2}\right)$ f) $F(0.01, -2)$

(C)

8. In *Example 1*, the graphs of $f(x) = \left(\frac{1}{3}\right)^x, f^{-1}(x) = \log_{\frac{1}{3}} x$, and $y = x$ are shown.

   Determine the coordinates of their point of intersection to 3 decimal places.

9. Given the function $f(x) = a^x$ and its inverse $f^{-1}(x) = \log_a x$, where $a > 0$
   a) For what values of a do the graphs of $y = f(x)$ and $y = f^{-1}(x)$ intersect?
   b) Find out as much as you can about the point of intersection of the graphs in part a).

10. Prove that if $f(x) = \log_a x$, then $f(xy) = f(x) + f(y)$.

5-9 TRANSLATING EXPONENTIAL AND LOGARITHMIC FUNCTIONS

A translation t(h,k) is applied to the graph of a logarithmic function $f(x) = \log_a x$. The graph of the image
can be obtained by applying the translation
$T(x,y) = (x + h, y + k)$ to every point (x,y) on the
graph of f. The function g corresponding to the translation image of f is defined by the equation
$g(x) = \log_a (x - h) + k$.

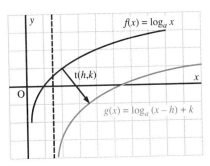

Example 1. Graph the function $g(x) = \log_2 (x + 2) + 1$. State the properties of this
function.

Solution. The graph of $g(x) = \log_2 (x + 2) + 1$ can
be obtained by applying a translation
t(-2, 1) to the graph of $f(x) = \log_2 x$.
For $\log_2 (x + 2) + 1$ to be defined,

$$x + 2 > 0$$
$$x > -2$$

For the horizontal intercept, solve

$$\log_2 (x + 2) + 1 = 0$$
$$\log_2 (x + 2) = -1$$
$$x + 2 = 0.5$$
$$x = -1.5$$

The properties of $g(x) = \log_2 (x + 2) + 1$
are:
—Vertical intercept is 2.
—Horizontal intercept is -1.5.
—Domain is $]-2,+\infty$.
—Range is $\mathbb{R}$.
—Asymptote is $x = -2$.
—The function is increasing on $]-2,+\infty$.

Example 2. For the function $g(x) = \log_2 (x + 2) + 1$, find the equation of g^{-1}. Sketch
the graphs of g and g^{-1}. State the properties of g^{-1}.

Solution. $g(x) = \log_2 (x + 2) + 1$
Replace $g(x)$ with y.
$y = \log_2 (x + 2) + 1$
Interchange x and y.
$x = \log_2 (y + 2) + 1$
Solve for y.

$$x - 1 = \log_2 (y + 2)$$
$$y + 2 = 2^{x-1}$$
$$y = 2^{x-1} - 2$$
$$g^{-1}(x) = 2^{x-1} - 2$$

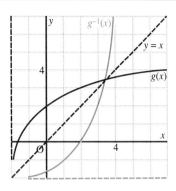

The properties of $g^{-1}(x) = 2^{x-1} - 2$ are:
—Vertical intercept is -1.5.
—Horizontal intercept is 2.
—Domain is $\mathbb{R}$.
—Range is $]-2,+\infty$.
—Asymptote is $y = -2$.
—The function is increasing over $\mathbb{R}$.

Compare the properties of the functions in *Examples 1* and *2*. Since $g^{-1}(x) = 2^{x-1} - 2$ is the inverse of $g(x) = \log_2 (x + 2) + 1$, the vertical intercept of g^{-1} is the same as the horizontal intercept of g, and vice versa; and the domain of g^{-1} is the same as the range of g, and vice versa.

EXERCISES 5-9

(A)

1. Draw the translation image of each graph under the given translation t.

a)

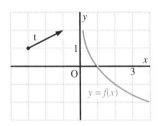

b)

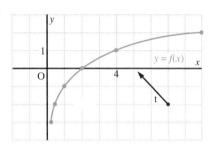

2. A logarithmic function f is given. Function g is the image of f under the given translation. Find the equation of g.
   a) $f(x) = \log_4 x$; t(2,-1)   b) $f(x) = \log_{0.2} x$; t(0,-2)   c) $f(x) = \log_2 x$; t(-3,0)

(B)

3. Graph each function and state its properties.
   a) $f(x) = \log_2 (x - 2) + 3$ b) $g(x) = \log_{\frac{1}{2}} (x + 1) - 2$ c) $h(x) = \log_3 x - 4$
   d) $k(x) = \log_{\frac{1}{3}} (x + 3) - 1$ e) $m(x) = 2^{x-1} + 1$ f) $n(x) = \left(\frac{1}{2}\right)^{x+2} - 3$

4. For each function, find the equation of its inverse and state its domain and range.
   a) $f(x) = \log_3 (x - 1) + 2$ b) $g(x) = \log_{\frac{1}{2}} (2 - x) + 4$ c) $h(x) = 4^{x-1} + 5$

(C)

5. Graph each function and state its properties.
   a) $f(x) = \log_2 (2 - x) + 1$ b) $g(x) = 3 \log_{\frac{1}{2}} x - 2$ c) $h(x) = \log_{0.1} (2x - 3)$

5-10 LOGARITHMS AS EXPONENTS

Recall that to find the inverse of a function from its equation, we interchange x and y in the equation and solve for y. Hence, to find the inverse of $y = a^x$:

Step 1. Interchange x and y. $x = a^y \ldots$ ①

Step 2. Solve for y. We can do this using common logarithms, but it is preferable to use the definition on page 246. According to the definition, the inverse is
$$y = \log_a x \ldots ②$$

Hence, this is the equation that results when equation ① is solved for y.

Comparing equations ① and ②, we see that

$$\underset{\text{base} \quad \text{exponent}}{\log_a x = y} \qquad \text{means that} \qquad x = a^y, x > 0.$$

Hence, $\log_a x$ is an exponent. It is the exponent that x would have if it were written in power form with base a ($a > 0$, $a \neq 1$). If the base is omitted, it is understood to be base 10.

Example 1. Evaluate each logarithm.

      a) $\log_5 25$ b) $\log_7 \sqrt{7}$ c) $\log_{\frac{1}{3}} 9$ d) $\log_a a$

Solution.   a) Since $25 = 5^2$, then $\log_5 25 = 2$

      b) Since $\sqrt{7} = 7^{\frac{1}{2}}$, then $\log_7 \sqrt{7} = \frac{1}{2}$

      c) Write 9 as a power of $\frac{1}{3}$. Since $\left(\frac{1}{3}\right)^2 = \frac{1}{9}$, then $\left(\frac{1}{3}\right)^{-2} = 9$

          Hence, $\log_{\frac{1}{3}} 9 = -2$

      d) Since $a = a^1$, then $\log_a a = 1$

Since any positive number can be expressed as a power of any other positive number (except 1), we can find approximations to the logarithm of any positive number to any positive base (except 1).

Example 2. Find $\log_5 9$ to the nearest thousandth.

Solution.   To find $\log_5 9$ means to find the exponent that 9 would have if it were expressed as a power of 5.

      Let $9 = 5^x$

      Take the logarithm of each side to base 10.

      $\log 9 = \log (5^x)$

      $\log 9 = x \log 5$

      $x = \dfrac{\log 9}{\log 5}$

      $\doteq 1.365\ 212\ 4$

      To the nearest thousandth, $9 \doteq 5^{1.365}$

      Therefore, $\log_5 9 \doteq 1.365$

Example 3. Simplify each expression.
  a) $\log_a a^x$
  b) $a^{\log_a x}$

Solution. a) $\log_a a^x$ is the exponent that a^x would have if it were written as a power of a. This exponent is x. Hence, $\log_a a^x = x$
  b) $a^{\log_a x}$ is a raised to the exponent that x would have if x were written as a power of a. Hence, $a^{\log_a x} = x$

Summary

- $\log_a x = y$ means that $x = a^y$, where $a > 0$, $a \neq 1$, and $x > 0$
- $\log_a a^x = x$ and $a^{\log_a x} = x$
- $\log_a a = 1$

Example 4. Write each expression in exponential form.
  a) $\log_2 16 = 4$
  b) $\log_2 0.5 = -1$

Solution. a) $\log_2 16 = 4$
        $16 = 2^4$
  b) $\log_2 0.5 = -1$
        $0.5 = 2^{-1}$

Example 5. Write each expression in logarithmic form.
  a) $3^5 = 243$
  b) $a^b = c$

Solution. a) $3^5 = 243$
        $5 = \log_3 243$
  b) $a^b = c$
        $b = \log_a c$

EXERCISES 5-10

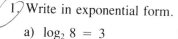

1. Write in exponential form.
  a) $\log_2 8 = 3$
  b) $\log_2 32 = 5$
  c) $\log_2 \left(\dfrac{1}{4}\right) = -2$

  d) $\log_5 625 = 4$
  e) $\log_3 9 = 2$
  f) $\log_9 3 = \dfrac{1}{2}$

2. Evaluate each logarithm.
  a) $\log_2 16$
  b) $\log_2 4$
  c) $\log_3 27$
  d) $\log_5 25$
  e) $\log_5 \left(\dfrac{1}{5}\right)$
  f) $\log_7 7$
  g) $\log_3 1$
  h) $\log_3 3^4$

3. In geography, sediments are classified by particle size, as shown.
  a) Write the logarithm to base 2 of each number.
  b) Write the logarithm to base 4 of each number.

Type of sediment	Size (mm)
Boulder	256
Cobble	64
Pebble	4
Granule	2
Sand	$\dfrac{1}{16}$
Silt	$\dfrac{1}{256}$

Ⓑ

4. Evaluate each logarithm.

a) $\log_5 \sqrt{5}$

b) $\log_{\frac{1}{2}}\left(\frac{1}{16}\right)$

c) $\log_{\frac{3}{2}}\left(\frac{9}{4}\right)$

d) $\log_{\sqrt{3}} 9$

e) $\log_{\frac{1}{2}} 8$

f) $\log_{\frac{2}{5}}\left(\frac{25}{4}\right)$

g) $\log_3 (\sqrt{3})^3$

h) $\log_{\sqrt{5}} 125$

5. Evaluate each logarithm to the nearest thousandth.

a) $\log_3 5$ b) $\log_7 4$ c) $\log_2 50$ d) $\log_5 12$ e) $\log_4 27$ f) $\log_{16} 8$

6. Write in logarithmic form.

a) $6^2 = 36$

b) $4^{-2} = \frac{1}{16}$

c) $3^5 = 243$

d) $7^3 = 343$

e) $8^{\frac{1}{3}} = 2$

f) $2^0 = 1$

g) $5^{-2} = 0.04$

h) $4^{-\frac{1}{2}} = \frac{1}{2}$

i) $\left(\frac{1}{2}\right)^2 = \frac{1}{4}$

j) $\left(\frac{2}{3}\right)^{-1} = \frac{3}{2}$

k) $\left(\frac{1}{9}\right)^2 = \frac{1}{81}$

l) $x^y = z$

7. Write in exponential form.

a) $\log_{20} 400 = 2$

b) $\log_7\left(\frac{1}{49}\right) = -2$

c) $\log_8 4 = \frac{2}{3}$

d) $\log_6 36^2 = 4$

e) $\log_{0.5} 8 = -3$

f) $\log_r s = t$

8. Solve for x.

a) $x = \log_5 25$

b) $\log_4 1 = x$

c) $\log_x 16 = 2$

d) $\log_x 3 = \frac{1}{2}$

e) $\log_2 x = 3$

f) $\log_3 x = 4$

9. Solve for x.

a) $\log_2 x = 9$

b) $\log_2 x = -2$

c) $\log_3\left(\frac{1}{3}\right) = x$

d) $\log_{\sqrt{2}} 32 = x$

e) $\log_x 16 = -2$

f) $\log_x 125 = -3$

10. If $\log_8 3 = x$ and $\log_4 7 = y$, find an expression in terms of x and y for:
a) $\log_2 21$ b) $\log_2 63$.

11. Given that $f(x) = x - \log_2 x$ and $g(x) = 2^x$, find: a) $f(g(x))$ b) $g(f(x))$.

12. If a telephone network is designed to carry N telephone calls simultaneously, then the number of switches needed per call must be at least $\log_2 N$. If the network can carry 10 000 calls simultaneously, how many switches would be needed:
a) for one call   b) for 10 000 simultaneous calls?

Ⓒ

13. a) Evaluate each logarithm. i) $\log_2 8$ and $\log_8 2$ ii) $\log_5 25$ and $\log_{25} 5$
b) On the basis of the results of part a), make a conjecture about how $\log_a b$ and $\log_b a$ are related, where $a, b > 0$. Prove your conjecture.

14. Let a and b be any two positive numbers. Prove that for all positive values of x, $\log_b x$ is directly proportional to $\log_a x$.

MATHEMATICS AROUND US

The Logarithmic Spiral

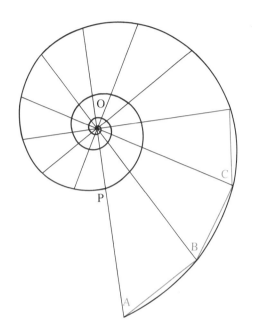

Some living creatures exhibit exponential growth in their dimensions. A well-known example is the chambered nautilus of the Indian and Pacific Oceans. As it grows, the shell extends continuously, generating a natural spiral.

QUESTIONS

1. The diagram shows a series of equally-spaced radii drawn from the centre of the spiral. The radii are spaced every 30°.
   a) Measure and record the length of each radius, starting with OP and proceeding clockwise around the spiral.
   b) Verify that the length of the radius L centimetres satisfies the equation $L = 1.5(1.0034)^\theta$, where θ degrees is the angle of rotation measured clockwise starting at OP.

2. a) Measure the angles represented by A, B, C, . . ., on the diagram.
   b) Prove that if the length of the radius is an exponential function of the angle of rotation, then the angles A, B, C, . . ., are all equal.

3. a) Suggest why the spiral is called a *logarithmic spiral*.
   b) The spiral is also referred to as an *equiangular spiral*. Suggest why.

USING TECHNOLOGY

Exponential and Logarithmic Functions

Discovering the Compound Interest Rule

If $100 is invested at a rate R percent with interest compounded at the end of each year, then the total amount A after n years can be calculated with the formula $A = 100(1 + R)^n$, where R is expressed as a decimal.

a) Suppose $100 is invested at 3% with the interest compounded annually. Enter $Y_1 = 100(1.03)^X$ on the functions menu. Display the graph in a viewing window of $[-1, 30]$ by $[-50, 250]$.

   Use the TRACE feature to determine the value of the investment after 10 years. Verify your answer numerically.

b) To the nearest year, how long would it take the investment in part a) to double in value? Use the TRACE feature to obtain the answer.

c) Suppose $100 is invested at 4% compounded annually. Display the graph of an equation that represents this. Find the number of years it would take for the investment to double.

d) Suppose $100 is invested at 6% compounded annually. Use your graphing calculator to find the number of years needed to double the investment.

e) From the results of parts b), c), and d), determine a pattern between the rate of interest and the number of years needed to double the investment. From the pattern, predict the number of years needed if the rate is 12%. Verify your prediction on your graphing calculator.

Population Growth

To calculate the future population P of a country, we can use a formula similar to the compound interest formula, $P = P_0(1 + R)^n$, where P_0 is the original population, R is the annual rate of growth of the population, and n is the number of years.

   In 1990, the population of the United States was 250 million and the population of Mexico was 90 million. Their annual rates of growth were 0.7% and 3.5% respectively.

a) On your graphing calculator, define two functions Y_1 and Y_2 that describe the future populations of the United States and Mexico.

b) Determine an appropriate viewing window to graph Y_1 and Y_2 and display these graphs simultaneously.

c) Use the TRACE feature to determine the year in which the population of Mexico will equal that of the United States.

d) What will their populations be in that year?

Exploring the Exponential Function

Graph $Y_1 = 2^X$, $Y_2 = 2^{X+2}$, and $Y_3 = 2^{X-2}$ in the same viewing window of your graphing calculator. Write your interpretation of the resulting graphs.

Solving Simultaneous Equations

To solve the equations $3x + 2y = 6$ and $y = 2^{x-1}$ simultaneously by algebraic methods is impractical. An approximate solution can be found by plotting the graphs of both equations and estimating their point of intersection.

a) Use both graphical procedures below, then compare them. Which one do you prefer?

   i) Graph each equation in the same viewing window and use the TRACE and magnification features to find the point where the graphs intersect. Recall that the linear function will have to be expressed as $y = \dfrac{6 - 3x}{2}$.

   ii) Find the roots of the equation $y = 2^{x-1} - \dfrac{6 - 3x}{2}$.

b) Use both procedures in part a) to solve the equations $y = 2^x$ and $y = x^2$ simultaneously.

Earthquakes

In western Canada, the area A square kilometres affected by an earthquake is related to the magnitude R of the quake by the formula
$R = 2.3 \log (A + 7500) - 6$
R is the reading on the Richter scale.
Display the graph of $Y_1 = 2.3 \log (X + 7500) - 6$ in an appropriate viewing window. Use the graph to answer these questions.

a) What area is affected by an earthquake which registers 5 on the Richter scale?

b) What is the magnitude of the earthquake which affects an area of 157 000 km²?

Looking Ahead

The equations below may or may not be identities.
Display the graph of each side of each equation in the viewing window $[-4, 10]$ by $[-2, 3]$. Decide whether or not the equation is an identity.

a) $\log (x + 3) = \log x + \log 3$ b) $\log x^2 = (\log x)^2$ c) $\log \dfrac{x}{5} = \dfrac{\log x}{\log 5}$

5-11 THE LAWS OF LOGARITHMS (BASE *a*)

In *Section 5-6* we developed the laws of logarithms for logarithms with base 10. The restriction to base 10 is not necessary, and the laws can be extended to logarithms with any positive base (except 1).

For example, an equation such as $2^3 \times 2^4 = 2^7$ can be written in logarithmic form as $\log_2 8 + \log_2 16 = \log_2 128$. This equation states that the sum of the exponents that 8 and 16 have when expressed as powers of 2 is equal to the exponent that 128 has when expressed as a power of 2.

Theorem   Law of Logarithms for Multiplication (Base *a*)

If *x* and *y* are positive real numbers, then

$\log_a xy = \log_a x + \log_a y \qquad a > 0, a \neq 1$

Given: Two positive real numbers *x* and *y*
Required to Prove: $\log_a xy = \log_a x + \log_a y \qquad a > 0, a \neq 1$
Proof: Let $\log_a x = M$ and $\log_a y = N$

$$x = a^M \qquad\qquad y = a^N$$

Hence, $xy = (a^M)(a^N)$
$$= a^{M+N}$$

Therefore, $\log_a xy = \log_a (a^{M+N})$
$$= M + N$$
$$= \log_a x + \log_a y$$

Corollary   Law of Logarithms for Division (Base *a*)

If *x* and *y* are positive real numbers, then

$\log_a \left(\dfrac{x}{y} \right) = \log_a x - \log_a y \qquad a > 0, a \neq 1$

Example 1. Write $\log_2 15$ as:
  a) a sum of two logarithms   b) a difference of two logarithms.

Solution.   a) Since $15 = 5 \times 3$, then $\log_2 15 = \log_2 5 + \log_2 3$
         b) Since $15 = 30 \div 2$, then $\log_2 15 = \log_2 30 - \log_2 2$

What other answers can you find for *Example 1*?

Example 2. Write each expression as a single logarithm and simplify it.
         a) $\log_3 6 + \log_3 1.5$ b) $\log_5 50 - \log_5 0.4$

Solution.   a) $\log_3 6 + \log_3 1.5 = \log_3 (6 \times 1.5)$
$$= \log_3 9$$
$$= 2$$

         b) $\log_5 50 - \log_5 0.4 = \log_5 \left(\dfrac{50}{0.4} \right)$
$$= \log_5 125$$
$$= 3$$

> **Theorem**   **Law of Logarithms for Powers (Base *a*)**
> If x and n are real numbers, and $x > 0$, then
> $\log_a (x^n) = n \log_a x$ $a > 0, a \neq 1$

Given: Two real numbers x and n, where $x > 0$
Required to Prove: $\log_a (x^n) = n \log_a x$
Proof: Let $\log_a x = M$
$$x = a^M$$
Hence, $x^n = (a^M)^n$
$$= a^{nM}$$
Therefore, $\log_a (x^n) = \log_a (a^{nM})$
$$= nM$$
$$= n \log_a x$$

> **Corollary**   **Law of Logarithms for Roots (Base *a*)**
> If x and n are real numbers, and $x > 0$, then
> $\log_a \sqrt[n]{x} = \dfrac{1}{n} \log_a x$ $a > 0, a \neq 1$

Example 3. a) Write $\log_5 16$ as a product of a whole number and a logarithm.

b) Write as a single logarithm.   i) $2 \log_6 5$ ii) $\dfrac{1}{3} \log_4 125$

Solution. a) Since $16 = 2^4$, then $\log_5 16 = \log_5 (2^4)$
$$= 4 \log_5 2$$

b) i) $2 \log_6 5 = \log_6 (5^2)$
$$= \log_6 25$$

ii) $\dfrac{1}{3} \log_4 125 = \log_4 (\sqrt[3]{125})$
$$= \log_4 5$$

Example 4. Given that $\log_2 7 \doteq 2.8074$, find an approximation for each logarithm.

a) $\log_2 14$ b) $\log_2 49$ c) $\log_2 \left(\dfrac{4}{7}\right)$ d) $\log_2 \sqrt[3]{7}$

Solution. a) $\log_2 14 = \log_2 (7 \times 2)$ b) $\log_2 49 = \log_2 (7^2)$
$$= \log_2 7 + \log_2 2 \qquad\qquad = 2 \log_2 7$$
$$\doteq 2.8074 + 1 \qquad\qquad\quad \doteq 2(2.8074)$$
$$\doteq 3.8074 \qquad\qquad\qquad \doteq 5.6148$$

c) $\log_2 \left(\dfrac{4}{7}\right) = \log_2 4 - \log_2 7$ d) $\log_2 \sqrt[3]{7} = \dfrac{1}{3} \log_2 7$
$$\doteq 2 - 2.8074 \qquad\qquad\qquad\quad \doteq \dfrac{1}{3}(2.8074)$$
$$\doteq -0.8074 \qquad\qquad\qquad\qquad \doteq 0.9358$$

Laws of Logarithms (Base *a*) $a > 0, a \neq 1$
- Multiplication $\log_a xy = \log_a x + \log_a y$ $x, y > 0$
- Division $\log_a \left(\dfrac{x}{y}\right) = \log_a x - \log_a y$ $x, y > 0$
- Powers $\log_a (x^n) = n \log_a x$ $x > 0$
- Roots $\log_a \sqrt[n]{x} = \dfrac{1}{n} \log_a x$ $x > 0$

We can solve equations involving logarithms by using the laws of logarithms and the definition of a logarithm.

Example 5. Solve each equation, and check.

a) $2 \log x = \log 8 + \log 2$ b) $\log_8 (2 - x) + \log_8 (4 - x) = 1$

Solution.   a) $2 \log x = \log 8 + \log 2$

$\log x^2 = \log 16$

Hence, $x^2 = 16$

$x = \pm 4$

To check, substitute each value of x into the original equation.

When $x = 4$,

L.S. $= 2 \log 4$ R.S. $= \log 8 + \log 2$

$= \log 16$ $= \log 16$

4 is a root.

When $x = -4$, the left side is not defined since $\log x$ is defined only when $x > 0$. Hence, -4 is an extraneous root.

b) $\log_8 (2 - x) + \log_8 (4 - x) = 1$

Simplify the left side using the law of logarithms for multiplication.

$\log_8 (2 - x)(4 - x) = 1$

Use the definition of a logarithm.

$(2 - x)(4 - x) = 8^1$

$8 - 6x + x^2 = 8$

$-6x + x^2 = 0$

$x = 0 \text{ or } x = 6$

When $x = 0$,

L.S. $= \log_8 2 + \log_8 4$ R.S. $= 1$

$= \log_8 8$

$= 1$

0 is a root.

When $x = 6$, the left side is not defined. Hence, 6 is an extraneous root.

In *Example 5b* we may ask, if 6 is an extraneous root, then where did it come from? The key to the answer is the quadratic equation $(2 - x)(4 - x) = 8$ which occurred in the solution. This equation may also be written as $(x - 2)(x - 4) = 8$ without changing the two roots. But then the associated logarithmic equation would be $\log_8 (x - 2) + \log_8 (x - 4) = 1$. Hence, if this equation were solved using the method of *Example 5b* the same two roots 0 and 6 would result, but this time 6 would be the root and 0 would be extraneous.

EXERCISES 5-11

Ⓐ

1. Write each expression as a single logarithm, and simplify it.
   a) $\log_6 9 + \log_6 4$　　b) $\log_5 15 - \log_5 3$　　c) $\log_4 2 + \log_4 32$
   d) $\log_2 48 - \log_2 6$　　e) $\log_3 54 - \log_3 2$　　f) $\log_3 9 + \log_3 9$

2. Write as a sum of logarithms.
   a) $\log_3 20$　　b) $\log_7 45$　　c) $\log_5 90$　　d) $\log_{12} 6$　　e) $\log_8 75$　　f) $\log_{20} 39$

3. Write as a difference of logarithms.
   a) $\log_4 11$　　b) $\log_3 12$　　c) $\log_9 5$　　d) $\log_6 7$　　e) $\log_{11} 21$　　f) $\log_2 13$

4. Write each expression as a single logarithm and simplify it.
   a) $\log_6 4 + \log_6 3 + \log_6 3$　　　　b) $\log_4 8 + \log_4 6 + \log_4 \left(\dfrac{4}{3}\right)$
   c) $\log_3 18 + \log_3 5 - \log_3 10$　　　　d) $\log_2 20 - \log_2 5 + \log_2 8$

5. Simplify.
   a) $\log_2 (8 \times 16)$　　　　b) $\log_3 (27 \times 81)$　　　　c) $\log_5 (625 \times 25)$
   d) $\log_2 \left(\dfrac{32}{4}\right)$　　　　e) $\log_3 \left(\dfrac{27}{3}\right)$　　　　f) $\log_5 \left(\dfrac{125}{25}\right)$

6. Write each logarithm as a product of a whole number and a logarithm.
   a) $\log_3 8$　　b) $\log_5 36$　　c) $\log_2 27$　　d) $\log_6 32$　　e) $\log_{12} 81$　　f) $\log_4 125$

7. Write as a single logarithm.
   a) $3 \log_2 5$　　b) $2 \log_7 4$　　c) $6 \log_3 8$　　d) $5 \log_{12} 4$　　e) $15 \log_2 3$

Ⓑ

8. Write as a single logarithm and simplify it.
   a) $\log_4 48 + \log_4 \left(\dfrac{2}{3}\right) + \log_4 8$　　　　b) $\log_8 24 + \log_8 4 - \log_8 3$
   c) $\log_9 36 + \log_9 18 - \log_9 24$　　　　d) $\log_4 20 - \log_4 5 + \log_4 8$
   e) $\log_3 \sqrt{45} - \log_3 \sqrt{5}$　　　　　　　　　　f) $\log_2 \sqrt{5} - \log_2 \sqrt{40}$
   g) $\log_5 \sqrt{10} + \log_5 \sqrt{\dfrac{25}{2}}$　　　　　　h) $\log_4 \sqrt{40} + \log_4 \sqrt{48} - \log_4 \sqrt{15}$

9. Given $\log_2 5 \doteq 2.3219$, find an approximation for each logarithm.
   a) $\log_2 20$　　　　b) $\log_2 25$　　　　c) $\log_2 2.5$　　　　d) $\log_2 \sqrt{5}$

10. Simplify.

a) $\log_2 24 - \log_2 \left(\frac{3}{4}\right)$

b) $\log_2 20 + \log_2 0.4$

c) $\log_8 48 + \log_8 4 - \log_8 3$

d) $\log_{21} 7 + \log_{21} 9 + \log_{21} \left(\frac{1}{3}\right)$

11. Given $\log_3 10 \doteq 2.0959$, find an approximation for each logarithm.

a) $\log_3 1000$

b) $\log_3 30$

c) $\log_3 \sqrt{0.3}$

d) $\log_3 \left(\frac{100}{9}\right)$

12. Express y as a function of x. What is the domain?
   a) $\log_2 xy = 3 \log_2 x$
   b) $\log_5 y = 2 \log_5 (x + 1) + \log_5 (x - 1)$
   c) $\log_3 (y - 3) = 1 + 2 \log_3 (x + 3)$

13. Use your calculator to evaluate each expression.
   a)   i) $\log_2 3000$ ii) $\log_2 300$ iii) $\log_2 30$ iv) $\log_2 3$
       v) $\log_2 0.3$ vi) $\log_2 0.03$ vii) $\log_2 0.003$ viii) $\log_2 0.0003$
   b) Can you find a pattern in the results of part a)? Account for the pattern.

14. If $\log_3 2 = x$, simplify each logarithm.
   a) $\log_3 8$

   b) $\log_3 24$

   c) $\log_3 \sqrt{2}$

   d) $\log_3 6\sqrt{2}$

15. If $\log_2 5 = x$, simplify each logarithm.

   a) $\log_2 20$

   b) $\log_2 100$

   c) $\log_2 10\sqrt{5}$

   d) $\log_2 \left(\frac{\sqrt[3]{5}}{2}\right)$

16. Given that $\log_2 x = 5$, evaluate each logarithm.

   a) $\log_2 2x$

   b) $\log_2 \left(\frac{x}{2}\right)$

   c) $\log_2 (x^2)$

   d) $\log_2 (4x^2)$

17. Given that $\log_3 x = 2$ and $\log_3 y = 5$, evaluate each logarithm.

   a) $\log_3 xy$

   b) $\log_3 (9x^2y)$

   c) $\log_3 \left(\frac{3x^2}{y}\right)$

   d) $\log_3 (27x^{-2}y)$

18. Solve and check.
   a) $2 \log x = \log 32 + \log 2$
   b) $2 \log x = \log 3 + \log 27$
   c) $\log_4 (x + 2) + \log_4 (x - 1) = 1$
   d) $\log_2 (x - 5) + \log_2 (x - 2) = 2$
   e) $\log_2 x + \log_2 (x + 2) = 3$
   f) $\log_6 (x - 1) + \log_6 (x + 4) = 2$

19. Solve and check.
   a) $2 \log m + 3 \log m = 10$
   b) $\log_3 x^2 - \log_3 2x = 2$
   c) $\log_3 s + \log_3 (s - 2) = 1$
   d) $\log (x - 2) + \log (x + 1) = 1$
   e) $\log_7 (x + 4) + \log_7 (x - 2) = 1$
   f) $\log_2 (2m + 4) - \log_2 (m - 1) = 3$

20. Solve each equation to the nearest thousandth.
   a) $\log_2 x + \log_4 x = 5$
   b) $\log_5 x + \log_{10} x = 5$

21. a) Show that: i) $\dfrac{1}{\log_3 10} + \dfrac{1}{\log_4 10} = \dfrac{1}{\log_{12} 10}$ ii) $\dfrac{1}{\log_3 x} + \dfrac{1}{\log_4 x} = \dfrac{1}{\log_{12} x}$.
   b) Using the results of part a) as a guide, state a general result and prove it.

5-12 APPLICATIONS OF EXPONENTIAL AND LOGARITHMIC FUNCTIONS: PART ONE

Exponential functions have defining equations of the form $y = ca^x$. In many applied problems, we are given three of the quantities c, a, x, and y, and are required to calculate the fourth quantity.

Compound Interest

Example 1.   What amount of money would grow to $1000 in 5 years if it is invested at 9% per annum compounded annually?

Solution.   Let the amount of money be P dollars. Then,

$$P(1.09)^5 = 1000$$
$$P = \frac{1000}{(1.09)^5}$$
$$= 1000(1.09)^{-5}$$
$$\doteq 649.93$$

Hence, $649.93 would grow to $1000 in 5 years at 9% per annum.

Solving an equation of the form $y = ca^x$ for the base a amounts to taking a root of both sides. We illustrate this in the next example.

Example 2.   In 1947 an investor bought Van Gogh's painting *Irises* for $84 000. In 1987 she sold it for $49 million. What annual rate of interest corresponds to an investment of $84 000 which grows to $49 million in 40 years?

Solution.   Let i represent the rate of interest. Then,

$$84\ 000(1 + i)^{40} = 49\ 000\ 000$$
$$(1 + i)^{40} = \frac{49\ 000}{84}$$

Take the 40th root of each side.

$$1 + i = \left(\frac{49\ 000}{84}\right)^{\frac{1}{40}}$$
$$1 + i \doteq 1.173$$
$$i \doteq 0.173$$

The annual rate of interest is approximately 17.3%.

Example 3.   Suppose you invest $500 at 8% per annum compounded annually. How many years would it take for your investment to double?

Solution.   Let n represent the number of years. Then,

$$500(1.08)^n = 1000$$
$$(1.08)^n = 2$$

Take the logarithm of each side (base 10).

$$n \log 1.08 = \log 2$$
$$n = \frac{\log 2}{\log 1.08}$$
$$\doteq 9.0$$

Hence, $500 earning interest at 8% per annum will double in approximately 9 years.

In many applications of exponential functions it is necessary to solve an equation of the form $y = ca^x$ for the exponent x. This was illustrated in *Example 3*.

Light Penetration

Example 4. For every metre a diver descends below the water surface, the light intensity is reduced by 2.5%. At what depth is the light intensity only 50% of that at the surface?

Solution. Let d metres represent the required depth.
Then,　　　$50 = 100(0.975)^d$
　　　　　$(0.975)^d = 0.5$
Take the logarithm of each side (base 10).
$d \log 0.975 = \log 0.5$
$$d = \frac{\log 0.5}{\log 0.975}$$
$$\doteq 27.4$$

The light intensity is only 50% of that at the surface at a depth of approximately 27 m.

Nuclear Fallout

Exponential functions occur in the study of nuclear fallout. This refers to the contamination of the atmosphere and the ground from radioactive particles released in a nuclear accident or explosion. The harmful effects arise when these particles decay into other particles and release radiation. Each radioactive substance decays with a characteristic *halflife*. This is the time required for one-half of the material to decay.

Example 5. In a nuclear test explosion, some strontium-90 is released. This substance has a halflife of 28 years.
　　a) Draw a graph showing the percent of strontium-90 remaining up to 140 years.
　　b) Express the percent P of strontium-90 remaining as a function of:
　　　i) the number of halflives elapsed, n
　　　ii) the number of years elapsed, t.
　　c) What percent of strontium-90 remains after 50 years?

Solution. 　a) Make a table of values for time intervals of 1 halflife. Plot the percent remaining against the time in years.

Halflives (n)	0	1	2	3	4	5
Years (t)	0	28	56	84	112	140
Percent remaining (P)	100	50	25	12.5	6.25	3.13

b) i) After each half life, the
       percent remaining is halved.
       Hence, the percent
       remaining after n half lives
       have elapsed is:

$$P = 100\left(\frac{1}{2}\right)^n \quad \text{...} \; \textcircled{1}$$

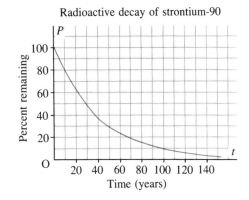

Radioactive decay of strontium-90

   ii) Since $t = 28n$, we can write
       equation $\textcircled{1}$ in terms of t.
       Substitute $\frac{t}{28}$ for n.

$$P = 100\left(\frac{1}{2}\right)^{\frac{t}{28}} \quad \text{...} \; \textcircled{2}$$

c) Substitute 50 for t in equation $\textcircled{2}$.

$$P = 100\left(\frac{1}{2}\right)^{\frac{50}{28}}$$
$$\doteq 29.003\,235$$

Hence, about 29% of the strontium-90 remains after 50 years.

Example 6. In April 1986 there was a major nuclear accident at the Chernobyl power
plant in the Soviet Union. The atmosphere was contaminated with quantities of radioactive iodine-131, which has a half life of 8.1 days. How
long did it take for the level of radiation to reduce to 1% of the level
immediately after the accident?

Solution. Let P represent the percent of the original radiation that was present after
t days. Then, since the half life is 8.1 days,

$$P = 100\left(\frac{1}{2}\right)^{\frac{t}{8.1}}$$

Substitute 1 for P and solve for t by taking the logarithm of each side.

$$1 = 100(0.5)^{\frac{t}{8.1}}$$

$$\log 1 = \log 100 + \frac{t}{8.1}\log 0.5$$

$$0 = 2 + \frac{t}{8.1}\log 0.5$$

$$t = -\frac{16.2}{\log 0.5}$$

$$\doteq 54$$

It took about 54 days for the level of radiation to reduce to 1% of the
level immediately after the accident.

EXERCISES 5-12

Compound Interest

1. How much should you invest at 7% per annum compounded annually so that $5000 will be available in 4 years?

2. The 50¢ Bluenose is one of Canada's most famous postage stamps. In 1930 it could be bought at the post office for 50¢. In 1987 a superb copy was sold at an auction for $500. What annual rate of interest corresponds to an investment of 50¢ in 1930 which grows to $500 in 1987?

3. In 1626, Manhattan Island was sold for $24. If that money had been invested at 8% per annum compounded annually, what would it have amounted to today?

4. Suppose you invest $200 at 9% per annum compounded annually. How many years would it take for your investment to grow to $500?

5. Mary invests $2500 at 11% per annum compounded annually. How many years will it take for her investment to double in value?

Light Penetration

6. For every metre a diver descends under water, the intensity of three colors of light is reduced as shown.

Color	Percent Reduction per metre
Red	35%
Green	5%
Blue	2.5%

   a) For each color, write an equation which expresses the percent P of surface light as a function of the depth d metres.
   b) For each color, determine the depth at which about half the light has disappeared.
   c) Let us agree that, for all practical purposes, the light has disappeared when the intensity is only 1% of that at the surface. At what depth would this occur for each color?

7. Several layers of glass are stacked together. Each layer reduces the light passing through it by 5%.
   a) What percent of light passes through 10 layers of glass?
   b) How many layers of glass are needed to reduce the intensity to only 1% of the original light?

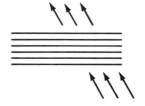

Growth of Populations

8. The town of Springfield is growing at a rate of 6.5% per annum. How many people are there in Springfield now, if there will be 15 000 in 4.5 years?

9. In 1950 the world population was approximately 2.5 billion. The population doubled to 5 billion in 1987. What was the average annual growth rate of the world population from 1950 to 1987?

10. A culture has 750 bacteria. The number of bacteria doubles every 5 h. How many bacteria are in the culture after 12 h?

11. A colony of bees increases by 25% every three months. How many bees should Raiman start with if he wishes to have 10 000 bees in 18 months?

12. If the population of a colony of bacteria doubles every 30 min, how long would it take for the population to triple?

13. Prove that if the growth rate is constant, the time required for a population to double is independent of the population size.

Nuclear Fallout

14. When strontium-90 decays, the percent P remaining is expressed as a function of the time t years by the equation $P \doteq 100(2)^{-0.0357t}$. How long is it until the percent remaining is: a) 10% b) 1%?

15. The halflives of two products of a nuclear explosion are shown. For each substance
    a) Draw a graph showing the percent remaining during the first five halflives.

Substance	Halflife
Iodine-131	8.1 days
Cesium-144	282 days

    b) Express the percent remaining as a function of:
       i) the number of halflives elapsed, n ii) the number of days elapsed, t.
    c) What percent of the substance remains after:
       i) one week   ii) 30 days   iii) one year?
    d) How long is it until the percent remaining of each substance is:
       i) 10%   ii) 0.1%?

16. Another product of a nuclear explosion is plutonium-239, which has a halflife of 24 000 years. What percent of plutonium-239 remains after:
    a) 100 years   b) 1000 years   c) 10 000 years   d) 100 000 years?

17. Polonium-210 is a radioactive element with a halflife of 20 weeks. From a sample of 25 g, how much would remain after:
    a) 30 weeks   b) 14 weeks   c) 1 year   d) 511 days?

Other Applications

18. Jacques bought a new car for $15 000. Each year the value of the car depreciates to 70% of its value the previous year. In how many years will the car be worth only $500?

19. A pan of water is brought to a boil and then removed from the heat. Every 5 min thereafter the difference between the temperature of the water and room temperature is reduced by 50%.
    a) Room temperature is 20°C. Express the temperature of the water as a function of the time since it was removed from the heat.
    b) How many minutes does it take for the temperature of the water to reach 30°C?

20. A cup of coffee contains approximately 100 mg of caffeine. When you drink the coffee, the caffeine is absorbed into the bloodstream, and is eventually metabolized by the body. Every 5 h the amount of caffeine in the bloodstream is reduced by 50%.
    a) Write an equation which expresses the amount of caffeine c milligrams in the bloodstream as an exponential function of the elapsed time t hours since drinking one cup of coffee.
    b) How many hours does it take for the amount of caffeine to be reduced to:
       i) 10 mg   ii) 1 mg?

21. In a steel mill, red-hot slabs of steel are pressed many times between heavy rollers. The drawings show two stages in rolling a slab.

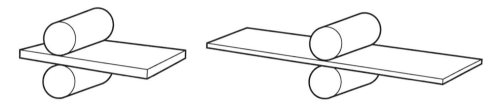

    A slab is 2.00 m long and 0.120 m thick. On each pass through the rollers, its length increases by 20%.
    a) Write the equation which expresses the length L metres of the slab as an exponential function of the number of passes n through the rollers.
    b) How many passes are needed to increase the length of the slab to 50 m?

22. a) For the slab in *Exercise 21*, by what factor does the thickness of the slab decrease on each pass through the rollers? Assume the width is constant.
    b) Write an equation which expresses the thickness t metres of the slab as an exponential function of the number of passes n through the rollers.
    c) How many passes are needed to reduce the thickness of the slab to 0.001 m?
    d) How long would the slab be when its thickness is 0.001 m?

Ⓒ

23. The total amount of arable land in the world is about 3.2×10^9 ha. At current population rates, about 0.4 ha of land is required to grow food for each person in the world.
    a) Assuming a 1987 world population of 5 billion and a constant growth rate of 1.5%, determine the year when the demand for arable land exceeds the supply.
    b) Compare the effect of each comment on the result of part a).
       i) doubling the productivity of the land so that only 0.2 ha is required to grow food for each person
       ii) reducing the growth rate by one-half, to 0.75%
       iii) doubling the productivity of the land *and* reducing the growth rate by 50%

5-13 APPLICATIONS OF EXPONENTIAL AND LOGARITHMIC FUNCTIONS: PART TWO

Growth of Populations
Occasionally we see statements such as this, in magazines and newspapers.

In favorable breeding conditions, the population of a swarm of desert locusts can multiply 10-fold in 20 days.

This information is not sufficient to calculate the population of a swarm of locusts, since an initial population figure is not given. But we can still use the statement to compare the populations of a swarm at two different times.

Example 1. Use the information above to compare the population of a swarm of locusts after 30 days with its population after 20 days.

Solution. Let P_0 represent the population of a swarm at $t = 0$. Then we can use the fact that the population is multiplied 10-fold in 20 days to express the population P as an exponential function of the time t days.

$$P = P_0(10)^{\frac{t}{20}}$$
or $\qquad P = P_0(10)^{0.05t} \quad \dots \text{①}$

Let P_{20} and P_{30} represent the populations after 20 and 30 days, respectively. Then, using equation ①, we obtain

$$P_{20} = P_0(10)^{0.05(20)}$$
$$= P_0(10) \qquad \dots \text{②}$$
$$P_{30} = P_0(10)^{0.05(30)}$$
$$= P_0(10)^{1.5} \qquad \dots \text{③}$$

Since we do not know the value of P_0, we cannot calculate P_{20} or P_{30}. But we can find their ratio by dividing equation ③ by equation ②.

$$\frac{P_{30}}{P_{20}} = \frac{P_0(10)^{1.5}}{P_0(10)}$$
$$= 10^{0.5}$$
$$\doteq 3.162\ 277\ 7$$

A swarm is about 3.2 times as large after 30 days as it was after 20 days.

Calculations such as those in *Example 1* are used in many applications of exponential and logarithmic functions.

Earthquakes
A scale for comparing the intensities of earthquakes was devised by Charles Richter about 50 years ago. The intensity of an earthquake is measured by the amount of ground motion as recorded on a seismometer.

When we use the Richter scale, we do not need to know the actual intensities, or seismometer readings. The scale is used simply to compare the intensities of two earthquakes using the following rule.

Each increase of 1 unit in magnitude
on the Richter scale represents a
10-fold increase in intensity as
measured on a seismometer.

Consider, for example, the Italy earthquake
of 1976 which had a magnitude of 6.5 on
the Richter scale. Notice that the Guatemala
earthquake the same year had a magnitude
of 7.5, which is exactly 1 unit greater. This
means that the second earthquake was *10
times* as intense as the first. Similarly, the
Alaska earthquake in 1964 was 10 × 10, or
100 times as intense as the 1976 Italy earthquake, and 10 × 10 × 10, or *1000 times* as
intense as the 1983 earthquake in Colombia.
But, how do we compare the intensities of
earthquakes such as the Alaska earthquake
in 1964 and the Turkey earthquake in 1966,
whose magnitudes do not differ by a whole
number?

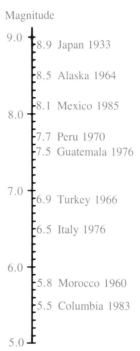

The Richter Scale

Magnitude

- 9.0 — 8.9 Japan 1933
- 8.5 Alaska 1964
- 8.1 Mexico 1985
- 8.0 — 7.7 Peru 1970
- 7.5 Guatemala 1976
- 7.0 — 6.9 Turkey 1966
- 6.5 Italy 1976
- 6.0 — 5.8 Morocco 1960
- 5.5 Columbia 1983
- 5.0

Example 2.   Use the information above to compare the intensity of the 1964 Alaska
earthquake with the intensity of the 1966 Turkey earthquake.

Solution.   Let I_0 represent the intensity of an earthquake with a magnitude of 0 on
the Richter scale. Then we can use the fact that the intensity is multiplied
10-fold for each increase in 1 unit of magnitude to express the intensity
I as an exponential function of the magnitude M.
$$I = I_0(10)^M \quad \ldots \; ①$$
Let I_A and I_T represent the intensities of the Alaska and Turkey earthquakes,
respectively. Then, using equation ①, we obtain
$$I_A = I_0(10)^{8.5} \quad \ldots \; ②$$
$$I_T = I_0(10)^{6.9} \quad \ldots \; ③$$
Since we do not know the value of I_0, we cannot calculate I_A or I_T. But
we can find their ratio by dividing equation ② by equation ③.
$$\frac{I_A}{I_T} = \frac{I_0(10)^{8.5}}{I_0(10)^{6.9}}$$
$$= 10^{8.5-6.9}$$
$$= 10^{1.6}$$
$$\doteq 39.810\,717$$
The Alaska earthquake was about 40 times as intense as the Turkey
earthquake.

Acid Rain

Acid rain has become a major environmental problem. The acidity of rainwater is measured on a special scale called a *pH scale*. Each 1 unit decrease in pH represents a 10-fold *increase* in acidity. For example, the pH of vinegar is 2 units less than that of tomatoes. Hence, vinegar is 10^2, or 100 times more acidic than tomatoes.

Let A represent the acid content of a substance with a pH of P. Then, since each increase of 1 unit in P represents a 10-fold decrease in A,

$$A = A_0(0.1)^P \ldots \text{①}$$

where A_0 represents the acid content of a substance with pH 0.
To express P as a function of A, solve equation ① for P.

$$\log A = \log A_0 + P \log 0.1$$

$$P \log 0.1 = \log A - \log A_0$$

$$P = \frac{\log \left(\frac{A}{A_0}\right)}{\log 0.1}$$

or $\quad P = -\log \left(\frac{A}{A_0}\right) \ldots \text{②}$

Equation ② expresses the pH of a substance as a logarithmic function of its acid content.

In the equation for pH, $P = -\log \left(\frac{A}{A_0}\right)$, notice that the value of A_0 is not given. Despite this, we can still use this equation to obtain useful information. This involves a comparison of the acid content, or pH of two substances.

Example 3. A lake in the Muskoka region of Ontario has a pH of 4.0. How many times as acidic as clean rain water, which has a pH of 5.6, is the water in this lake?

Solution. Use the equation developed above. $P = -\log \left(\frac{A}{A_0}\right)$

Let P_1 and A_1 represent the pH and acid content of clean rain water, and let P_2 and A_2 represent the pH and acid content of the lake. Then,

$$P_1 = -\log \left(\frac{A_1}{A_0}\right)$$

$$P_2 = -\log \left(\frac{A_2}{A_0}\right)$$

Subtract and then use the law of logarithms for division.

$$P_1 - P_2 = -\log \left(\frac{A_1}{A_0}\right) + \log \left(\frac{A_2}{A_0}\right)$$

$$= \log \left(\frac{A_2}{A_0}\right) - \log \left(\frac{A_1}{A_0}\right)$$

$$= \log \left(\frac{A_2}{A_1}\right)$$

Substitute 5.6 for P_1 and 4.0 for P_2.

$$5.6 - 4.0 = \log\left(\frac{A_2}{A_1}\right)$$

$$1.6 = \log\left(\frac{A_2}{A_1}\right)$$

By the definition of a logarithm

$$\frac{A_2}{A_1} = 10^{1.6}$$

$$\doteq 39.8$$

Hence, the lake is about 40 times as acidic as clean rain water.

EXERCISES 5-13

Ⓑ

Growth of Populations

1. The population of a swarm of insects can multiply 5-fold in 4 weeks. Let P_0 represent the population at time $t = 0$.
   a) Write expressions to represent the population after:
      i) 4 weeks   ii) 6 weeks.
   b) How many times as great is the population after 6 weeks as it was after 4 weeks?

2. The population of a nest of ants can multiply 3-fold in 5 weeks. After 8 weeks, how many times as great is the population as it was after 5 weeks?

3. The population of a colony of bacteria can double in 25 min. After one hour, how many times as great is the population as it was after 25 min?

Earthquakes

4. On July 26, 1986, an earthquake with magnitude 5.5 hit California. The next day a second earthquake with magnitude 6.2 hit the same region. How many times as intense as the first earthquake was the second earthquake?

5. In 1985/86, three earthquakes hit Mexico City. How many times as intense as:
   a) the second earthquake was the first
   b) the third earthquake was the second
   c) the third earthquake was the first?

Mexico City Earthquakes	
Date	**Magnitude**
Sept. 19, 1985	8.1
Sept. 21, 1985	7.5
April 30, 1986	7.0

6. It has been observed that for every decrease of 1 unit in magnitude, earthquakes are about 6 or 7 times as frequent. In a given year, how should the number of earthquakes with magnitudes between 4.0 and 4.9 compare with the number of earthquakes with magnitudes between:
   a) 5.0 and 5.9   b) 6.0 and 6.9   c) 7.0 and 7.9?

Acid Rain

7. Between 1956 and 1976 the annual average pH of precipitation at Sault Ste. Marie, Ontario, dropped from 5.6 to 4.3. How many times as acidic as the precipitation in 1956 was the precipitation in 1976?

8. In the spring, the pH of a stream dropped from 6.5 to 5.5 during a 3-week period in April.
   a) How many times as acidic did the stream become?
   b) Why would this happen in April?
   c) The mean pH of Lake Huron is 8.2. How many times as acidic was the stream:
      i) before the 3-week period   ii) after the 3-week period?

9. When the pH of the water in a lake falls below 4.7, nearly all species of fish in the lake are deformed or killed. How many times as acidic as clean rainwater, which has a pH of 5.6, is such a lake?

Ⓒ

Other Applications

10. If the temperature is constant, the pressure of the Earth's atmosphere decreases by 5% for every 300 m increase in altitude.
    a) Let P_1 and P_2 represent the pressures at altitudes h_1 and h_2 respectively. Derive an equation which expresses the ratio $\dfrac{P_2}{P_1}$ as an exponential function of the difference in altitudes $h_2 - h_1$.
    b) A jet gains 1000 m in altitude. By what percent did the atmospheric pressure decrease?

11. One of the most remarkable technological trends ever recorded is the growth of the number of components on a silicon chip. Since 1970, the number of components on each chip has quadrupled every three years. It is expected that this level should persist until the early 1990s.
    a) Let N_1 and N_2 represent the numbers of components on a chip in the years t_1 and t_2 respectively. Derive an equation which expresses the ratio $\dfrac{N_2}{N_1}$ as an exponential function of the time difference $t_2 - t_1$.
    b) How did the number of components on a chip in 1985 compare with the number in: i) 1980   ii) 1975   iii) 1970?

INVESTIGATE

The ⬚ln key on a Calculator

Your calculator should have a key marked ⬚ln. This key calculates logarithms of numbers to a base different from 10. Find the base of these logarithms as accurately as you can.

THE MATHEMATICAL MIND

Natural Logarithms

Logarithms were introduced into mathematics almost four hundred years ago by the Scotsman, John Napier. The invention was enthusiastically hailed throughout Europe as a great breakthrough in computation. This was because logarithms can be used to reduce multiplication and division to the simpler operations of addition and subtraction. For example, the law of logarithms, $\log xy = \log x + \log y$, can be applied to multiply two numbers x and y by adding their logarithms. In the past, extensive tables of logarithms were prepared for this purpose. Of course, modern technology has rendered this method of computation obsolete.

Originally, Napier's logarithms had a certain base which was different from 10. These logarithms are called *natural logarithms*.

You can evaluate natural logarithms using the $\boxed{\ln}$ key on your calculator. For example, key in: 3 $\boxed{\ln}$ to display 1.0986123. We write $\ln 3 \doteq 1.098\ 612\ 3$, and we say "lawn 3 is approximately 1.098 612 3''. To explain what this means, we need to know the base of the logarithms. The base of the natural logarithms is always represented by the letter e.

You can use your calculator to find the value of e. Key in: 1 $\boxed{e^x}$ or 1 $\boxed{\text{INV}}$ $\boxed{\ln}$ to display 2.7182818. Hence, $e \doteq 2.718\ 281\ 8$
Therefore, $\ln 3 \doteq 1.098\ 612\ 3$ means that $e^{1.0986123} \doteq 3$, where $e \doteq 2.718\ 281\ 8$.

Natural logarithms are a particular case of logarithms to base a, which were studied earlier in this chapter. Hence, natural logarithms have all the properties of logarithms to base a. This means that we can use natural logarithms to solve problems like those solved earlier.

For example, to solve the equation $e^x = 3.5$ for x, take the natural logarithm of both sides, and write $x \ln e = \ln 3.5$. Since $\ln e = 1$, then $x = \ln 3.5$. Key in: 3.5 $\boxed{\ln}$ to display 1.2527630. Hence, $x \doteq 1.252\ 763$.

QUESTIONS

1. Use your calculator to evaluate each logarithm. Then write the result in exponential form and check with the calculator.
   a) ln 2
   b) ln 4
   c) ln 30
   d) ln 100
   e) ln 8750
   f) ln 0.5
   g) ln 0.1
   h) ln 0.000 44

2. Solve for x.
   a) $e^x = 5$
   b) $e^x = 15$
   c) $e^x = 53.9$
   d) $e^x = 266$
   e) $e^x = 1$
   f) $e^x = 0.25$
   g) $e^x = 0.092$
   h) $e^x = 0.0003$

3. Solve for x.
   a) $\ln x = 1$
   b) $\ln x = 1.6$
   c) $\ln x = 3$
   d) $\ln x = 4.5$
   e) $\ln x = 0.33$
   f) $\ln x = -1$
   g) $\ln x = -1.4$
   h) $\ln x = -2.2$

4. Write as a single logarithm, and check with your calculator.
   a) $\ln 5 + \ln 3$
   b) $\ln 2 + \ln 10$
   c) $2 \ln 6$
   d) $\ln 18 - \ln 2$
   e) $\ln 21 - \ln 3$
   f) $\frac{1}{2} \ln 25$

5. a) Simplify each expression.
      i) $\ln e$
      ii) $\ln e^2$
      iii) $\ln e^{-3}$
      iv) $\ln e^{0.2}$
   b) Based on the results of part a), state a general result.

6. About 200 years ago, at age 15, Carl Friedrich Gauss noticed that the number of primes less than a given natural number n can be approximated by $\dfrac{n}{\ln n}$.
   Use this expression to approximate the number of primes less than:
   a) 10
   b) 100
   c) 1000
   d) 10^6
   e) 10^9.

7. Although it has never been proved, mathematicians have observed that the number of twin primes less than a given number n is approximately equal to $\dfrac{2n}{(\ln n)^2}$. Use this result to approximate the number of twin primes less than:
   a) 10
   b) 100
   c) 1000
   d) 10^6
   e) 10^9.

8. It has been proved that the average spacing of the prime numbers near a given natural number n is approximately equal to $\ln n$. For example, the six prime numbers closest to 50, and the successive differences between them are:

   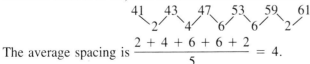

   The average spacing is $\dfrac{2 + 4 + 6 + 6 + 2}{5} = 4$.
   a) Find $\ln 50$, and compare it with the above result.
   b) Check that the average spacing of the six primes closest to:
      i) 100 is approximately $\ln 100$
      ii) 150 is approximately $\ln 150$.

MATHEMATICS AROUND US

Applications of Natural Logarithms

In the applications of exponential and logarithmic functions studied in *Sections 5-12* and *5-13*, many different bases were used. For example, in compound interest applications the base depended on the interest rate. In other applications we used bases 2, $\frac{1}{2}$, and 10. It would simplify matters to use the same base every time, and mathematicians have found that there is an advantage to using base e.

For example, consider population growth. In 1987 the world population reached 5 billion, and was increasing at about 1.6% per annum. Hence, an equation expressing the population P billion as a function of time t years relative to 1987 is

$$P = 5(1.016)^t \ldots \text{①}$$

Let's investigate what would happen if we express this equation with base e instead of base 10. To do this, we must write 1.016 as a power of e.

Let $1.016 = e^k$. Then, by definition, $k = \ln 1.016$
Key in: 1.016 $\boxed{\ln}$ to display 0.0158733
To two significant figures, $k \doteq 0.016$
Hence, $1.016 \doteq e^{0.016}$, and equation ① can be written as follows.

$$P = 5e^{0.016t}$$

Initial population Growth rate

Look at that! The constant in the exponent is 0.016, which is the growth rate. We now see an advantage of using base e. When an exponential function is expressed with base e, the constant in the exponent is the rate of growth. e is the only number with this property. Hence, it is the natural base to use in problems involving exponential growth and decay.

There is another advantage. Notice that the value of k obtained was not exactly 0.016. This slight discrepancy is caused by the way in which e is defined in higher mathematics. The definition assumes that the population grows continuously, and that the new members are not added all at once at the end of the year. In this case, the growth rate is called *instantaneous*. In the above example, the instantaneous rate of growth is 0.015 873 3, whereas the annual rate is 0.016. In some applications the difference may not be significant. Since a rigorous development of instantaneous rates of growth requires calculus, we will ignore its effect.

Example 1.   In 1986 the population of Canada was 25.5 million, and was growing at the rate of approximately 1.0% per annum.
a) Write an equation for the population P million after t years.
b) Assuming that the growth rate remains constant, use the equation to determine:
  i) the predicted population in the year 2000
  ii) the number of years required for the population to reach 40 million.

Solution.   a) The equation is $P = 25.5e^{0.01t}$.
b) i) The year 2000 is 14 years later than 1986. Hence, substitute 14 for t.
$$P = 25.5e^{0.01(14)}$$
$$= 25.5e^{0.14}$$
$$\doteq 29.331\ 982$$
The population will be approximately 29.3 million in the year 2000.
  ii) Substitute 40 for P.
$$40 = 25.5e^{0.01t}$$
To solve for t, take the natural logarithm of each side.
$$\ln 40 = \ln 25.5 + 0.01t$$
$$t = \frac{\ln 40 - \ln 25.5}{0.01}$$
$$\doteq 45.020\ 100$$
The population will reach 40 million 45 years after 1986, or in the year 2031.

Example 2.   In 1987 the world population reached 5 billion. According to United Nations forecasts, the population will reach 6.1 billion in the year 2001. Calculate the average annual rate of growth from 1987 to 2001.

Solution.   Let $P = P_0e^{kt}$
Substitute 5 for P_0, 6.1 for P, and 14 for t.
$$6.1 = 5e^{14k}$$
Take the natural logarithm of each side.
$$\ln 6.1 = \ln 5 + 14k$$
$$k = \frac{\ln 6.1 - \ln 5}{14}$$
$$\doteq 0.014\ 203\ 6$$
Hence, the average annual rate of growth is about 1.42%.

The conventions of writing log x to mean the logarithm to base 10 of x, and ln x to mean the logarithm to base e of x are by no means universal. In higher mathematics, natural logarithms are usually the only logarithms that are used, and log x often refers to the natural logarithm of x. Also, many computer languages use LOG(X) for the natural logarithm function.

QUESTIONS

1. Each equation represents the population P million of a country t years after 1985. State the 1985 population and the growth rate for each country.
   a) Italy $P = 57e^{0.007t}$
   b) Kenya $P = 20e^{0.030t}$
   c) Costa Rica $P = 2.6e^{0.038t}$

2. In 1985 the population of India was 770 million, and was growing at approximately 1.6% per annum.
   a) Write an equation for the population P million after t years, using an exponential function with base e.
   b) Assuming that the growth rate is constant, determine:
      i) the predicted population in 1995
      ii) when the population will reach 1 billion
      iii) when the population was 500 million.

3. When uranium-238 decays, the percent P remaining after t years is given by the equation $P = 100e^{-1.53 \times 10^{-10}t}$.
   a) What percent remains after 10 million years?
   b) Determine the halflife of uranium-238.

4. The altitude of an aircraft can be determined by measuring the air pressure. In the stratosphere (between 12 000 m and 30 000 m) the pressure P kilopascals is expressed as an exponential function of the altitude h metres by the equation $P = 130e^{-0.000155h}$.
   a) What is the altitude if the pressure is 8.5 kPa; 2.5 kPa?
   b) What is the pressure at an altitude of 20 000 m?
   c) Solve the equation for h to obtain an equation expressing the altitude as a logarithmic function of the pressure.

5. A rule of thumb which is used to approximate the time required for an investment to double in value is to divide 70 by the interest rate. For example, if the interest rate is 8%, then an investment will double in approximately $\frac{70}{8}$, or 9 years. Explain why the rule of thumb works.

1. Evaluate.

   a) $8^{-\frac{2}{3}}$ b) $27^{\frac{1}{3}}$ c) $32^{\frac{3}{5}}$ d) $\left(\dfrac{1}{125}\right)^{-\frac{2}{3}}$

   e) $(2.25)^{1.5}$ f) $\left(\dfrac{16}{81}\right)^{-0.75}$ g) $(0.0144)^{0}$ h) $(0.0016)^{1.25}$

2. A bacteria culture doubles in size every 8 h. If there are now 1000 bacteria in the culture, how many:
   a) will there be in   i) 16 h   ii) 44 h
   b) were there   i) 24 h ago   ii) 1.5 days ago?

3. Simplify.

   a) $\dfrac{-15x^{-3}y^2 \times 8x^5y^3}{-24x^{-1}y^7}$ b) $\dfrac{18m^2n^{-5} \times (-5m^{-4}n^2)}{-15m^3n^{-4} \times 12m^{-7}n^0}$

   c) $(2a^2b)^{-3}(5ab^{-2})^2$ d) $(x^{\frac{1}{2}}y^{-\frac{2}{3}})^3 \times \left(\dfrac{3}{5}x^{-\frac{3}{4}}y^{\frac{1}{3}}\right)^2$

   e) $\dfrac{21a^{-\frac{3}{4}}b^{\frac{2}{3}}}{-35a^{-\frac{1}{2}}b}$ f) $\dfrac{6m^{\frac{1}{4}}n^{-\frac{1}{3}} \times 35m^{-\frac{3}{4}}n^{\frac{1}{2}}}{14m^{\frac{1}{2}}n^{\frac{5}{6}} \times 10m^{\frac{3}{2}}n^{-\frac{1}{2}}}$

4. Simplify.

   a) $\dfrac{(x^{3a})(x^{-5a})}{x^{-2a}}$ b) $\dfrac{(m^{3x+y})(2m^{x-2y})}{(3m^{-2x+3y})}$ c) $\dfrac{(a^{\frac{x}{4}})(b^{\frac{2x}{3}})^3}{(a^{\frac{3x}{2}})^{-\frac{1}{2}}(b^{\frac{3x}{4}})^2}$

5. How much must be invested at 7.5% interest compounded annually, so that there will be $5600 in 12 years?

6. There are 5400 red ants in a particular colony. If there were 1200 ants in the colony 8 months ago, what is the monthly rate of growth?

7. A diamond ring worth $12 500 increases in value by 12% per year. In how many years will it be worth $50 000?

8. Write in exponential form.

   a) $\log 1000 = 3$ b) $\log \sqrt{10} = \dfrac{1}{2}$ c) $\log_3 81 = 4$

9. Write in logarithmic form.
   a) $10^4 = 10\,000$ b) $10^{-3} = 0.001$ c) $5^4 = 625$

10. Solve for x.
    a) $\log x = 2$ b) $\log x = -5$ c) $\log_x 64 = 2$
    d) $\log_3 x = 3$ e) $\log_5 0.04 = x$ f) $\log_2 x = 5$

11. Write in terms of $\log x$ and $\log y$.
    a) $\log (xy^2)$ b) $\log (x\sqrt{y})$ c) $\log (10x^3y^2)$

    d) $\log (\sqrt[3]{xy^2})$ e) $\log \left(\dfrac{x}{\sqrt{y}}\right)$ f) $\log \left(\dfrac{x^2}{\sqrt[3]{y}}\right)$

12. Write as a single logarithm.
a) $\log x + \log y - \log z$ b) $2 \log x - \log y$

c) $3 \log x + 5 \log y$ d) $\frac{1}{2} \log x + 3 \log y$

e) $\log (2x - 3) + \log (y + 5)$ f) $3 \log (x + y) - \log (x - y)$

13. Express.
a) 8 as a power of 3   b) 24 as a power of 6
c) 12 as a power of 1.3   d) 0.78 as a power of 2

14. Solve for x. Give the answers to 4 decimal places.
a) $5^x = 9$ b) $14^x = 8$ c) $3^{2x-1} = 25$ d) $4^{5-x} = 45$
e) $7^{3-x} = 4$ f) $8^{5x-2} = 69$ g) $2^{1-x} = 9^{x+1}$ h) $5^{3x+1} = 12^{x+4}$

15. Evaluate.

a) $\log 10\ 000$ b) $\log_2 16$ c) $\log_3 243$ d) $\log_2 \left(\frac{1}{8} \right)$

e) $\log_{\frac{1}{3}} 27$ f) $\log_{\sqrt{2}} 32$ g) $\log_5 0.008$ h) $\log_7 343$

16. Solve and check.
a) $3 \log x = \log 512 - \log 8$ b) $\log_2 x + \log_2 (x - 3) = 2$
c) $\log_{\sqrt{2}} (x - 2) + \log_{\sqrt{2}} (x + 1) = 4$ d) $\log_6 (x + 3) + \log_6 (x - 2) = 1$

17. Graph each function and its inverse on the same grid.
a) $y = 3^x$ b) $y = \log_5 x$ c) $y = \log_{\frac{1}{3}} x$

18. The halflife of a radioactive substance is 23 days. How long is it until the percent remaining is:
a) 10%   b) 3% ?

19. a) An air filter loses about 0.3% of its effectiveness each day. What is its effectiveness after 145 days as a percent of its initial effectiveness?
b) The filter should be replaced when its effectiveness has decreased to 20% of its initial value. After how long should it be replaced?

20. In 1951 the UNIVAC computer performed approximately 1000 arithmetic operations per second. Since then, the speed of computers has doubled, on the average, about every 2 years.
a) Express the number of operations per second N as an exponential function of the time n years since 1951.
b) Predict when computers will be able to perform a billion operations per second. What assumption are you making?

21. On each bounce a ball rises to 70% of the height from which it fell. Let us agree that, for all practical purposes, the ball stops bouncing when the height to which it rises is only 0.1% of the height from which it was dropped originally. How many bounces will this take?

Andy and Brinkley are seated at opposite ends of a diameter of a Ferris wheel. What is Andy's angle of elevation as seen from the bottom of the Ferris wheel, in terms of his angle of elevation as seen by Brinkley? (See Section 6-5 *Example 3*.)

6-1 REVIEW

In our study of the geometry of circles and right triangles, we will introduce new properties or facts by stating, and sometimes proving, theorems and associated corollaries.

A *theorem* is a fact to be established with a chain of reasoning, by using accepted or proved statements.
A *corollary* is an additional fact generated by a theorem (usually self-evident—a consequence of that theorem).

Many of the geometric facts which you used when studying geometry in previous years were theorems which have been established by logical reasoning. These will be the basis for all our new discoveries and proofs. To refresh your memory, here is a list of theorems with which you should be familiar.

In any triangle, the sum of the measures of the three angles is 180°.

$$m\angle A + m\angle B + m\angle C = 180°$$

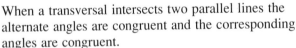

When two lines intersect, the vertically opposite angles are congruent.
$m\angle 1 = m\angle 2$

In any isosceles triangle, the angles opposite the congruent sides are congruent.
If $m\overline{AB} = m\overline{AC}$, then $m\angle B = m\angle C$

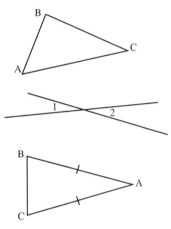

When a transversal intersects two parallel lines the alternate angles are congruent and the corresponding angles are congruent.
$m\angle 3 = m\angle 6$; $m\angle 4 = m\angle 5$;
$m\angle 1 = m\angle 5$; $m\angle 2 = m\angle 6$;
$m\angle 3 = m\angle 7$; $m\angle 4 = m\angle 8$;

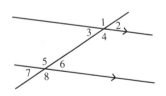

In a right triangle, the area of the square on the hypotenuse is equal to the sum of the areas of the squares on the other two sides.
Pythagorean Theorem
If $m\angle C = 90°$, then $c^2 = a^2 + b^2$

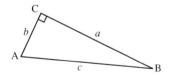

The image of a figure under an isometric transformation is congruent to the original figure. △AOB is rotated 180° about O.

△ABO ≅ △A′B′O

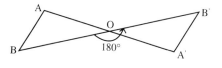

Any point on the right bisector of a line segment is equidistant from the end points of the segment. The bisector is the axis of symmetry (line of reflection).

If m∠PDA = 90° and m$\overline{AD}$ = m$\overline{DB}$,

then m$\overline{PA}$ = m$\overline{PB}$

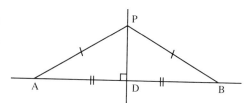

Any point on the bisector of an angle is equidistant from the two rays which form the angle. The bisector is the axis of symmetry of the angle.

If m∠BAP = m∠CAP, then m$\overline{PB}$ = m$\overline{PC}$

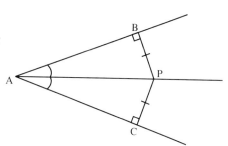

Two triangles are congruent if the congruent corresponding parts are SSS or SAS or AAS or HL

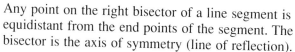

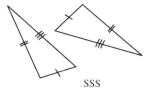

SSS

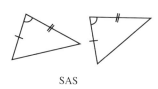

SAS

AAS

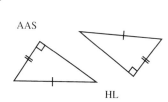

HL

Two triangles are similar if:
- the measures of corresponding sides are proportional, SSS~

$$\frac{m\overline{A'B'}}{m\overline{AB}} = \frac{m\overline{A'C'}}{m\overline{AC}} = \frac{m\overline{B'C'}}{m\overline{BC}}$$

- two corresponding angles are congruent, AA~
  m∠A = m∠A′ and m∠B = m∠B′
- the measures of two corresponding sides are proportional *and* the corresponding angles between the two sides are congruent, SAS~

$$\frac{m\overline{A'B'}}{m\overline{AB}} = \frac{m\overline{A'C'}}{m\overline{AC}} \text{ and } m\angle A' = m\angle A$$

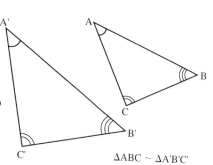

△ABC ~ △A′B′C′

The image of a size transformation (dilatation) or a composition of transformations on a figure is similar to the original figure.

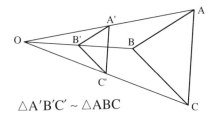

$$\triangle A'B'C' \sim \triangle ABC$$

Geometry is based on logical reasoning so it is important to remember the conditional logical connective. $p \rightarrow q$ is read "If p then q," and the truth table shows that this statement is true for all cases except when p is true and q is false.

After we prove a theorem, which is usually in the form $p \rightarrow q$, we may consider its *converse*, which is $q \rightarrow p$. Recall that the converse is not necessarily true; *Example 2* illustrates this.

In the exercises, you will be required to justify all answers by referring to the theorem or fact on which you based your calculation or solution. There is no need to state each theorem formally, but the progression of steps in your work should be clear to anyone reading your solution.

Example 1. From the diagram, calculate these measures.

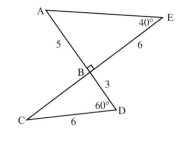

    a) $m\overline{AE}$

    b) $m\angle BAE$

    c) $m\overline{BC}$

    Give the answers to 1 decimal place where necessary.

Solution.   a) $\triangle AEB$ is a right triangle because $m\angle ABE = 90°$
          Using the Pythagorean Theorem, $(m\overline{AE})^2 = 5^2 + 6^2$
$$m\overline{AE} = \sqrt{61}$$
$$\doteq 7.8$$

    b) Since the sum of the angles in a triangle is $180°$,
       in $\triangle ABE$, $m\angle BAE = 180° - (90° + 40°)$
$$= 50°$$

    c) Since $\angle CBD$ and $\angle ABE$ are vertically opposite angles, they are congruent. Hence, $m\angle CBD = 90°$
      Since $\triangle BCD$ is a right triangle, using the Pythagorean Theorem,
$$(m\overline{BC})^2 = 6^2 - 3^2$$
$$m\overline{BC} = \sqrt{27}$$
$$\doteq 5.2$$

Example 2. For each conditional statement, write the converse statement and state whether it is true.

    a) In an isosceles triangle if two sides are congruent, then the angles opposite those sides are congruent.

    b) If a quadrilateral is a square, then the measures of all four sides are the same.

Solution.   a) Converse: If an isosceles triangle has two angles congruent, then the sides opposite those angles are congruent. This is a true statement.

    b) Converse: If a quadrilateral has all four sides the same measure, then it is a square. This is not a true statement, as the diagram shows.

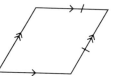

EXERCISES 6-1

(A)

1. a) For the diagram at the right, list the properties which justify each statement.

    i) m∠ABE = m∠CDE = 45°

    ii) △AEB ~ △DEC

    iii) $(m\overline{EB})^2 = (m\overline{AB})^2 - (m\overline{AE})^2$

  b) Calculate the measure of each segment. Give the answers to 1 decimal place.

    i) $\overline{EB}$ ii) $\overline{DE}$ iii) $\overline{AC}$

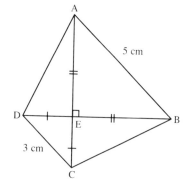

2. Calculate each value of *a*, *b*, *c*, and *d*.

  a)

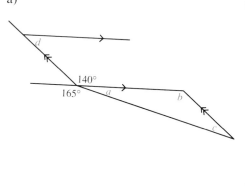

  b)

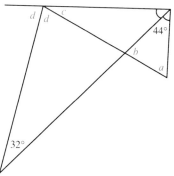

3. In the diagram shown

   a) Find and name two pairs of congruent triangles.

   b) For each pair of congruent triangles, list facts which prove the congruence and give reasons.

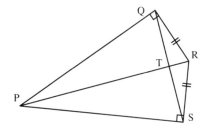

4. Write the converse of each statement. Is the converse true?

   a) If a quadrilateral is a square, then it is a rectangle.

   b) A rectangle has congruent diagonals.

5. For the diagram (below left)

   a) Find and name a pair of similar triangles.

   b) Give reasons why these triangles are similar.

   c) Write the proportion for the corresponding sides.

   d) If $m\overline{EC}$ = 2.5 cm, $m\overline{DB}$ = 6 cm, $m\overline{CD}$ = 3.5 cm, find $m\overline{AB}$ and $m\overline{AD}$.

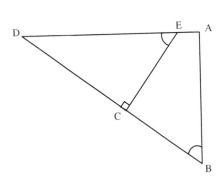

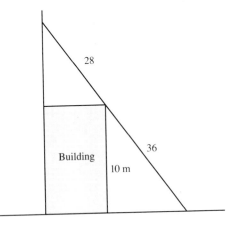

6. A window cleaner places a ladder to reach the window of a building (above right). The ladder just clears a smaller building 10 m tall. The window cleaner keeps track of her progress by counting the rungs of the ladder on the way up. She passes the roof of the low building at rung 36 and counts 28 rungs more to the window of the higher building. How high is the window? Give the answer to 1 decimal place. Your calculation should show all steps and a justification for each step.

6-2 DEFINITIONS AND CONCEPTS OF A CIRCLE

The concept of a circle has intrigued the human intellect since the beginnings of recorded time. The circle has been used by various religious groups as the symbol of eternity, perfection, and completeness. Circles are also employed in a variety of logos, such as the familiar Olympic symbol.

The association of the circle with qualities such as perfection, eternity, and completeness derives from the following geometric properties of circles.

- A circle is a closed curve.
- There is a unique point, the centre of the circle, which is equidistant from all points on the circle.
- Any line which passes through the centre of a circle is a line of symmetry of the circle.
- A circle has an infinite number of lines of symmetry.
- The intersection of a sphere with a plane is a circle.

The ancient Ptolemaic theory of planetary motion asserted that each planet moved in a circle about the sun, which in turn moved in a circle about the Earth. This theory was predominant for about 1500 years, until the publication in 1543 of the Copernican theory which asserted that all planets, including the Earth, travel in circular orbits around the sun. We know today that the planets actually travel in elliptical orbits but their orbits are in most cases almost circular. The successive theories of planetary motion are suggestive of the all-pervasive role of the circle in scientific models. This fact alone makes the study of the circle and its geometric properties of critical importance.

Definition: A *circle* is the set of all points which lie a fixed distance r (called the *radius*) from a fixed point C (called the *centre*).

This diagram illustrates examples of familiar terms.

- Point O is the centre of the circle.
- Point A is any point on the circle.
- Line segment OA is a radius.
- Line segment DT (which contains O) is a diameter.
- Line segment MN is a chord.
- $\overset{\frown}{TC}$ is a minor arc. $\overset{\frown}{TMC}$ is a major arc.
- The shaded region TOC is a sector, and $\angle TOC$ is the sector angle.
- $\angle TOC$ is also called the central angle of the sector.

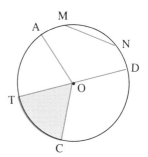

Any two distinct points A and B on a circle divide
the circle into two parts or arcs. If the two arcs are
equal in length, each arc is called a *semicircle*. Otherwise, the arcs have different lengths. The diagram
shows that the points A, B, and P divide the circle into
a shorter arc, called the *minor arc*, and denoted $\overset{\frown}{AB}$ as
well as a longer arc, called the *major arc*, and denoted
$\overset{\frown}{APB}$.

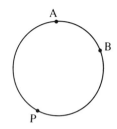

The following definition enables us to associate with each arc a
unique angle measure.

Definition: The *degree measure* of an arc of a circle is the measure (in degrees) of the
central angle that intercepts that arc.

In the diagram, the degree measure of minor arc $\overset{\frown}{AB}$ is
the measure of ∠AOB in degrees. The degree measure
of major arc $\overset{\frown}{APB}$ is the measure of reflex ∠AOB.

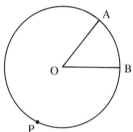

The diagrams below show the three possible cases for the intersection
of a line with a circle. Recall these diagrams from *Section 4-4*.

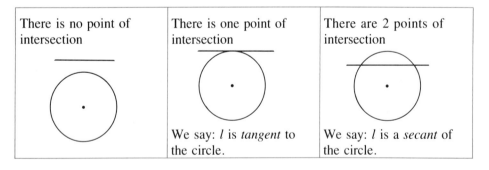

There is no point of intersection	There is one point of intersection	There are 2 points of intersection
	We say: *l* is *tangent* to the circle.	We say: *l* is a *secant* of the circle.

In *Section 6-5* we will study interesting and important properties of
tangents and secants of circles.

Consider a circle, centre O, with any chord AB.
∠AOB is a central angle and $\overset{\frown}{AB}$ is the intercepted
arc. By definition, the degree measure of $\overset{\frown}{AB}$ equals
the degree measure of ∠AOB.

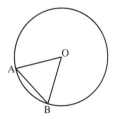

△OAB is rotated 100° clockwise about O to an image △OA'B'.

Compare m$\overline{AB}$ to m$\overline{A'B'}$.

Compare m∠AOB to m∠A'OB'.

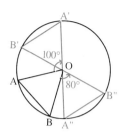

What is true about the measures of $\overline{AB}$ and $\overline{A'B'}$?

△AOB is rotated 80° counterclockwise about O to an image △OA"B". Compare the lengths and angles, as before.

Since a rotation is an isometry, the chord and its images are congruent. Angle measure is preserved so the central angles are congruent. This means that the intercepted arcs are congruent. Hence, congruent chords intercept congruent arcs.

Rotations can also be used to show that if arcs of a circle are congruent, corresponding chords are congruent. This statement and its converse can be combined into a single statement using the "iff" notation.

Theorem

Chords of a circle are congruent iff they intercept congruent arcs.

By using a translation, the theorem can be extended to include chords in congruent circles. In the diagram below, the circle, centre O', is the translated image of the circle, centre O.

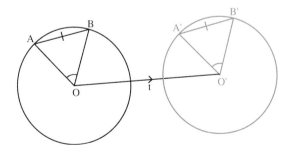

Since translation is an isometry, the measures of the chord and central angle are preserved.

m$\overline{AB}$ = m$\overline{A'B'}$ and m∠AOB = m∠A'O'B'

Therefore the arcs are congruent.   m$\overarc{AB}$ = m$\overarc{A'B'}$

Corollary

Congruent chords in congruent circles intercept congruent arcs.

Example. $\overline{AOC}$ is a diameter of a circle, centre O.
If m∠AOB = 110° and m$\overline{OA}$ = 6, find:

a) m$\overarc{AB}$ b) m$\overarc{AC}$ c) m$\overarc{BC}$

d) m$\overline{OB}$ e) m∠OAB.

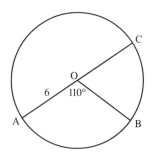

Solution.   a) By definition of arc measure,
    m$\overarc{AB}$ = 110°

b) Since $\overline{AOC}$ is a diameter, $\overarc{AC}$ is a semicircle.
    By definition of a semicircle,
    m$\overarc{AC}$ = 180°

c) Since $\overline{AOC}$ is a straight line, ∠COB and ∠AOB are supplementary
    angles.
    Hence, m$\overarc{BC}$ = m∠COB
        = 180° − 110°
        = 70°

d) $\overline{OB}$ is a radius of the circle, which is given as 6.
    Hence, m$\overline{OB}$ = 6

e) △AOB is isosceles, with m$\overline{AO}$ = m$\overline{OB}$
    Hence, m∠OBA = m∠OAB
    Since the sum of the angles in a triangle is 180°,
    m∠OAB = $\frac{1}{2}$(180° − 110°)
        = 35°

EXERCISES 6-2

1. What point is equidistant from all the points that lie on a circle?

2. What is the greatest possible distance between two points which lie on a circle
    with radius R?

3. Define each term as it pertains to a circle.
    a) centre   b) radius   c) diameter   d) chord   e) arc

4. a) Define the term sector.   b) Can a semicircle be a sector?

5. Explain the difference between a secant and a tangent to a circle.

6. How many secants pass through a particular point on a circle?

7. Use the diagram at the right to name
   these parts of a circle.

   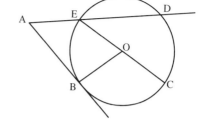

   a) three radii

   b) a diameter

   c) a secant

   d) a tangent

   e) two semicircles

   f) two central angles

8. a) What is the greatest number of points in which three circles can intersect?

   b) What is the least number of points in which three circles can intersect?

   c) Draw diagrams to illustrate three circles intersecting in all possible numbers of
      points from the least to the greatest.

9. $\overline{AB}$ is a diameter of a circle, centre
   O. Find each measure.

   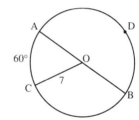

   a) ∠COB

   b) $\overparen{CB}$

   c) $\overparen{ADB}$

   d) $\overline{AB}$

10. Calculate the perimeter of each inscribed regular polygon.

    a)

    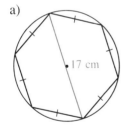

    17 cm

    b)

    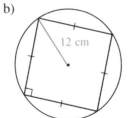

    12 cm

    c)

    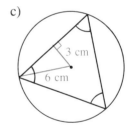

    3 cm

    6 cm

Ⓒ

11. In the diagram at the right, C is the
    midpoint of chord AB. Prove that
    radius OD is the right bisector of $\overline{AB}$.

12. The point of intersection of the
    perpendicular bisectors of two
    (non-parallel) chords of a circle is
    the centre of the circle. Describe
    how to locate the centre of a circular
    disk using only a ruler (marked in
    millimetres) and a set square.

    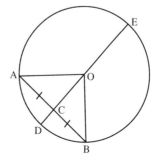

6-3 PROPERTIES OF ARCS AND CHORDS IN A CIRCLE

In the construction of a wheel for a train, a
disk is cut from a steel cylinder. A hole is
then drilled in the centre of the circular
disk.

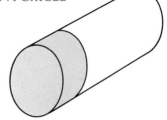

How can the centre of the disk be
located?

The following theorem suggests a method for finding the centre of a
circle using a property of its chords.

Theorem
The perpendicular (right) bisector of a chord of a circle passes through the
centre of the circle.

Consider the circle at the right, centre O and chord
AB. Since radii OA and OB are congruent, O is equidistant from A and B. Since any point equidistant from
the end points of a line segment is on the perpendicular bisector of the segment, O is on the perpendicular
bisector of $\overline{AB}$.

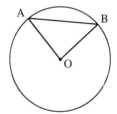

It follows from the theorem above that the centre of a circle is the
point of intersection of the perpendicular bisectors of any two (non-
parallel) chords of the circle.
l is the perpendicular bisector of chord AB.
m is the perpendicular bisector of chord CD.
O is the centre of the circle.

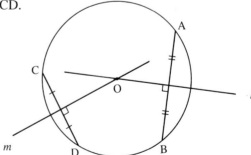

Consider the circle at the right, centre O, with chord
AB, and radius OC perpendicular to $\overline{AB}$ at D.
Join OA and OB.
Rotate the figure about O.
The image of $\overline{OD}$ is $\overline{OD'}$, so $\overline{OD} \cong \overline{OD'}$.
Hence, $m\overline{OD} = m\overline{OD'}$
Since we know that OD is the right bisector of $\overline{AB}$,
then OD′ is the right bisector of $\overline{A'B'}$.
Hence, $\overline{AB}$ and $\overline{A'B'}$ are equidistant from O.
This result enables us to make the following statement.

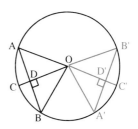

> If chords in a circle are congruent, then the chords are equidistant from the centre
> of the circle.

We can use a rotation to show that the converse of this statement is
also true.

> If two chords are equidistant from the centre of a circle, then the chords are
> congruent.

Consider a circle, centre O, with radius OD which is perpendicular to
chord AB at E. We extend DO to intersect the circumference at C.
Since $\overline{CD}$ is a diameter, it is an axis of symmetry of
the circle. The reflection image of $\overline{AE}$ in $\overline{CD}$ is $\overline{EB}$.
Hence, $m\overline{AE} = m\overline{BE}$
Therefore, E is the midpoint of chord AB, and radius
OD cuts $\overline{AB}$ into two congruent segments, $\overline{AE}$ and
$\overline{EB}$.
Similarly, the reflection image of $\overset{\frown}{AD}$ in $\overline{CD}$ is $\overset{\frown}{BD}$, so
$\overset{\frown}{AD} \cong \overset{\frown}{DB}$.

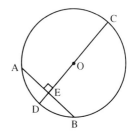

We can conclude that a radius perpendicular to a chord bisects the
chord and the intercepted arc.

Theorem
If a radius is perpendicular to a chord in a circle, then the radius divides the
chord into two congruent segments and the intercepted arc into two
congruent arcs.

The proof of the converse of this theorem is left as an exercise.

> **Converse**
> If the radius bisects a chord or the subtended arc, then the radius is perpendicular to the chord.

Example.   Calculate the perimeter of a regular octagon inscribed in a circle of diameter 15 cm. Each side of the octagon is 6.9 cm from the centre of the circle.

Solution.   Draw a diagram.
Figure ABCDEFGH is a regular octagon.
Join AO and OB, which are radii of the circle.
Then $m\overline{AO} = m\overline{OB} = 7.5$ cm
Drop the perpendicular from O onto AB at R.
Then $m\overline{OR} = 6.9$ cm
Use the Pythagorean Theorem in $\triangle BOR$.
$$(m\overline{RB})^2 = (m\overline{OB})^2 - (m\overline{OR})^2$$
$$= 7.5^2 - 6.9^2$$
$$m\overline{RB} = \sqrt{7.5^2 - 6.9^2}$$
$$\doteq 2.939$$
$$m\overline{AB} = 2(m\overline{RB})$$
$$\doteq 5.878$$
The perimeter of the octagon is 8(5.878) cm, or about 47 cm.

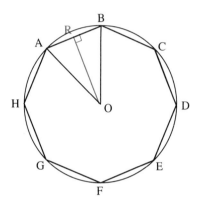

EXERCISES 6-3

Ⓐ

1. Find each value of x to 1 decimal place where necessary.

a)

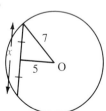

b)

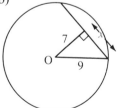

c)

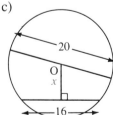

2. Find each value of *x* to 1 decimal place where necessary.

a)

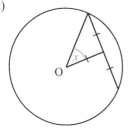

b)

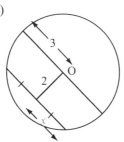

c)

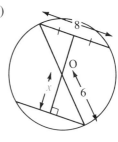

3. A circle has a diameter of 14 cm. How far from the centre of the circle is a chord of length 7 cm?

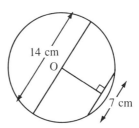

4. Find each value of *z* to 1 decimal place where necessary.

a)

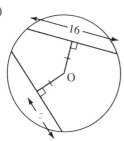

b)

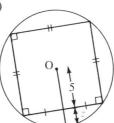

c)

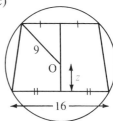

Ⓑ

5. $\overline{EF}$ is a diameter of a circle, centre O. $\overline{AB}$ and $\overline{CD}$ are parallel chords. Use a reflection to show that $\overparen{AC} \cong \overparen{BD}$.

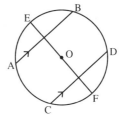

6. Two intersecting circles of equal radii are drawn. How many points on each circle are equidistant from both centres?

7. How far is a chord of length 8 cm from the centre of a circle with diameter 10 cm?

8. Two paths through a circular garden intersect at the centre of the garden (below left). One of the central angles is 115°. Find the degree measure of the 4 minor arcs determined by the paths.

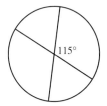

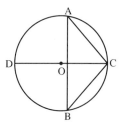

9. Find the degree measure of $\overset{\frown}{AC}$ if the degree measure of $\overset{\frown}{DB}$ is 98° (above right).

10. What is the diameter of a circle in which a chord 16 cm long is 15 cm from the centre?

Ⓒ

11. In the diagram (below left), $\overline{PQ}$ and $\overline{RS}$ are equal chords of a circle, centre O. T is the point of intersection of $\overline{PQ}$ and $\overline{RS}$. Show that $\overset{\frown}{PR} \cong \overset{\frown}{SQ}$.

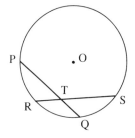

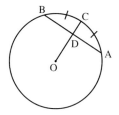

12. In the diagram (above right), radius OC of circle, centre O, cuts chord AB at D and bisects $\overset{\frown}{AB}$ at C. Show that OD is perpendicular to AB.

13. A student of woodwork is building a 3-legged stool for her term project. She uses her knowledge of geometry of the circle to determine where to attach the 3 legs to the circular top. With the aid of a diagram, show a method she can use as a guide to assemble the stool.

14. Write an algebraic expression for the area of a regular hexagon inscribed in a circle with radius R.

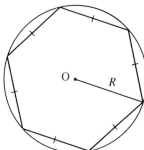

6-4 PROPERTIES OF ANGLES IN A CIRCLE

When the balls on a billiard table are positioned as shown, the ⑦ ball is easier to sink than the ⑥ ball even though both balls are the same distance from the pocket.

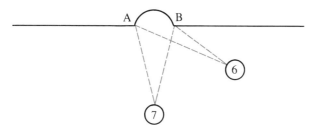

The diagram shows why. The dotted lines show the boundary of the paths for each ball. The permissible paths for the ⑥ ball lie within a small angle. The permissible paths for the ⑦ ball lie within a larger angle. We say that the angle subtended by line segment AB at the ⑦ ball is greater than the angle subtended by $\overline{AB}$ at the ⑥ ball.

The central angle AOB of the circle is *subtended* by the arc AB or by the chord AB.

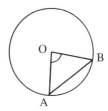

The vertex C of ∠ACB is on the circumference of the circle. ACB is an *inscribed* angle subtended by arc AB or by chord AB. We say that ∠ACB *intercepts* $\overset{\frown}{AB}$ or that $\overset{\frown}{AB}$ *inscribes* ∠ACB.

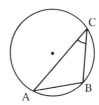

Definition: Points which are on the same circle are said to be *concyclic*. An inscribed polygon is one in which the vertices are concyclic. An inscribed quadrilateral is called a *cyclic quadrilateral*.

In the following examples, we will see how the measure of an inscribed angle is related to the measure of its intercepted arc.

Example 1.   ACB is an inscribed angle and $\overline{AC}$ is a diameter of the circle, centre O. How is m∠C related to m$\overset{\frown}{AB}$?

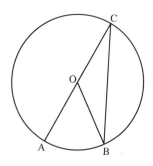

Solution.   Since AOB is an exterior angle to isosceles △BOC,
m∠AOB = m∠C + m∠B
But m∠C = m∠B,
so m∠AOB = 2(m∠C) or
m∠C = $\frac{1}{2}$(m∠AOB)
Since m∠AOB = m$\overset{\frown}{AB}$
then m∠C = $\frac{1}{2}$(m$\overset{\frown}{AB}$)

Example 1 shows that the measure of the inscribed angle is half the measure of the intercepted arc.

We will investigate whether this relationship is true for other cases. Compare the measures of the central angle AOB and the inscribed angle ACB in the diagrams below.

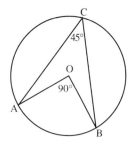
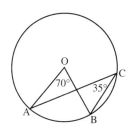
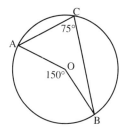

We see that m∠AOB is twice m∠ACB in each case. It can be proved that this is true for all circles. The proof is similar to the solution of *Example 1*. Since the measure of the central angle is equal to the measure of the intercepted arc AB, we can make the following statement.

Theorem
The degree measure of an inscribed angle is half the degree measure of its intercepted arc.

We can use the preceding theorem to show that angles subtended by the same arc are congruent.

In the diagram, angles C, D, and E are subtended by the same arc AB. Since the measure of each angle is equal to half the measure of $\overarc{AB}$, then $m\angle C = m\angle D = m\angle E$.

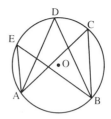

Furthermore we can show, by using a rotation, that angles subtended by congruent arcs in the same circle are congruent.

> **Corollary**
>
> In a circle, inscribed angles subtended by the same arc or by congruent arcs are congruent.

The corollary can be extended to include angles subtended by congruent arcs in congruent circles. This can be verified by a translation.

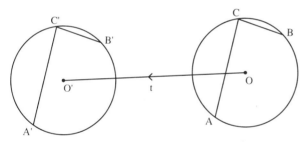

The circle, centre O', is a translation image of the circle, centre O. Hence, $m\overarc{AB} = m\overarc{A'B'}$ and $m\angle ACB = m\angle A'C'B'$

We now consider an angle inscribed in a semicircle.
$\overline{AB}$ is a diameter of a circle, centre O. Angle ACB is subtended by $\overarc{ADB}$. Since $\overarc{ADB}$ is a semicircle, its measure is 180°.
Hence, $m\angle ACB = 90°$

> **Corollary**
>
> An inscribed angle subtended by a semicircle is a right angle.

Example 2.   Points A, B, C, and D are located on a circle, centre O. If AB is parallel to DC, show that m$\overset{\frown}{AD}$ = m$\overset{\frown}{BC}$.

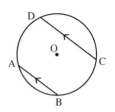

Solution.   Join DB. ABD and BDC are alternate angles between parallel lines.
Hence, m∠ABD = m∠BDC
Since congruent angles intercept congruent arcs, m$\overset{\frown}{AD}$ = m$\overset{\frown}{BC}$

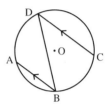

The result of *Example 2* can be expressed as a corollary.

Corollary
In a circle, the two arcs between two parallel chords are congruent.

Example 3. $\overline{AB}$ is a diameter of a circle, centre O, with points D and E on one arc AB, and point C on the other arc AB.
m∠CAB = 40°, m$\overset{\frown}{AD}$ = 46°, and
m∠EOB = 50°
Find the measures of these arcs and angles.

   a) $\overset{\frown}{BC}$ b) $\overset{\frown}{AC}$

   c) ∠ACB   d) ∠CEB

Solution.   a) Since ∠CAB is subtended by $\overset{\frown}{CB}$,
     m$\overset{\frown}{BC}$ = 2(m∠CAB)
         = 80°

   b) Since $\overset{\frown}{ACB}$ is a semicircle,
     m$\overset{\frown}{AC}$ = 180° − m$\overset{\frown}{BC}$
         = 100°

   c) Since ∠ACB is inscribed in a semicircle, its measure is 90°.

   d) Inscribed angle CEB is subtended by $\overset{\frown}{CB}$. Since the degree measure of an inscribed angle is half the degree measure of its intercepted arc,
     m∠CEB = $\frac{1}{2}$(m$\overset{\frown}{CB}$)
          = 40°

EXERCISES 6-4

1. Use the diagram to name these angles.

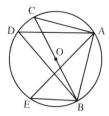

   a) three inscribed angles subtended by $\overset{\frown}{AB}$

   b) two angles inscribed on $\overset{\frown}{CD}$

   c) two inscribed angles subtended by $\overset{\frown}{DE}$

   d) an angle subtended by a semicircle

2. a) What is the measure of an angle at the circumference of a circle, subtended by a diameter?

   b) What is the measure of an angle at the centre of a circle, subtended by a diameter?

3. Find each value of x.

   a)

   b)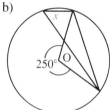

   c)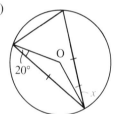

4. Find the values of x, y, and z.

   a)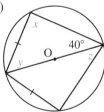

   b)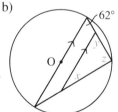

   c)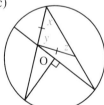

5. $\overline{PS}$ is a diameter of a circle, centre O. Find each measure.

   a) $\angle QPR$ b) $\overset{\frown}{PR}$

   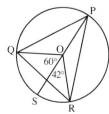

6. $\overline{AB}$, $\overline{BC}$, $\overline{DE}$, and $\overline{EF}$ are congruent chords of a circle, centre O, and m∠BAC = 30° (below left). Find the measures of ∠DEF and ∠DFE.

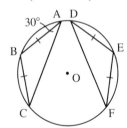
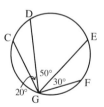

7. Use the diagram (above right) to find the measure of each arc.
   a) $\overset{\frown}{CD}$ b) $\overset{\frown}{DF}$ c) $\overset{\frown}{CGF}$

Ⓑ

8. Trapezoid ABCD (below left) is inscribed in a circle and AD is parallel to BC. If m∠ABD = 35° and m∠DAC = 40°, find the measures of ∠DAB and ∠ADC.

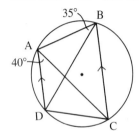
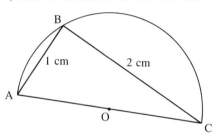

9. Calculate the radius of the semicircle (above right).

10. In the diagram (below left), $m\overset{\frown}{PR} = m\overset{\frown}{QS}$; show that PQ is parallel to RS.

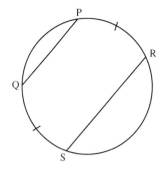
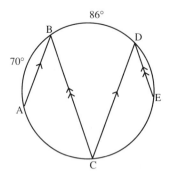

11. In the circle (above right), $m\overset{\frown}{AB} = 70°$ and $m\overset{\frown}{BD} = 86°$; find each measure.
    a) ∠CDE   b) $\overset{\frown}{AC}$ c) $\overset{\frown}{DE}$

12. ABCD is a cyclic quadrilateral in a circle, centre O (below left). Use the fact that the sum of the degree measures of a minor arc and the corresponding major arc is 360° to show that m∠A + m∠C = 180° and m∠B + m∠D = 180°.

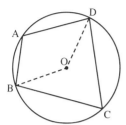
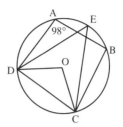

13. In the diagram (above right), m∠BCO = 44° and m∠A = 98°; find each measure.
    a) ∠DCO   b) ∠DOC   c) ⌢DC   d) ∠DEC

14. An urban planner responsible for parks and recreation areas presents a plan for a playground. The position of a swing set, S, is shown with the walkways connecting the location points of the other equipment. Paths AC and BD are diagonals of the quadilateral ABCD.
    If m∠ABC = 98° and m⌢CD = 100°, find each measure.

    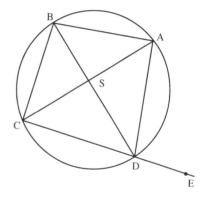

    a) ∠ABD
    b) ∠ADE
    c) ⌢AD

15. The sum of the measures of an inscribed angle and central angle subtended by the same arc is 162°. Find the measure of each angle.

16. Trapezoid PQRS, with parallel sides PQ and RS, is inscribed in a circle, centre O. If m⌢PS = 54° and m⌢SR = 68°, find the measure of each angle of the trapezoid.

17. CDEF is a cyclic quadrilateral. If m∠C = 4x + 10°, m∠D = 7x + 20°, and m∠E = 6x + 30°, find the measure of each angle of the quadrilateral.

Ⓒ

18. In the diagram, ⌢VX and ⌢XY are congruent arcs. Prove that the angles of △VWZ are respectively congruent to the angles of △XYZ.

    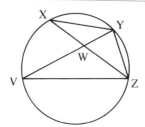

 PROBLEM SOLVING

The Nine-Point Circle

''Mathematics, rightly viewed, possesses not only truth but supreme beauty.''

Bertrand Russell

△ABC is any triangle. Prove that these *nine* points lie on a circle.

- the midpoints of the sides: D, E, F
- the feet of the altitudes: P, Q, R
- the midpoints of the segments joining the orthocentre, H, to the vertices: X, Y, Z

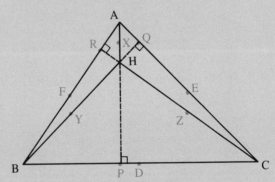

Understand the problem
- What is the orthocentre?

Think of a strategy
- Since altitudes are involved, we can see some right angles on the diagram.
- This suggests that to prove certain points lie on a circle, we may need to use the property of angles in a semicircle.

Carry out the strategy
- Can you prove that the quadrilaterals FEZY and FXZD are rectangles?
- Does this prove that the points F, E, Z, Y, X, and D lie on the same circle?
- Why do the points P, Q, and R also lie on this circle?
- Complete a proof that the points D, E, F, P, Q, R, X, Y, and Z lie on the same circle.

Look back
- For what kind of triangle do the three altitudes intersect outside the triangle? Would the result still be true for this kind of triangle?
- What happens if the triangle is a right triangle?
- What happens if the triangle is isosceles? equilateral?
- Discuss why Bertrand Russell might have felt that the nine-point circle is a good example to illustrate the quotation above.

PROBLEMS

1. A triangle has sides of length 6 cm, 8 cm, and 10 cm. If a circle is drawn through its vertices, what is the diameter of the circle?

2. Two numbers have a sum of 6 and a product of 7.
   a) Find the sum of their squares.
   b) Find the difference of their squares.
   c) Find the sum of the squares of their reciprocals.

3. Write the numbers from 1 to 9 in a 3 by 3 grid such that the sums of the three numbers along any row, any column, or any diagonal are all different.

4. The Great Pyramid of Cheops has a base 230 m square. Its faces are congruent isosceles triangles, making an angle of 51.87° with the ground.
   a) Calculate the height of the pyramid, to the nearest metre.
   b) Discuss how close the faces are to being equilateral triangles.

5. A cylindrical fuel tank has a diameter of 1.6 m and a length of 3.0 m. It is installed underground at a gasoline station, lying on its side. By measuring, it is found that the maximum depth of the fuel in the tank is 0.5 m. Calculate the number of litres of fuel in the tank.

6. How many real roots does this equation have?
   $(x - 1)^2 + (x - 2)^2 + (x - 3)^2 + (x - 4)^2 = 0$

7. a) If $p \neq q$, explain why this equation has no real roots:
      $(x + p)^2 + (x + q)^2 = 0.$
   b) Prove that every quadratic equation $ax^2 + bx + c = 0$ $(a \neq 0)$ which has no real roots can be written in the form $(x + p)^2 + (y + q)^2 = 0$, where p and q are real numbers.

8. Prove that the centre of the nine-point circle of any triangle is the midpoint of the line segment joining the orthocentre and the circumcentre.

6-5 PROPERTIES OF TANGENTS AND SECANTS

AB is a secant that intersects radius OP at right angles in a circle, centre O. Consider a translation that moves AB along $\overline{OP}$. As AB moves away from O, the distances between the intersection points of the secant and the circle decrease. When the secant reaches point P, it becomes a tangent to the circle. Since the translation image A′B′ is parallel to AB, then A′B′ is perpendicular to OP at P.

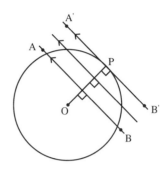

Theorem
A tangent to a circle is perpendicular to the radius of the circle at the point of contact.

The converse of this theorem is true.

Converse
A line perpendicular to a radius of a circle at a point of intersection with the circle is tangent to the circle at that point.

Example 1. Two tangents PQ and PR intersect a circle, centre O, at Q and R respectively. Show that $\overline{PQ} \cong \overline{PR}$.

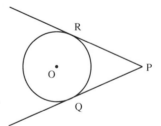

Solution. Join PO, OR, and OQ.
△PQO ≅ △PRO   HL
Since the triangles are congruent, $\overline{PQ} \cong \overline{PR}$

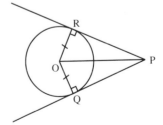

In *Example 1,* note that △PRO is the reflection image of △PQO in $\overline{OP}$. Also, $\overline{PQ}$ and $\overline{PR}$ are called *tangent segments*.

In the diagram (below left), AB is a diameter of a circle, centre O. CA is tangent to the circle at A. D is any point on $\overset{\frown}{AB}$.
Since a tangent to a circle is perpendicular to the radius at the point of contact, m∠BAC = 90°
Since the degree measure of a semicircle is 180°, $m\overset{\frown}{ADB}$ = 180°
These two statements illustrate that the measure of the angle between a tangent and a diameter is half the measure of the intercepted arc.
That is, m∠BAC = $\frac{1}{2}$(m$\overset{\frown}{ADB}$)

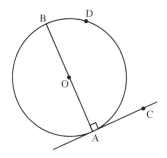 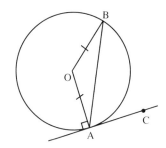

Consider the angle formed by a tangent and a chord. In the diagram (above right), $\overline{AB}$ is a chord of a circle, centre O. CA is tangent to the circle at A.
m∠OAC = 90°
Since △AOB is isosceles, m∠OAB = m∠OBA
The sum of the angles in a triangle is 180°.
m∠AOB = 180° − 2(m∠OAB)
Since ∠OAB and ∠BAC are complementary,
m∠OAB = 90° − m∠BAC
Hence, m∠AOB = 180° − 2(90° − m∠BAC)
$\qquad\qquad$ = 2(m∠BAC)
Hence, m∠BAC = $\frac{1}{2}$(m∠AOB)
$\qquad\qquad$ = $\frac{1}{2}$(m$\overset{\frown}{AB}$)
This result can be expressed as a theorem.

Theorem
The measure of an angle formed by a secant and a tangent, at the point of contact in a circle, is half the measure of its intercepted arc.

Example 2. DC is tangent to a circle at A. B and E are two points on the circle. If m∠BAC = 52° and m∠EAD = 44°, find the measure of each angle.

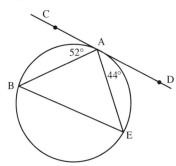

   a) ∠AEB

   b) ∠EBA

   c) ∠EAB

Solution. a) Since the angle formed by a tangent and a secant is half the measure of the intercepted arc,

$$m\angle BAC = \tfrac{1}{2}(m\stackrel{\frown}{BA})$$
$$52° = \tfrac{1}{2}(m\stackrel{\frown}{BA})$$
$$m\stackrel{\frown}{BA} = 104°$$

But the degree measure of an inscribed angle is half the degree measure of its intercepted arc.

Hence, $m\angle AEB = \tfrac{1}{2}(m\stackrel{\frown}{BA})$
$$= 52°$$

   b) Similarly, $m\angle EAD = \tfrac{1}{2}(m\stackrel{\frown}{EA})$
$$m\stackrel{\frown}{EA} = 88°$$
And $m\angle EBA = \tfrac{1}{2}(m\stackrel{\frown}{EA})$
$$= 44°$$

   c) Since ∠EAD, ∠EAB, and ∠BAC are supplementary,
$$m\angle EAB = 180° - (44° + 52°)$$
$$= 84°$$

The following definition will be required in the next example.

Definition: The *angle of elevation* of an object is the angle (up to 90° maximum) between the horizontal plane and the line segment joining the observer's eye to the object.

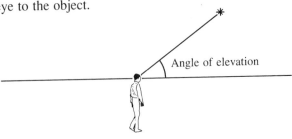

Angle of elevation

Example 3. Andy and Brinkley are seated at opposite ends of a diameter of a Ferris wheel. What is Andy's angle of elevation as seen from the bottom of the Ferris wheel when his angle of elevation as seen by Brinkley is $x°$? (Assume the ground is a tangent to the Ferris wheel.)

Solution. Let A and B denote Andy's and Brinkley's positions respectively and let O denote the centre of the Ferris wheel. $x°$ is the angle of elevation of A from B. G marks the position of the Ferris wheel where it is tangent to the ground, GE. Let OC and BD be lines parallel to the ground.

We want an expression for $\angle AGE$, the angle of elevation of A from G.

Since $\overline{OC}$ and $\overline{BD}$ are parallel, corresponding angles are congruent.
$m\angle AOC = m\angle ABD = x°$

Since $\overline{OC}$ and $\overline{GE}$ are parallel, interior angles are supplementary.
$m\angle COG + m\angle OGE = 180°$

Since the tangent to a circle is perpendicular to the radius,
$m\angle OGE = 90°$

Therefore, $m\angle COG = 90°$
$m\angle AOG = m\angle COG + m\angle AOC$
$\qquad = (90 + x)°$

Since the measure of the angle between secant and tangent is half the measure of the intercepted arc,
$m\angle AGE = \frac{1}{2}(m\angle AOG)$
$\qquad\quad = 45° + \frac{1}{2}x°$

Andy's angle of elevation from the bottom of the Ferris wheel is $45° + \frac{1}{2}x°$.

Example 3 shows the power of the theorem relating secant and tangent in finding angles in a circle.

When two secants intersect inside a circle, there is a relationship between the intersection angle and the intercepted arcs. Consider a circle, centre O, with secants AB and CD intersecting at E. $\overset{\frown}{AC}$ and $\overset{\frown}{DB}$ are the intercepted arcs. Join AD.

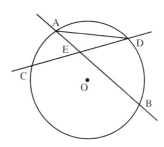

Since the exterior angle of a triangle is equal to the sum of the interior opposite angles,

m∠CEA = m∠ADC + m∠DAB

Since the degree measure of an inscribed angle is half the degree measure of its intercepted arc,

m∠ADC = $\frac{1}{2}$(m$\overarc{AC}$) and m∠DAB = $\frac{1}{2}$(m$\overarc{DB}$)

Hence, m∠CEA = $\frac{1}{2}$(m$\overarc{AC}$ + m$\overarc{DB}$)

This result can be expressed as a theorem.

Theorem
The measure of an angle formed by two secants intersecting inside a circle is half the sum of the measures of the intercepted arcs.

Consider the angle between two secants intersecting outside a circle. Secant CDE intersects secant ABE at E, which is outside the circle, centre O. Join AD.
Since the exterior angle of a triangle is equal to the sum of the interior opposite angles,

m∠CDA = m∠EAD + m∠E

Therefore, m∠E = m∠ADC − m∠EAD

Since the degree measure of an inscribed arc is half the degree measure of its intercepted arc,

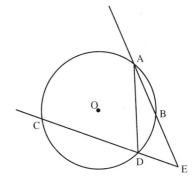

m∠ADC = $\frac{1}{2}$(m$\overarc{AC}$) and m∠EAD = $\frac{1}{2}$(m$\overarc{BD}$)

Hence, m∠E = $\frac{1}{2}$(m$\overarc{AC}$ − m$\overarc{BD}$)

This result can be expressed as a theorem.

Theorem
The measure of an angle formed by two secants intersecting outside a circle is the absolute value of half the difference of the measures of the intercepted arcs.

This relationship is also true for an angle formed by two tangents, or an angle formed by a tangent and a secant. (The proofs of these relationships are left as exercises.)

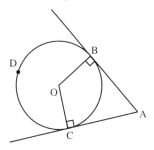

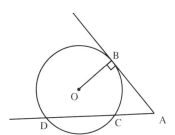

For a circle, centre O, tangents are drawn from an exterior point A to intersect the circle at B and C. D is on the major arc BC.

$m\angle A = \frac{1}{2}(m\overset{\frown}{BDC} - m\overset{\frown}{BC})$

For a circle, centre O, from an exterior point A a tangent is drawn to intersect the circle at B and a secant is drawn to intersect the circle at C and D.

$m\angle A = \frac{1}{2}(m\overset{\frown}{BD} - m\overset{\frown}{BC})$

Example 4. $\overline{ABC}$ and $\overline{ADE}$ are secants, and $\overline{AF}$ is tangent to a circle. $\overline{CF}$ and $\overline{DE}$ intersect at H.
If $m\overset{\frown}{CB} = 120°$, $m\angle EAC = 20°$, $m\overset{\frown}{DF} = 54°$, and $m\overset{\frown}{EC} = 64°$; find each measure.

a) $\angle CHE$

b) $\overset{\frown}{BD}$

c) $\angle CFG$

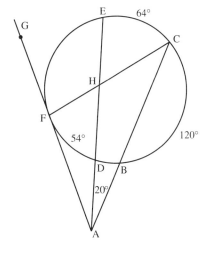

Solution. a) $m\angle CHE = \frac{1}{2}(m\overset{\frown}{EC} + m\overset{\frown}{DF})$

$= \frac{1}{2}(64° + 54°)$

$= 59°$

b) $m\angle A = \frac{1}{2}(m\overset{\frown}{CE} - m\overset{\frown}{BD})$

$20° = \frac{1}{2}(64° - m\overset{\frown}{BD})$

$m\overset{\frown}{BD} = 64° - 40°$

$= 24°$

c) Since ∠CHE and ∠EHF are supplementary,

$$m\angle EHF = 180° - 59°$$
$$= 121°$$

But $m\angle EHF = \frac{1}{2}(m\overset{\frown}{EF} + m\overset{\frown}{CB} + m\overset{\frown}{BD})$

$$121° = \frac{1}{2}(m\overset{\frown}{EF} + 120° + 24°)$$
$$m\overset{\frown}{EF} = 242° - 120° - 24°$$
$$= 98°$$

Then, $m\angle CFG = \frac{1}{2}(m\overset{\frown}{CEF})$

$$= \frac{1}{2}(64° + 98°)$$
$$= 81°$$

EXERCISES 6-5

Ⓐ

1. Find each value of *y*.

a)

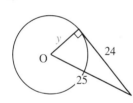

b)

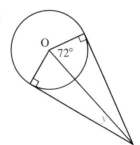

c)

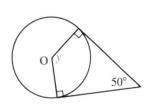

2. Find each value of *x*.

a)

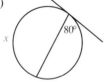

b)

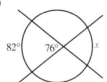

c)

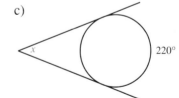

d)

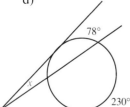

e)

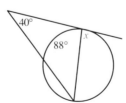

f)

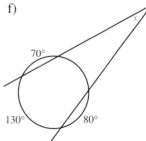

3. Find each value of *x*.

a) 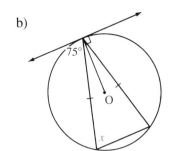   b)   c)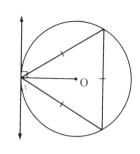

(B)

4. Tangents are drawn from an external point P to points A and B on a circle (below left). $\overline{AD}$ is a chord parallel to tangent PB. If m∠PAB = 60° and m$\overline{AP}$ = 7 cm, find:

a) the measure of ∠ADB   b) the measure of ∠BAD   c) the length of AD.

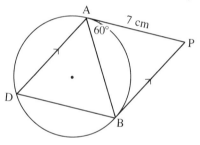

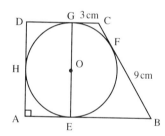

5. The sides of the trapezoid (above right) are tangent to a circle, centre O, at E, F, G, and H. The diameter of the circle is 10 cm. Find the perimeter of ABCD.

6. Find the values of *x* and *y*.

a) AB is tangent to the circle.   b)   c) AB and AC are tangent to the circle.

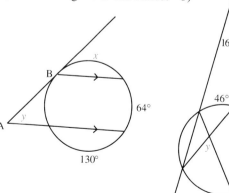

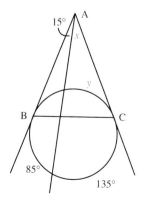

7. The sides of quadrilateral ABCD are tangent to a circle at P, Q, R, and S (below left). If m∠A = 100°, m∠B = 96°, and m∠C = 50°, find the measure of each angle of quadrilateral PQRS.

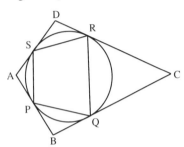
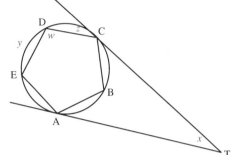

8. ABCDE is a regular pentagon inscribed in a circle (above right). $\overline{TA}$ and $\overline{TC}$ are tangent segments. Find the values of w, x, y, and z.

9. A circular wading pool with a fountain at the centre is planned for a city park. Two paths, with a 30° angle between them, lead from a point on the sidewalk to the edge of the pool. The paths are tangent to the pool. What is the degree measure of the arc of the pool between the two paths?

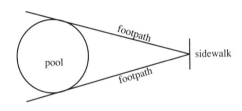

10. $\overline{AB}$ and $\overline{AC}$ are tangent segments to a circle, centre O. $\overline{BOD}$ is a diameter and m∠BCA = 48°. Find m∠DOC.

11. A chord AB cuts a circle so that the ratio of the degree measures of the minor and major arcs is 2:3. CB is tangent to the circle. Find the measure of the acute angle between the tangent and the chord.

Ⓒ

12. The measure of an angle formed by a tangent and a secant is 32°. If the measure of one of the intercepted arcs is 70°, what are all the possible values of the measure of the other intercepted arc?

13. $\overline{PA}$ and $\overline{PB}$ are tangent segments to a circle, centre O. Show that ∠APB and ∠AOB are supplementary.

14. A tangent and a secant to a circle intersect outside the circle. Prove that the degree measure of the angle between the tangent and the secant is one-half the difference between the degree measures of the intercepted arcs.

15. Two tangents to a circle intersect outside the circle. Prove that the degree measure of the angle between the tangents is equal to one-half the difference between the degree measures of the intercepted arcs.

6-6 METRIC RELATIONS BETWEEN TWO CIRCLES

Circles with the same centre are said to be *concentric*.
Consider two concentric circles with centre O.
A dilatation, centre O, maps the smaller circle onto the
larger circle.
Radius OP is mapped onto radius OP′.

The scale factor is $\dfrac{m\overline{OP'}}{m\overline{OP}}$.

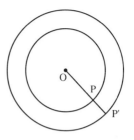

Consider any two circles with centres O and M. The composite transformation of a translation and a dilatation will map one circle onto the
other. To map the smaller circle, centre O, radius r, onto the larger
circle, centre M, radius R, translate the smaller circle a distance equal
to $m\overline{OM}$ along $\overline{OM}$, then perform a dilatation, centre M, scale factor
$\dfrac{R}{r}$.

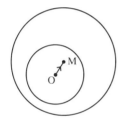

   In this manner, any circle can be mapped onto any other circle.
Since a figure and its dilatation image are similar, all circles have the
same shape and are similar. In any two circles, the scale factor of the
dilatation is equal to the ratio of their radii. The ratio of the circumfer-
ences is equal to the ratio of the radii.
   Recall that the circumference C of a circle, radius r, is given by
$C = 2\pi r$, and the area A is πr^2. Consider the ratio of the areas, A_1 and
A_2, of two circles with radii r_1 and r_2.

$$\frac{A_1}{A_2} = \frac{\pi r_1^{\,2}}{\pi r_2^{\,2}}$$

The relationship between the areas of two circles can be written as
$A_1 : A_2 = r_1^{\,2} : r_2^{\,2}$. That is, the ratio of the areas is equal to the ratio of
the squares of the radii.

In the following examples, we will investigate other relationships between two circles. In the diagrams, r_1 and r_2 represent the radii of the smaller circle, centre O_1, and the larger circle, centre O_2, respectively, and d represents the distance between the centres.

Two circles can intersect at most in two points. Here are two special cases.

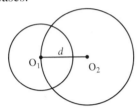

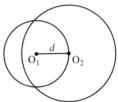

$d = r_2$ $d = r_1$

Two common tangents can be drawn from an external point to a pair of circles intersecting in two points.

Since a tangent is perpendicular to the radius drawn to the point of contact, $m\angle TP_1O_1 = m\angle TP_2O_2 = 90°$

Since corresponding angles are equal, O_1P_1 is parallel to O_2P_2.

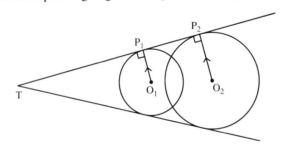

Circles with only one common point are either internally or externally tangent.

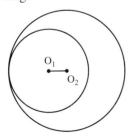

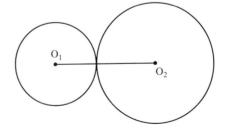

$d = r_2 - r_1$ $d = r_1 + r_2$

A tangent can be drawn at the point of contact of two internally or externally tangent circles. This is the only common tangent possible for internally tangent circles (below left). However, two additional tangents can be drawn from a given point to externally tangent circles (below right). Relationships among the angles, the radii, and the arcs in these situations will be investigated in the exercises.

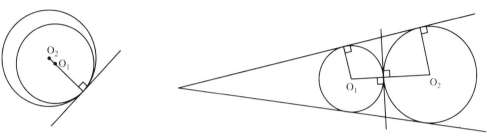

Nonconcentric circles with no points in common are either internally disjoint (below left) or externally disjoint (below right).

It is not possible to draw a common tangent to internally disjoint circles.

The diagram below illustrates that externally disjoint circles have four common tangents.

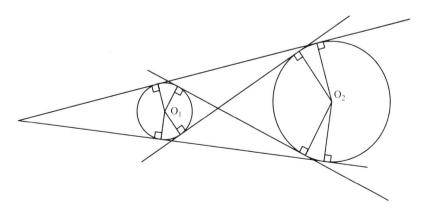

Example 1. A belt is driven by a set of two pulleys, centres O_1 and O_2. Find a formula for the distance between the centres of the pulleys in terms of their radii, r_1 and r_2, and the length t of the belt between the two points of contact, P_1 and P_2.

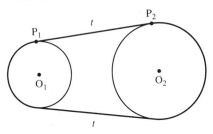

Solution.   Join O_1O_2, O_1P_1, and O_2P_2. Draw $\overline{O_1A}$ parallel to $\overline{P_1P_2}$. Let d represent $m\overline{O_1O_2}$. t represents $m\overline{P_1P_2}$.

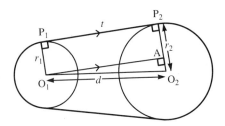

Since $\overline{P_1P_2}$ is tangent to both circles, $m\angle O_1P_1P_2 = m\angle O_2P_2P_1 = 90°$
Since $O_1AP_2P_1$ is a rectangle, $m\overline{O_1A} = t$ and $m\overline{AP_2} = m\overline{O_1P_1} = r_1$
Then, $m\overline{O_2A} = r_2 - r_1$
Since $P_1P_2 \parallel O_1A$, $m\angle O_1AO_2 = 90°$
In right $\triangle AO_1O_2$, using the Pythagorean Theorem,
$d^2 = t^2 + (r_2 - r_1)^2$
$d = \sqrt{t^2 + (r_2 - r_1)^2}$
The distance between the centres of the pulleys is $\sqrt{t^2 + (r_2 - r_1)^2}$.

In a circle, we know that the degree measure of an intercepted arc is equal to the degree measure of the central angle. Sometimes it is useful to know the measure of an arc in linear units. The linear measure of a complete circle is its circumference. The ratio of the linear measures of an arc and the complete circle is equal to the ratio of their degree measures.

In the diagram,

$$\frac{m\widehat{AB} \text{ in linear units}}{\text{circumference}} = \frac{\text{degree measure of central angle AOB}}{\text{degree measure of the complete circle}}$$

Let *s* represent the linear measure of $\widehat{AB}$ and let *r* represent the radius of the circle.

Then $\dfrac{s}{2\pi r} = \dfrac{m\angle AOB}{360°}$

$$s = \frac{2\pi r \, (m\angle AOB)}{360°}$$

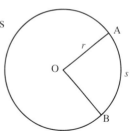

> The measure, in linear units, of an intercepted arc is equal to the product of the circumference of the circle and the degree measure of the central angle divided by 360°.

Example 2.   In the diagram, m∠COD = 60°

 a) Find the degree measures of $\widehat{AB}$ and $\widehat{CD}$.

 b) Find the linear measures of $\widehat{AB}$ and $\widehat{CD}$.

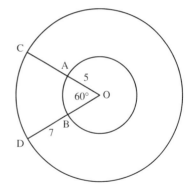

Solution.   a) Since the central angle COD subtends arcs AB and CD, their degree measures are the same. Hence, $m\widehat{AB}$ = 60° and $m\widehat{CD}$ = 60°

 b) $m\widehat{AB} = \dfrac{2\pi(5)(60°)}{360°}$

 $= \dfrac{5\pi}{3}$

 $m\widehat{CD} = \dfrac{2\pi(12)(60°)}{360°}$

 $= 4\pi$

In *Example 2*, if an exact measure is required, leave the answer in terms of π. An approximation is found by substituting for π, using a calculator.

EXERCISES 6-6

Ⓐ

1. In the diagram (below left), $\overline{BD}$ is a line segment and $\overline{AB}$ is a common tangent to two internally tangent circles. If m$\stackrel{\frown}{BD}$ = 100°, what is m$\stackrel{\frown}{BC}$?

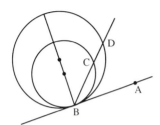

2. A graphic artist is commissioned to design a logo representing the four aspects of health care provided by a local hospital. The artist submits a design (above right) consisting of a triangle formed by joining the centres of three externally tangent circles. Each circle has a radius of 2 cm. What is the perimeter of the triangle?

3. What is the distance between the centres of two externally tangent circles with radii 11 cm and 17 cm?

4. Explain why $\overline{AB} \cong \overline{BC}$ in each diagram.

   a) AC is tangent to the smaller circle at B.

   b) BA and BC are tangent to the smaller circle at D and E respectively.

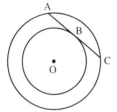
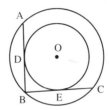

Ⓑ

5. Two circles are externally tangent at P (below left). Line segments AB and CD contain P. Show that the degree measures of arcs AC and DB are equal.

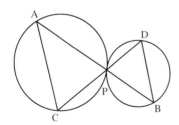
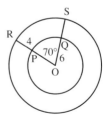

6. In the diagram (above right), find the linear measures of arcs PQ and RS. Give the answers to 1 decimal place.

7. Find each value of x. Give the answer to 1 decimal place where necessary.

a)   b)   c)

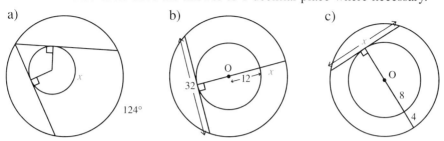

8. Find the values of x and y. O and M mark the centres of the circles.

a)   b)

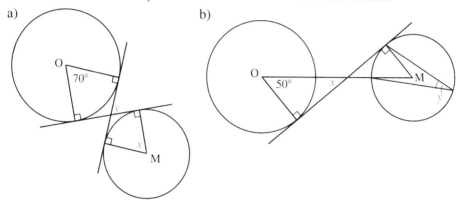

9. In the diagram (below left), $\overline{DF}$ and $\overline{AE}$ are line segments; $\overline{BC}$ is a common chord. Find the values of x and y.

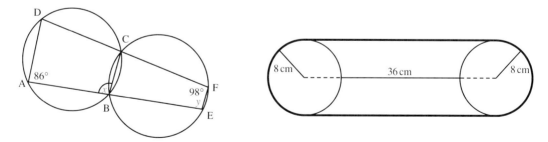

10. Two pulleys, with the same radius of 8 cm, are 36 cm apart (above right). Find the length of the belt around the pulleys. Give the answer to 1 decimal place.

11. Each of the smaller circles has a radius of 3 cm. Find the area of the shaded region of each diagram to the nearest tenth of a centimetre.

a)

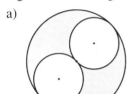

b)

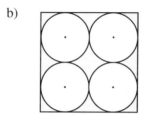

12. In the diagram, find the length of the belt around a system of two pulleys with radii 12 cm and 7 cm. The distance between the pulleys, measured along the line joining their centres, is 18 cm. Give the answer to 1 decimal place.

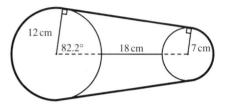

13. In the diagram (below left), A, B, and C are the centres of three externally tangent circles, each with a radius of 5 cm. Find the distance around the outside of the figure. Give the answer to 1 decimal place.

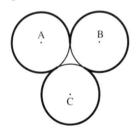

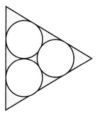

14. In the diagram (above right), a logo is created with three tangent circles inscribed in a triangle. The radius of each circle is 1 cm. Find the perimeter of the triangle.

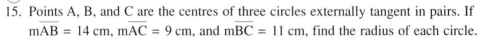

Ⓒ

15. Points A, B, and C are the centres of three circles externally tangent in pairs. If $m\overline{AB}$ = 14 cm, $m\overline{AC}$ = 9 cm, and $m\overline{BC}$ = 11 cm, find the radius of each circle.

16. Two circles of radii r and R intersect in two points A and B. The distance between the centres of the circles is d units. Write an algebraic expression in terms of r, R, and d for the distance of chord AB from the centre of each circle.

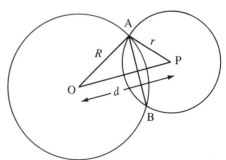

6-7 THE MEAN PROPORTIONAL THEOREM

How high is the moon above the Earth?
We can say that the surface of the moon
is about 380 000 km above the Earth's
surface, but this does not provide us with a
visual sense of this height. Sometimes it
is helpful to make comparisons such as this.
"The height of the moon above the Earth is
to the height of the CN tower as the height
of the CN tower is to the height (thickness)
of a dime."

That is, $\dfrac{\text{height of the moon}}{\text{height of the CN tower}} = \dfrac{\text{height of the CN tower}}{\text{height of a dime}}$

This equation is a proportion in which the denominator of one ratio is
the same as the numerator of the other ratio. That is, it has the form

$$\frac{a}{b} = \frac{b}{c}.$$

The common element b is called the *mean proportional* between a
and c. In the example above, we say that the height of the CN tower
is the mean proportional between the thickness of a dime and the height
of the moon.

In general, if b is the mean proportional between a and c, then

$$\frac{a}{b} = \frac{b}{c}$$
$$b^2 = ac$$

That is, $b = \pm \sqrt{ac}$ $ac \geqslant 0$

This shows that there are two mean proportionals between any two non-
zero numbers with the same sign.
The mean proportional is sometimes called the *geometric mean.*
We can check the relationship above by substituting values for two
of the distances, and calculating the third distance.
Let d kilometres represent the distance from the Earth to the moon.
Let c metres represent the height of the CN tower.
Let t centimetres represent the thickness of a dime.

Then, the relationship is $\dfrac{d}{c} = \dfrac{c}{t}$

Substitute $d = 380\,000$ km and $t = 0.1$ cm.
Convert both measurements to metres.

$$\frac{380\ 000\ 000}{c} = \frac{c}{0.001}$$

$$c^2 = 380\ 000$$

$$c \doteq 616$$

An almanac gives the height of the CN tower at 553 m, so our estimate
of 616 m is a good approximation.

Consider △ABC, with a right angle at A. $\overline{AD}$ is the altitude from A to
the hypotenuse BC.
From the sum of the angles in △ABC,
m∠ABD + m∠ACD = 90°
From the sum of the angles in △ABD,
m∠ABD + m∠BAD = 90°
Hence, m∠ACD = m∠BAD
Similarly, m∠ABD = m∠DAC
    Using D as the centre of rotation,
rotate △ABD clockwise through an angle
of 90° so that the image △A′B′D is on top
of △ADC and the sides are aligned as shown
in the diagram.
Since the size and shape of a triangle are
invariant under a rotation, △ABD ≅ △A′B′D.
Triangles ACD and BAD are equiangular
and therefore similar.

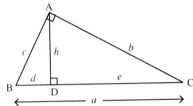

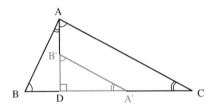

We can write a proportion relating
corresponding sides.

$$\frac{m\overline{BD}}{m\overline{AD}} = \frac{m\overline{AD}}{m\overline{CD}} \text{ or } \frac{d}{h} = \frac{h}{e}$$

h is the mean proportional between the
segments d and e.

Theorem
The altitude to the hypotenuse of a right triangle is the mean proportional
between the segments into which the altitude divides the hypotenuse.

△ABC is similar to each of the smaller right triangles formed by the
altitude.
We can demonstrate this by considering the following transformations.

● Reflect △ABD in the line BC to an image △A′BD (below left).

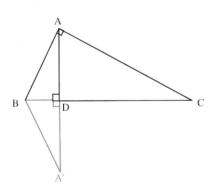 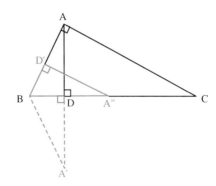

● Rotate △A′BD, with centre of rotation point B, counterclockwise through an angle equal to the measure of angle B (above right). The rotation image is △A″BD′. △ABC is similar to △D′BA″ and hence to △DBA. The proportion relating corresponding sides is

$$\frac{m\overline{BC}}{m\overline{BA}} = \frac{m\overline{BA}}{m\overline{BD}} \text{ or } \frac{a}{c} = \frac{c}{d}$$

c is the mean proportional between side a and segment d.

A similar reflection of △ACD in $\overline{BC}$, followed by a clockwise rotation about C of the image triangle A′DC through an angle equal to the measure of ∠C produces this diagram. △ABC is similar to △D′A″C and hence to △DAC. The proportion relating the corresponding sides is

$$\frac{m\overline{DC}}{m\overline{AC}} = \frac{m\overline{AC}}{m\overline{BC}} \text{ or } \frac{e}{b} = \frac{b}{a}$$

b is the mean proportional between side a and segment e.

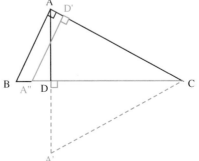

Corollary
Each of the shorter sides of a right triangle is the mean proportional between the hypotenuse and its adjacent segment.

The similarity of the three triangles generates one more interesting proportion (though not a mean proportional).

Since $\triangle ABC \sim \triangle DBA$, then $\dfrac{m\overline{AC}}{m\overline{DA}} = \dfrac{m\overline{BC}}{m\overline{BA}}$

$$\frac{b}{h} = \frac{a}{c}$$
$$ah = bc$$

This proportion illustrates a metric relation between the lengths of the sides of the right triangle and the length of the altitude to the hypotenuse.

Example 1. Find each value of x.

a)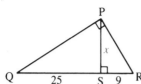

b)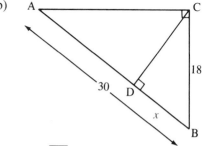

Solution.   a) Since $\overline{PS}$ is the mean proportional between $\overline{QS}$ and $\overline{RS}$,

$$\frac{m\overline{QS}}{m\overline{PS}} = \frac{m\overline{PS}}{m\overline{RS}}$$
$$\frac{25}{x} = \frac{x}{9}$$
$$x^2 = 225$$
$$x = 15$$

b) Since $\overline{BC}$ is the mean proportional between $\overline{BD}$ and $\overline{BA}$,

$$\frac{m\overline{BD}}{m\overline{BC}} = \frac{m\overline{BC}}{m\overline{BA}}$$
$$\frac{x}{18} = \frac{18}{30}$$
$$x = 10.8$$

Example 2. Triangle PQR is inscribed in a circle, centre O. Side QR is a diameter whose length is 24 cm. Chord PS is perpendicular to $\overline{QR}$ and intersects $\overline{QR}$ at T. If $m\overline{TR} = 6$ cm, what is the length of the chord PS, to 1 decimal place?

Solution.   Draw a diagram.
Since $\angle QPR$ is subtended by a semicircle, $m\angle QPR = 90°$
Since $\overline{PT}$ is the mean proportional between $\overline{TR}$ and $\overline{QT}$,

$$(m\overline{PT})^2 = m\overline{TR} \times m\overline{QT}$$
$$m\overline{PT} = \sqrt{6(24 - 6)}$$
$$\doteq 10.39$$

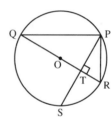

Diameter QR is perpendicular to chord PS and therefore bisects the chord.

Hence, $m\overline{PS} = 2(m\overline{PT})$
$$\doteq 2(10.39)$$
$$\doteq 20.8$$

Chord PS is 20.8 cm long.

Example 3. For $\triangle ABC$, with a right angle at A and altitude AD, prove the Pythagorean Theorem using the mean proportional theorem.

Solution. We need to show that $a^2 = b^2 + c^2$.
Use the corollary.
$\overline{AC}$ is the mean proportional between $\overline{CD}$
and $\overline{CB}$.
$b^2 = ad \ldots ①$
$\overline{AB}$ is the mean proportional between $\overline{BD}$
and $\overline{BC}$.
$c^2 = ae \ldots ②$
Add ① and ②.
$b^2 + c^2 = ad + ae$
$$= a(d + e)$$
$$= a(a)$$
Hence, $b^2 + c^2 = a^2$

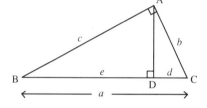

EXERCISES 6-7

Ⓐ

1. Find the mean proportionals between each pair of numbers.
   a) 2 and 8   b) 9 and 4   c) 4 and 16
   d) 3 and 27   e) 9 and 16   f) 8 and 50

2. Find the mean proportionals between each pair of terms.
   a) 6 and 10   b) -12 and -20 c) $4a$ and $18a$
   d) mn and $\dfrac{m}{n}$ e) $15xy$ and $75x$ f) $-\dfrac{18s^2}{t}$ and $-\dfrac{8t^2}{s}$

3. b is the mean proportional between a and c. If $b = 30$, find the value of c for each value of a.
   a) 25   b) -12 c) 50   d) 45   e) -150 f) -10

Ⓑ

4. Find two numbers which have a mean proportional of 4 and a sum of 10.

5. The length of a virus is to the length of a shoelace as the length of the shoelace is to the length of the St. Lawrence River. The lengths of the shoelace and the St. Lawrence River are approximately 60 cm and 3000 km. About how long is the virus?

6. The mass of a 320 kg polar bear is to the mass of a 6300 kg elephant as the mass of the elephant is to the mass of a blue whale. What is the mass of the blue whale?

7. Find each value of x to 1 decimal place.

a)

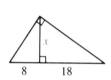

b)

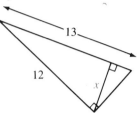

c)

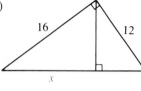

8. Find the values of x and y to 1 decimal place.

a)

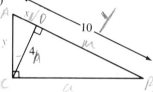

b)

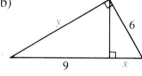

c)

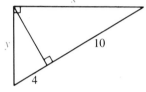

9. In the diagram (below left), name the mean proportional between each pair of sides.

a) $\overline{QS}$ and $\overline{RS}$

b) $\overline{QS}$ and $\overline{QR}$

c) $\overline{PT}$ and $\overline{QT}$

d) $\overline{RS}$ and $\overline{RQ}$

e) $\overline{PT}$ and $\overline{PQ}$

f) $\overline{QT}$ and $\overline{PQ}$

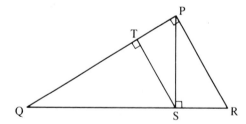

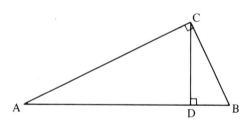

10. In $\triangle ABC$ (above right), $\angle C = 90°$, and $\overline{CD}$ is perpendicular to $\overline{AB}$.

a) If $m\overline{CD}$ is 12 cm and $m\overline{AD} : m\overline{DB} = 3 : 1$, find the measure of $\overline{AD}$.

b) If $m\overline{AD}$ is 9 cm and $m\overline{DB}$ is 7 cm, find the area of $\triangle ABC$.

Give the answers to the nearest whole number.

11. An inflated model of a gorilla is displayed at the front of a flat roof of a newly opened video store and is secured by 4 guy wires (below left). The gorilla is 12 m horizontally from the left top corner of the building and 7 m horizontally from the right top corner. Two of the guy wires, which are attached to the top of the model, are perpendicular. How high is the top of the gorilla above the flat roof? Give the answer to the nearest metre.

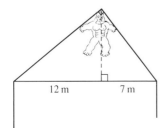

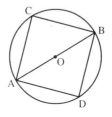

12. In the diagram (above right), the circle, centre O, has radius 15 cm. Triangle ACB is congruent to △ADB and $\overline{AB}$ is a diameter. If mAC = 22 cm, find the area of the shaded region. Give the answer to the nearest whole number.

13. Two circles, centres O and P, intersect in a common chord XY and $\overline{OX}$ is perpendicular to $\overline{XP}$. The radius of the larger circle is 16 cm and the length of the common chord is 20 cm.
   a) Calculate the distance between the centres O and P.
   b) Calculate the radius of the smaller circle.
   Give the answers to 1 decimal place.

Ⓒ

14. In rectangle ABCD (below left), $\overline{AE}$ and $\overline{CF}$ are perpendiculars from A and C to the diagonal $\overline{BD}$. Find an expression for the length of $\overline{EF}$.

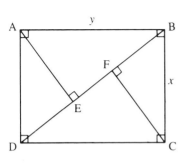

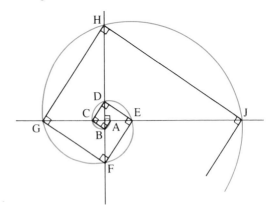

15. A chambered nautilus shell (above right) can be approximated by a sequence of perpendicular line segments. Prove that the length of each segment is the geometric mean between the lengths of the preceding and succeeding segments.

USING TECHNOLOGY

Maximum and Minimum Values

Cutting Construction Costs

A construction company is building a single-story house which contains 100 m² of living space. The base of the house is rectangular. The local building codes require both the length and width of the base to be greater than 7 m. To keep the costs to a minimum, the builder wants to minimize the perimeter of the foundation.

a) Find an equation that expresses the perimeter y in terms of x, the length of the base.

b) On your graphing calculator define a viewing window that contains only the values of X that make sense. Display the graph of Y in this window.

c) Use the TRACE feature to find the value of the length that minimizes the perimeter. What is the minimum perimeter?

Cutting Wire

A 200-cm piece of wire is cut into two pieces. Let x be the length of one of these pieces. Each piece of wire is bent to make a square frame.

a) Find an equation that defines the total area of the squares as a function of x.

b) Define an appropriate viewing window on your graphing calculator and display the graph of the function in part a).

c) Use the TRACE feature to find the lengths of the two pieces of wire that will form squares of minimum total area. What is this minimum total area?

d) Suppose each piece of wire was used to make a wire circle. Find the minimum total area of the two circles, by graphical methods.

e) Suppose the two pieces of wire were used to make a square and a circle. Find the minimum total area of the square and the circle, by graphical methods.

Quadrilaterals

Display the graphs of $Y_1 = |X| - 8$ and $Y_2 = -|X| + 8$ in an appropriate viewing window of your graphing calculator.

a) What type of quadrilateral is formed by these two graphs?

b) Prove your answer in part a) algebraically.

Manufacturing Cans

The capacity of a cylindrical soft-drink can is 355 mL. To minimize costs, the manufacturer wishes to find the radius r and the height h of the can with the smallest surface area. The volume V and the surface area S can be calculated using the formulas $V = \pi r^2 h$ and $S = 2\pi rh + 2\pi r^2$.

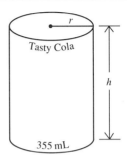

a) Since the volume is 355 mL, substitute this value in the formula for V and solve for h in terms of r.

b) Substitute this expression for h into the formula for the surface area and obtain an equation for S in terms of r.

c) Enter this equation for S in the functions menu of your graphing calculator and define a suitable viewing window to display its graph.

d) Display the graph in the viewing window and determine the value of r that will yield the minimum surface area. What is the minimum surface area?

e) From the formula for V, calculate the height of the can that results in the minimum surface area.

f) Obtain a soft-drink can with a capacity of 355 mL. Measure its radius and height. How close are these measurements to the values you determined in parts d) and e)? Write what you think may account for any differences.

Triangles

a) Define three linear functions Y_1, Y_2, and Y_3 whose graphs will make an isosceles right triangle when they are displayed simultaneously on your graphing calculator.

b) Define three other functions whose graphs will form a $30° - 60° - 90°$ triangle on your graphing calculator.

Solving Systems Graphically

Solve each system of equations graphically to the nearest hundredth. Verify your solutions numerically.

a) $y = 5 - x^2$
   $y = x^2 - 3$

b) $y = 3x$
   $y = x^3 - 4x$

c) $y = x^3 - 3x$
   $y = 4 - x^2$

THE MATHEMATICAL MIND

The Mystic Hexagram

The great French mathematician, Blaise Pascal, was a child prodigy. His father realized that he was bright, and taught him languages with great care. Since Blaise was of frail health, his father did not permit him to study mathematics. He thought that Blaise needed to conserve his energy, and that the strain would be too great if he studied mathematics as well.

But the ban on mathematics naturally aroused the boy's curiosity, and when he was 12 years old he asked what geometry was. His father told him, and Blaise immediately became very interested. Without assistance from anyone, he soon discovered many theorems of elementary geometry. By age 16 he had discovered and proved many original results. His work astonished some of the leading mathematicians of the time, who could not believe that it had been done by a teenager.

One of these results concerns a pattern formed when any six points on a circle are joined in a certain way.

Step 1. Draw a circle and mark any six points on it. Make an X using the four points on the left. This locates point P.

Step 2. Make an X using the two points on the left and the two on the right. This locates point Q.

Step 3. Make an X using the four points on the right. This locates point R. Join P, Q, and R.

When he was only 15 years old, Blaise discovered and proved the remarkable fact that no matter where the six points are marked on the circle, P, Q, and R will always lie on a straight line. For this reason, he called the figure formed by joining the six points the *mystic hexagram*. Blaise also proved that the same result occurs when six points are marked on certain figures other than circles.

QUESTIONS

1. Construct a circle and follow the steps described above. Do P, Q, and R lie on the same line?

2. Construct a circle and locate any three points P, Q, and R inside it which lie on a straight line. Can you find the six points on the circle which form the mystic hexagram?

1. In the diagram, m$\overline{PQ}$ = m$\overline{PR}$ and PQ is parallel to CA. Which of the following statements are true?

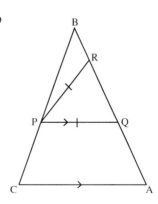

a) $\dfrac{m\overline{BP}}{m\overline{BC}} = \dfrac{m\overline{PQ}}{m\overline{AC}}$

b) $\dfrac{m\overline{BP}}{m\overline{BC}} = \dfrac{m\overline{PR}}{m\overline{AC}}$

c) $\dfrac{m\overline{BP}}{m\overline{BC}} = \dfrac{m\overline{PQ}}{m\overline{CA}}$, m∠PBQ = m∠CBA, and △PBQ ~ △CBA

d) $\dfrac{m\overline{BP}}{m\overline{BC}} = \dfrac{m\overline{PR}}{m\overline{AC}}$, m∠PBQ = m∠CBA, and △PBR ~ △CBA

2. Given a circle and a point outside the circle

   a) How many secants can be drawn from the point to the circle?

   b) How many tangents can be drawn from the point to the circle?

3. Points A and B divide a circle into a major arc and a minor arc. What is the sum of the degree measures of these two arcs?

4. The base of a large hemispherical dome is a circle of diameter 80 m (below left). How far apart are two 20 m parallel support beams which form "chords" of the circular base?

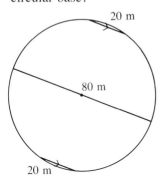

20 m

80 m

20 m

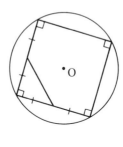

•O

5. A square is inscribed in a circle of diameter 20 cm (above right). What is the distance between the midpoints of adjacent sides of the square?

6. The Sun Stone is a work of art featuring the face of the Aztec sun god at the centre of several concentric circles. The radius of the stone is 1.8 m. What is the circumference of the stone, to the nearest tenth of a metre?

1. Identify the locus of each point P and sketch its graph.
   a) P is the same distance from A($-3,-5$) as it is from B($2,3$).
   b) P is always 4 units from Q($-2,-3$).

2. Find the equation of an ellipse with major axis on the x-axis if:
   a) the x- and y-intercepts are ± 4 and ± 1 respectively
   b) the semi-major axis is 6 units and the minor axis is 8 units.

3. A rectangular hyperbola with centre O($0,0$) and vertices on the y-axis passes through P($-6,8$). Find the equation of the hyperbola.

4. Simplify.
   a) $\dfrac{12x^3y^{-2} \times 5x^{-7}y^5}{15xy^{-3}}$

   b) $\dfrac{-18m^{-4}n^{-2} \times 15m^2n^{-7}}{-10m^2n^{-3} \times 6m^9n^{-4}}$

5. Solve.
   a) $\log x = -2$
   b) $\log_x 27 = \dfrac{3}{2}$
   c) $\log_4 x = \dfrac{7}{2}$
   d) $3^x = 12$
   e) $5^{x+3} = 83$
   f) $7^{x-3} = 3^{x+1}$

6. Express as a single logarithm.
   a) $\log 12 + \log 8 - \log 16$
   b) $\log_4 (x + 5) + \log_4 (2x - 3) - \log_4 (x + 4)$

7. If $\log 12 = x$ and $\log 4 = y$, write each logarithm in terms of x and y.
   a) $\log 3$
   b) $\log 0.75$
   c) $\log 480$
   d) $\log \left(\dfrac{16}{3}\right)$

8. If $\log 11 \doteq 1.0414$, find an approximation for each logarithm.
   a) $\log 121$
   b) $\log \sqrt{11}$
   c) $\log 110$
   d) $\log \left(\dfrac{1}{11}\right)$

9. Solve and check.
   a) $\log_3 x + \log_3 (x + 24) = 4$
   b) $\log_{\sqrt{7}} (x + 4) + \log_{\sqrt{7}} (x - 2) = 2$

10. Find the values of x and y.
    a)

    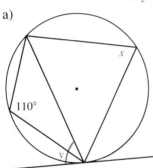

    b)

    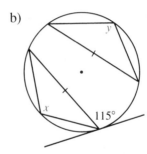

7 Cosine and Sine Functions

The tides in the Bay of Fundy are among the highest in the world. Suppose you know how high the water is at high tide, and the time of day this occurs, and also how high it is at low tide, and the time it occurs. How can you determine the height of the water at any other time of the day? (See Section 7-11 *Example 3.*)

7-1 INTRODUCTION TO PERIODIC FUNCTIONS

In this chapter we will describe many applications of mathematics involving quantities that change in a regular way. Applications concerned with the sun and human physiology are shown on these pages.

The time of the sunset

In summer, the sun sets later than it does in winter. The graph below shows how the time of the sunset at Ottawa varies during a two-year period. The times are given on a 24 h clock in hours and decimals of hours. For example, on June 21 the sun sets at 20.3 h. This means 20 h and 0.3 × 60 min, or 20 h 18 min.

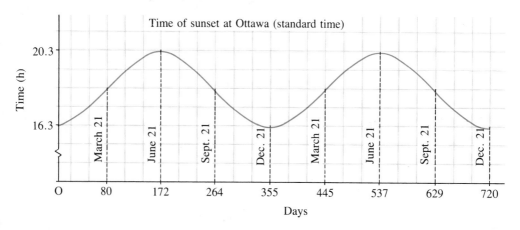

1. a) Estimate the time of the sunset at Ottawa on these dates.
    i)   February 2   ii) July 25   iii) October 30
   b) Estimate the dates when the sun sets at these times.
    i)   8 P.M.   ii) 7 P.M.   iii) 6 P.M.   iv) 5 P.M.

2. Suppose similar graphs were drawn for Yellowknife and Mexico City. In what ways would the graphs for these cities differ from the graph above? In what ways would they be similar?

	Approximate time of sunset on			
	March 21	June 21	September 21	December 21
Mexico City	18.8 h	19.3 h	18.6 h	17.9 h
Yellowknife	18.9 h	22.4 h	18.7 h	15.2 h

Sunspots

Sunspots are dark spots that appear from time to time on the surface of the sun. The periodic variation in the number of sunspots has been recorded for hundreds of years. The following graph shows how the number of sunspots varied from 1944 to 1986.

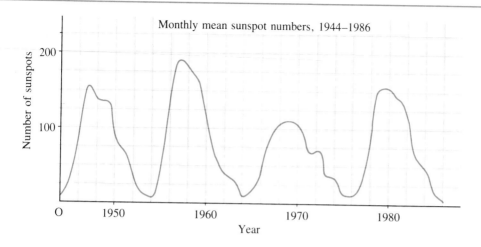

Monthly mean sunspot numbers, 1944–1986

3. The graph shows that sunspot activity increases and decreases at fairly regular intervals. Estimate the number of years, on the average, between the times when there is a maximum number of sunspots.

Lengths of shadows

The graph below shows how the length of the shadow of a 100-m building varies during a three-day period. It is assumed that the sun is directly overhead at noon.

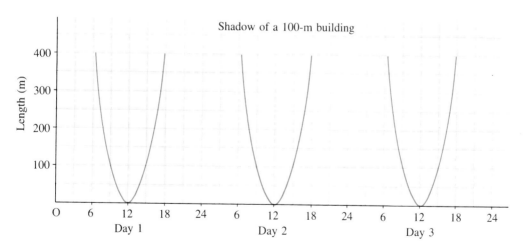

Shadow of a 100-m building

4. a) How long is the shadow at 8 A.M.? at 2 P.M.?
   b) For about how many hours during the day is the shadow longer than 100 m?

5. In many localities the sun is never directly overhead. What change would be needed in the graph if it were drawn for such a locality?

Blood pressure and volume

There are two significant phases to a heartbeat. During the systolic phase, the heart contracts, and pumps blood into the arteries. This phase is marked by a sudden increase in the pressure and a decrease in the volume of blood in the heart. The second phase is the diastolic phase, when the heart relaxes. The pressure decreases and the volume increases as more blood is drawn into the heart from the veins.

Graphs showing how the pressure and volume of blood in the left ventricle of the heart vary during five consecutive heartbeats are shown below. The time scale is the same for both graphs.

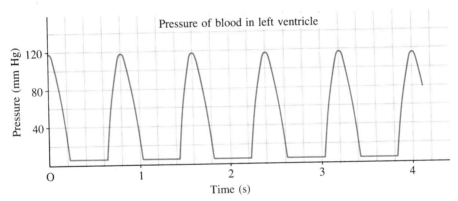

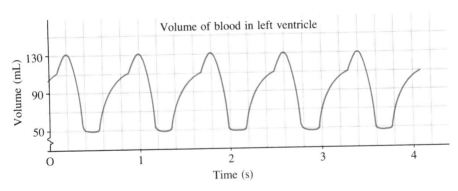

6. During intense physical activity the heart beats faster to satisfy the body's demand for more oxygen. Suppose graphs showing the variation of blood pressure and volume were drawn in this situation. How would the graphs differ from those above? In what ways would they be similar?

Volume of air in the lungs

The volume of air in your lungs is a periodic function of time. This graph shows how the volume of air in the lungs varies during normal breathing.

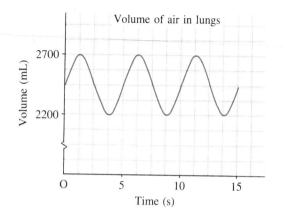

Volume of air in lungs

7. According to the graph, how long does it take to inhale and exhale once?

8. When the average person takes a deep breath, about 5000 mL of air can be inhaled. But only about 4000 mL of this air can be exhaled. Suppose that such a breath takes twice as much time as a normal breath. If a graph similar to the one shown were drawn for deep breathing, in what ways would it differ?

Summary

The graphs in this section suggest what is meant by a *periodic function*. The graph of such a function repeats in a regular way. The length of the part that repeats, measured along the horizontal axis, is called the *period* of the function.

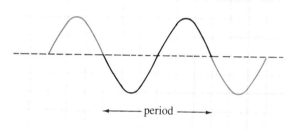

period

9. All periodic functions have a period. Estimate the period for the functions illustrated above.

10. State the period of this function.

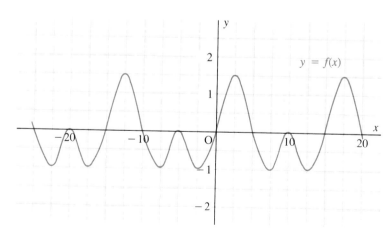

$y = f(x)$

11. One of the examples in this section suggests a periodic function, but it is not a periodic function. Which example is this?

7-2 RADIAN MEASURE

When we construct a circle graph, we assume that the area of a *sector* of a circle is proportional to the *sector angle*. The length of the arc bounding the sector is proportional to the sector angle and is called the *arc length*.

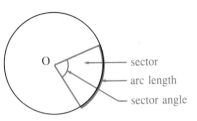

Example 1.   Calculate the arc length of a sector of a circle of radius 20 cm if the sector angle is 140°.

Solution.   Since the angle subtended at the centre of the circle by the circumference is 360°,

the arc length of the sector shown is $\frac{140}{360}$

of the circumference.

$$\frac{\text{Arc length}}{\text{Circumference}} = \frac{140}{360}$$

The circumference of the circle is $2\pi(20)$, or 40π.

Therefore, arc length $= \frac{140}{360}(40\pi)$

$\doteq 48.9$

The arc length is about 49 cm.

Example 1 illustrates the following relationship.

$$\frac{\text{Arc length of a sector}}{\text{Circumference}} = \frac{\text{Sector angle}}{\text{Full-turn angle}}$$

Using this relationship, we can calculate the sector angle that corresponds to a given arc length.

Example 2.   Find the measure of the angle, to the nearest tenth of a degree, subtended at the centre of a circle, radius R, by an arc of each length.

a) R b) $2R$ c) $3R$

Solution.   a) Rewrite the proportion above.

$$\frac{\text{Sector angle}}{\text{Full-turn angle}} = \frac{\text{Arc length}}{\text{Circumference}}$$

For an arc length R

$$\frac{\text{Sector angle}}{360°} = \frac{R}{2\pi R}$$

Therefore, sector angle $= \frac{360°}{2\pi}$

$= \frac{180°}{\pi}$

$\doteq 57.3°$

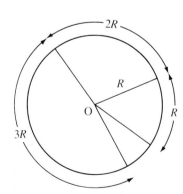

b) Since the sector angle is proportional to the arc length, for an arc
length 2R the sector angle is twice as large as in part a).

$$\text{Sector angle} = 2\left(\frac{180°}{\pi}\right)$$
$$\doteq 114.6°$$

c) Similarly, for an arc length 3R

$$\text{Sector angle} = 3\left(\frac{180°}{\pi}\right)$$
$$\doteq 171.9°$$

In *Example 2* we discovered that an angle of $\frac{180°}{\pi}$ (approximately
57°) is subtended at the centre of a circle by an arc of length R, where
R is the radius.

Definition: One *radian* is the measure of an angle which
is subtended at the centre of a circle by
an arc equal in length to the radius of the
circle.

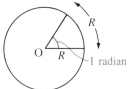

From this definition, $1 \text{ radian} = \frac{180°}{\pi}$

Multiply both sides by π, to get the following result.

$$\boxed{\pi \text{ radians} = 180°}$$

Hence, a full-turn angle, 360°, is equal to 2π radians.

We can use this result to derive a simple relation between the arc
length, the radius, and the sector angle measured in radians. Let a
represent the arc length which subtends an angle θ radians at the centre
of a circle, radius R.

Substitute in this proportion.

$$\frac{\text{Arc length of a sector}}{\text{Circumference}} = \frac{\text{Sector angle}}{\text{Full-turn angle}}$$
$$\frac{a}{2\pi R} = \frac{\theta}{2\pi}$$
$$a = R\theta$$

This formula can be used to find an arc length if the angle it subtends
at the centre of the circle is measured in radians.

The arc length a subtended by an angle
θ radians in a circle with radius R is
given by the formula: $a = R\theta$

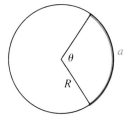

The fact that π radians is equal to $180°$ can be used to convert from radians to degrees, and vice versa.

Example 3. Express each angle to 2 decimal places.

      a) 4 radians in degrees   b) $138°$ in radians

Solution.   a) π radians $= 180°$ b) $180° = \pi$ radians

$$1 \text{ radian} = \frac{180°}{\pi}$$
$$1° = \frac{\pi}{180} \text{ radians}$$

$$4 \text{ radians} = 4\left(\frac{180°}{\pi}\right)$$
$$138° = 138\left(\frac{\pi}{180}\right) \text{ radians}$$

$$\doteq 229.18°$$
$$\doteq 2.41 \text{ radians}$$

Most scientific calculators have keys which enable you to convert from radians to degrees, and vice versa. Read your calculator manual to determine how to make these conversions. Verify the answers in *Example 3*.

Example 4. A circle has radius 6.5 cm. Calculate the length of an arc of this circle subtended by each angle.

      a) 2.4 radians   b) $75°$

Solution.   a) $a = R\theta$

$$a = (6.5)(2.4)$$
$$= 15.6$$

The arc length is 15.6 cm.

b) To use the formula $a = R\theta$, the angle must be in radians.

$$180° = \pi \text{ radians}$$

$$1° = \frac{\pi}{180} \text{ radians}$$

$$75° = 75\left(\frac{\pi}{180}\right) \text{ radians}$$

$$\doteq 1.309 \text{ radians}$$

Substitute in the formula $a = R\theta$.

$$a = R\theta$$
$$\doteq (6.5)(1.309)$$
$$\doteq 8.5085$$

The arc length is approximately 8.5 cm.

EXERCISES 7-2

1. Convert from degrees to radians. Express the answer in terms of π.

    a) $30°$ b) $45°$ c) $60°$ d) $90°$ e) $120°$ f) $135°$

    g) $150°$ h) $180°$ i) $210°$ j) $225°$ k) $240°$ l) $270°$

    m) $300°$ n) $315°$ o) $330°$ p) $360°$ q) $390°$ r) $405°$

2. Convert from radians to degrees.

a) $\frac{\pi}{2}$ radians   b) $\frac{3\pi}{4}$ radians   c) $-\frac{2\pi}{3}$ radians   d) $\frac{7\pi}{6}$ radians

e) $\frac{\pi}{4}$ radians   f) $-\frac{3\pi}{2}$ radians   g) $\frac{7\pi}{4}$ radians   h) 2π radians

i) $-\frac{5\pi}{3}$ radians   j) $\frac{5\pi}{4}$ radians   k) $\frac{\pi}{6}$ radians   l) $-\frac{11\pi}{6}$ radians

3. Convert from degrees to radians. Give the answers to 2 decimal places.

a) $100°$ b) $225°$ c) $57.3°$ d) $-125°$ e) $75x°$ f) $\frac{60°}{\pi}$

g) $-65°$ h) $24.5x°$ i) $150°$ j) $30°$ k) $\frac{180°}{\pi}$ l) $-90x°$

4. Convert from radians to degrees. Give the answers to 1 decimal place.
a) 2 radians   b) -5 radians   c) 3.2 radians   d) 1.8 radians
e) -0.7 radians   f) 1.4θ radians   g) 6.7 radians   h) $-2\pi x$ radians

5. Find the length of the arc which subtends each angle at the centre of a circle of radius 5 cm. Give the answers to 1 decimal place.
a) 2.0 radians   b) 3.0 radians   c) 1.8 radians
d) 6.1 radians   e) 4.2 radians   f) 0.6 radians

6. Find the length of the arc of a circle with radius 12 cm that subtends each sector angle. Give the answers to 1 decimal place where necessary.
a) $135°$ b) $75°$ c) $105°$ d) $165°$
e) $240°$ f) $180°$ g) $310°$ h) $200°$

7. Find the arc length to the nearest centimetre of the sector of a circle with radius:
a) 7 m, if the sector angle is   i) $120°$ ii) $210°$
b) 90 cm, if the sector angle is   i) $30°$ ii) $225°$
c) 216 mm, if the sector angle is   i) $135°$ ii) $300°$.

B

8. How many radians are there in:
a) a full turn   b) a half turn   c) a quarter turn?

9. Calculate the arc length to the nearest metre of a sector of a circle with radius 6 m if the sector angle is $140°$.

10. Two sectors of the same circle have sector angles of $35°$ and $105°$ respectively. The arc length of the smaller sector is 17 cm. What is the arc length of the larger sector?

11. Write an expression for the measure in radians of the sector angle of a sector, in a circle graph with radius r, which represents $x\%$ of the total area.

12. The Earth travels in a nearly circular orbit around the sun. The radius of the orbit is about 149 000 000 km.

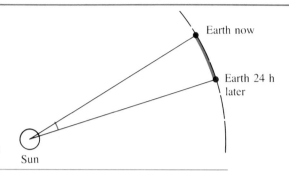

Earth now

Earth 24 h later

Sun

a) What is the measure in radians of the angle subtended at the sun by the positions of the Earth at two different times 24 h apart?

b) About how far does the Earth travel in one day in its orbit around the sun?

Ⓒ

13. The *angular velocity* of an object is the angle per unit time through which an object rotates about a rotation centre.

a) What is the angular velocity in radians per second of a car tire of diameter 64 cm when the car is travelling at 100 km/h?

b) Write an expression for the angular velocity in radians per second for a car tire of diameter *d* centimetres when the car is travelling at *x* kilometres per hour?

14. a) Write expressions for the distance from A to B:
   i) along the line segment AB
   ii) along the circular arc from A to B.

b) How many times as long as the straight-line distance is the distance along the circular arc from A to B?

c) Write an expression for the area of the shaded segment of the circle.

d) Write an expression for the shortest distance from the vertex of the right angle to the line segment AB.

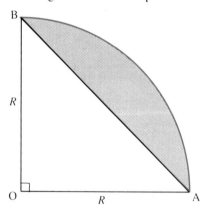

B

R

O   R   A

INVESTIGATE

A Reason for Introducing Radian Measure

1. The formula $a = R\theta$ for the arc length subtended by an angle θ radians in a circle with radius R was derived in this section. Derive a similar formula if the measure of the angle is degrees instead of radians. Then compare the two formulas.

2. a) Derive a formula for the area of a sector formed by an angle θ radians in a circle with radius R.

   b) Derive a similar formula if the measure of the angle is degrees. Then compare the two formulas.

3. Suggest an advantage of using radian measure instead of degree measure for angles.

7-3 THE WRAPPING FUNCTION

A point P moving around a circle is an example of periodic motion, because P returns to its previous positions on successive rotations.

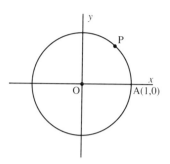

Consider P moving around a circle with radius 1 unit. This is a unit circle. The centre of the circle is at the origin, hence the equation of the circle is $x^2 + y^2 = 1$. The circumference of the circle is 2π.

We shall associate the distance P has travelled, from its starting position A, with the coordinates of P on the unit circle.

The diagrams below illustrate various positions of P on the first rotation.

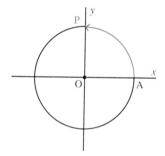
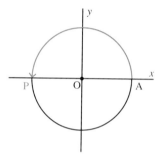
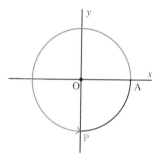

distance of P from A is $\frac{\pi}{2}$

P is at $(0,1)$

distance of P from A is π

P is at $(-1,0)$

distance of P from A is $\frac{3\pi}{2}$

P is at $(0,-1)$

P is rotating continuously so, for example, a distance of $\frac{9\pi}{2}$ is illustrated in the diagram at the right. P terminates in the same position it was for the distance of $\frac{\pi}{2}$. The periodic nature of the motion means that every time the arc length is increased by an integral multiple of 2π, the coordinates of P are the same. Arcs which have the same end point are called *coterminal arcs*.

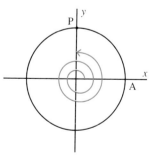

The relation that maps the distance from A onto the end point P is formalized in what we call the wrapping function.

Consider an infinite number line with zero coinciding with A. Imagine the number line wrapped around the unit circle like a tape measure. Positive numbers on the number line are wrapped in a counterclockwise direction. Negative numbers are wrapped in a clockwise direction. For every point on the number line, there will be an ordered pair (x,y) which represents the horizontal and vertical distances of P from the origin.

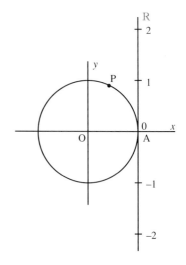

The *wrapping function*, $W(s)$, maps any real number, s, onto the coordinates of a point on the unit circle.
$W:s \rightarrow (x,y)$
The domain of $W(s)$ is $\mathbb{R}$.
The range of $W(s)$ is $\{(x,y) \in \mathbb{R} \times \mathbb{R} \mid x^2 + y^2 = 1\}$.
$W(s)$ is periodic with a period of 2π, that is,
$W(s) = W(s + 2k\pi), k \in \mathbb{Z}$

The wrapping function can be expressed in terms of θ, the central angle, since for every value of s there is a corresponding value of θ. θ is measured in degrees or radians.
$W:\theta \rightarrow (x,y)$

Example 1. Draw an arc on the unit circle to represent each arc length.

a) $-\dfrac{3\pi}{2}$ b) $\dfrac{5\pi}{2}$ c) 4

Solution. a) 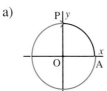 b)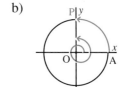

c) Express 4 radians in terms of π.

$$4 \text{ radians} = \left(\frac{4}{\pi}\right)\pi$$

$$\doteq 1.27\pi$$

Example 2. In which quadrant will the arc representing each real number terminate?

a) 3   b) −5   c) 7.3

Solution. a) $3 \doteq 0.95\pi$
The arc will terminate in Quadrant II.

b) $-5 \doteq -1.6\pi$
The arc will terminate in Quadrant I.

c) $7.3 \doteq 2.3\pi$
The arc will terminate in Quadrant I.

Example 3. Which ordered pair is not an element of the range for $W(s)$?

a) $\left(\frac{3}{5}, \frac{4}{5}\right)$ b) $(1, -1)$ c) $\left(\frac{\sqrt{3}}{2}, -\frac{1}{2}\right)$

Solution. For all elements (x, y) of the range, $x^2 + y^2 = 1$

a) $\left(\frac{3}{5}\right)^2 + \left(\frac{4}{5}\right)^2 = 1$, so $\left(\frac{3}{5}, \frac{4}{5}\right)$ is an element of the range

b) $(1)^2 + (-1)^2 = 2$, so $(1, -1)$ is not an element of the range

c) $\left(\frac{\sqrt{3}}{2}\right)^2 + \left(-\frac{1}{2}\right)^2 = 1$, so $\left(\frac{\sqrt{3}}{2}, -\frac{1}{2}\right)$ is an element of the range

Example 4. Onto which point P(x,y) does the wrapping function map $\frac{\pi}{4}$?

Solution. Show P on the unit circle: $\frac{\pi}{4} = 45°$.

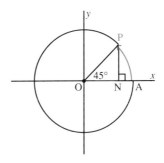

Drop the perpendicular from P onto the
x-axis at N.
Then $\angle NOP = \angle OPN = 45°$
Hence, PN = NO
Using the Pythagorean Theorem
$PN^2 + NO^2 = 1$
$PN = NO = \dfrac{1}{\sqrt{2}}$

The wrapping function maps $\frac{\pi}{4}$ onto the

point $P\left(\dfrac{1}{\sqrt{2}}, \dfrac{1}{\sqrt{2}}\right)$.

EXERCISES 7-3

Ⓐ

1. Draw an arc on a unit circle to represent each arc length.

   a) 3π

   b) $-\frac{\pi}{2}$

   c) $\frac{3\pi}{4}$

   d) $-\frac{5\pi}{4}$

   e) 6.3

   f) -2

   g) $-\frac{21\pi}{2}$

   h) $\frac{13\pi}{4}$

2. In which quadrant will the arc representing each real number terminate?

   a) -0.5

   b) $\frac{\pi}{6}$

   c) $\frac{2\pi}{3}$

   d) $-\frac{7\pi}{5}$

   e) 2

   f) 8

   g) -10

   h) -17.8

Ⓑ

3. Copy and complete this mapping diagram for the elements of $W(s)$.

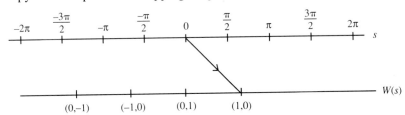

4. For each ordered pair in the range of $W(s)$, find 3 values of s.

   a) $(1,0)$

   b) $(0,-1)$

   c) $(-1,0)$

   d) $\left(\frac{\sqrt{2}}{2}, -\frac{\sqrt{2}}{2}\right)$

5. Copy and complete this table for values of $W(s)$.

s	0	$\frac{\pi}{4}$	$\frac{\pi}{2}$	$\frac{3\pi}{4}$	π	$\frac{5\pi}{4}$	$\frac{3\pi}{2}$	$\frac{7\pi}{4}$	2π
$W(s)$									

6. Find the element of the range of $W(\theta)$ for each central angle.

   a) $-270°$

   b) $540°$

   c) $405°$

   d) $-1170°$

7. For each ordered pair in the range of $W(\theta)$, find 2 values of θ in the interval $]-360°, 360°]$.

   a) $(0,1)$

   b) $\left(-\frac{\sqrt{2}}{2}, -\frac{\sqrt{2}}{2}\right)$

   c) $(1,0)$

   d) $\left(\frac{\sqrt{2}}{2}, \frac{\sqrt{2}}{2}\right)$

8. Find a value of k so that each ordered pair is an element of $W(s)$. Give the answers to 2 decimal places where necessary.

   a) $(0.2, k)$

   b) $\left(-\frac{1}{3}, k\right)$

   c) $\left(\frac{1}{2}, k\right)$

   d) $(k, 0.4)$

9. For the wrapping function $W(s)$, if $s \in [0,2\pi[$, find the domain for each restricted range.

   a) $\{ s \mid x < 0, y < 0 \}$

   b) $\{ s \mid x > 0, y < 0 \}$

7-4 ANGLES IN STANDARD POSITION

As illustrated in *Section 7-3*, one of the simplest examples of periodic motion is motion in a circle. To study motion in a circle, we need to define the standard position of an angle.

Let $P(x,y)$ represent a point which moves around a circle with radius r and centre $(0,0)$. P starts at the point $A(r,0)$ on the x-axis. For any position of P, an angle θ is defined, which represents the amount of rotation about the origin. When the vertex of the angle is $(0,0)$, the *initial arm* is OA, the *terminal arm* is OP, and we say that the angle θ is in *standard position*. The measure of the angle may be in degrees or in radians.

If $\theta > 0$, the rotation is counterclockwise.   If $\theta < 0$, the rotation is clockwise.

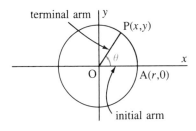   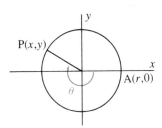

When P moves around the circle, the motion is repeated after P has rotated 360°, or 2π radians. If any angle θ is given, we can always determine other angles for which the position of P is the same. All these angles are in standard position.

Given an angle of 60°, or $\dfrac{\pi}{3}$

Add 360°, or 2π
$$60° + 360° = 420°$$
$$\frac{\pi}{3} + 2\pi = \frac{7\pi}{3}$$

Add 360°, or 2π again
$$420° + 360° = 780°$$
$$\frac{7\pi}{3} + 2\pi = \frac{13\pi}{3}$$

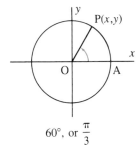   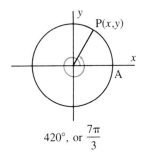   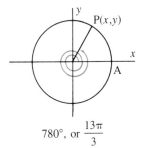

60°, or $\dfrac{\pi}{3}$ 420°, or $\dfrac{7\pi}{3}$ 780°, or $\dfrac{13\pi}{3}$

The angles shown above are in standard position, and have the same terminal arm. For this reason, they are called coterminal angles. If θ is any angle in standard position, other angles which are coterminal with θ can be found by adding or subtracting multiples of 360° if θ is in degrees, or multiples of 2π if θ is in radians.

Coterminal Angles
- Two or more angles in standard position are *coterminal angles* if the position of P is the same for each angle.
- If θ represents any angle, then any angle coterminal with θ is represented by these expressions, where n is an integer.
  $\theta + n(360°)$, if θ is in degrees
  $\theta + 2\pi n$, if θ is in radians

Example 1. Given   a) $\theta = 150°$ b) $\theta = \dfrac{\pi}{6}$

   i) Draw the angle θ in standard position.
   ii) Find two other angles which are coterminal with θ and illustrate them on diagrams.
   iii) Write an expression to represent any angle coterminal with θ.

Solution.   a) i)   ii) $150° + 360° = 510°$ $150° - 360° = -210°$

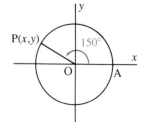 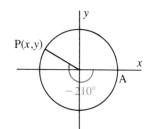

   iii) Any angle coterminal with θ is represented by the expression $150° + n(360°)$, where n is an integer.

   b) i)   ii) $\dfrac{\pi}{6} + 2\pi = \dfrac{13\pi}{6}$ $\dfrac{\pi}{6} - 2\pi = -\dfrac{11\pi}{6}$

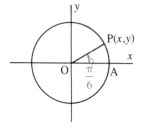 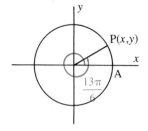 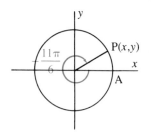

   iii) Any angle coterminal with θ is represented by the expression $\dfrac{\pi}{6} + 2\pi n$, where n is an integer.

We can determine which quadrant P is in for any given angle expressed in degrees or in radians.

Example 2. Suppose P has rotated 830° about (0,0) from A.
a) How many complete rotations have been made?
b) In which quadrant is P located now?
c) Draw a diagram to show the position of P.

Solution. a) Since a complete rotation is 360°, divide 830 by 360.
830 ÷ 360 ≐ 2.3056
Since the result is between 2 and 3, P has made 2
complete rotations around the circle, and part of a third
rotation.
b) Two complete rotations amount to 2(360°), or 720°.
The additional rotation beyond 720° is 830° − 720°,
or 110°. Since 90° < 110° < 180°, P is now in the
second quadrant.

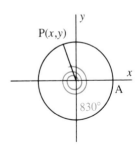

Example 3. Suppose P has rotated 3π radians about (0,0) from A.
a) How many complete rotations have been made?
b) In which quadrant is P located now?
c) Draw a diagram to show the position of P.

Solution. a) Since a complete rotation is 2π radians,
divide 3π by 2π.
3π ÷ 2π = 1.5
P has made 1 complete rotation, and half
of a second rotation.
b) P is on the x-axis, between the second
and third quadrants.

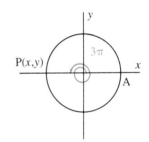

EXERCISES 7-4

Ⓐ

1. An angle in standard position is shown. What is the value of θ, in degrees and in radians?

a)   b)   c)   d)

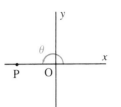 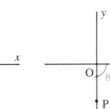 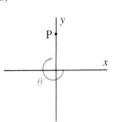

2. Draw each angle in standard position.
a) $\theta = 50°$ b) $\theta = 120°$ c) $\theta = 165°$ d) $\theta = 240°$
e) $\theta = \dfrac{\pi}{2}$ f) $\theta = \dfrac{\pi}{4}$ g) $\theta = \dfrac{2\pi}{3}$ h) $\theta = \dfrac{3\pi}{2}$

3. In *Exercise 2*, find two angles which are coterminal with θ.

4. An angle θ in standard position is shown. Find two other angles which are coterminal with θ.

a)

b)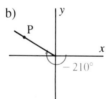

c)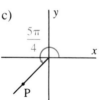

d)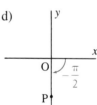

5. Find two angles which are coterminal with θ.
   a) $\theta = \pi$
   b) $\theta = \frac{\pi}{2}$
   c) $\theta = -\frac{\pi}{3}$
   d) $\theta = -2\pi$

(B)

6. P is a point on the terminal arm of an angle θ in standard position. Suppose P has rotated 420°.
   a) How many complete rotations have been made?
   b) In which quadrant is P located now?
   c) Draw a diagram to show the position of P.

7. Repeat *Exercise 6* if P has rotated:
   a) 480°
   b) 660°
   c) 870°
   d) 1000°.

8. Draw each angle in standard position.
   a) $\theta = 400°$
   b) $\theta = 750°$
   c) $\theta = -270°$
   d) $\theta = -60°$

9. Repeat *Exercise 6* if P has rotated $\frac{7\pi}{3}$ radians.

10. Repeat *Exercise 6* if P has rotated:
    a) π
    b) $\frac{3\pi}{2}$
    c) 2π
    d) $\frac{5\pi}{2}$.

11. Draw each angle in standard position.
    a) $\theta = \frac{9\pi}{2}$
    b) $\theta = \frac{10\pi}{3}$
    c) $\theta = -\frac{5\pi}{4}$
    d) $\theta = -7\pi$

12. Write an expression to represent any angle coterminal with θ.
    a) $\theta = 45°$
    b) $\theta = 150°$
    c) $\theta = 240°$
    d) $\theta = -30°$
    e) $\theta = \pi$
    f) $\theta = -\frac{\pi}{4}$
    g) $\theta = \frac{5\pi}{2}$
    h) $\theta = 1$

(C)

13. P is a point on the terminal arm of an angle θ in standard position. Explain how you could determine the quadrant in which P is located, if you know the value of θ in:
    a) degrees
    b) radians.

14. Let θ represent any angle, where θ is in radians. Let α represent the angle which is coterminal with θ, where $0 \leqslant \alpha < 2\pi$.
    a) Draw a graph to represent α as a function of θ.
    b) What are the domain and the range of the function?

7-5 THE COSINE AND SINE FUNCTIONS

A point moving around a circle is an example of periodic motion because the point returns to its previous positions on each successive rotation.

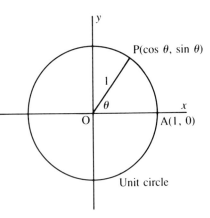

Imagine that a point P rotates around a unit circle. Suppose that this circle is centred at the origin on a coordinate grid, and that P is on the terminal arm of an angle θ in standard position.

For any position of P on the unit circle, we define the first coordinate of P to be the *cosine* of θ, and the second coordinate of P to be the *sine* of θ. We write the coordinates of P as (cos θ, sin θ). As P rotates around the circle, the values of cos θ and sin θ change periodically. These values can be found for any given angle using a scientific calculator. Some typical values of cos θ and sin θ are illustrated below.

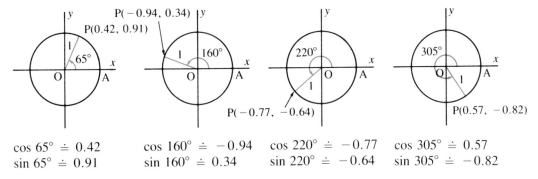

| cos 65° ≐ 0.42 | cos 160° ≐ −0.94 | cos 220° ≐ −0.77 | cos 305° ≐ 0.57 |
| sin 65° ≐ 0.91 | sin 160° ≐ 0.34 | sin 220° ≐ −0.64 | sin 305° ≐ −0.82 |

> The coordinates of any point P on a unit circle with centre (0,0) are (cos θ, sin θ),
> where P is on the terminal arm of an angle θ in standard position.

We can use the definitions to determine values for cos θ and sin θ for certain angles. For example, if the terminal arm of an angle coincides with one of the axes the angles are multiples of 90° or $\frac{\pi}{2}$ radians. These angles are called *quadrantal angles*. We can determine the sines and cosines of the quadrantal angles from diagrams like those on the next page.

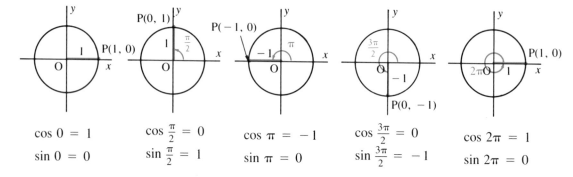

$$\cos 0 = 1$$

$$\sin 0 = 0$$

$$\cos \frac{\pi}{2} = 0$$

$$\sin \frac{\pi}{2} = 1$$

$$\cos \pi = -1$$

$$\sin \pi = 0$$

$$\cos \frac{3\pi}{2} = 0$$

$$\sin \frac{3\pi}{2} = -1$$

$$\cos 2\pi = 1$$

$$\sin 2\pi = 0$$

We can use a scientific calculator to find the cosine or sine of any angle when its measure is given in degrees or radians. Consult your manual to determine how to put your calculator in degree mode or in radian mode. When the angle is in radians, it is customary to indicate no unit.

Example 1.   Find each value to five decimal places. Explain the sign of each result.
a) cos 125° and sin 125°   b) cos 4.3 and sin 4.3

Solution.   a) First, be sure that the calculator is in *degree mode*.
cos 125° $\doteq$ −0.573 58   sin 125° $\doteq$ 0.819 15
Since θ is in the second quadrant, the first coordinate of P is negative and the second coordinate is positive. Hence, cos 125° < 0 and sin 125° > 0

b) Since there is no unit for the angle, the angle is in radians. Be sure that the calculator is in *radian mode*.
cos 4.3 $\doteq$ −0.400 80   sin 4.3 $\doteq$ −0.916 17
Since θ is in the third quadrant, both coordinates of P are negative. Hence, cos 4.3 < 0 and sin 4.3 < 0.

As θ rotates around the circle, past 360° or 2π, the same values of cos θ and sin θ are encountered as before. Hence, in *Example 1*, there are infinitely many other angles having the same cosine as 125°, or the same sine as 4.3 radians. For example,

these expressions are also equal to cos 125°
cos (125° + 360°), or cos 485°
cos (125° + 720°), or cos 845°
cos (125° − 360°), or cos (−235°)

these expressions are also equal to sin 4.3.
sin (4.3 + 2π)
sin (4.3 + 4π)
sin (4.3 − 2π)

Relating the values of cos θ and sin θ

Since (cos θ, sin θ) are the coordinates of a point on the unit circle, they satisfy its equation. We obtain this equation by applying the Pythagorean Theorem to $\triangle$PON in the diagram shown.

The result is $x^2 + y^2 = 1$.

Substituting cos θ for x and sin θ for y, we obtain (cos θ)^2 + (sin θ)^2 = 1.

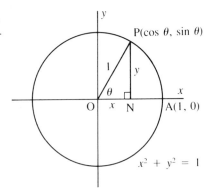

An expression such as (cos θ)^2 occurs so frequently that it is abbreviated as cos$^2\theta$. Similarly, (sin θ)^2 is written as sin$^2\theta$. Hence, we obtain the following result:

For any value of θ, $\cos^2\theta + \sin^2\theta = 1$

If we know the value of either of the functions cos θ or sin θ for any given angle, we can use this equation to determine the value of the other function.

Example 2. If θ is an angle in the second quadrant and sin θ = 0.6425, determine the value of cos θ to four decimal places.

Solution. Sketch a unit circle showing P in the second quadrant.

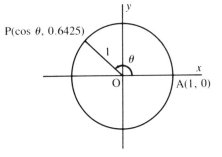

Substitute 0.6425 for sin θ in the equation.
$$\cos^2\theta + \sin^2\theta = 1$$
$$\cos^2\theta + (0.6425)^2 = 1$$
$$\cos^2\theta = 1 - (0.6425)^2$$
$$= 0.587\ 193\ 75$$
$$\cos \theta = \pm\sqrt{0.587\ 193\ 75}$$
$$\doteq \pm 0.766\ 285\ 684$$

Since θ is an angle in the second quadrant, the first coordinate of P is negative.
Therefore, we reject the positive root and obtain cos $\theta \doteq -0.7663$ to four decimal places.

In *Example 2*, if θ were in the third quadrant, we would obtain the same value for cos θ. But if θ were in the first or the fourth quadrants, the value of cos θ would be $+0.7663$. In problems of this kind, observe how the diagram helps us determine the sign of the function.

EXERCISES 7-5

(A)

1. Use a scientific calculator in degree mode. Find each value to 5 decimal places. Explain the sign of each result.
   a) cos 20°   b) sin 38°   c) cos 123°
   d) sin 240°   e) cos 324°   f) sin 347°

2. Use a scientific calculator in radian mode. Find each value to 5 decimal places. Explain the sign of each result.
   a) cos 1.5   b) cos 2.35   c) sin 7.485
   d) cos 2   e) sin 1   f) sin 3.47

3. Suppose P starts at A(1,0) and makes two complete rotations counterclockwise around the unit circle. Describe how the values of cos θ and sin θ change as θ increases from 0° to 720°.

(B)

4. a) Find cos 125° to 5 decimal places.
   b) Find three other angles that have the same cosine as 125°, and verify with your calculator.

5. a) Find sin 5.6 to 5 decimal places.
   b) Find three other angles that have the same sine as 5.6 radians, and verify with your calculator.

6. Without using your calculator, determine if each function is positive or negative. Justify your answer.
   a) sin 145°   b) cos 160°   c) cos 210°
   d) sin 255°   e) cos 335°   f) sin 328°

7. a) Determine cos 73° and sin 73° as accurately as you can using your calculator.
   b) Using the results of part a), evaluate $\cos^2 73° + \sin^2 73°$. Explain the result.

8. Use your calculator to evaluate $\cos^2 2.85 + \sin^2 2.85$.

9. Determine each result to 4 decimal places.
   a) If θ is in the first quadrant and sin θ = 0.7625, find cos θ.
   b) If θ is in the second quadrant and cos θ = −0.3865, find sin θ.
   c) If θ is in the third quadrant and sin θ = −0.1406, find cos θ.
   d) If θ is in the fourth quadrant and cos θ = 0.6981, find sin θ.

(C)

10. You can use a scientific calculator to find the sine or the cosine of any angle in standard position.
    a) Determine the largest angle your calculator will accept: in degrees; in radians.
    b) Are these two angles equal?

7-6 COSINE AND SINE FUNCTIONS OF SPECIAL ANGLES

When we use a scientific calculator to find the cosine and sine of a given angle, the results are decimal approximations, which are not exact. Although the approximations are useful for most purposes, it is important to realize that exact values of these functions can be determined from geometrical relationships, for a limited number of angles.

Angles of $\frac{\pi}{4}$ and its multiples

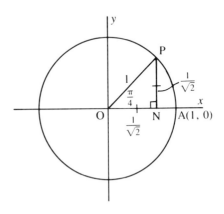

This diagram shows the angle 45°, or $\frac{\pi}{4}$ in standard position. If P is on a unit circle and PN is perpendicular to OA, then △PON is a right isosceles triangle with OP = 1. Let ON = NP = x. Then, by the Pythagorean Theorem,

$$ON^2 + NP^2 = OP^2$$
$$2x^2 = 1$$
$$x = \pm\frac{1}{\sqrt{2}}, \text{ or } \pm\frac{\sqrt{2}}{2}$$

Since P is in the first quadrant, $x = \frac{1}{\sqrt{2}}$. Hence, the coordinates of P are $\left(\frac{1}{\sqrt{2}}, \frac{1}{\sqrt{2}}\right)$. Therefore, $\cos\frac{\pi}{4} = \frac{1}{\sqrt{2}}$ and $\sin\frac{\pi}{4} = \frac{1}{\sqrt{2}}$

$$\boxed{\cos\frac{\pi}{4} = \frac{1}{\sqrt{2}} \qquad \sin\frac{\pi}{4} = \frac{1}{\sqrt{2}}}$$

Since the unit circle is symmetric about the coordinate axes, we can determine the cosine and sine of any multiple of $\frac{\pi}{4}$ by reflecting the right isosceles triangle above in the *y*-axis, the *x*-axis, or both.

Example 1. Determine $\cos\frac{3\pi}{4}$ and $\sin\frac{3\pi}{4}$.

Solution. Draw the diagram shown.
Since $\angle POA = \frac{3\pi}{4}$,

$$\angle PON = \pi - \frac{3\pi}{4}, \text{ or } \frac{\pi}{4}.$$

△PON is a right isosceles triangle with sides $\frac{1}{\sqrt{2}}$, $\frac{1}{\sqrt{2}}$, and 1. Since P is in the second quadrant, $\cos\frac{3\pi}{4}$ is negative and $\sin\frac{3\pi}{4}$ is positive. Hence,

$$\cos\frac{3\pi}{4} = -\frac{1}{\sqrt{2}} \text{ and } \sin\frac{3\pi}{4} = \frac{1}{\sqrt{2}}$$

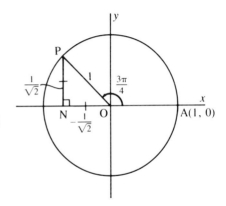

In *Example 1*, ∠PON is called the reference angle. A *reference angle* is the acute angle between OP and the *x*-axis.

Angles of $\frac{\pi}{6}$ and its multiples

This diagram shows the angle 30°, or $\frac{\pi}{6}$ in standard position. If P is on a unit circle and PN is perpendicular to OA, then △PON is a 30-60-90 triangle with OP = 1. We can determine the lengths of the other two sides of this triangle as follows. By reflecting △PON in the *x*-axis, an equilateral △POP′ is formed, in which N is the midpoint of PP′. Hence, NP = $\frac{1}{2}$

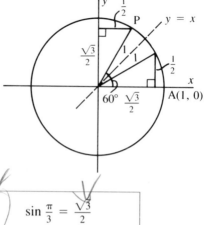

To determine the length of ON, let ON = *x*. Then, by the Pythagorean Theorem,
ON² + NP² = OP²

$$x^2 + \frac{1}{4} = 1$$
$$x^2 = \frac{3}{4}$$
$$x = \pm\frac{\sqrt{3}}{2}$$

Since P is in the first quadrant, $x = \frac{\sqrt{3}}{2}$.

Hence, the coordinates of P are $\left(\frac{\sqrt{3}}{2}, \frac{1}{2}\right)$.

Therefore, $\cos\frac{\pi}{6} = \frac{\sqrt{3}}{2}$ and $\sin\frac{\pi}{6} = \frac{1}{2}$

To determine the cosine and sine of 60°, or $\frac{\pi}{3}$, reflect the 30-60-90 triangle in the above diagram in the line $y = x$. The coordinates of P are now $\left(\frac{1}{2}, \frac{\sqrt{3}}{2}\right)$. Therefore,

$\cos\frac{\pi}{3} = \frac{1}{2}$ and $\sin\frac{\pi}{3} = \frac{\sqrt{3}}{2}$

$$\cos\frac{\pi}{6} = \frac{\sqrt{3}}{2} \qquad \sin\frac{\pi}{6} = \frac{1}{2} \qquad \cos\frac{\pi}{3} = \frac{1}{2} \qquad \sin\frac{\pi}{3} = \frac{\sqrt{3}}{2}$$

By reflecting the 30-60-90 triangle in the *y*-axis, the *x*-axis, or both, we can determine the cosine and sine of any multiple of $\frac{\pi}{6}$ and $\frac{\pi}{3}$.

Example 2. Determine $\cos \frac{4\pi}{3}$ and $\sin \frac{4\pi}{3}$.

Solution. Draw the diagram shown. Since reflex $\angle POA = \frac{4\pi}{3}$, the reference angle is $\angle PON = \frac{4\pi}{3} - \pi$, or $\frac{\pi}{3}$. $\triangle PON$ is a 30-60-90 triangle with sides $\frac{1}{2}$, 1, and $\frac{\sqrt{3}}{2}$. Since P is in the third quadrant, both $\cos \frac{4\pi}{3}$ and $\sin \frac{4\pi}{3}$ are negative. Hence, $\cos \frac{4\pi}{3} = -\frac{1}{2}$ and $\sin \frac{4\pi}{3} = -\frac{\sqrt{3}}{2}$

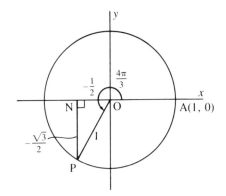

EXERCISES 7-6

(A)

1. What is the advantage of using geometrical relationships instead of a scientific calculator to determine the cosines and sines of angles of 30°, 45°, and their multiples?

2. Find the exact value of each expression.

   a) $\sin \frac{\pi}{4}$　　　b) $\sin \frac{3\pi}{4}$　　　c) $\sin \frac{5\pi}{4}$　　　d) $\sin \frac{7\pi}{4}$

   e) $\sin \frac{\pi}{6}$　　　f) $\sin \frac{5\pi}{6}$　　　g) $\sin \frac{7\pi}{6}$　　　h) $\sin \frac{11\pi}{6}$

   i) $\sin \frac{\pi}{3}$　　　j) $\sin \frac{2\pi}{3}$　　　k) $\sin \frac{4\pi}{3}$　　　l) $\sin \frac{5\pi}{3}$

3. Repeat *Exercise 2* by replacing all the sines with cosines.

4. Develop a method for remembering the results of *Exercises 2* and *3*.

(B)

5. Find the exact value of each expression.

   a) $\sin \frac{7\pi}{3}$　　　b) $\cos \frac{7\pi}{3}$　　　c) $\sin \frac{9\pi}{4}$　　　d) $\cos \frac{9\pi}{4}$

   e) $\sin \frac{8\pi}{3}$　　　f) $\cos \frac{8\pi}{3}$　　　g) $\sin \frac{11\pi}{4}$　　　h) $\cos \frac{11\pi}{4}$

6. Evaluate.

   a) $\sin^2\left(\frac{\pi}{4}\right) + \cos^2\left(\frac{\pi}{4}\right)$　　b) $\sin^2\left(\frac{\pi}{6}\right) + \cos^2\left(\frac{\pi}{6}\right)$　　c) $\sin^2\left(\frac{\pi}{3}\right) + \cos^2\left(\frac{\pi}{3}\right)$

7. a) $\triangle ABC$ is an isosceles right triangle. Verify that $\sin 2A + \sin 2B + \sin 2C = 4 \sin A \sin B \sin C$.

   b) Determine if the equation in part a) holds for a 30-60-90 triangle.

 **PROBLEM SOLVING**

Write an Expression in Two Different Ways

"Mathematics is the queen of sciences and number theory the queen of mathematics."

Carl Friedrich Gauss

What is the sum of the natural numbers from 1 to 20?

Understand the problem
- We could merely add the numbers, but that would be of little use for related problems involving, say, the sum of the natural numbers from 1 to 1000.
- Hence, the problem is really asking for a method of adding the natural numbers from 1 to n.

Think of a strategy
- Let S represent the required sum. Then:
$$S = 1 + 2 + 3 + \ldots + 18 + 19 + 20 \ldots ①$$
and also, $$S = 20 + 19 + 18 + \ldots + 3 + 2 + 1 \ldots ②$$

Carry out the strategy
- Notice that the sums of the numbers occurring above each other on the right sides are all the same.
- Hence, we might try adding both sides of equations ① and ②.
- What is the sum of the expressions on the left side?
- When you add the pairs of numbers on the right side, the sum is always 21. How many 21s are there in all?
- What is the sum of all the numbers on the right side in both ① and ②?
- What does S equal?

Look back
- The strategy of writing two expressions for S led to a simpler problem of adding $21 + 21 + 21 + \ldots + 21 + 21 + 21$. Since there were 20 terms, the sum could be found.
- Use the same method to find the sum of the first 50 natural numbers.
- Generalize to prove this formula for the sum of the first n natural numbers.

$$1 + 2 + 3 + \ldots + n = \frac{n(n + 1)}{2}$$

PROBLEMS

Ⓑ

1. A right triangle has sides 3 cm, 4 cm, and 5 cm. Determine the length of the altitude to the hypotenuse.

2. Three cylindrical logs with radius 10 cm are strapped together at each end. Determine the length of strapping required if 5 cm is needed for overlapping.

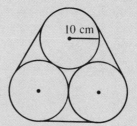

10 cm

3. The numbers 23 and 5678 are two examples of numbers with consecutive digits. How many numbers are there in all with consecutive digits?

4. Carry out calculations to determine the length of time it takes the sun to drop out of sight once it reaches the horizon during a sunset. The diameter of the sun is 1.38×10^6 km and its distance from the Earth 1.49×10^8 km. List some of the assumptions you are making.

Ⓒ

5. An isosceles triangle has sides of length 6 cm, 6 cm, and 4 cm. Determine the lengths of the three altitudes.

6. Write the numbers from 1 to 64 on an 8 by 8 grid. Then circle eight numbers as follows:
   - Select any number and draw a circle around it.
   - Strike out the row and column containing the number.
   - Repeat until 8 numbers have been circled.

   Find the sum of the 8 circled numbers.

1	2	3	4	5	6	7	8
9	10	11	12	13	14	15	16
17	18	19	20	21	22	23	24
25	26	27	28	29	30	31	32
33	34	35	36	37	38	39	40
41	42	43	44	45	46	47	48
49	50	51	52	53	54	55	56
57	58	59	60	61	62	63	64

7. The natural numbers are written in a triangle as shown. Show that the sum of the numbers in the nth row is $\dfrac{n(n^2 + 1)}{2}$.

$$
\begin{array}{c}
1 \\
2 \quad 3 \\
4 \quad 5 \quad 6 \\
7 \quad 8 \quad 9 \quad 10 \\
11 \quad 12 \quad 13 \quad 14 \quad 15
\end{array}
$$

Ⓓ

8. Solve the inequality $\left(\dfrac{x}{1 - \sqrt{x + 1}} \right)^2 > x + 5.$

7-7 GRAPHING THE COSINE AND SINE FUNCTIONS

To draw graphs of the functions $y = \sin \theta$
and $y = \cos \theta$, recall their definitions. If P
is any point on a unit circle with centre (0,0),
then the coordinates of P are $(\cos \theta, \sin \theta)$.

Imagine that P rotates around the circle
counterclockwise starting at A(1,0). As θ
increases, the coordinates of P change periodically. This causes a periodic change in
the values of $\cos \theta$ and $\sin \theta$. We will graph
the function $y = \sin \theta$ first.

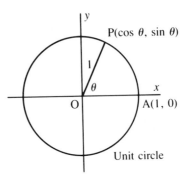

Graphing the function $y = \sin \theta$

Suppose θ starts at 0 and increases to π. Then $\sin \theta$ changes as follows.

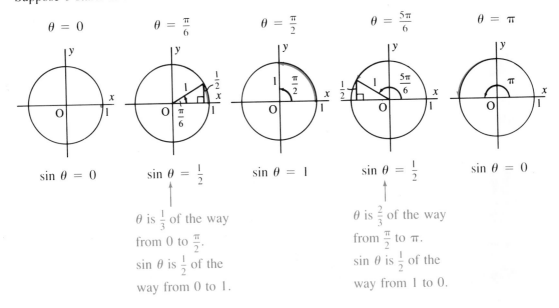

We use these results to sketch the graph for $0 \le \theta \le \pi$.

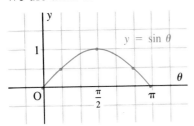

For $0 \le \theta < \frac{\pi}{2}$, $\sin \theta$ is increasing.

For $\frac{\pi}{2} < \theta \le \pi$, $\sin \theta$ is decreasing.

Suppose θ continues from π to 2π. Then $\sin \theta$ changes as follows.

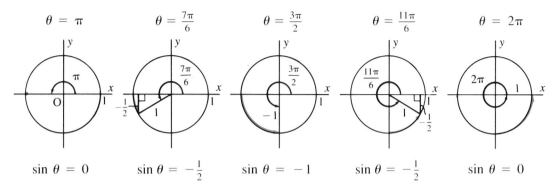

We use these results to sketch the graph for $\pi \leqslant \theta \leqslant 2\pi$.

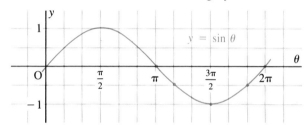

For $\pi \leqslant \theta < \frac{3\pi}{2}$, $\sin \theta$ continues to decrease.

For $\frac{3\pi}{2} < \theta \leqslant 2\pi$, $\sin \theta$ is increasing.

As θ continues beyond 2π, P rotates around the circle again, and the same values of $\sin \theta$ are encountered. Hence, the graph can be continued to the right. Similarly, the graph can be continued to the left, corresponding to a rotation in the opposite direction. Hence, the patterns in the graph repeat every 2π in both directions.

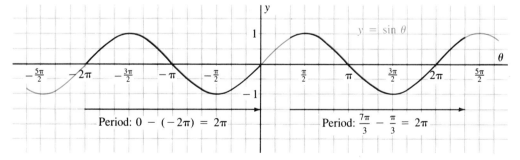

This graph shows two different cycles of the function $y = \sin \theta$. When θ is in radians, the period of this function is 2π.

A *cycle* of a periodic function is a part of its graph from any point to the first point where the graph starts repeating.

The *period* of a periodic function of θ may be expressed as the difference in the values of θ for the points at the ends of a cycle.

Graphing the function $y = \cos \theta$

We can graph the function $y = \cos \theta$ using the same method as we used to graph the function $y = \sin \theta$. The result is shown below.

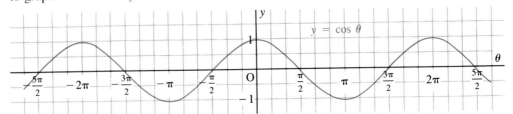

The function $y = \cos \theta$ has a period of 2π. Its graph is congruent to the graph of $y = \sin \theta$, but it is shifted horizontally so that it intersects the y-axis at $(0,1)$ instead of $(0,0)$.

Up to now, we have used the variable θ, but any symbol can be used. Since we often use the variable x when we work with functions, we will use x with sine and cosine functions.

Properties of the function $y = \sin x$

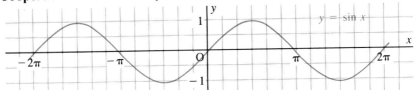

Period: 2π Maximum value of y: 1   Minimum value of y: -1

Domain: x may represent any real number

Range: $\{y \mid -1 \leqslant y \leqslant 1\}$ Symmetric about: $x = \pm\frac{\pi}{2}, \pm\frac{3\pi}{2}, \ldots$

x-intercepts: $\ldots, -\pi, 0, \pi, \ldots$ y-intercept: 0

Increasing: $\ldots]-\frac{\pi}{2}, \frac{\pi}{2} [,] \frac{3\pi}{2}, \frac{5\pi}{2} [, \ldots$ Decreasing: $\ldots] -\frac{3\pi}{2}, -\frac{\pi}{2} [,] \frac{\pi}{2}, \frac{3\pi}{2} [, \ldots$

Properties of the function $y = \cos x$

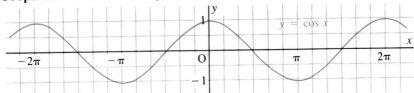

Period: 2π Maximum value of y: 1   Minimum value of y: -1

Domain: x may represent any real number

Range: $\{y \mid -1 \leqslant y \leqslant 1\}$ Symmetric about: $x = 0, \pm\pi, \pm 2\pi, \ldots$

x-intercepts: $\ldots, -\frac{\pi}{2}, \frac{\pi}{2}, \frac{3\pi}{2}, \frac{5\pi}{2}, \ldots$ y-intercept: 1

Increasing: $\ldots]-\pi, 0 [,] \pi, 2\pi [, \ldots$ Decreasing: $\ldots]-2\pi, -\pi [,] 0, \pi [, \ldots$

These curves are called *sinusoids*, meaning "like sine curves". To use sinusoidal functions in applications involving quantities that change periodically, we must be able to work with them when their maximum and minimum values are different from 1 and −1, and their periods are different from 2π. This involves taking the basic graphs described in this section, and expanding or compressing them in the vertical or horizontal directions, as well as changing their positions relative to the axes. When changes such as these are made to the graphs of these functions, corresponding changes occur in the equations. In the following sections we will investigate how the changes in the equations are related to the changes in the graphs.

EXERCISES 7-7

(A)

1. In the following diagrams, graphs of $y = \sin \theta$ have been started using different scales. Copy each graph on graph paper, and then extend it for the number of cycles indicated.

   a) 2 cycles   b) 2 cycles   c) 1 cycle

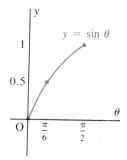 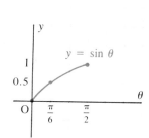 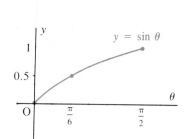

2. **Graphing the function $y = \cos \theta$**

Let P be a point on the terminal arm of an angle θ in standard position on a circle with radius $r = 2$.

   a) Suppose θ starts at 0 and increases to π. Use diagrams like those on page 362 corresponding to $\theta = 0, \frac{\pi}{3}, \frac{\pi}{2}, \frac{2\pi}{3}$, and π to determine values of $\cos \theta$, and use the results to sketch the graph of $y = \cos \theta$ for $0 \le \theta \le \pi$.

   b) Suppose θ continues from π to 2π. Determine values of $\cos \theta$ for $\theta = \frac{4\pi}{3}, \frac{3\pi}{2}, \frac{5\pi}{3}$, and 2π, and use the results to continue the graph from π to 2π.

   c) Continue the graph of $y = \cos \theta$ for values of θ greater than 2π and less than 0.

   d) For what values of θ in the interval $0 \le \theta \le 2\pi$ does:

      i) $\cos \theta$ increase   ii) $\cos \theta$ decrease?

3. In the following diagrams, graphs of $y = \cos \theta$ have been started using different scales. Copy each graph on graph paper, and then extend it for the number of cycles indicated.

   a) 2 cycles   b) 2 cycles   c) 4 cycles

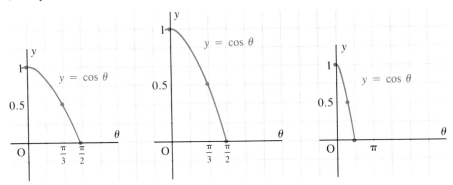

4. Without making a table of values, draw graphs of $f(x) = \sin x$ and $f(x) = \cos x$ for $-2\pi \leqslant x \leqslant 2\pi$.

5. For the graph of $y = \sin x$
   a) What is the maximum value of y? For what values of x does this occur?
   b) What is the minimum value of y? For what values of x does this occur?
   c) What is the range of the function?
   d) What is the y-intercept?
   e) What are the x-intercepts?
   f) In which interval(s) is $\sin x$ decreasing?
   g) In which interval(s) is $\sin x$ increasing?

6. Repeat *Exercise 5* for the graph of $y = \cos x$.

7. Which of the following statements are true?
   a) For $\theta \in \;] \frac{\pi}{2}, \pi[$, both $\cos \theta$ and $\sin \theta$ are decreasing.
   b) If $\frac{3\pi}{2} \leqslant \theta \leqslant 2\pi$, then $\cos \theta$ is decreasing.
   c) In Quadrant III, $\sin \theta < 0$ and $\cos \theta < 0$
   d) For $\theta \in [0, 2\pi]$, $\sin \theta$ increases only when $\theta \in \;]0, \frac{\pi}{2}[$.
   e) The function $f(x) = \cos x$ is increasing in the interval $\;] -2\pi, -\pi[$.

8. Compare the graphs of $f(x) = \sin x$ and $f(x) = \cos x$. In what ways are they alike? In what ways are they different?

9. A function $y = f(x)$ is defined to be *periodic* if there is a number p such that $f(x + p) = f(x)$ for all values of x in the domain. Use this definition to prove that the functions $y = \sin \theta$ and $y = \cos \theta$ are periodic.

Graphing the Sine and Cosine Functions Using a Unit Circle

If P is any point on the unit circle with centre O, and ∠POA = θ, then
sin θ is the second coordinate of P and cos θ is the first coordinate
of P.

   Suppose P rotates counterclockwise so that θ increases from 0° to
360°. The diagram shows how to graph the sine function by projecting
the second coordinates of P horizontally. Observe that it is not necessary
to know the actual coordinates of any of the points on the circle or on
the graph.

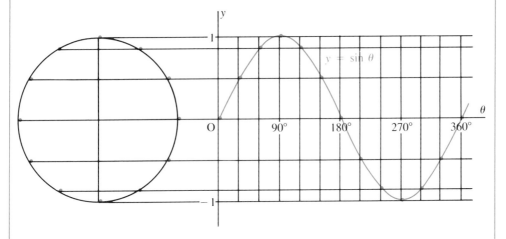

1. a) Describe how the coordinates of points on the graph at the right are
      related to the position of P as P moves around the unit circle.
   b) Use this method to draw your own graph of *y* = sin θ.

2. In the above diagram, the second coordinates of P are vertical distances in
   the unit circle, and these are projected horizontally to produce the graph
   of *y* = sin θ.
   a) Since the first coordinates of P are horizontal distances in the unit circle,
      in which direction do you think they should be projected to produce
      the graph of *y* = cos θ?
   b) Use this method to graph *y* = cos θ.
   c) Describe how the coordinates of points on your graph are related to the
      position of P as P moves around the unit circle.

$$\text{USING TECHNOLOGY}$$

Periodic Functions, Part I

Viewing the Sine Function

The graphing calculator allows us to view the graph of $y = \sin x$ without plotting points. Enter the equation $Y_1 = \sin X$ on the functions menu. Since $\pi \doteq 3.14$, set the viewing window to be $[-6.28, 6.28]$ by $[-1, 1]$. The graph should resemble the one below (without the numbers).

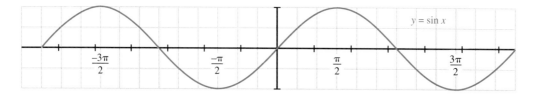

a) Use the TRACE feature or the independent cursor to determine the values of Y when X equals -2π, $-\pi$, 0, $\frac{\pi}{2}$, π, $\frac{3\pi}{2}$, and 2π. How do these values compare to what you have learned previously?

Parametric Equations

When we study a relation that is not a function, it is often convenient to express its equations in parametric form. In this form, the variables x and y are expressed in terms of another quantity, like T or θ, called a *parameter*. The curve representing an equation can be plotted, point by point, by giving the parameter different values.

Even a fairly simple relation such as the one defined by the vertical line $x = 3$ cannot be expressed as y in terms of x. However, the line $x = 3$ can be expressed as the pair of parametric equations:

$x = 3$
$y = t$

Graph this pair of equations in the parametric mode on your graphing calculator. Express the equations as $X_1(T) = 3$ and $Y_1(T) = T$, then press the graphing key.

The Unit Circle and the Sine Function

Previously, you have studied the unit circle whose equation is $x^2 + y^2 = 1$. It is not possible to express this equation in functional form, $y = f(x)$.

The coordinates of any point P on the unit circle are (cos θ, sin θ). We can define the unit circle in parametric form as:

$x = \cos \theta$
$y = \sin \theta$

where θ is the angle of rotation.
Each value of the parameter θ determines a point on the circle.

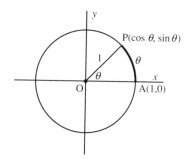

Set your graphing calculator to parametric mode. Enter the equations for the unit circle: $X_1(T) = \cos T$ and the sine function: $X_2(T) = T$
$\qquad\qquad\qquad\qquad\quad Y_1(T) = \sin T \qquad\qquad\qquad\qquad\qquad\qquad\quad Y_2(T) = \sin T$
Let T vary from 0 to 6.28 in steps of 0.105 and set the viewing window to be $[-1, 6.28]$ by $[-2, 2]$.

a) Describe what you see when you graph these 2 sets of equations on the same screen.

b) Use the TRACE feature to place the cursor at any point P on the unit circle and record the values of X, Y, and T.

c) Move the cursor horizontally to the sine curve. Which values of X, Y, and T are the same as those in part b)?

d) What is the relationship between the values of X and Y on the sine curve and the values of T and Y on the unit circle?

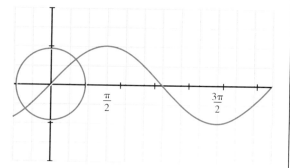

Looking Ahead

a) Without graphing the equations, describe some similarities and differences in the graphs of $y = x$ and $y = x + 1$.

b) On your graphing calculator, display the graph of $y = \sin x$. Describe what you think the graph of $y = \sin x + 1$ will look like. Display the graphs of $y = \sin x$ and $y = \sin x + 1$ on the same screen. Was your description accurate?

c) Describe the similarities and differences you think there are between the graphs of $y = \sin x$ and $y = 2 \sin x$. Graph these two functions on your calculator. Does your description fit the graphs you see?

d) How do you think the graph of $y = \sin 8x$ differs from the graph of $y = \sin x$? Graph these two functions on your calculator. Is the graph of $y = \sin 8x$ what you expected it to be?

7-8 VERTICAL TRANSLATION AND AMPLITUDE VARIATION OF COSINE AND SINE FUNCTIONS

In this section and the next we shall develop a technique for graphing a sinusoidal function without making a table of values.

Vertical Translation

As you pedal a bicycle, the heights of the pedals above the ground are changing. A graph of the height of a pedal against time is a sinusoidal curve with a vertical translation corresponding to the mean height of the pedal above the ground.

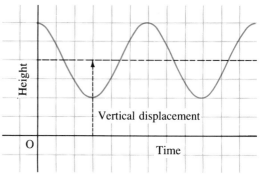

Suppose the graph of $y = \cos x$ is translated one unit up. Then the y-coordinates of all points on the graph are increased by 1 unit. Hence, the equation of the translated graph is $y = \cos x + 1$. Similarly, if the graph is translated 0.5 units down, its equation becomes $y = \cos x - 0.5$.

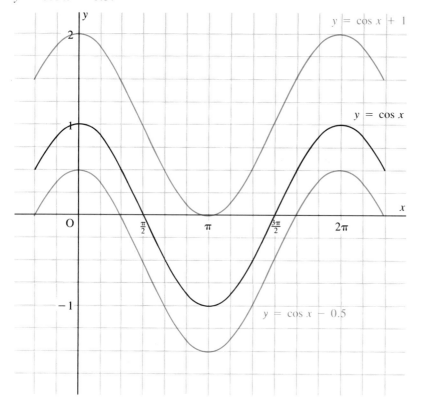

In general, adding a constant to sin x or cos x in the equations of the functions $y = \sin x$ or $y = \cos x$ causes a vertical translation of the graph. The sign of the constant indicates whether the graph is translated up or down. A positive constant causes a translation up; a negative constant causes a translation down.

Varying the Amplitude

This graph shows how the top of a building sways in a high wind. The distance the building sways from the centre is called the amplitude of the vibration.

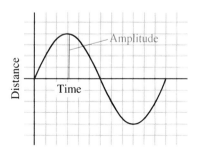

Suppose the y-coordinates of all points on the graph of $y = \sin x$ are doubled. Then, the new points lie on a sinusoidal curve that is expanded vertically relative to the graph of $y = \sin x$. Its equation is $y = 2 \sin x$. Similarly, if the y-coordinates of all points on the graph of $y = \sin x$ are divided by 2, the new points lie on a sinusoidal curve that is compressed vertically relative to $y = \sin x$. Its equation is $y = 0.5 \sin x$.

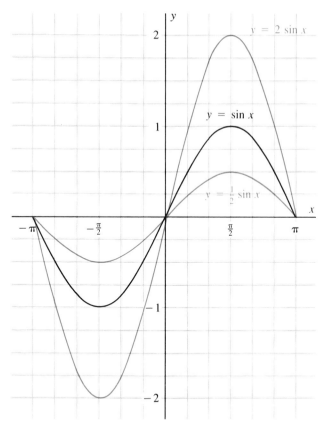

In general, multiplying sin x or cos x by a positive constant a causes a vertical expansion or compression of the graphs of $y = \sin x$ or $y = \cos x$. That is, for $0 < a < 1$, there is a compression; for $a > 1$, there is an expansion.

Example.   Draw a graph of the function $f(x) = 2 \sin x + 3$ over two cycles.

Solution.   Draw a graph of $y = \sin x$, and expand it vertically by a factor of 2. Then translate the image 3 units up.

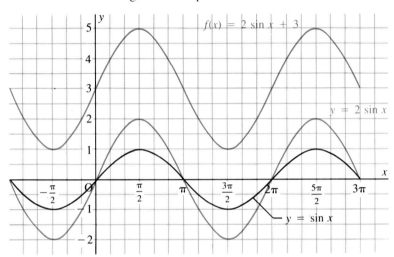

We can use the graph in the *Example* to derive a definition for the amplitude of a periodic function. In this graph, the maximum value of the function is 5, and the minimum value is 1. The amplitude is one-half the way from the minimum to the maximum, measured in the vertical direction. For this function, the amplitude is $\frac{1}{2}(5 - 1)$, or 2.

If M represents the maximum value of a periodic function in any cycle, and m represents the minimum value in that cycle, then the *amplitude A* of the function is

$$A = \frac{M - m}{2}$$

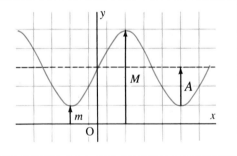

EXERCISES 7-8

Ⓐ

1. a) Graph each set of functions on the same grid for $-\pi \leqslant x \leqslant \pi$.
   i) $f(x) = \sin x$ $f(x) = \sin x + 1.5$ $f(x) = \sin x - 2$
   ii) $f(x) = \cos x$ $f(x) = \cos x - 3$ $f(x) = \cos x + 4$
   b) Graph each set of functions on the same grid for $-\pi \leqslant x \leqslant \pi$.
   i) $f(x) = 2 \cos x$ $f(x) = \cos x$ $f(x) = \frac{1}{2} \cos x$

   ii) $f(x) = 3 \sin x$ $f(x) = \sin x$ $f(x) = \frac{1}{4} \sin x$

2. Each function graphed below is sinusoidal. Write an equation for each function.
   State the maximum and minimum values of y, and the amplitude.
   a)   b)

   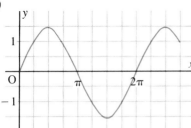   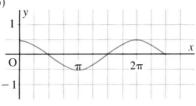

3. Write an equation to represent each function. State the vertical translation, the
   maximum value of y, the minimum value of y, and the y-intercept.
   a)   b)

   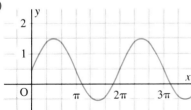   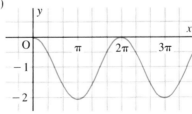

Ⓑ

4. Graph each sinusoidal function over two complete cycles. Determine the maximum
   and minimum values of the function, and its range.
   a) $y = 5 \sin x$ b) $y = 3 \cos x$ c) $y = 3 \sin x + 4$

   d) $f(x) = 2 \cos x - 3$ e) $f(x) = 4 \sin x - 2$ f) $f(x) = \frac{1}{2} \cos x + 3$

   g) $f(x) = \frac{1}{2} \sin x - 1$ h) $f(x) = 2 + 2 \sin x$ i) $f(x) = 3 + 3 \cos x$

5. Given the function $f(x) = a \sin x + q$
   a) What is the maximum value of $f(x)$? For what values of x does this occur?
   b) What is the minimum value of $f(x)$? For what values of x does this occur?

6. Repeat *Exercise 5* for the function $g(x) = a \cos x + q$.

Ⓒ

7. Find the equation of a function of the form $f(x) = \sin x + p$ whose graph just
   touches the x-axis. How many such functions are there?

7-9 VARYING THE PHASE SHIFT OF COSINE AND SINE FUNCTIONS

In a certain region the number of rabbits increases and decreases periodically. This variation is caused by wolves which feed on the rabbits. If the number of wolves is small, the rabbits will flourish. But then the number of wolves will increase, since food is easy to find. This, in turn, causes a decrease in the number of rabbits, which causes the number of wolves to decrease, and the cycle begins all over again. The population graph for the wolves is translated horizontally relative to the population graph for the rabbits.

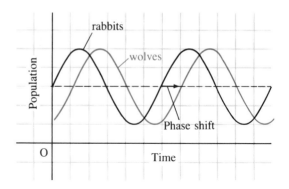

In $y = \sin x$, if x is replaced with $x - \frac{\pi}{2}$, we obtain $y = \sin \left(x - \frac{\pi}{2} \right)$. If we were to graph this function using a table of values, we would start with values of x, subtract $\frac{\pi}{2}$, and then find the sines of the results. To give the same y-coordinates as in $y = \sin x$, the values of x must be $\frac{\pi}{2}$ greater than those in $y = \sin x$. Hence, the x-coordinates of all points on the graph of $y = \sin \left(x - \frac{\pi}{2} \right)$ are $\frac{\pi}{2}$ *greater* than the x-coordinates of corresponding points on the graph of $y = \sin x$. Therefore, the graph of $y = \sin \left(x - \frac{\pi}{2} \right)$ is translated $\frac{\pi}{2}$ units to the *right* relative to the graph of $y = \sin x$. We say that its phase shift is $\frac{\pi}{2}$. Similarly, the graph of $y = \sin \left(x + \frac{\pi}{3} \right)$ is translated $\frac{\pi}{3}$ units to the left relative to the graph of $y = \sin x$, and its phase shift is $-\frac{\pi}{3}$.

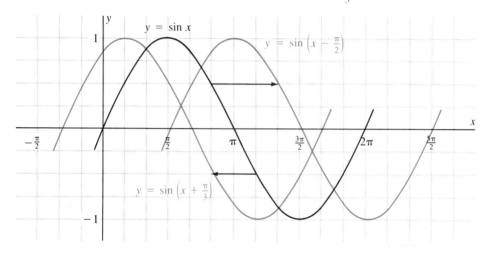

The *phase shift* of a periodic function is the amount by which the graph of the function is translated horizontally with respect to the basic function. A negative phase shift corresponds to a translation to the left. A positive phase shift corresponds to a translation to the right.

Similar results will be found for other values of x, and for cosine functions. In general, adding a constant to the variable x in the equations of the functions $y = \sin x$ or $y = \cos x$ causes a horizontal translation of the graph. A positive constant causes a translation to the left; a negative constant causes a translation to the right.

In general, the phase shift of $y = \sin (x - p)$ or $y = \cos (x - p)$ is the value of x for which $x - p = 0$; that is, p.

Vertical translation, phase shift, and amplitude are often combined in the same function.

Example. Draw a graph of the function $f(x) = 3 \sin \left(x - \frac{2\pi}{3}\right) + 2$ over two cycles. State the vertical translation, the phase shift, and the amplitude.

Solution. Draw a graph of $y = \sin x$, and expand it vertically by a factor of 3. Then translate the image $\frac{2\pi}{3}$ units to the right and 2 units up.

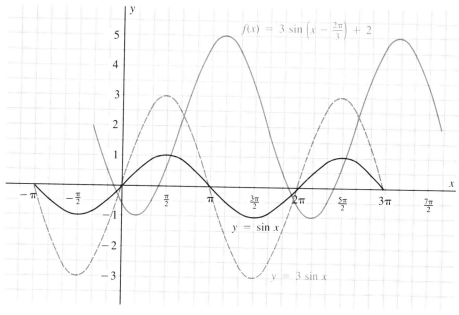

The vertical translation is 2, the phase shift is $\frac{2\pi}{3}$, and the amplitude is 3.

EXERCISES 7-9

Ⓐ

1. a) Graph these functions on the same grid for $-\pi \leqslant x \leqslant \pi$.

$$y = \sin x \qquad y = \sin\left(x - \frac{\pi}{6}\right) \qquad y = \sin\left(x - \frac{\pi}{3}\right) \qquad y = \sin\left(x + \frac{\pi}{4}\right)$$

b) Graph these functions on the same grid for $-\pi \leqslant x \leqslant \pi$.

$$y = \cos x \qquad y = \cos\left(x + \frac{\pi}{3}\right) \qquad y = \cos\left(x - \frac{\pi}{3}\right) \qquad y = \cos\left(x - \frac{\pi}{4}\right)$$

2. The function graphed below can be considered as a sine function. Find two possible values for the phase shift. What is the equation of the function for each phase shift?

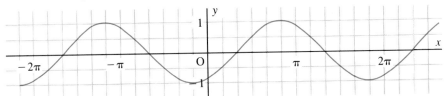

3. The function in *Exercise 2* can also be considered as a cosine function. Find two possible values for the phase shift. What is the equation of the function for each phase shift?

Ⓑ

4. Graph each sinusoidal function over two cycles.

a) $y = \sin\left(x - \frac{\pi}{4}\right)$ b) $y = \sin\left(x - \frac{4\pi}{3}\right)$ c) $y = 2\sin\left(x + \frac{5\pi}{6}\right)$

d) $y = 3\cos\left(x - \frac{\pi}{6}\right)$ e) $y = 2\cos\left(x + \frac{5\pi}{3}\right)$ f) $y = 5\cos\left(x - \frac{7\pi}{6}\right)$

5. Graph each sinusoidal function, and determine its domain and range.

a) $f(x) = 2\sin\left(x - \frac{\pi}{4}\right) + 3$ b) $g(x) = 2\cos\left(x - \frac{\pi}{6}\right) + 2$

c) $h(x) = 4\cos\left(x - \frac{4\pi}{3}\right) - 1$ d) $k(x) = 4\sin\left(x + \frac{2\pi}{3}\right) - 2$

6. Find values of p for which the graph of $y = \sin(x - p)$ coincides with the graph of:

a) $y = \sin x$ b) $y = \cos x$.

7. Repeat *Exercise 6* for the function $y = \cos(x - p)$.

Ⓒ

8. Given the function $f(x) = a\sin(x - p) + q$, where $a > 0$
   a) What is the maximum value of $f(x)$? For what values of x does this occur?
   b) What is the minimum value of $f(x)$? For what values of x does this occur?

9. Repeat *Exercise 8* for the function $f(x) = a\cos(x - p) + q$, where $a > 0$.

7-10 VARYING THE PERIOD OF COSINE AND SINE FUNCTIONS

In 1968 the scientific world was astonished when two astronomers detected extremely massive stars that spin on their axes in a fraction of a second. Since a pulse of radio energy is sent out on each rotation, these stars are called pulsars, or rotating stars. One pulsar, in the Crab Nebula, pulses every 0.033 s. This time is called the period.

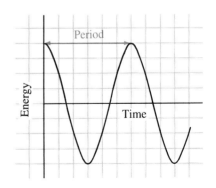

In $y = \cos x$, if x is replaced with $2x$, we obtain $y = \cos 2x$. If we were to graph this function using a table of values, we would start with values of x, multiply by 2, and then find the cosines of the results. To give the same y-coordinates as in $y = \cos x$, the values of x must be one-half of those in $y = \cos x$. Hence, the x-coordinates of all points on the graph of $y = \cos 2x$ are *one-half* of the x-coordinates of corresponding points on the graph of $y = \cos x$. Therefore, the graph of $y = \cos 2x$ is *compressed* horizontally relative to the graph of $y = \cos x$. The period of $y = \cos 2x$ is π, since one cycle is completed in π units along the x-axis. Similarly, the graph of $y = \cos \frac{1}{2}x$ is *expanded* horizontally relative to the graph of $y = \cos x$, and its period is 4π.

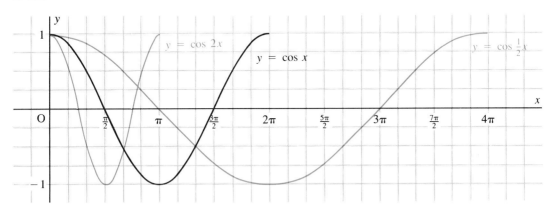

In general, multiplying the variable x in the equations of the functions $y = \cos x$ or $y = \sin x$ by a positive constant k affects the period and causes a horizontal expansion or compression of its graph. If $0 < k < 1$, there is an expansion; if $k > 1$, there is a compression.

To discover how k is related to the period, we compare the three functions graphed on the previous page with their periods.

Function	Value of k	Period
$y = \cos x$	1	2π
$y = \cos 2x$	2	π
$y = \cos \frac{1}{2}x$	$\frac{1}{2}$	4π

In each case, if we multiply the value of k by the period, the product is 2π.

$$(k)(\text{period}) = 2\pi$$
$$\text{period} = \frac{2\pi}{k}$$

Very often, horizontal expansions or compressions are combined with horizontal translations. The result depends on the order in which these two transformations are applied. With sinusoidal functions we will assume that the expansion or compression is applied first, since there is no need to consider the reverse order in applications.

Suppose the graph of the function $y = \cos x$ is compressed horizontally by a factor of $\frac{1}{2}$. To find the equation of the image, replace x with $2x$. The equation becomes $y = \cos 2x$.

Now suppose the resulting graph is translated $\frac{\pi}{3}$ units to the right. To find the image equation after the translation, replace x with $\left(x - \frac{\pi}{3}\right)$. The equation becomes $y = \cos 2\left(x - \frac{\pi}{3}\right)$.

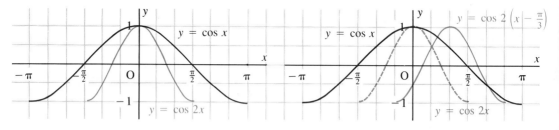

In the above example, the magnitude and direction of the translation give the phase shift. Also, the translation does not affect the period.

The phase shift of $y = \cos 2\left(x - \frac{\pi}{3}\right)$ is $\frac{\pi}{3}$.

The period of $y = \cos 2\left(x - \frac{\pi}{3}\right)$ is $\frac{2\pi}{2}$, or π.

Similar results will be found for other functions.

The graphs of $y = \cos k(x - p)$ and $y = \sin k(x - p)$ are related to the graphs of $y = \cos x$ and $y = \sin x$ by a horizontal expansion or compression followed by a horizontal translation. For $y = \cos k(x - p)$ and $y = \sin k(x - p)$:

- the phase shift is p • the period is $\frac{2\pi}{k}$.

Example.   Graph the function $y = 2 \cos 3\left(x - \frac{\pi}{2}\right)$ over two cycles, and state its amplitude, phase shift, and period.

Solution.   Graph $y = 2 \cos x$, then compress horizontally by a factor of $\frac{1}{3}$. At this point, the equation of the curve is $y = 2 \cos 3x$. Then translate the image $\frac{\pi}{2}$ units to the right.

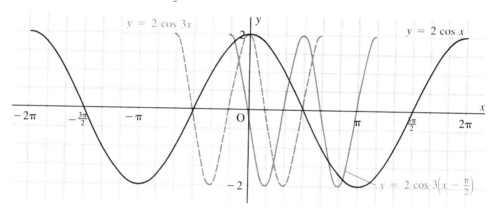

The amplitude of the function is 2.
The phase shift is $\frac{\pi}{2}$.
The period is $\frac{2\pi}{3}$.

EXERCISES 7-10

(A)

1. a) Graph these functions on the same grid for $-\pi \leqslant x \leqslant \pi$.
     $y = \sin 2x$ $y = \sin x$ $y = \sin \frac{1}{2}x$

   b) Graph these functions on the same grid for $-\pi \leqslant x \leqslant \pi$.
     $y = \cos 3x$ $y = \cos x$ $y = \cos \frac{1}{3}x$

   c) Describe the effect on the graphs of $y = \sin kx$ and $y = \cos kx$ as the value of k varies.

2. Each function graphed below is sinusoidal. Write an equation for each function.
a)   b)

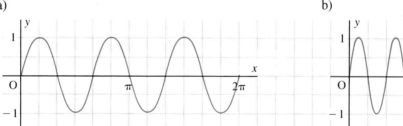

(B)

3. Graph each sinusoidal function, and state its amplitude and period.
   a) $y = 2 \sin 2x$
   b) $y = 3 \sin \frac{1}{2}x$
   c) $y = 4 \sin 2x$
   d) $y = 4 \cos \frac{1}{2}x$
   e) $y = 5 \cos 2x$
   f) $y = 3 \cos 3x$

4. State the amplitude, the period, and the phase shift for each function.
   a) $f(x) = 5 \cos 3(x - \pi)$
   b) $f(x) = 2 \sin 4\left(x + \frac{\pi}{2}\right)$
   c) $f(x) = 2.5 \sin 6\left(x - \frac{2\pi}{3}\right)$
   d) $f(x) = 0.5 \cos 5\left(x + \frac{5\pi}{4}\right)$

5. Graph each function over two cycles, and state its amplitude, period, and phase shift.
   a) $y = \sin 2\left(x - \frac{\pi}{3}\right)$
   b) $y = 2 \cos 3\left(x - \frac{\pi}{2}\right)$
   c) $y = 4 \cos \frac{1}{2}(x + \pi)$
   d) $y = 0.5 \sin \frac{1}{2}\left(x - \frac{5\pi}{4}\right)$

(C)

6. **Negative values of k in $y = \sin kx$ and $y = \cos kx$**
   a) Draw graphs of these functions.
      i) $y = \sin(-x)$ ii) $y = \sin(-2x)$ iii) $y = \sin\left(-\frac{1}{2}x\right)$
   b) How are the graphs of the functions in part a) related to the graph of the function $y = \sin x$?
   c) Draw diagrams to illustrate how the graphs of $y = \sin kx$ and $y = \cos kx$ are related to the graphs of $y = \sin x$ and $y = \cos x$ if $k < 0$.
   d) Do negative values of k affect the period? In what way?

7. Graph each function over two cycles, and state the period.
   a) $y = \sin(-3x)$
   b) $y = 4 \cos\left(-\frac{1}{2}x\right)$
   c) $y = 3 \sin(-2x) + 3$

8. Compare the graphs of each pair of functions. What conclusions can you make?
   a) $y = \sin x$ and $y = \sin(-x)$
   b) $y = \cos x$ and $y = \cos(-x)$

7-11 APPLICATIONS OF COSINE AND SINE FUNCTIONS

In the first section of this chapter several graphs were shown illustrating some examples of periodic functions. These graphs differ from the graphs we studied in the preceding sections in one major way. They show periodic functions without the use of angles.

Up to now the horizontal axes have been scaled in terms of π. These scales are not very useful in applications such as those in *Section 7-1*, where the horizontal axes are usually marked in time intervals. To use sinusoidal functions in applications we must scale the horizontal axis with rational numbers in decimal form. We do this by adjusting the period of the function.

For example, the graph below shows a sine function with period 5. Its equation can be written in the form $y = \sin kt$. Since the period of this function is $\frac{2\pi}{k}$, we can write $\frac{2\pi}{k} = 5$, or $k = \frac{2\pi}{5}$. Therefore, the equation of this function is $y = \sin \frac{2\pi t}{5}$.

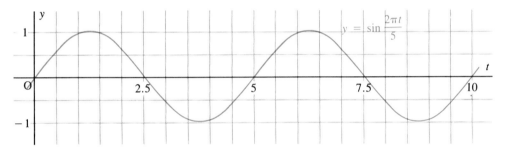

Observe that if π does not occur on the axis, then it must occur in the equation. When the coefficient of t in the equation is written in the form $\frac{2\pi}{k}$, the denominator is the period of the function. We can use this information, and the results of the preceding sections, to write an equation representing any sinusoidal function.

Example 1. The volume of air in the lungs is a sinusoidal function of time. A graph illustrating this variation for normal breathing is shown on page 339. Write an equation for this function.

Solution. The vertical translation is 2450 mL. The amplitude is 250 mL. The period is 5 s. If V millilitres represents the volume of air in the lungs at time t seconds, then an equation for the function is:

$$V = 250 \sin \frac{2\pi t}{5} + 2450.$$

Example 2.   Write an equation of this sinusoidal function.

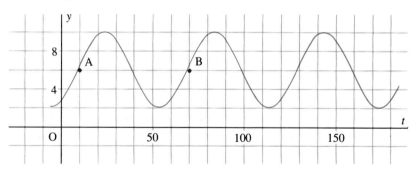

Solution.   The vertical translation is 6.
The amplitude is 4.
For a sine function, the phase shift is the horizontal coordinate of A: 10.
The period is the difference between the horizontal coordinates of A and B: 70 − 10; or 60.

An equation of the function is $y = 4 \sin 2\pi \dfrac{(t - 10)}{60} + 6$.

In *Example 2*, the period, amplitude, phase shift, and vertical translation are all represented by numbers in the equation.

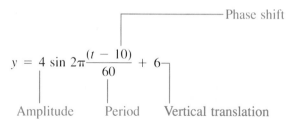

Notice the factor 2π in the equation. This factor must be present for the period to be as indicated. We can use this pattern to write the equation when these data are given or when they can be read from a graph.

In *Example 2*, the function can also be expressed as a cosine function. The only difference is the phase shift. Since the first maximum occurs when $t = 25$, the phase shift is 25. An equation of the function is $y = 4 \cos 2\pi \dfrac{(t - 25)}{60} + 6$. What are other equations for this function?

A common example of sinusoidal functions occurs at the coast. The tides are the periodic rise and fall of the water in the oceans, caused almost entirely by the gravitational attraction of the moon and the sun. An equation representing the depth of the water as a function of time is extremely complicated, since the distances and relative positions of the moon and sun are constantly changing. However, over a period of one or two days, the depth can be approximated by a sinusoidal function. The amplitude of the function depends on the location, and at any particular location it varies considerably at different times of the year.

Some of the highest tides in the world occur in the Bay of Fundy, where the Annapolis Tidal Generating Station has been in operation since 1984. The graph below shows how the depth of the water at the station varies during a typical day. Notice that times are given in decimal form using a 24 h clock.

When we work with sinusoidal functions involving time in hours, a fractional part of an hour must be expressed in decimal form. For example, the period of the tidal motion (below) is 12 h 25 min. Converting to decimal form,

$$12 \text{ h } 25 \text{ min} = \left(12 + \frac{25}{60}\right) \text{h}$$

$$\doteq 12.4 \text{ h}$$

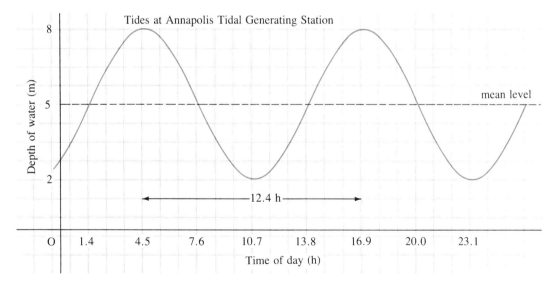

We can find the vertical translation, the phase shift, the period, and the amplitude of the function from the graph, and use these to write an equation of the function.

Since the mean level is 5 m, the vertical translation is 5 m.

The amplitude is the difference between high tide level and mean level, 3 m.

The first high tide occurs at 4.5 h. If we think of the function as a cosine function, then the phase shift is 4.5 h.

The period is the time between two high tides, 12.4 h.

Therefore, if h metres represents the depth, and t hours represents the time, an equation of the function is:

$$h = 3 \cos 2\pi \frac{(t - 4.5)}{12.4} + 5$$

Phase shift
(time at first high tide)

Amplitude   Period   Mean level

We can use this equation to calculate the depth of the water at any time during the day.

Example 3.   Calculate the depth of the water to the nearest tenth of a metre at:

a) 9:30 A.M.   b) 6:45 P.M.

Solution.   Convert the times to decimals of hours, on a 24 h clock.

9:30 A.M. = 09.50 h   6:45 P.M. = (12 + 6.75) h
                                         = 18.75 h

a) Substitute $t = 9.5$ in the above equation.

$$h = 3 \cos 2\pi \frac{(t - 4.5)}{12.4} + 5$$

$$= 3 \cos 2\pi \frac{(9.5 - 4.5)}{12.4} + 5$$

Use a scientific calculator in *radian mode* to evaluate this expression.

$h \doteq 2.537\ 709\ 7$

At 9:30 A.M., the depth of the water is approximately 2.5 m.

b) Substitute $t = 18.75$ in the above equation.

$$h = 3 \cos 2\pi \frac{(t - 4.5)}{12.4} + 5$$

$$= 3 \cos 2\pi \frac{(18.75 - 4.5)}{12.4} + 5$$

$\doteq 6.775\ 631$

At 6:45 P.M., the depth of the water is approximately 6.8 m.

If your calculator requires the function key to be pressed first you may need to use the memory or brackets to evaluate expressions such as those in *Example 3*.

The pattern suggested by *Example 3* can be used to solve other problems involving quantities which change periodically. In each case, we use a sinusoidal function to approximate the data. The general pattern in the equation of the function is shown below.

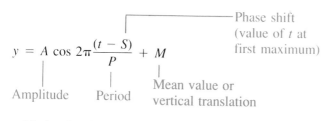

$$y = A \cos 2\pi \frac{(t - S)}{P} + M$$

Phase shift (value of t at first maximum)

Amplitude   Period   Mean value or vertical translation

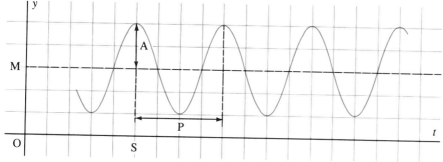

Example 4. A Ferris wheel with a radius of 20 m rotates once every 40 s. Passengers get on at point S, which is 1 m above level ground. Suppose you get on at S and the wheel starts to rotate.

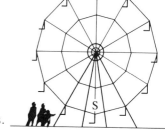

a) Draw a graph showing how your height above the ground varies during the first two cycles.

b) Write an equation which expresses your height as a function of the elapsed time.

c) Calculate your height above the ground after 15 s.

Solution.   a) *Step 1.* Draw a sinusoidal curve.

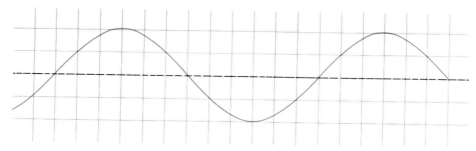

Step 2. Find the phase shift and the period, and use them to establish a horizontal scale.

For a cosine function, the phase shift is the *t*-coordinate of the first maximum, point A. Since you take 20 s to reach A, the phase shift is 20 s. Since the Ferris wheel rotates once every 40 s, the period is 40 s. Hence, the *t*-coordinates of two consecutive maximum points are 20 and 60.

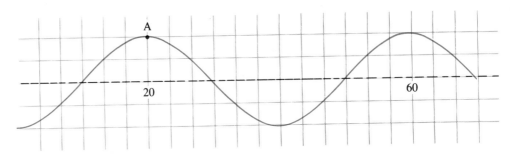

Step 3. Complete the graph by drawing the axes and their scales. The vertical translation is 21 m, and the amplitude is 20 m. Since the people get on at the bottom, draw the vertical axis as shown.

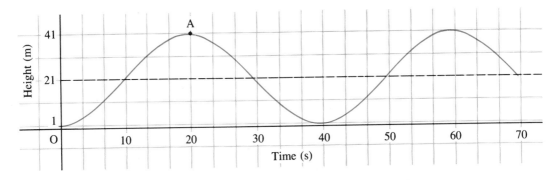

b) An equation which expresses your height as a function of time is:

$$h = 20 \cos 2\pi \frac{(t - 20)}{40} + 21.$$

c) To calculate your height above the ground after 15 s, substitute 15 for *t* in the above equation.

$$h = 20 \cos 2\pi \frac{(t - 20)}{40} + 21$$

$$= 20 \cos 2\pi \frac{(15 - 20)}{40} + 21$$

$$\doteq 35.142\ 136$$

After 15 s you will be about 35 m above the ground.

EXERCISES 7-11

Ⓐ

1. At a seaport, the depth of the water h metres at time t hours during a certain day is given by this formula.

$$h = 1.8 \sin 2\pi \frac{(t - 4.00)}{12.4} + 3.1$$

   a) Calculate the depth of the water at 5 A.M. and at 12 noon.
   b) What is the maximum depth of the water? When does it occur?

2. The equation below gives the depth of the water h metres at an ocean port at any time t hours during a certain day.

$$h = 2.5 \sin 2\pi \frac{(t - 1.5)}{12.4} + 4.3$$

   Calculate the approximate depth of the water at 9:30 A.M.

Ⓑ

3. At an ocean port, the water has a maximum depth of 4 m above the mean level at 8 A.M., and the period is 12.4 h.
   a) Assuming that the relation between the depth of the water and time is a sinusoidal function, write an equation for the depth of the water at any time t.
   b) Find the depth of the water at 10 A.M.

4. Tidal forces are greatest when the Earth, the sun, and the moon are in line. When this occurs at the Annapolis Tidal Generating Station, the water has a maximum depth of 9.6 m at 4:30 A.M. and a minimum depth of 0.4 m 6.2 h later.
   a) Write an equation for the depth of the water at any time t.
   b) Calculate the depth of the water at 9:30 A.M. and at 6:45 P.M.
   c) Compare the results of part b) with *Example 3*.

5. Repeat *Exercise 4* when the tidal forces are weakest. The maximum and minimum depths of the water at this time are 6.4 m and 3.6 m.

6. a) In *Example 3*, if the calculator is in *degree mode*, what change would have to be made in the equation?
   b) Solve *Example 3* using your calculator in degree mode.

7. In the solution of *Example 3*, a cosine function was used. Solve *Example 3* using sine function.

8. Write an equation for the volume of air in the lungs during deep breathing, when the variation is from 1000 mL to 5000 mL. Assume that the period is 10 s.

9. The twin towers of the World Trade Center in New York were once the tallest buildings in the world. During a strong wind, the top of each tower swings back and forth as much as 80 cm, with a period of 10 s.
   a) Draw a graph showing the departure of the top of one of the buildings from the normal position as a function of time, for 20 s.
   b) Write an equation for the function in part a).

10. The fundamental tone of a guitar string with length L is associated with a sinusoidal function with a period of $2L$. The period of the first overtone is $\frac{2L}{2}$; the period of the second overtone is $\frac{2L}{3}$; and so on.

    a) Assuming that the string is 50 cm long, and that the amplitude of the vibration is 0.5 cm, write the equations of the functions associated with the fundamental tone and the first three overtones.

    b) Draw the graphs of the functions in part a) on the same axes.

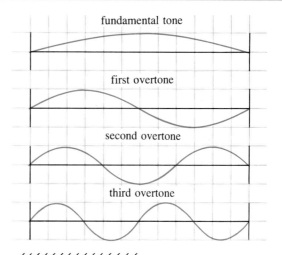

11. A certain mass is supported by a spring so that it is at rest 0.5 m above a table top. The mass is pulled down 0.4 m and released at time $t = 0$, creating a periodic up and down motion, called *simple harmonic motion*. It takes 1.2 s for the mass to return to the low position each time.

    a) Draw a graph showing the height of the mass above the table top as a function of time for the first 2.0 s.

    b) Write an equation for the function in part a).

    c) Use your equation to determine the height of the mass above the table top after:
    i) 0.3 s ii) 0.7 s iii) 1.2 s.

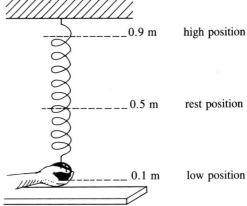

12. A piston in an engine moves up and down in the cylinder, as shown in the diagram. The height h centimetres of the piston at time t seconds is given by this formula.

    $h = 20 \sin \frac{2\pi t}{0.05} + 20$

    a) State the piston's:
    i) maximum height
    ii) minimum height
    iii) period.

    b) If the piston operates for exactly one hour, how many complete cycles does it make?

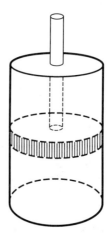

13. A Ferris wheel has a radius of 25 m, and its centre is 26 m above the ground. It rotates once every 50 s. Suppose you get on at the bottom at $t = 0$.
    a) Draw a graph showing how your height above the ground changes during the first two minutes.
    b) Write an equation for the function in part a).
    c) Use your equation to determine how high you will be above the ground after:
       i)   10 s   ii)   20 s   iii)   40 s   iv)   60 s.

14. The pedals of a bicycle are mounted on a bracket whose centre is 29.0 cm above the ground. Each pedal is 16.5 cm from the bracket. Assume that the bi-cycle is pedaled at the rate of 12 cycles per minute.

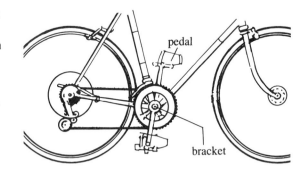

    a) Draw a graph showing the height of a pedal above the ground for the first few cycles. Assume that the pedal starts at the topmost position at $t = 0$.
    b) Write an equation for the function in part a).
    c) Use your equation to determine the height of the pedal after:
       i)   5 s   ii)   12 s   iii)   18 s.

15. On December 21 each year, the sun is closest to the Earth, at approximately 147.2 million kilometres. On June 21 the sun is at its greatest distance, approximately 152.2 million kilometres.

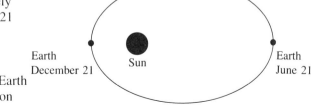

    a) Express the distance d from the Earth to the sun as a sinusoidal function of the number of the day of the year.
    b) Use the function to calculate the approximate distance from the Earth to the sun on:
       i) March 1   ii) April 30   iii) September 2.

16. On the nth day of the year, the number of hours of daylight at Seattle is given by this formula.

$$h = 3.98 \sin 2\pi \frac{(n - 80)}{365} + 12.16$$

    a) About how many hours of daylight should there be today?
    b) On what dates should there be about 10 h of daylight?

17. In *Example 3*, calculate to the nearest minute the first time after 4:30 A.M. when the depth of the water is: a) 6.0 m   b) 3.0 m.

Review Exercises

1. Convert from radians to degrees. Give the answers to 1 decimal place where necessary.

   a) $\frac{\pi}{3}$ radians

   b) $-\frac{7\pi}{4}$ radians

   c) $\frac{5\pi}{6}$ radians

   d) 4.7 radians

2. Convert from degrees to radians. Give the answers to 2 decimal places where necessary.

   a) 135°

   b) 270°

   c) 330°

   d) −47°

3. Calculate the arc length to the nearest centimetre of a sector of a circle with radius 9 cm if the sector angle is 220°.

4. Draw each angle in standard position.

   a) 240°

   b) 495°

   c) 690°

   d) $\frac{9\pi}{4}$

   e) 3π

   f) $\frac{7\pi}{3}$

5. Find the values of sin θ and cos θ for each angle in *Exercise 4*.

6. Determine each result to 4 decimal places.

   a) If θ is in the first quadrant and cos θ = 0.1234, find sin θ.

   b) If θ is in the second quadrant and sin θ = 0.2476, find cos θ.

   c) If θ is in the third quadrant and cos θ = −0.5891, find sin θ.

   d) If θ is in the fourth quadrant, and sin θ = −0.8223, find cos θ.

7. State the exact value of each expression.

   a) $\cos \frac{5\pi}{6}$

   b) $\sin \frac{\pi}{3}$

   c) $\cos \frac{7\pi}{4}$

   d) $\sin \frac{5\pi}{4}$

   e) $\sin \frac{4\pi}{3}$

   f) $\cos \frac{11\pi}{6}$

8. Draw graphs of $y = \sin θ$ and $y = \cos θ$ for $-2\pi \leqslant θ \leqslant 2\pi$. For each graph

   a) State the maximum value of y, and the values of θ for which it occurs.

   b) State the minimum value of y, and the values of θ for which it occurs.

   c) State the θ- and y-intercepts.

9. Find the amplitude, the period, the phase shift, and the vertical translation for each function.

   a) $y = 3 \sin 2\left(θ - \frac{\pi}{4}\right) - 4$

   b) $y = 2 \cos 5\left(θ + \frac{\pi}{3}\right) + 1$

10. Sketch the graphs of each set of functions on the same grid for $-2\pi \leqslant θ \leqslant 2\pi$.

   a) $y = \sin θ$ $y = 3 \sin θ$ $y = 3 \sin θ + 2$

   b) $y = \frac{1}{2} \cos θ$ $y = \frac{1}{2} \cos \left(θ + \frac{\pi}{3}\right)$ $y = \frac{1}{2} \cos \left(θ + \frac{\pi}{3}\right) + 2$

8 Trigonometric Functions and Identities

In the 17th and 18th centuries many important achievements were made in navigation and astronomy. What development in mathematics contributed significantly to these achievements? (See *The Mathematical Mind*, pages 434, 435.)

8-1 THE TANGENT FUNCTION

Another function associated with an angle in
standard position is called the tangent function. This name is used because the function
involves the tangent to the unit circle at
A(1,0).

Let P be any point on the unit circle. Then
P is on the terminal arm of an angle θ in
standard position. Let Q be the point where
the line OP intersects the tangent at A(1,0).
We define the *tangent* of θ to be the second
coordinate of Q, and we write it as tan θ.

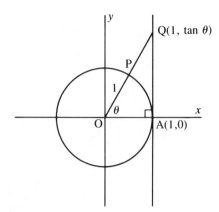

Therefore, (1, tan θ) are the coordinates of the point where the line
OP intersects the tangent to the circle passing through A(1,0). As P
rotates around the circle, the value of tan θ changes periodically.
Some values of tan θ are illustrated in the diagrams below.

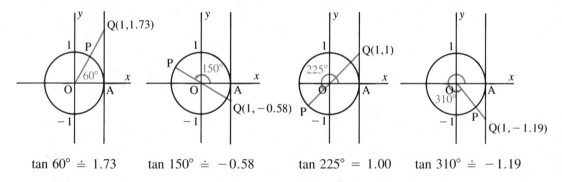

tan 60° ≐ 1.73   tan 150° ≐ −0.58   tan 225° = 1.00   tan 310° ≐ −1.19

We can use this definition to determine tan θ for certain quadrantal
angles. For other quadrantal angles, the line OP is parallel to the tangent
through A, and the tangent function is not defined.

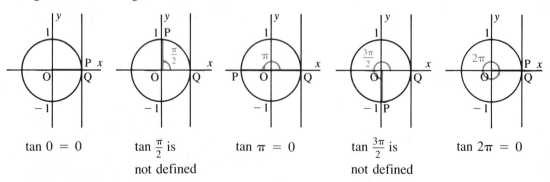

tan 0 = 0   tan $\frac{\pi}{2}$ is   tan π = 0   tan $\frac{3\pi}{2}$ is   tan 2π = 0

          not defined   not defined

We can use a scientific calculator to determine $\tan \theta$ for any angle θ.

Example 1. Find each value to five decimal places. Explain the sign of each result.
a) $\tan 232°$ b) $\tan 5.7$

Solution.   a) In degree mode, $\tan 232° \doteq 1.279\ 94$
Since θ is in the third quadrant, the line OP intersects the tangent through A above the x-axis. Hence, the second coordinate of P is positive, and so $\tan 232° > 0$.
b) In radian mode, $\tan 5.7 \doteq -0.659\ 73$
Since θ is in the fourth quadrant, the line OP intersects the tangent through A below the x-axis. Hence, the second coordinate of P is negative, and so $\tan 5.7 < 0$.

Relating tan θ with sin θ and cos θ

In the diagram, since $\triangle PON$ and $\triangle QOA$ are

similar triangles, $\dfrac{QA}{OA} = \dfrac{PN}{ON}$

Therefore, $\dfrac{\tan \theta}{1} = \dfrac{\sin \theta}{\cos \theta}$

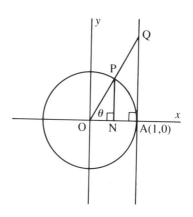

$$\tan \theta = \dfrac{\sin \theta}{\cos \theta}$$

The diagram shows θ in the first quadrant. Using similar diagrams showing θ in the other quadrants, we can show that this equation holds for any value of θ, except those for which $\cos \theta = 0$.

> For any value of θ, $\tan \theta = \dfrac{\sin \theta}{\cos \theta}$, $\cos \theta \neq 0$

If we know the value of $\sin \theta$ or $\cos \theta$, we can determine the value of $\tan \theta$.

Example 2. If θ is an angle in the fourth quadrant and $\cos \theta = 0.2784$, determine the value of $\tan \theta$ to four decimal places.

Solution.   Sketch a unit circle showing P in the fourth quadrant.
Substitute 0.2784 for $\cos \theta$ in the equation

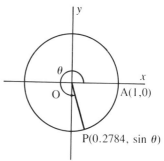

$$\cos^2\theta + \sin^2\theta = 1$$
$$(0.2784)^2 + \sin^2\theta = 1$$
$$\sin^2\theta = 1 - 0.077\ 506\ 56$$
$$= 0.922\ 493\ 44$$
$$\sin \theta = \pm\sqrt{0.922\ 493\ 44}$$
$$\doteq \pm 0.960\ 465\ 22$$

Since θ is in the fourth quadrant, the second coordinate of P is negative. Hence, we reject the positive root and obtain $\sin \theta \doteq -0.960\ 465\ 22$

Therefore, $\tan \theta = \dfrac{\sin \theta}{\cos \theta}$

$\doteq \dfrac{-0.960\ 465\ 22}{0.2784}$

$\doteq -3.4499$

In *Chapter 7* we found exact values for the cosines and sines of certain special angles and their multiples. Hence, we can use those results to find the tangents of the same angles.

$$\tan \frac{\pi}{6} = \frac{\sin \frac{\pi}{6}}{\cos \frac{\pi}{6}} \qquad \tan \frac{\pi}{4} = \frac{\sin \frac{\pi}{4}}{\cos \frac{\pi}{4}} \qquad \tan \frac{\pi}{3} = \frac{\sin \frac{\pi}{3}}{\cos \frac{\pi}{3}}$$

$$= \frac{\frac{1}{2}}{\frac{\sqrt{3}}{2}} \qquad\qquad = \frac{\frac{1}{\sqrt{2}}}{\frac{1}{\sqrt{2}}} \qquad\qquad = \frac{\frac{\sqrt{3}}{2}}{\frac{1}{2}}$$

$$= \frac{1}{2} \times \frac{2}{\sqrt{3}} \qquad\quad = 1 \qquad\qquad = \frac{\sqrt{3}}{2} \times \frac{2}{1}$$

$$= \frac{1}{\sqrt{3}} \qquad\qquad\qquad\qquad\qquad\quad = \sqrt{3}$$

$$\boxed{\tan \frac{\pi}{6} = \frac{1}{\sqrt{3}} \qquad \tan \frac{\pi}{4} = 1 \qquad \tan \frac{\pi}{3} = \sqrt{3}}$$

Example 3. Determine $\tan \dfrac{11\pi}{6}$.

Solution.   Draw the diagram shown. The reference angle is $\dfrac{\pi}{6}$.

Since P is in the fourth quadrant, $\cos \dfrac{11\pi}{6}$ is positive, and $\sin \dfrac{11\pi}{6}$ is negative. Hence,

$\cos \dfrac{11\pi}{6} = \dfrac{\sqrt{3}}{2}$ and $\sin \dfrac{11\pi}{6} = -\dfrac{1}{2}$

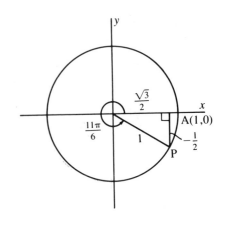

Therefore, $\tan \dfrac{11\pi}{6} = -\dfrac{\frac{1}{2}}{\frac{\sqrt{3}}{2}}$

$= -\dfrac{1}{\sqrt{3}}$

The three trigonometric functions sin θ, cos θ, and tan θ are called the *primary trigonometric functions*. There are three other trigonometric functions, which will be introduced in a later section.

EXERCISES 8-1

Ⓐ

1. Use a scientific calculator in degree mode. Find each value to 5 decimal places. Explain the sign of each result.
   a) tan 32°   b) tan 87°   c) tan 155°   d) tan 244°   e) tan 306°

2. Use a scientific calculator in radian mode. Find each value to 5 decimal places. Explain the sign of each result.
   a) tan 1   b) tan 2   c) tan 3.5   d) tan 5.38   e) tan 6.62

3. Suppose P starts at A(1,0) and makes one complete rotation counterclockwise around the unit circle. Describe how the values of tan θ change as θ increases from 0° to 360°.

Ⓑ

4. a) Find tan 75° to 5 decimal places.
   b) Find three other angles which have the same tangent as 75°, and verify with your calculator.

5. Without using your calculator, determine if each function is positive or negative. Justify your answer.
   a) tan 123°   b) tan 342°   c) tan 249°   d) tan 400°   e) tan 272°

6. Determine tan θ to 4 decimal places.
   a) θ is in the first quadrant and sin θ = 0.6524.
   b) θ is in the second quadrant and cos θ = −0.8269.
   c) θ is in the third quadrant and sin θ = −0.0993.
   d) θ is in the fourth quadrant and cos θ = 0.3305.

7. Determine the exact value of each expression.
   a) $\tan \frac{3\pi}{4}$ b) $\tan \frac{5\pi}{4}$ c) $\tan \frac{7\pi}{4}$ d) $\tan \frac{\pi}{3}$ e) $\tan \frac{2\pi}{3}$
   f) $\tan \frac{4\pi}{3}$ g) $\tan \frac{5\pi}{3}$ h) $\tan \frac{\pi}{6}$ i) $\tan \frac{5\pi}{6}$ j) $\tan \frac{7\pi}{6}$

8. Using diagrams similar to that on page 393, show that the equation $\tan \theta = \frac{\sin \theta}{\cos \theta}$ holds for values of θ in the second, third, and fourth quadrants.

Ⓒ

9. Express tan θ in terms of: a) cos θ only   b) sin θ only.

10. a) Suppose θ is a very small angle, in radians. Use your calculator to compare the values of tan θ, sin θ, and θ. Explain the result.
    b) Repeat part a) if θ is in degrees.

8-2 GRAPHING THE TANGENT FUNCTION

To draw a graph of the tangent function $y = \tan \theta$, recall the definition. Let P be a point on the unit circle, and P is also on the terminal arm of an angle θ in standard position. Then $\tan \theta$ is the y-coordinate of the point Q where the line OP intersects the tangent to the circle at A(1,0).

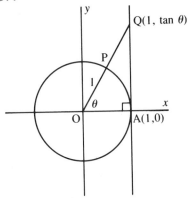

Imagine that P rotates around the circle counterclockwise, starting at A. As θ increases, the position of Q changes periodically. This causes a periodic change in the values of $\tan \theta$.

Suppose θ starts at 0 and increases to $\frac{\pi}{2}$. Then $\tan \theta$ changes as follows.

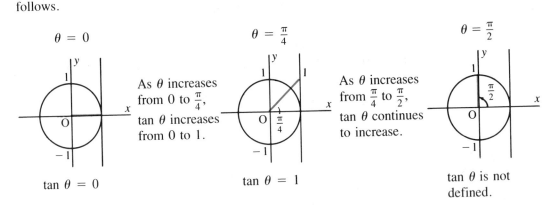

$\theta = 0$ As θ increases from 0 to $\frac{\pi}{4}$, $\tan \theta$ increases from 0 to 1. $\theta = \frac{\pi}{4}$ As θ increases from $\frac{\pi}{4}$ to $\frac{\pi}{2}$, $\tan \theta$ continues to increase. $\theta = \frac{\pi}{2}$

$\tan \theta = 0$ $\tan \theta = 1$ $\tan \theta$ is not defined.

Suppose θ continues from $\frac{\pi}{2}$ to π.

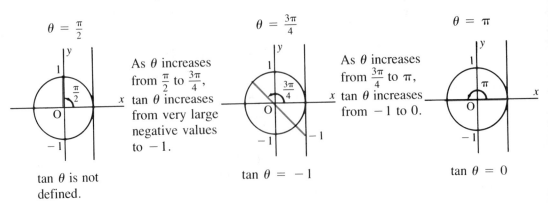

$\theta = \frac{\pi}{2}$ As θ increases from $\frac{\pi}{2}$ to $\frac{3\pi}{4}$, $\tan \theta$ increases from very large negative values to -1. $\theta = \frac{3\pi}{4}$ As θ increases from $\frac{3\pi}{4}$ to π, $\tan \theta$ increases from -1 to 0. $\theta = \pi$

$\tan \theta$ is not defined. $\tan \theta = -1$ $\tan \theta = 0$

We use these results to sketch the graph of $y = \tan \theta$ for $0 < \theta \leqslant \pi$, as shown. Notice that no value is plotted for $\tan \theta$ when $\theta = \frac{\pi}{2}$.

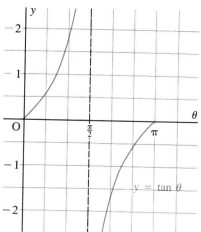

As θ continues beyond π, the line OP intersects the tangent at A at the same locations as before, and the same values of $\tan \theta$ are encountered. Hence, the graph can be continued to the right. Similarly, the graph can be continued to the left, corresponding to a rotation in the opposite direction.

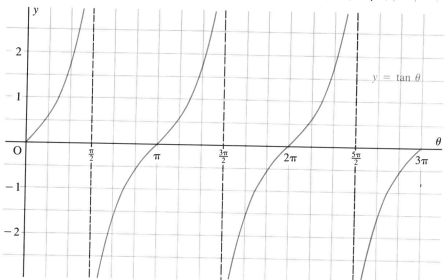

From the graph, we see that the period of the tangent function is π.

As with the cosine and sine functions, we will often use the variable x instead of θ with the tangent function.

Properties of the function $y = \tan x$

Period: π

Domain: x may represent any angle in standard position, except $\ldots -\frac{3\pi}{2}, -\frac{\pi}{2}, \frac{\pi}{2}, \frac{3\pi}{2}, \ldots$

Range: All real numbers

x-intercepts: $\ldots -2\pi, -\pi, 0, \pi, 2\pi, \ldots$

y-intercept: 0

EXERCISES 8-2

Ⓐ

1. In the following diagrams, graphs of $y = \tan \theta$ have been started using different scales. Copy each graph on graph paper, and then extend it for at least two cycles.

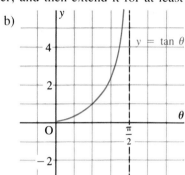

a)   b)

Ⓑ

2. Without making a table of values, draw a graph of $f(x) = \tan x$ for $-2\pi \leqslant x \leqslant 2\pi$.

3. For the graph of $y = \tan x$
   a) Are there any maximum or minimum values of y? Explain your answer.
   b) What are the domain and the range?
   c) What is the y-intercept?
   d) What are the x-intercepts?
   e) In which intervals is y increasing?
   f) In which intervals is y decreasing?

4. Which statements are true for $f(x) = \tan x$?
   a) If $x \in]\frac{\pi}{2}, \pi[$, then $f(x) > 0$
   b) $f(x)$ is undefined when $x = \pi$.
   c) If $x \in [-\pi, \pi]$ and $f(x) < 0$, then $x \in]-\frac{\pi}{2}, 0[\cup]\frac{\pi}{2}, \pi[$
   d) The period of $f(x)$ is π.
   e) $f(x)$ is an increasing function for all values of x for which $\tan x$ is defined.

5. Compare the graph of $f(x) = \tan x$ with the graphs of $f(x) = \sin x$ and $f(x) = \cos x$. In what ways are they alike? In what ways are they different?

Ⓒ

6. Use the definition in Exercises 7-7, *Exercise 9*, to prove that the function $f(x) = \tan x$ is periodic.

7. A function $y = f(x)$ is defined to be an *even* function if $f(-x) = f(x)$ for all values of x in the domain. A function $y = f(x)$ is defined to be an *odd* function if $f(-x) = -f(x)$ for all values of x in the domain. Is the function $f(x) = \tan x$ an even function or an odd function?

8. Graph each function.   a) $y = |\tan x|$ b) $y = \tan |x|$

8-3 THE RECIPROCAL TRIGONOMETRIC FUNCTIONS

The reciprocals of the cosine, sine, and tangent functions are called respectively, the *secant*, *cosecant*, and *cotangent* functions, and are abbreviated as sec θ, csc θ, and cot θ. They are defined as follows:

$$\sec \theta = \frac{1}{\cos \theta}, \quad \cos \theta \neq 0 \qquad \csc \theta = \frac{1}{\sin \theta}, \quad \sin \theta \neq 0$$

$$\cot \theta = \begin{cases} \dfrac{1}{\tan \theta}, & \tan \theta \neq 0 \\ 0 \text{ when } \theta = \pm\frac{\pi}{2}, \pm\frac{3\pi}{2}, \pm\frac{5\pi}{2}, \ldots \end{cases}$$

The values of all six trigonometric functions for angles of 0° and 90°, and for the special angles of 30°, 45°, and 60° are summarized below.

θ	$\cos \theta$	$\sin \theta$	$\tan \theta$	$\sec \theta$	$\csc \theta$	$\cot \theta$
0°	1	0	0	1	—	—
30°	$\dfrac{\sqrt{3}}{2}$	$\dfrac{1}{2}$	$\dfrac{1}{\sqrt{3}}$	$\dfrac{2}{\sqrt{3}}$	2	$\sqrt{3}$
45°	$\dfrac{1}{\sqrt{2}}$	$\dfrac{1}{\sqrt{2}}$	1	$\sqrt{2}$	$\sqrt{2}$	1
60°	$\dfrac{1}{2}$	$\dfrac{\sqrt{3}}{2}$	$\sqrt{3}$	2	$\dfrac{2}{\sqrt{3}}$	$\dfrac{1}{\sqrt{3}}$
90°	0	1	—	—	1	0

Example 1. Determine csc $\frac{4\pi}{3}$.

Solution. The reference angle is $\frac{\pi}{3}$.

Since P is in the third quadrant, sin $\frac{4\pi}{3}$ is negative.

Hence, sin $\frac{4\pi}{3} = -\frac{\sqrt{3}}{2}$

Therefore, csc $\frac{4\pi}{3} = -\frac{2}{\sqrt{3}}$

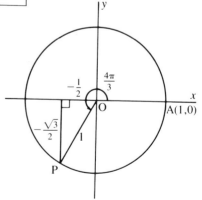

Often, there are no secant, cosecant, or cotangent keys on a scientific calculator. These are not necessary, since you can easily find the cosine, sine, or tangent of an angle and then take its reciprocal.

Example 2. Determine csc 230° to five decimal places.

Solution. Using *degree mode*, find the sine of 230°, then take its reciprocal. Since sin 230° $\doteq$ −0.766 04, then csc 230° $\doteq$ −1.305 41

To graph the secant and cosecant functions we graph the corresponding cosine or sine function, and use it to graph the reciprocal
function.

Example 3. Graph the function $y = \csc x$ over two cycles.

Solution. *Step 1.* Graph the function $y = \sin x$ and draw vertical dotted lines
through the points where the graph intersects the *x*-axis. At these points,
$\sin x = 0$, and hence $\csc x$ is not defined.

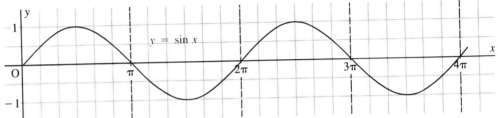

Step 2. Consider values of x from 0 to π.
Since $\sin 0 = 0$, $\csc 0$ is not defined.
From the graph, we can see that as θ
increases from 0 to $\frac{\pi}{2}$ and then to π, $\sin \theta$
is positive and increases from 0 to 1, and
then decreases to 0. Hence, $\csc x$ is positive and decreases to 1 and then increases. Since $\sin \pi = 0$, $\csc \pi$ is not
defined.

   When *x* is close to 0 or close to π, $\csc x$
is very large.

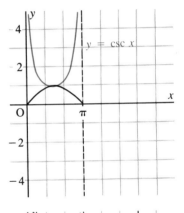

Step 3. Consider values of x from π to 2π.
From the graph, as *x* increases from π
to $\frac{3\pi}{2}$ and then to 2π, $\sin x$ is negative
and decreases from 0 to -1, and then
increases to 0. Hence, $\csc x$ is negative
and increases to -1 and then decreases.
Since $\sin 2\pi = 0$, $\csc 2\pi$ is not defined.

   When *x* is close to π or close to 2π,
$\csc x$ is negative, but has a very large
absolute value.

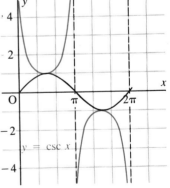

Step 4. This completes one cycle. Other cycles can be graphed similarly.

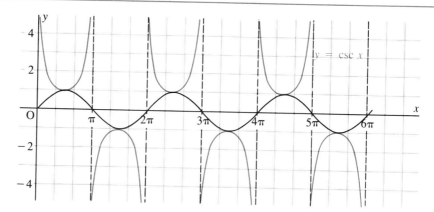

The reciprocal function of any sinusoidal function can be graphed in a similar way.

EXERCISES 8-3

Ⓐ

1. Use a scientific calculator in degree mode. Find each value to 3 decimal places.
   a) csc 110°   b) csc 256°   c) sec 95°   d) sec 272°   e) cot 184°

2. Use a scientific calculator in radian mode. Find each value to 3 decimal places.
   a) csc 1.75   b) csc 3.22   c) sec 2.16   d) sec 6.75   e) cot 6.25

Ⓑ

3. Determine the exact value of each expression.
   a) $\sec \frac{\pi}{4}$ b) $\csc \frac{\pi}{6}$ c) $\cot \frac{\pi}{6}$ d) $\sec \frac{\pi}{3}$ e) $\cot \frac{\pi}{4}$

   f) $\csc \frac{4\pi}{3}$ g) $\sec \frac{5\pi}{4}$ h) $\cot \frac{7\pi}{4}$ i) $\sec \frac{2\pi}{3}$ j) $\csc \frac{11\pi}{6}$

   k) $\cot \frac{5\pi}{3}$ l) $\csc \frac{3\pi}{4}$ m) $\sec \frac{5\pi}{6}$ n) $\cot \frac{4\pi}{3}$ o) $\csc \frac{7\pi}{3}$

4. Graph each function for $-2\pi \leqslant x \leqslant 2\pi$.
   a) $y = \csc x$ b) $y = \sec x$ c) $y = \tan x$ d) $y = \cot x$

5. a) Compare the graphs of $y = \sin x$ and $y = \csc x$. In what ways are they similar? In what ways are they different?
   b) Repeat part a) for the graphs of $y = \cos x$ and $y = \sec x$.
   c) Repeat part a) for the graphs of $y = \tan x$ and $y = \cot x$.

6. Make a list of the properties of the functions $y = \csc x$ and $y = \sec x$ that is similar to the one on page 364 for $y = \sin x$ and $y = \cos x$.

Ⓒ

7. Graph each function, and state its period and phase shift.
   a) $y = 2 \csc (x - \pi)$ b) $y = 3 \sec (x + \pi)$

INVESTIGATE

Defining and Graphing the Trigonometric Functions Using a Unit Circle

In *Sections 7-5* and *8-1*, the primary trigonometric functions were
defined in terms of line segments associated with a unit circle. This
suggests that we might look for other line segments that represent the
other trigonometric functions of an angle in standard position. If we
can find these segments, we can use them to draw the graphs of these
functions.

The cosecant function
Let P represent any point in the
first quadrant on the unit circle,
and construct the tangent to the
circle at P. Let the tangent
intersect the *y*-axis at C and the
x-axis at D.

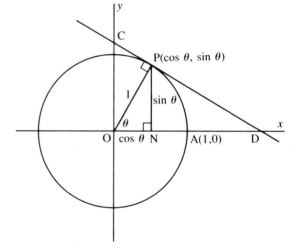

1. a) Use similar triangles to
      find a line segment on this
      diagram whose length is
      equal to csc θ.
   b) Use the result of part a) to
      write a definition of csc θ
      in terms of a unit circle.

2. Draw diagrams to illustrate
   the definition for angles in
   quadrants other than the first.

3. Recall how the graph of the sine function was drawn in a previous
   INVESTIGATE by projecting the second coordinate of P horizontally to the right.
   a) Use a similar method to draw the graph of the cosecant function.
   b) Describe how the coordinates of points on your graph are related
      to the position of P as P moves around the unit circle.

The secant function
4. a) Use similar triangles to find a line segment on the diagram above
      whose length is equal to sec θ.
   b) Use the result of part a) to write a definition of sec θ in terms of
      a unit circle.

5. Draw diagrams to illustrate the definition for angles in quadrants other than the first.

6. Draw the graph of the secant function by projecting line segments. Use a method that is similar to the method that was used for the cosine function in the previous *INVESTIGATE*.

The tangent function

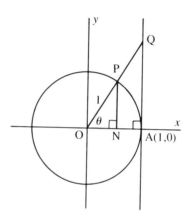

7. a) Recall how the graph of the sine function was drawn by projecting line segments horizontally to the right. Use a similar method to draw the graph of the tangent function.
   b) Describe how the coordinates of points on your graph are related to the position of P as P moves around the unit circle.

The cotangent function

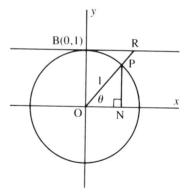

8. a) Let P be any point on the unit circle, and construct the tangent to the circle at B(0,1) Extend the segment OP to intersect this tangent at R. Find a line segment on this diagram whose length is equal to cot θ.
   b) Write a definition of cot θ in terms of a unit circle.

9. Draw diagrams to illustrate the definition for angles in quadrants other than the first.

10. a) Recall how the graph of the cosine function was drawn by projecting line segments below a unit circle. Use a similar method to draw the graph of the cotangent function.
    b) Describe how the coordinates of points on your graph are related to the position of P as P moves around the unit circle.

8-4 PYTHAGOREAN, RECIPROCAL, AND QUOTIENT IDENTITIES

Let P be any point on the unit circle with centre O, corresponding to an angle θ in standard position. Let Q be the point of intersection of the line OP and the tangent to the unit circle at A(1,0). Recall that the six trigonometric functions of θ are defined as shown below. These definitions apply for any quadrant.

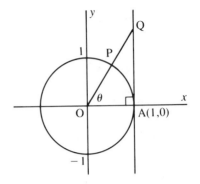

cos θ is the first coordinate of P. $\sec \theta = \dfrac{1}{\cos \theta}$, $\cos \theta \neq 0$

sin θ is the second coordinate of P. $\csc \theta = \dfrac{1}{\sin \theta}$, $\sin \theta \neq 0$

tan θ is the second coordinate of Q. $\cot \theta = \dfrac{1}{\tan \theta}$, $\tan \theta \neq 0$

Observe that the definitions involve only the coordinates of two points, P and Q. One of those points is on the unit circle, and the other is on the tangent at A(1,0). Further, P and Q lie on a line through O. For these reasons, the trigonometric functions are related in a wide variety of different ways. The equations, $\cos^2\theta + \sin^2\theta = 1$ and

$\tan \theta = \frac{\sin \theta}{\cos \theta}$, established in Chapter 7 are examples of how the functions are related. Equations such as these are called *identities* because they are satisfied for all values of the variable for which they are defined.

The definitions of the reciprocal functions are often called *reciprocal identities*. The identity for tan θ above is called a *quotient identity*. There is a similar quotient identity for cot θ, which is a direct consequence of the definition of cot θ.

Reciprocal Identities

$\csc x = \dfrac{1}{\sin x}$ $\sec x = \dfrac{1}{\cos x}$ $\cot x = \dfrac{1}{\tan x}$

Quotient Identities

$\dfrac{\sin x}{\cos x} = \tan x$ $\dfrac{\cos x}{\sin x} = \cot x$

The definitions of csc θ, sec θ, and tan θ at the top of the preceding page include the restrictions that the denominators are not equal to zero. When we work with identities, it is inconvenient to write these restrictions every time the reciprocal functions are used. Hence, we will assume that the restrictions apply without stating them explicitly.

The reciprocal and quotient identities can be used to prove other identities, such as those in the following example.

Example 1. Prove each identity.
   a) $\sec \theta (1 + \cos \theta) = 1 + \sec \theta$
   b) $\sec x = \tan x \csc x$

Solution. a) $\sec \theta (1 + \cos \theta) = 1 + \sec \theta$

$$\begin{aligned} \text{Left side} &= \sec \theta (1 + \cos \theta) \\ &= \sec \theta + \sec \theta \cos \theta \\ &= \sec \theta + 1 \qquad \text{(using a reciprocal identity)} \\ &= \text{Right side} \end{aligned}$$

Since the left side simplifies to the right side, the identity is correct.

   b) $\sec x = \tan x \csc x$

$$\begin{aligned} \text{Left side} &= \sec x \\ &= \frac{1}{\cos x} \qquad \text{(reciprocal identity)} \end{aligned}$$

$$\begin{aligned} \text{Right side} &= \tan x \csc x \\ &= \frac{\sin x}{\cos x} \times \frac{1}{\sin x} \qquad \text{(quotient, reciprocal identities)} \\ &= \frac{1}{\cos x} \end{aligned}$$

Since both sides simplify to the same expression, the identity is correct.

Observe the methods used in *Example 1* to prove the identities. We use the reciprocal and quotient identities, along with algebraic simplification, to show that one side of the identity is equal to the other side, or that both sides of the identity simplify to the same expression.

The identity $\cos^2 x + \sin^2 x = 1$ was established in Chapter 7. Since the Pythagorean Theorem was used in its development, this identity is known as a *Pythagorean identity*. We can obtain two additional Pythagorean identities from this one and the reciprocal identities.

$\cos^2 x + \sin^2 x = 1$
Divide both sides by $\cos^2 x$.

$$1 + \frac{\sin^2 x}{\cos^2 x} = \frac{1}{\cos^2 x} \qquad (\cos x \neq 0)$$

$$1 + \tan^2 x = \sec^2 x$$

$\cos^2 x + \sin^2 x = 1$
Divide both sides by $\sin^2 x$.

$$\frac{\cos^2 x}{\sin^2 x} + 1 = \frac{1}{\sin^2 x} \qquad (\sin x \neq 0)$$

$$\cot^2 x + 1 = \csc^2 x$$

Pythagorean Identities

$$\cos^2 x + \sin^2 x = 1 \qquad 1 + \tan^2 x = \sec^2 x \qquad 1 + \cot^2 x = \csc^2 x$$

The reciprocal, quotient, and Pythagorean identities are rather like theorems in geometry, because they are used to prove other identities.

Example 2. Prove the identity $1 - \cos^2\theta = \cos^2\theta \tan^2\theta$.

Solution.   Left side $= 1 - \cos^2\theta$
$$= \sin^2\theta \qquad \text{(Pythagorean identity)}$$
Right side $= \cos^2\theta \tan^2\theta$
$$= \cos^2\theta \times \frac{\sin^2\theta}{\cos^2\theta} \qquad \text{(quotient identity)}$$
$$= \sin^2\theta$$
Since both sides simplify to the same expression, the identity is correct.

Example 3. a) Prove the identity $\dfrac{\sin x}{1 + \cos x} = \dfrac{1 - \cos x}{\sin x}$.

b) Predict a similar identity for the expression $\dfrac{\cos x}{1 + \sin x}$, and prove that it is correct.

Solution.   a) Left side $= \dfrac{\sin x}{1 + \cos x}$

$$= \frac{\sin x}{1 + \cos x} \times \frac{1 - \cos x}{1 - \cos x} \qquad \text{(multiplying by 1)}$$

$$= \frac{\sin x\,(1 - \cos x)}{1 - \cos^2 x}$$

$$= \frac{\sin x\,(1 - \cos x)}{\sin^2 x} \qquad \text{(Pythagorean identity)}$$

$$= \frac{1 - \cos x}{\sin x}$$

$$= \text{Right side}$$

Since the left side simplifies to the right side, the identity is correct.

b) The pattern of the terms $\sin x$ and $\cos x$ in part a) suggests that a similar identity might be:

$$\frac{\cos x}{1 + \sin x} = \frac{1 - \sin x}{\cos x}.$$

We can prove this identity in a similar way.

Another way to prove this identity (and the one in part a)) is to start with the Pythagorean identity $\sin^2 x + \cos^2 x = 1$ and perform the same operation to both sides. That is, we may write

$$\sin^2 x + \cos^2 x = 1$$
$$\cos^2 x = 1 - \sin^2 x$$
$$\cos^2 x = (1 - \sin x)(1 + \sin x)$$

Hence, $\dfrac{\cos x}{1 + \sin x} = \dfrac{1 - \sin x}{\cos x}$

EXERCISES 8-4

(A)

1. Prove each identity.
   a) $\tan \theta \cos \theta = \sin \theta$
   c) $\sin x \cot x = \cos x$
   e) $\sin \theta = \dfrac{\tan \theta}{\sec \theta}$

   b) $\cot x \sec x = \csc x$
   d) $\tan \theta \csc \theta = \sec \theta$
   f) $\dfrac{\cot x}{\csc x} = \cos x$

2. Prove each identity.
   a) $\csc x (1 + \sin x) = 1 + \csc x$
   c) $\cos \theta (\sec \theta - 1) = 1 - \cos \theta$
   e) $\dfrac{1 - \tan x}{1 - \cot x} = -\tan x$

   b) $\sin \theta (1 + \csc \theta) = 1 + \sin \theta$
   d) $\sin x \sec x \cot x = 1$
   f) $\cot \theta = \dfrac{1 + \cot \theta}{1 + \tan \theta}$

(B)

3. Prove each identity.
   a) $\sin \theta \tan \theta + \sec \theta = \dfrac{\sin^2 \theta + 1}{\cos \theta}$
   b) $\dfrac{1 + \cos \theta}{1 - \cos \theta} = \dfrac{1 + \sec \theta}{\sec \theta - 1}$
   c) $\dfrac{1 + \sin x}{1 - \sin x} = \dfrac{\csc x + 1}{\csc x - 1}$
   d) $\dfrac{1 + \tan \theta}{1 + \cot \theta} = \dfrac{1 - \tan \theta}{\cot \theta - 1}$
   e) $\dfrac{1 + \sin \theta}{1 + \csc \theta} = \sin \theta$
   f) $\dfrac{\sin x + \tan x}{\cos x + 1} = \tan x$

4. Prove each identity.
   a) $\sin^2 x \cot^2 x = 1 - \sin^2 x$
   b) $\csc^2 \theta - 1 = \csc^2 \theta \cos^2 \theta$
   c) $\sin^2 \theta = \dfrac{\tan^2 \theta}{1 + \tan^2 \theta}$
   d) $\dfrac{\sin x + \cos x \cot x}{\cot x} = \sec x$
   e) $\sin x \cos x \tan x = 1 - \cos^2 x$
   f) $\dfrac{\cos \theta}{1 + \sin \theta} + \dfrac{\cos \theta}{1 - \sin \theta} = 2 \sec \theta$

5. a) Prove this identity. $\dfrac{1}{1 + \sin \theta} + \dfrac{1}{1 - \sin \theta} = 2 \sec^2 \theta$

   b) Establish a similar identity for this expression. $\dfrac{1}{1 + \cos \theta} + \dfrac{1}{1 - \cos \theta}$

6. a) Prove this identity. $\tan^2x \, (1 + \cot^2x) = \sec^2x$
   b) Predict a similar identity for the expression $\cot^2x \, (1 + \tan^2x)$, and prove that it is correct.

7. a) Prove each identity.
      i) $(1 - \cos^2\theta)(1 + \tan^2\theta) = \tan^2\theta$ ii) $(1 - \sin^2\theta)(1 + \cot^2\theta) = \cot^2\theta$
   b) Establish another identity like those in part a).

8. Prove each identity.
   a) $\tan x + \cot x = \sec x \csc x$
   b) $\sec^2\theta + \csc^2\theta = \sec^2\theta \csc^2\theta$
   c) $\sec^2\theta + \csc^2\theta = (\tan \theta + \cot \theta)^2$
   d) $\sin^2x = \cos x \, (\sec x - \cos x)$

Ⓒ

9. In *Exercise 5*, identities for $\dfrac{1}{1 + f(x)} + \dfrac{1}{1 - f(x)}$, where $f(x) = \sin x$ and $f(x) = \cos x$, were established. Establish similar identities where $f(x)$ represents each of the other four trigonometric functions.

10. Establish an identity which involves all six trigonometric functions.

 INVESTIGATE

We can use identities to express $\sin \theta$ and $\tan \theta$ in terms of $\cos \theta$:

$\cos^2\theta + \sin^2\theta = 1$ $\tan \theta = \dfrac{\sin \theta}{\cos \theta}$
$\quad\quad\; \sin^2\theta = 1 - \cos^2\theta$
$\quad\quad\;\; \sin \theta = \pm\sqrt{1 - \cos^2\theta}$ $\quad\quad = \dfrac{\pm\sqrt{1 - \cos^2\theta}}{\cos \theta}$

1. Express the three reciprocal functions in terms of $\cos \theta$.

2. Investigate whether or not any trigonometric function can be expressed in terms of any other trigonometric function.

 INVESTIGATE

1. On this diagram, ON $= \cos \theta$ and NP $= \sin \theta$. Find line segments whose lengths are equal to sec θ, csc θ, tan θ, and cot θ.

2. Use the results of part a), the Pythagorean Theorem, and similar triangles to illustrate as many different identities as you can.

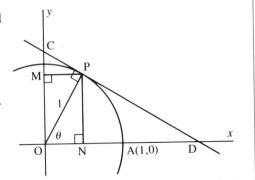

8-5 ODD-EVEN, RELATED-ANGLE, AND COFUNCTION IDENTITIES

In addition to the reciprocal, quotient, and Pythagorean identities, and identities that can be derived from them, there are many other identities relating the trigonometric functions.

Odd-Even Identities

Let P be any point on the unit circle, and on the terminal arm of an angle θ. Then the coordinates of P are $(\cos \theta, \sin \theta)$.
Let Q be the reflection of P in the x-axis; the coordinates of Q are $(\cos \theta, -\sin \theta)$ ... ①
Then, by the SAS congruence theorem,
$\triangle QNO \cong \triangle PNO$
Since the triangles are congruent, $\angle QON = \angle PON$
Therefore, Q is on the terminal arm of an angle $-\theta$.
Hence, by the definitions of the cosine and sine functions, the coordinates of Q are also
$(\cos (-\theta), \sin (-\theta))$ ... ②
Comparing ① and ②, we obtain these identities:
$\cos (-\theta) = \cos \theta$
$\sin (-\theta) = -\sin \theta$
These identities are called *odd-even identities*, because they are similar to a property of powers: if n is a natural number, then $(-x)^n = -x^n$ if n is odd, and $(-x)^n = x^n$ if n is even. Odd-even identities for the other trigonometric functions can be proved in the same way.

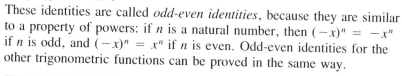

Odd-Even Identities		
$\sin (-x) = -\sin x$	$\cos (-x) = \cos x$	$\tan (-x) = -\tan x$
$\csc (-x) = -\csc x$	$\sec (-x) = \sec x$	$\cot (-x) = -\cot x$

The identities $\cos (-x) = \cos x$ and $\sin (-x) = -\sin x$ can be seen on the graphs of the cosine and sine functions.

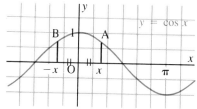

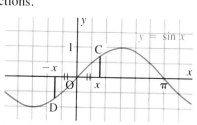

$\cos x$ is the y-coordinate of A.
$\cos (-x)$ is the y-coordinate of B.
Since these y-coordinates are equal,
$\cos (-x) = \cos x$

$\sin x$ is the y-coordinate of C.
$\sin (-x)$ is the y-coordinate of D.
Since these y-coordinates are equal in absolute value, but have opposite signs,
$\sin (-x) = -\sin x$

Related-Angle Identities

Let R be the reflection of P in the y-axis; the coordinates of R are $(-\cos \theta, \sin \theta)$ ... ③
Also, by the SAS congruence theorem,
$\triangle RMO \cong \triangle PNO$
Since the triangles are congruent, $\angle ROM = \angle PON$, and so $\angle ROA = \pi - \theta$. Therefore, R is on the terminal arm of an angle in standard position equal to $\pi - \theta$. Hence, by definition, the coordinates of R are $(\cos (\pi - \theta), \sin (\pi - \theta))$ ... ④
Comparing ③ and ④, we obtain
$\cos (\pi - \theta) = -\cos \theta$
$\sin (\pi - \theta) = \sin \theta$
These identities are called *related-angle identities* because they show how the trigonometric functions of angles greater than 90° can be related to functions of acute angles.

Similar identities relating the other trigonometric functions can be proved in the same way.

Related-Angle Identities	
$\sin (\pi - x) = \sin x$	$\csc (\pi - x) = \csc x$
$\cos (\pi - x) = -\cos x$	$\sec (\pi - x) = -\sec x$
$\tan (\pi - x) = -\tan x$	$\cot (\pi - x) = -\cot x$

These identities can be seen on graphs.

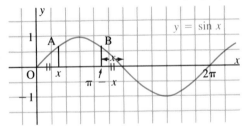

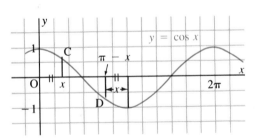

sin x is the y-coordinate of A.
$\sin (\pi - x)$ is the y-coordinate of B.
Since these y-coordinates are equal,
$\sin (\pi - x) = \sin x$

cos x is the y-coordinate of C.
$\cos (\pi - x)$ is the y-coordinate of D.
Since these y-coordinates are equal in absolute value, but have opposite signs,
$\cos (\pi - x) = -\cos x$

Cofunction Identities

Let S be the reflection of P in the line $y = x$. Hence, OL = ON and LS = NP, so that the coordinates of S are $(\sin \theta, \cos \theta)$ ... ⑤
Since $\triangle SLO \cong \triangle PNO$, $\angle SOL = \angle PON = \theta$, and $\angle SOA = \frac{\pi}{2} - \theta$. Therefore, S is on the terminal arm of an angle in standard position equal to $\frac{\pi}{2} - \theta$. Hence, the coordinates of S are also
$$\left(\cos\left(\frac{\pi}{2} - \theta\right), \sin\left(\frac{\pi}{2} - \theta\right)\right) \quad ... ⑥$$
Comparing ⑤ and ⑥, we obtain
$$\cos\left(\frac{\pi}{2} - \theta\right) = \sin \theta$$
$$\sin\left(\frac{\pi}{2} - \theta\right) = \cos \theta$$

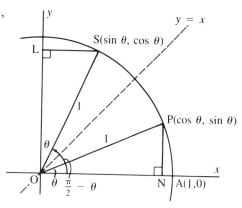

These identities are called *cofunction identities*, because they involve complementary angles and the *co*sine and sine functions. They state that:
● the *co*sine of an angle is equal to the sine of the *complementary* angle.
● the sine of an angle is equal to the *co*sine of the *complementary* angle.

Similar identities relating the other trigonometric functions can be proved in the same way.

Cofunction Identities

$$\sin\left(\frac{\pi}{2} - x\right) = \cos x \qquad \csc\left(\frac{\pi}{2} - x\right) = \sec x$$

$$\cos\left(\frac{\pi}{2} - x\right) = \sin x \qquad \sec\left(\frac{\pi}{2} - x\right) = \csc x$$

$$\tan\left(\frac{\pi}{2} - x\right) = \cot x \qquad \cot\left(\frac{\pi}{2} - x\right) = \tan x$$

The cofunction identities can be seen on graphs. For example, on the graph (below left), $\cos x$ is the y-coordinate of A. On the other graph, $\sin\left(\frac{\pi}{2} - x\right)$ is the y-coordinate of B. Since these y-coordinates are equal, $\sin\left(\frac{\pi}{2} - x\right) = \cos x$.

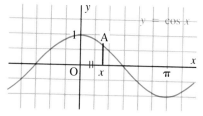

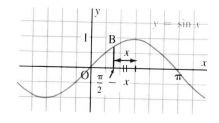

To remember these identities, we can think of the graphs as illustrated above, or we can think of the unit circle. All the identities result from the fact that a circle is symmetric about any diameter.

This diagram shows an angle of 25° corresponding to point P. P is reflected in the *x*-axis, the *y*-axis, and the line *y* = *x*. The images are also reflected to produce the diagram shown. Then we can read many results from the diagram such as those below. Observe that cosines correspond to horizontal segments and sines correspond to vertical segments. The signs of the results are determined by the quadrant of the angle.

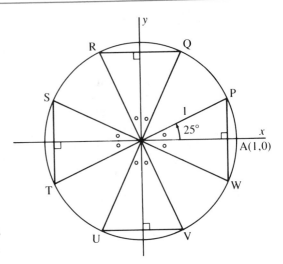

An example illustrating odd-even identities:
Since P and W have the same *x*-coordinate and opposite *y*-coordinates,
$$\cos(-25°) = \cos 25° \qquad \sin(-25°) = -\sin 25°$$

An example illustrating related-angle identities:
Since P and S have opposite *x*-coordinates and the same *y*-coordinates,
$$\cos 155° = -\cos 25° \qquad \sin 155° = \sin 25°$$

An example illustrating cofunction identities:
Compare the coordinates of R and P.
$$\cos 115° = -\sin 25° \qquad \sin 115° = \cos 25°$$

We can obtain similar identities by comparing the coordinates of other points.

Example 1. Express as a function of a positive acute angle.
a) cos 140°
b) sin 235°
c) tan (−65°)
d) sec (−130°)

Solution. a)

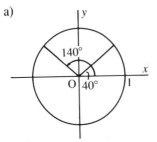

The reference angle is 40°.
$$\cos 140° = \cos(180° - 40°)$$
$$= -\cos 40°$$

b)

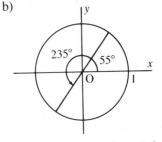

The reference angle is 55°.
$$\sin 235° = \sin(180° + 55°)$$
$$= -\sin 55°$$

c)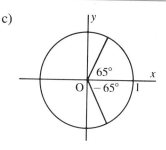

The reference angle is 65°.
$\tan(-65°) = -\tan 65°$

d)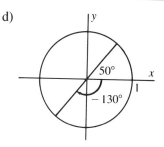

The reference angle is 50°.
$\sec(-130°) = \sec 230°$
$= \sec(180° + 50°)$
$= -\sec 50°$

Example 2. Use the related-angle identities to determine the value of each function.

a) $\sin \dfrac{5\pi}{6}$

b) $\cos \dfrac{3\pi}{4}$

Solution.

a) $\sin \dfrac{5\pi}{6} = \sin\left(\pi - \dfrac{\pi}{6}\right)$

$= \sin \dfrac{\pi}{6}$

$= \dfrac{1}{2}$

b) $\cos \dfrac{3\pi}{4} = \cos\left(\pi - \dfrac{\pi}{4}\right)$

$= -\cos \dfrac{\pi}{4}$

$= -\dfrac{1}{\sqrt{2}}$

Example 3. Use your calculator to check.

a) $\cos 2.4 = -\cos(\pi - 2.4)$ b) $\sin 1.5 = \cos\left(\dfrac{\pi}{2} - 1.5\right)$

Solution.   Be sure the calculator is in radian mode.

a) $\cos 2.4 \doteq -0.737\ 393\ 7$ and $\cos(\pi - 2.4) \doteq 0.737\ 393\ 7$

b) $\sin 1.5 \doteq 0.997\ 495$ and $\cos\left(\dfrac{\pi}{2} - 1.5\right) \doteq 0.997\ 495$

The identities established in this section are special cases of more general identities involving trigonometric functions of the sum or the difference of two angles. These identities will be developed in the next section.

EXERCISES 8-5

Ⓐ

1. Use your calculator to check each equation. Explain why the two sides are equal.
   a) $\cos(-40°) = \cos 40°$
   b) $\sin(-40°) = -\sin 40°$
   c) $\tan(-100°) = -\tan 100°$
   d) $\cos 165° = -\cos 15°$
   e) $\sin 165° = \sin 15°$
   f) $\sec 165° = -\sec 15°$
   g) $\cos 70° = \sin 20°$
   h) $\sin 100° = \cos 10°$
   i) $\cos 100° = -\sin 10°$

2. Make up some examples like those in *Exercise 1*, in which the angle on the left side is in the third or the fourth quadrant.

3. Use your calculator to check that:
   a) $\sin 1 = \sin (\pi - 1)$

   b) $\cos 1 = -\cos (\pi - 1)$

   c) $\cos 0.8 = -\cos (\pi - 0.8)$

   d) $\sin 1 = \cos \left(\frac{\pi}{2} - 1\right)$

   e) $\cos 1 = \sin \left(\frac{\pi}{2} - 1\right)$

   f) $\sin 0.8 = \cos \left(\frac{\pi}{2} - 0.8\right)$

4. Each diagram shows P reflected in a diameter of the unit circle. State the corresponding identities for all six trigonometric functions.

   a) 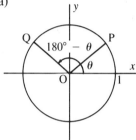   b) 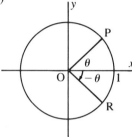   c)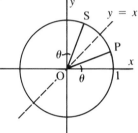

5. Express as a function of a positive acute angle.
   a) $\cos 110°$ b) $\sin 220°$ c) $\tan 160°$ d) $\cos (-20°)$
   e) $\sin (-50°)$ f) $\tan (-75°)$ g) $\cot 100°$ h) $\sec 175°$
   i) $\sin 325°$ j) $\sec 200°$ k) $\csc 115°$ l) $\cot (-40°)$

6. On the graph, the y-coordinates of A and B are equal; the y-coordinates of C and B are equal in absolute value but opposite in sign. State the corresponding identities.

   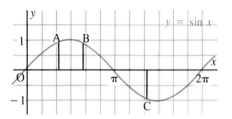

7. Express as a function of a positive acute angle.
   a) $\sin (\pi - 1.2)$ b) $\cos (\pi - 1.2)$ c) $\sin (\pi + 1.2)$ d) $\cos (\pi + 1.2)$
   e) $\tan (\pi + 1)$ f) $\cot (\pi + 1)$ g) $\csc (\pi - 1.5)$ h) $\sec (\pi + 1.5)$
   i) $\sin \left(\frac{\pi}{2} + 1.2\right)$ j) $\cos \left(\frac{\pi}{2} + 1.2\right)$ k) $\tan \left(\frac{\pi}{2} + 1\right)$ l) $\csc \left(\frac{\pi}{2} + 1\right)$

8. Use the related-angle identities to determine the value of each function.
   a) $\sin \frac{2\pi}{3}$ b) $\cos \frac{2\pi}{3}$ c) $\sin \frac{5\pi}{4}$ d) $\cos \frac{5\pi}{4}$
   e) $\sin \frac{11\pi}{6}$ f) $\cos \frac{11\pi}{6}$ g) $\tan \frac{7\pi}{6}$ h) $\cot \frac{5\pi}{3}$

9. Use the cofunction identities to determine the value of each function.
   a) $\sin 120°$ b) $\cos 120°$ c) $\tan 150°$ d) $\sec 150°$

10. Determine the exact value of each function.
   a) $\sin \frac{3\pi}{4}$ b) $\sin \frac{5\pi}{4}$ c) $\cos \frac{5\pi}{6}$ d) $\cos \frac{7\pi}{6}$

   e) $\tan \frac{2\pi}{3}$ f) $\tan \frac{4\pi}{3}$ g) $\sec \frac{7\pi}{4}$ h) $\cot \left(-\frac{2\pi}{3} \right)$

11. Draw a diagram like the one on page 412, where P corresponds to an angle of 40°. Write as many examples as you can illustrating the odd-even, related-angle, and cofunction identities. Organize your examples in some systematic way.

12. Express as a function of a positive acute angle less than 45°.
   a) $\cos 70°$ b) $\sin 80°$ c) $\tan 55°$ d) $\csc 65°$
   e) $\sin 130°$ f) $\cos 115°$ g) $\cos 205°$ h) $\sec 245°$

13. a) Related-angle identities for the sine and cosine functions were developed on page 410. Establish the related-angle identities for the other four trigonometric functions.

   b) Cofunction identities for the sine and cosine functions were developed on page 411. Establish the cofunction identities for the other four trigonometric functions.

14. In the identity $\sin \left(\frac{\pi}{2} - x \right) = \cos x$, substitute $\frac{\pi}{2} - x$ for x and simplify the result.

   What do you notice?

©

15. a) Prove each identity.
   i) $\sin \left(\frac{\pi}{2} + x \right) = \sin \left(\frac{\pi}{2} - x \right)$ ii) $\cos \left(\frac{\pi}{2} + x \right) = -\cos \left(\frac{\pi}{2} - x \right)$

   b) Establish similar identities involving π, $\frac{3\pi}{2}$, and 2π.

 INVESTIGATE

Relations Among the Identities

A variety of other identities can be obtained from the related-angle identities and the cofunction identities, by substitution. For example, in *Exercise 14* the expression $\frac{\pi}{2} - x$ was substituted for x in one of the cofunction identities. This substitution can be made in any of the identities of this section. Similarly, other expressions such as $-x$ and $\pi + x$ can also be substituted for x in the identities.

1. Investigate the effect of substituting expressions such as those above in the identities of this section. Look for patterns in the results, and classify the results in some way.

USING TECHNOLOGY

Tangent and Reciprocal Trigonometric Functions

Viewing the Tangent Function

On your graphing calculator, enter the equation $Y_1 = \tan X$ on the functions menu. Count the number of seconds your calculator takes to graph this function. Next, count the number of seconds it takes for your calculator to graph the function

$Y_2 = \frac{\sin X}{\cos X}$

a) What is the difference in times?

b) Since $\tan X = \frac{\sin X}{\cos X}$, why do you think your calculator takes a longer time to graph one of these functions?

c) Use your graphing calculator to show that $Y = \tan X$ is an odd function.

Viewing the Reciprocal Trigonometric Functions

Most graphing calculators do not have keys for the secant, cosecant, and cotangent functions. To display these on the graphing calculator, you must express them as the reciprocals of the cosine, sine, and tangent functions respectively.

Enter the cosecant function on the functions menu as $Y_1 = \frac{1}{\sin X}$ or as $Y_1 = (\sin X)^{-1}$. (Do not enter it as $Y_1 = \sin^{-1} X$.)

Let $Y_2 = \sin X$ and graph Y_1 and Y_2 on the same screen.

Let $Y_3 = (Y_1)(Y_2)$. Describe what you think the graph of Y_3 will look like. Display the graph of Y_3 on your calculator screen.

Transforming Trigonometric Functions

Graph each pair of equations on the same screen. Describe the results in writing.

a) $Y_1 = \sin(-X)$
   $Y_2 = -\sin X$

b) $Y_1 = \cos(-X)$
   $Y_2 = -\cos X$

c) $Y_1 = \tan(-X)$
   $Y_2 = -\tan X$

d) $Y_1 = \sin X$
   $Y_2 = \sin(\pi - X)$

e) $Y_1 = \sin X$
   $Y_2 = \sin\left(\frac{\pi}{2} - X\right)$

Investigating Identities

Your graphing calculator can be used to indicate visually whether or not an equation is an identity. You can do this by graphing each side of the equation as a function.

To show that $\dfrac{1 + \cos^2 x}{\sin x} = \sin x$ is not an identity, let

$Y_1 = \dfrac{1 + \cos^2 X}{\sin X}$ and $Y_2 = \sin X$. Display the graphs of Y_1 and Y_2 on the same screen. The graphs are not identical and we can conclude that the equation is not an identity; that is, it is not true for all values of x.

Although this equation is not an identity, nevertheless it is true for some values of x. Use the TRACE feature to find the values of x for which the equation is true. What is the solution set for this equation?

To verify the identity $\dfrac{\sin x}{1 - \cos x} = \dfrac{1 + \cos x}{\sin x}$, plot $Y_1 = \dfrac{\sin X}{1 - \cos X}$

and $Y_2 = \dfrac{1 + \cos X}{\sin X}$.

Do the graphs of $Y_1 = \dfrac{\sin X}{1 - \cos X}$ and $Y_2 = \dfrac{1 + \cos X}{\sin X}$ appear to be identical?

What do you see when you display the graph of $Y_1 - Y_2$? Now graph $Y_1 - Y_2 + 1$. Write an explanation of what you have observed.

It is important to note that the graphical display of Y_1 and Y_2 is not a proof that $Y_1 = Y_2$ is an identity. A formal proof can only be done algebraically.

Looking Ahead

a) Use your graphing calculator to help you decide if any of these equations is an identity.
   i) $\sin (x + 2) = \sin x + \sin 2$ ii) $\cos (x - 3) = \cos x - \cos 3$
   iii) $\tan (x + 4) = \tan x + \tan 4$

b) Write a brief explanation of why the distributive property cannot be applied to the trigonometric functions.

c) Is either of these equations an identity?
   i) $\cos 2x = 2 \cos x$ ii) $\sin 3x = 3 \sin x$

d) Display $Y_1 = \cos 3X$ and $Y_2 = 3 \cos X$ on the same screen. To the nearest hundredth, find 2 values of X between 0 and 2π where $Y_1 = Y_2$.

8-6 SUM AND DIFFERENCE IDENTITIES

In mathematics we often combine the operation of evaluating a function with the operations of addition or subtraction. These operations frequently give different results if they are carried out in different orders.

For example:

1. Triple a sum
$3(x + y)$

The sum of the numbers tripled
$3x + 3y$

2. The square of a sum
$(x + y)^2$

The sum of the squares
$x^2 + y^2$

3. The square root of a sum
$\sqrt{x + y}$

The sum of the square roots
$\sqrt{x} + \sqrt{y}$

4. The reciprocal of a sum
$\dfrac{1}{x + y}$

The sum of the reciprocals
$\dfrac{1}{x} + \dfrac{1}{y}$

5. The sine of a sum
$\sin (x + y)$

The sum of the sines
$\sin x + \sin y$

6. The cosine of a sum
$\cos (x + y)$

The sum of the cosines
$\cos x + \cos y$

The expressions in the first pair are equal for all values of the variables. That is, we can write $3(x + y) = 3x + 3y$. We say that the operation of multiplication is *distributive* over addition.

   In general, function operations are not distributive over addition. For example, the expressions in the next three pairs above are not equal.

$$(x + y)^2 \neq x^2 + y^2, \quad \sqrt{x + y} \neq \sqrt{x} + \sqrt{y}, \quad \text{and } \frac{1}{x + y} \neq \frac{1}{x} + \frac{1}{y}$$

We can show that $\cos (x + y) \neq \cos x + \cos y$ by using a counterexample. Suppose $x = \frac{\pi}{6}$ and $y = \frac{\pi}{3}$.

Then $\cos (x + y) = \cos \left(\frac{\pi}{6} + \frac{\pi}{3} \right)$ but $\cos x + \cos y = \cos \frac{\pi}{6} + \cos \frac{\pi}{3}$

$$= \cos \frac{\pi}{2} \qquad\qquad\qquad\qquad = \frac{\sqrt{3}}{2} + \frac{1}{2}$$

$$= 0 \qquad\qquad\qquad\qquad\qquad \neq 0$$

Therefore, $\cos \left(\frac{\pi}{6} + \frac{\pi}{3} \right) \neq \cos \frac{\pi}{6} + \cos \frac{\pi}{3}$

Hence, $\cos (x + y) \neq \cos x + \cos y$

Similarly, $\sin (x + y) \neq \sin x + \sin y$

   Therefore, in general, the operation of evaluating a sine or a cosine is not distributive over addition or subtraction. Hence, we now consider the problem of finding expressions for $\cos (x + y)$ and $\sin (x + y)$.

Deriving Identities for cos (α − β) and sin (α − β)

Let A(cos α, sin α) and B(cos β, sin β) be points on a unit circle, where α and β are the angles in standard position corresponding to A and B, respectively. Let C be on the circle such that OC is perpendicular to OB. Since the slopes of OC and OB are negative reciprocals, the coordinates of C may be represented by (−sin β, cos β).

Rotate quadrilateral OBAC clockwise about the origin through angle β. Then B coincides with E(1,0), C coincides with F(0,1), and A coincides with D, where ∠DOE = α − β. Hence, the coordinates of D are (cos (α − β), sin (α − β)).

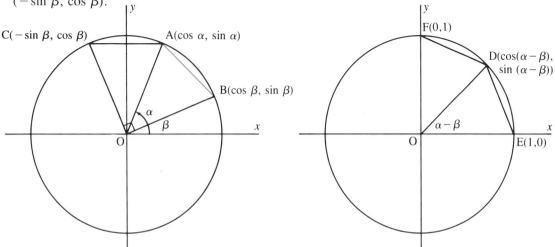

Since ∠AOB = ∠DOE, △AOB ≅ △DOE.
Since the triangles are congruent,

$$AB = DE$$
$$\sqrt{(\cos \alpha - \cos \beta)^2 + (\sin \alpha - \sin \beta)^2} = \sqrt{(\cos (\alpha - \beta) - 1)^2 + (\sin (\alpha - \beta) - 0)^2}$$

Square both sides to eliminate the radicals.

$$(\cos \alpha - \cos \beta)^2 + (\sin \alpha - \sin \beta)^2 = (\cos (\alpha - \beta) - 1)^2 + \sin^2(\alpha - \beta)$$

Expand the binomial squares and use the Pythagorean identity.

$$\cos^2\alpha - 2 \cos \alpha \cos \beta + \cos^2\beta + \sin^2\alpha - 2 \sin \alpha \sin \beta + \sin^2\beta$$
$$= \cos^2(\alpha - \beta) - 2 \cos (\alpha - \beta) + 1 + \sin^2(\alpha - \beta)$$
$$(\cos^2\alpha + \sin^2\alpha) + (\cos^2\beta + \sin^2\beta) - 2 (\cos \alpha \cos \beta + \sin \alpha \sin \beta)$$
$$= (\cos^2(\alpha - \beta) + \sin^2(\alpha - \beta)) + 1 - 2 \cos (\alpha - \beta)$$
$$2 - 2(\cos \alpha \cos \beta + \sin \alpha \sin \beta) = 2 - 2 \cos (\alpha - \beta)$$

Hence, cos (α − β) = cos α cos β + sin α sin β . . . ①

Similarly, using AC = DF, we can derive the following identity for sin (α − β).

sin (α − β) = sin α cos β − cos α sin β . . . ②

Equations ① and ② are the identities for cos (α − β) and sin (α − β) we have been seeking.

Deriving Identities for cos ($\alpha + \beta$) and sin ($\alpha + \beta$)

It is possible to obtain identities for cos ($\alpha + \beta$) and sin ($\alpha + \beta$) using diagrams similar to those on page 419. However, it is simpler to apply the odd-even identities to the identities ① and ② we already have. We can do this because the sum of two angles can also be expressed as a difference. That is, $\alpha + \beta = \alpha - (-\beta)$. Hence, we can write:

$$\cos (\alpha + \beta) = \cos (\alpha - (-\beta))$$
$$= \cos \alpha \cos (-\beta) + \sin \alpha \sin (-\beta)$$
$$= \cos \alpha \cos \beta - \sin \alpha \sin \beta$$

Similarly, we can obtain sin ($\alpha + \beta$) = $\sin \alpha \cos \beta + \cos \alpha \sin \beta$.

Deriving Identities for tan ($\alpha + \beta$) and tan ($\alpha - \beta$)

We can now derive an identity for tan ($\alpha + \beta$) as follows.

$$\tan (\alpha + \beta) = \frac{\sin (\alpha + \beta)}{\cos (\alpha + \beta)}$$

$$= \frac{\sin \alpha \cos \beta + \cos \alpha \sin \beta}{\cos \alpha \cos \beta - \sin \alpha \sin \beta}$$

To obtain tangent functions on the right side, divide numerator and denominator by cos α cos β. Hence,

$$\tan (\alpha + \beta) = \frac{\dfrac{\sin \alpha \cos \beta}{\cos \alpha \cos \beta} + \dfrac{\cos \alpha \sin \beta}{\cos \alpha \cos \beta}}{\dfrac{\cos \alpha \cos \beta}{\cos \alpha \cos \beta} - \dfrac{\sin \alpha \sin \beta}{\cos \alpha \cos \beta}}$$

$$= \frac{\dfrac{\sin \alpha}{\cos \alpha} + \dfrac{\sin \beta}{\cos \beta}}{1 - \dfrac{\sin \alpha}{\cos \alpha} \times \dfrac{\sin \beta}{\cos \beta}}$$

Hence,

$$\tan (\alpha + \beta) = \frac{\tan \alpha + \tan \beta}{1 - \tan \alpha \tan \beta}$$

We can derive an identity for tan ($\alpha - \beta$) in a similar way, or by replacing β with $-\beta$ in the above identity. The result is:

$$\tan (\alpha - \beta) = \frac{\tan \alpha - \tan \beta}{1 + \tan \alpha \tan \beta}$$

Sum and Difference Identities

$\sin (x + y) = \sin x \cos y + \cos x \sin y$

$\sin (x - y) = \sin x \cos y - \cos x \sin y$

$\tan (x + y) = \dfrac{\tan x + \tan y}{1 - \tan x \tan y}$

$\cos (x + y) = \cos x \cos y - \sin x \sin y$

$\cos (x - y) = \cos x \cos y + \sin x \sin y$

$\tan (x - y) = \dfrac{\tan x - \tan y}{1 + \tan x \tan y}$

We can use the sum and difference identities to find expressions for the sine, cosine, or tangent of an angle obtained by adding or subtracting multiples of $\frac{\pi}{6}$ or $\frac{\pi}{4}$. For example, since $\frac{5\pi}{12} = \frac{\pi}{4} + \frac{\pi}{6}$, we can find an expression for $\sin \frac{5\pi}{12}$ without using a calculator.

Example 1. Find an exact expression for $\sin \frac{5\pi}{12}$, and check with a calculator.

Solution.
$$\sin \frac{5\pi}{12} = \sin \left(\frac{\pi}{4} + \frac{\pi}{6} \right)$$
$$= \sin \frac{\pi}{4} \cos \frac{\pi}{6} + \cos \frac{\pi}{4} \sin \frac{\pi}{6}$$
$$= \frac{1}{\sqrt{2}} \left(\frac{\sqrt{3}}{2} \right) + \frac{1}{\sqrt{2}} \left(\frac{1}{2} \right)$$
$$= \frac{\sqrt{3} + 1}{2\sqrt{2}}$$

Both sides of this equation are equal to approximately 0.965 925 8.

We can use the sum and difference identities to prove the cofunction identities, and many other related identities.

Example 2. Prove each identity.

a) $\cos \left(\frac{\pi}{2} + x \right) = -\sin x$ b) $\sin (\pi - x) = \sin x$

Solution.
a) $\cos \left(\frac{\pi}{2} + x \right) = \cos \frac{\pi}{2} \cos x - \sin \frac{\pi}{2} \sin x$
$$= (0)\cos x - (1)\sin x$$
$$= -\sin x$$

b) $\sin (\pi - x) = \sin \pi \cos x - \cos \pi \sin x$
$$= (0)\cos x - (-1)\sin x$$
$$= \sin x$$

To use the sum and difference identities, we must know both the sine and the cosine of the two angles involved in the expression.

Example 3. Given $\cos \theta = \frac{3}{5}$, where θ is in Quadrant I, evaluate $\cos \left(\theta + \frac{\pi}{6} \right)$.

Solution. The two angles are θ and $\frac{\pi}{6}$. Hence, we need to know the sine and the cosine of each angle.
We know that $\sin \frac{\pi}{6} = \frac{1}{2}$ and $\cos \frac{\pi}{6} = \frac{\sqrt{3}}{2}$. The value of $\cos \theta$ is given, and we can obtain the value of $\sin \theta$ from the identity $\cos^2\theta + \sin^2\theta = 1$. Substitute $\frac{3}{5}$ for $\cos \theta$ to obtain:
$$\frac{9}{25} + \sin^2\theta = 1$$
$$\sin^2\theta = \frac{16}{25}$$
$$\sin \theta = \frac{+4}{-5}$$

Since θ is in Quadrant I, $\sin \theta$ is positive. Hence, $\sin \theta = \frac{4}{5}$

$$\cos \left(\theta + \frac{\pi}{6} \right) = \cos \theta \cos \frac{\pi}{6} - \sin \theta \sin \frac{\pi}{6}$$

$$= \frac{3}{5}\left(\frac{\sqrt{3}}{2} \right) - \frac{4}{5}\left(\frac{1}{2} \right)$$

$$= \frac{3\sqrt{3} - 4}{10}$$

EXERCISES 8-6

Ⓐ

1. Use a calculator to verify the sum and difference identities for $x = 2.2$ and $y = 1.4$.

2. Expand and simplify each expression.
   a) $\sin (30° + 60°)$ b) $\cos (45° + 45°)$
   c) $\sin \left(\frac{\pi}{3} - \frac{\pi}{6} \right)$ d) $\cos \left(\frac{\pi}{2} - \frac{\pi}{6} \right)$

3. Evaluate $\cos 120°$ by expanding and simplifying each expression.
   a) $\cos (60° + 60°)$ b) $\cos (90° + 30°)$ c) $\cos (180° - 60°)$

4. Evaluate $\sin \frac{3\pi}{4}$ by expanding and simplifying each expression.
   a) $\sin \left(\frac{\pi}{2} + \frac{\pi}{4} \right)$ b) $\sin \left(\pi - \frac{\pi}{4} \right)$

Ⓑ

5. a) Use the fact that $\frac{\pi}{12} = \frac{\pi}{3} - \frac{\pi}{4}$ to prove that $\sin \frac{\pi}{12} = \frac{\sqrt{3} - 1}{2\sqrt{2}}$.
   b) Find a similar expression for $\cos \frac{\pi}{12}$.
   c) Check the results in parts a) and b) with a calculator.

6. Find an exact expression for each sine or cosine.
   a) $\cos \frac{7\pi}{12}$ b) $\sin \frac{11\pi}{12}$ c) $\cos \frac{5\pi}{12}$ d) $\sin \frac{5\pi}{12}$

7. Show that the cofunction identities provide counterexamples to prove that $\cos (\alpha - \beta) \neq \cos \alpha - \cos \beta$ and $\sin (\alpha - \beta) \neq \sin \alpha - \sin \beta$.

8. Prove each identity.
   a) $\sin (90° + \theta) = \cos \theta$ b) $\cos (180° + \theta) = -\cos \theta$
   c) $\cos \left(\frac{3\pi}{2} + \theta \right) = \sin \theta$ d) $\sin \left(\frac{3\pi}{2} - \theta \right) = -\cos \theta$

9. Simplify each expression.
   a) $\cos (180° - x)$ b) $\sin (90° - x)$ c) $\sin (\pi - x)$ d) $\cos \left(x - \frac{\pi}{2} \right)$

10. Given $\sin \theta = \frac{4}{5}$, where θ is in Quadrant I, evaluate each expression.

   a) $\sin (\theta + 30°)$ b) $\sin (\theta + 45°)$ c) $\cos (\theta - 60°)$

11. Given $\cos \theta = -\frac{2}{3}$, where θ is in Quadrant II, evaluate each expression.

   a) $\sin \left(\theta + \frac{\pi}{6} \right)$ b) $\cos \left(\theta + \frac{\pi}{3} \right)$ c) $\cos \left(\theta - \frac{\pi}{4} \right)$

12. Given $\sin \theta = 0.75$, where $\frac{\pi}{2} < \theta < \pi$, evaluate each expression.

   a) $\sin \left(\theta + \frac{\pi}{3} \right)$ b) $\cos \left(\theta - \frac{\pi}{6} \right)$ c) $\cos \left(\theta + \frac{\pi}{4} \right)$

13. a) Prove that $\sin \left(\frac{\pi}{4} + x \right) + \sin \left(\frac{\pi}{4} - x \right) = \sqrt{2} \cos x$.

   b) Find a similar expression for:

   i) $\sin \left(\frac{\pi}{6} + x \right) + \sin \left(\frac{\pi}{6} - x \right)$ ii) $\sin \left(\frac{\pi}{3} + x \right) + \sin \left(\frac{\pi}{3} - x \right)$.

   c) State a general result suggested by parts a) and b), and prove it.

14. Given that $\sin \alpha = \frac{3}{5}$ and $\cos \beta = \frac{5}{13}$, where both α and β are in Quadrant I, evaluate each expression.

   a) $\cos (\alpha + \beta)$ b) $\cos (\alpha - \beta)$ c) $\sin (\alpha + \beta)$ d) $\sin (\alpha - \beta)$

15. Given that $\cos \alpha = -\frac{4}{5}$ and $\sin \beta = \frac{2}{3}$, where both α and β are in Quadrant II, evaluate each expression.

   a) $\cos (\alpha + \beta)$ b) $\cos (\alpha - \beta)$ c) $\sin (\alpha + \beta)$ d) $\sin (\alpha - \beta)$

16. Determine whether or not there are any values of α and β such that:

   a) $\sin (\alpha + \beta) = \sin \alpha + \sin \beta$ b) $\cos (\alpha + \beta) = \cos \alpha + \cos \beta$
   c) $\tan (\alpha + \beta) = \tan \alpha + \tan \beta$.

17. Derive the identity $\sin (\alpha - \beta) = \sin \alpha \cos \beta - \cos \alpha \sin \beta$ in two ways.
   a) using the diagram on page 419
   b) using the identity for $\cos (\alpha + \beta)$ and a cofunction identity

18. a) Prove the identity $\cos x \cos y = \frac{\cos (x + y) + \cos (x - y)}{2}$.

   b) Establish similar identities for:
   i) $\sin x \sin y$ ii) $\sin x \cos y$ iii) $\cos x \sin y$.

19. a) Prove the identity $\cos x + \cos y = 2 \cos \left(\frac{x + y}{2} \right) \cos \left(\frac{x - y}{2} \right)$.

   b) Establish similar identities for:
   i) $\cos x - \cos y$ ii) $\sin x + \sin y$ iii) $\sin x - \sin y$.

 PROBLEM SOLVING

The Golden Ratio

"Geometry has two great treasures: one is the theorem of Pythagoras; the other, the division of a line segment into extreme and mean ratio. The first we may compare to a measure of gold; the second we may name a precious jewel."

Johannes Kepler

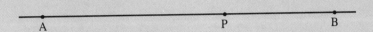

Given any line segment AB, there is a point P which divides the segment into two parts such that the length of the longer part is to the length of the shorter part as the length of the entire segment is to the length of the longer part. That is, $\dfrac{AP}{PB} = \dfrac{AB}{AP}$. This is what Kepler meant by "division . . . into extreme and mean ratio". The ratio is now known as the *golden ratio*.

The golden ratio occurs frequently and unexpectedly in a wide variety of problems. The problems below and in the problems section provide only a glimpse of this variety.

Problem 1. Find the numerical value of the golden ratio.

Understand the problem
- How can a ratio have a numerical value?

Think of a strategy and carry it out
- On the diagram above, let $AP = x$ and $PB = 1$.
- Use the definition of the golden ratio to write an equation in x, then solve the equation.
- The golden ratio is the positive root of this equation.

Look back
- Did you get the equation $x^2 - x - 1 = 0$?
- Did you obtain the root $\dfrac{1 + \sqrt{5}}{2}$? This is the golden ratio expressed as a real number.
- Why is the golden ratio the positive root rather than the negative root?
- Use a calculator to express the golden ratio in decimal form.

Problem 2. Prove that the diagonals of a regular pentagon divide each other in the golden ratio.

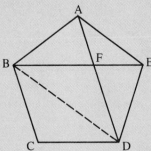

Understand the problem
- What is a regular pentagon?
- Do all the diagonals have the same length?

Think of a strategy
- Since the pentagon is regular, what properties would certain angles and segments have in a diagram like the one above?
- Could you prove these properties?
- There is no loss of generality in letting the sides of the pentagon have length 1. Hence, let the diagonals have length x.
- Write what is required to prove about point F and the diagonal BE. Are some of the segments involved sides of triangles?
- What kind of triangles might they be?

Carry out the strategy
- BF and FE are sides of $\triangle$BFD and $\triangle$EFA. Use properties of a regular pentagon to prove that these triangles are similar.
- Then use the result to prove that F divides BE in the same ratio that a diagonal bears to a side.
- Is this true about every diagonal and every side?
- Complete the proof that F divides BE in the golden ratio.

Look back
- Did you obtain the equation $x^2 - x - 1 = 0$?
- Does F divide DA in the golden ratio?
- What is the ratio of a diagonal to a side?
- Why is there no loss of generality in assuming that the sides of the pentagon have length 1?

PROBLEMS

Ⓑ

1. Prove each identity.
   a) $\sin 3\theta = 3 \sin \theta - 4 \sin^3\theta$ b) $\cos 3\theta = 4 \cos^3\theta - 3 \cos \theta$

2. The function $z(n)$ is defined as the number of zeros at the end of $n!$. For example, since $5! = 120$, which ends in one zero, then $z(5) = 1$.
   a) Determine.   i) $z(10)$ ii) $z(20)$ iii) $z(30)$
   b) Is it possible to find a value of n such that $z(n) = 5$?
   c) Given any natural number n, describe a method you could use to determine the value of $z(n)$.

3. If $\triangle ABC$ is a right triangle, prove that
   $\sin^2 A + \sin^2 B + \sin^2 C = 2(\cos^2 A + \cos^2 B + \cos^2 C)$.

4. Prove that $\cos 36° = \dfrac{\sqrt{5} + 1}{4}$ and $\cos 72° = \dfrac{\sqrt{5} - 1}{4}$.

5. Find the equations of the lines with slope $\dfrac{3}{4}$ that are 2 units from the point P(5, −1).

Ⓒ

6. Find the equations of two parallel lines passing through A(0, 2) and B(0, 7) which are 3 units apart.

7. Triangle ABC has vertices A(4, 9), B(1, 2), and C(9, 6). Find the area of $\triangle ABC$.

8. T is any point on a circle with centre C. P is a point on the tangent at T such that PT = 2CT. With centre P a second circle is drawn tangent to the given circle to intersect PT at N.
   a) Prove that N divides PT in the golden ratio.
   b) Use the result of part a) to construct a regular pentagon with one side PN.

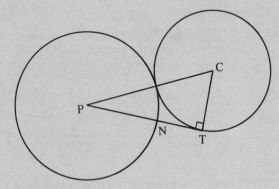

Ⓓ

9. In $\triangle ABC$, $\angle B = 90°$, and the ratio of the sides is AB : BC : CA = 3 : 4 : 5. O is the point of intersection of BC and the bisector of $\angle A$. With centre O and radius OB, a circle is drawn to intersect AO at P and Q. Prove that P divides QA in the golden ratio.

8-7 DOUBLE-ANGLE IDENTITIES

In *Section 8-6* we developed identities for the sine, cosine, and tangent of the sum of two angles.

$\sin (\alpha + \beta) = \sin \alpha \cos \beta + \cos \alpha \sin \beta$

$\cos (\alpha + \beta) = \cos \alpha \cos \beta - \sin \alpha \sin \beta$

$$\tan (\alpha + \beta) = \frac{\tan \alpha + \tan \beta}{1 - \tan \alpha \tan \beta}$$

If the two angles α and β are equal, then these identities reduce to identities for $\sin 2\alpha$, $\cos 2\alpha$, and $\tan 2\alpha$.

$$\begin{aligned} \sin 2\alpha &= \sin (\alpha + \alpha) \\ &= \sin \alpha \cos \alpha + \cos \alpha \sin \alpha \\ &= 2 \sin \alpha \cos \alpha \end{aligned} \qquad \begin{aligned} \cos 2\alpha &= \cos (\alpha + \alpha) \\ &= \cos \alpha \cos \alpha - \sin \alpha \sin \alpha \\ &= \cos^2\alpha - \sin^2\alpha \quad \dots \; \text{①} \end{aligned}$$

We can use the Pythagorean identity $\sin^2\alpha + \cos^2\alpha = 1$ to express the identity for $\cos 2\alpha$ in two other forms.

Since $\sin^2\alpha + \cos^2\alpha = 1$, then

$$\sin^2\alpha = 1 - \cos^2\alpha$$

Substitute this expression in ①

$$\begin{aligned} \cos 2\alpha &= \cos^2\alpha - \sin^2\alpha \\ &= \cos^2\alpha - (1 - \cos^2\alpha) \\ &= 2 \cos^2\alpha - 1 \end{aligned}$$

Since $\sin^2\alpha + \cos^2\alpha = 1$, then

$$\cos^2\alpha = 1 - \sin^2\alpha$$

Substitute this expression in ①

$$\begin{aligned} \cos 2\alpha &= \cos^2\alpha - \sin^2\alpha \\ &= (1 - \sin^2\alpha) - \sin^2\alpha \\ &= 1 - 2 \sin^2\alpha \end{aligned}$$

$$\begin{aligned} \tan 2\alpha &= \tan (\alpha + \alpha) \\[2mm] &= \frac{\tan \alpha + \tan \alpha}{1 - \tan \alpha \tan \alpha} \\[2mm] &= \frac{2 \tan \alpha}{1 - \tan^2\alpha} \end{aligned}$$

Double-Angle Identities

$$\sin 2x = 2 \sin x \cos x \qquad \begin{aligned} \cos 2x &= \cos^2x - \sin^2x \\ &= 2 \cos^2x - 1 \\ &= 1 - 2 \sin^2x \end{aligned} \qquad \tan 2x = \frac{2 \tan x}{1 - \tan^2x}$$

Example 1.   If $\cos \theta = -\frac{1}{3}$, and $\frac{\pi}{2} < \theta < \pi$, evaluate each expression.

　　　　　a) $\sin 2\theta$　　　　　　b) $\cos 2\theta$　　　　　　c) $\tan 2\theta$

Solution.   To find the values of these expressions, we need the value of $\sin \theta$ in addition to the given value of $\cos \theta$.

Substitute $-\frac{1}{3}$ for $\cos \theta$ in the identity $\cos^2\theta + \sin^2\theta = 1$.

$$\frac{1}{9} + \sin^2\theta = 1$$

$$\sin^2\theta = \frac{8}{9}$$

$$\sin\theta = \frac{2\sqrt{2}}{3} \qquad \text{(since } \theta \text{ is in Quadrant II)}$$

a) $\sin 2\theta = 2\sin\theta\cos\theta$

$$= 2\left(\frac{2\sqrt{2}}{3}\right)\left(-\frac{1}{3}\right)$$

$$= -\frac{4\sqrt{2}}{9}$$

b) We can find $\cos 2\theta$ using the Pythagorean identity, or any of the three identities for $\cos 2\theta$. For example,

$$\cos 2\theta = 2\cos^2\theta - 1$$

$$= 2\left(-\frac{1}{3}\right)^2 - 1$$

$$= -\frac{7}{9}$$

c) To find $\tan 2\theta$, we can use the double-angle identity or the quotient identity for $\tan 2\theta$.

$$\tan 2\theta = \frac{\sin 2\theta}{\cos 2\theta}$$

$$= \frac{-\dfrac{4\sqrt{2}}{9}}{-\dfrac{7}{9}}$$

$$= \frac{4\sqrt{2}}{7}$$

The patterns in the double-angle identities can be used to simplify certain trigonometric expressions.

Example 2. Write each expression in terms of a single trigonometric function.

a) $2\sin 0.45 \cos 0.45$ b) $\cos^2 5 - \sin^2 5$

Solution. a) $2\sin 0.45 \cos 0.45$

This expression can be obtained by substituting 0.45 for α in the right side of the identity $\sin 2\alpha = 2\sin\alpha\cos\alpha$. Hence, we substitute 0.45 for α in the left side of the identity. Therefore, $2\sin 0.45 \cos 0.45 = \sin 0.90$

b) $\cos^2 5 - \sin^2 5$

Similarly, by substituting 5 for α in the identity $\cos 2\alpha = \cos^2\alpha - \sin^2\alpha$, we obtain $\cos^2 5 - \sin^2 5 = \cos 10$.

Example 3. Prove the identity $\dfrac{1 + \cos 2x}{\sin 2x} = \cot x$.

Solution. In the left side, we use the double-angle identities for $\cos 2x$ and $\sin 2x$. There are three expressions we could substitute for $\cos 2x$. We choose the one which eliminates the 1 from the numerator.

$$\text{Left side} = \frac{1 + \cos 2x}{\sin 2x}$$

$$= \frac{1 + (2 \cos^2 x - 1)}{2 \sin x \cos x} \qquad \text{(double-angle identities)}$$

$$= \frac{2 \cos^2 x}{2 \sin x \cos x}$$

$$= \frac{\cos x}{\sin x}$$

$$= \cot x \qquad \text{(quotient identity)}$$

$$= \text{Right side}$$

Since the left side simplifies to the right side, the identity is correct.

EXERCISES 8-7

(A)

1. Use a calculator to verify the double-angle identities for $x = 0.45$.

2. Use a calculator to verify the double-angle identities for $x = 5$.

3. Write each expression in terms of a single trigonometric function.
   a) $2 \sin 0.6 \cos 0.6$
   b) $2 \sin 3 \cos 3$
   c) $2 \sin 2 \cos 2$
   d) $\cos^2 0.45 - \sin^2 0.45$
   e) $2 \cos^2 5 - 1$
   f) $1 - 2 \sin^2 3$

4. Write each expression in terms of a single trigonometric function.
   a) $2 \sin \frac{\pi}{6} \cos \frac{\pi}{6}$
   b) $\cos^2 \frac{\pi}{10} - \sin^2 \frac{\pi}{10}$
   c) $2 \cos^2 0.5 - 1$

5. Given that $\sin 60° = \dfrac{\sqrt{3}}{2}$ and $\cos 60° = \dfrac{1}{2}$, use the double-angle identities to determine the values of $\sin 120°$ and $\cos 120°$.

6. Given that $\sin \frac{\pi}{4} = \dfrac{1}{\sqrt{2}}$ and $\cos \frac{\pi}{4} = \dfrac{1}{\sqrt{2}}$, use the double-angle identities to determine the values of $\sin \frac{\pi}{2}$ and $\cos \frac{\pi}{2}$.

(B)

7. The identity $\cos 2x = 2 \cos^2 x - 1$ was used to prove the identity in *Example 3*. Prove the identity using one of the other identities for $\cos 2x$.

8. If $\sin \theta = \dfrac{1}{3}$, and θ is in Quadrant I, evaluate each expression.
   a) $\sin 2\theta$
   b) $\cos 2\theta$
   c) $\tan 2\theta$

9. A value of θ is defined. Evaluate the expressions $\sin 2\theta$, $\cos 2\theta$, and $\tan 2\theta$.
   a) $\cos \theta = -\frac{1}{2}$, and θ is in Quadrant II
   b) $\sin \theta = -\frac{2}{3}$, and θ is in Quadrant III
   c) $\tan \theta = 0.75$ and $\pi < \theta < \frac{3\pi}{2}$

10. Prove each identity.
    a) $1 + \sin 2\theta = (\sin \theta + \cos \theta)^2$ b) $\sin 2\theta = 2 \cot \theta \sin^2\theta$
    c) $\cos 2x = \dfrac{1 - \tan^2 x}{1 + \tan^2 x}$ d) $\sec^2 x = \dfrac{2}{1 + \cos 2x}$

11. a) Show that the expression $\dfrac{1 - \cos 2x}{2}$ is equivalent to $\sin^2 x$.
    b) Find a similar expression equivalent to $\cos^2 x$. Try to do this in more than one way.

12. Show that the expression $\dfrac{\sin^2\theta + \cos^2\theta}{\sin^2\theta - \cos^2\theta}$ is equivalent to $-\sec 2\theta$.

13. a) Show that the expression $\dfrac{(\sin \theta + \cos \theta)^2}{\sin 2\theta}$ is equivalent to $\csc 2\theta + 1$.
    b) Find a similar expression equivalent to $\csc 2\theta - 1$.

14. In *Example 3*, an identity for $\dfrac{1 + \cos 2x}{\sin 2x}$ was proved. Establish a similar identity for each expression.
    a) $\dfrac{1 - \cos 2x}{\sin 2x}$ b) $\dfrac{\sin 2x}{1 + \cos 2x}$ c) $\dfrac{\sin 2x}{1 - \cos 2x}$

15. a) If $\sin x + \cos x = \frac{1}{2}$, find the value of $\sin 2x$.
    b) Check the result of part a) with your calculator.

16. a) Sketch the graphs of the functions $y = \sin 2x$ and $y = 2 \sin x$.
    b) Use the graphs to explain why $\sin 2x \neq 2 \sin x$.
    c) Are there any values of x such that $\sin 2x$ is equal to $2 \sin x$?

17. Repeat *Exercise 16* using the cosine function.

INVESTIGATE

Triple-Angle Identities

By writing $3x = 2x + x$, use the sum identities for the sine and cosine functions to establish identities for $\sin 3x$ and $\cos 3x$.

THE MATHEMATICAL MIND

Evaluating Trigonometric Functions

By Measurement

We can determine rough approximations to the values of cos θ and sin θ by measuring.

Step 1. Construct a quarter circle with radius 100 mm. This distance represents 1 unit. Use a protractor to construct an angle of 40°. Locate point P and construct the perpendicular from P to the *x*-axis. Measure the lengths of ON and NP in millimetres. Since 100 mm represents 1 unit, divide the lengths by 100 to determine the values of cos 40° and sin 40°.

Hence, cos 40° $\doteq$ 0.77
and   sin 40° $\doteq$ 0.64

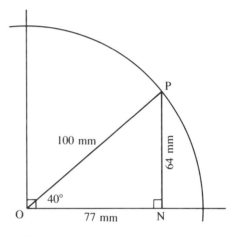

Step 2. Repeat for other angles such as 10°, 20°, 30°, ..., 90°.

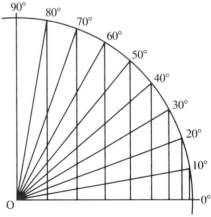

QUESTIONS

1. Use this method to determine the values of the trigonometric functions for 0°, 10°, 20°, ..., 90°. Summarize the results in a table.

2. Look for patterns in the results. Account for the patterns you see.

3. Do you think it would be possible to use this method to obtain 3-digit or 4-digit accuracy? Explain your answer.

Finding Exact Values Algebraically

We can determine exact values of the trigonometric functions for certain angles in a variety of ways.

Using the Pythagorean Theorem
In earlier sections we used the Pythagorean Theorem to find exact values of the trigonometric functions for angles of 30°, 45°, and 60°.

θ	$\cos \theta$	$\sin \theta$	$\tan \theta$
30°	$\dfrac{\sqrt{3}}{2}$	$\dfrac{1}{2}$	$\dfrac{1}{\sqrt{3}}$
45°	$\dfrac{1}{\sqrt{2}}$	$\dfrac{1}{\sqrt{2}}$	1
60°	$\dfrac{1}{2}$	$\dfrac{\sqrt{3}}{2}$	$\sqrt{3}$

Using the sum and difference identities
If we know the function values for two angles we can use the identities for sin $(x \pm y)$, cos $(x \pm y)$, and tan $(x \pm y)$ to determine the values for the sum and the difference of those angles. For example, we can find sin 15° by writing it as sin (45° − 30°) and using the identity sin $(x - y) = \sin x \cos y - \cos x \sin y$. The result is
sin 15° $= \dfrac{\sqrt{3} - 1}{2\sqrt{2}}$. See *Question 4* below.

Using the double-angle identities
We can use the double-angle identities to determine function values, but this is not really a different method because it amounts to using the sum identities with equal values for x and y. However, we can use these identities in another way, because two of the identities for cos $2x$ contain only one trigonometric expression on the right side:
$$\cos 2x = 2 \cos^2 x - 1 \quad \dots \text{①}$$
$$\cos 2x = 1 - 2 \sin^2 x \quad \dots \text{②}$$
Observe that the expression on the right side involves *half* the angle in the expression on the left side. Therefore, if we know the cosine of an angle, we can use these identities to determine the cosine and the sine of half the angle. By replacing x with $\frac{x}{2}$ in ① and ②, we can solve ① for $\cos \frac{x}{2}$ and we can solve ② for $\sin \frac{x}{2}$ to determine identities for $\cos \frac{x}{2}$ and $\sin \frac{x}{2}$. The results are as follows:

Half-Angle Identities

$$\cos \frac{x}{2} = \pm \sqrt{\frac{1 + \cos x}{2}} \qquad \sin \frac{x}{2} = \pm \sqrt{\frac{1 - \cos x}{2}}$$

Using symmetry

Once we know a function value for an angle, we can determine function values for other related angles. For example, we found above that $\sin 15° = \dfrac{\sqrt{3} - 1}{2\sqrt{2}}$. The diagram shows that these expressions are equal to $\sin 15°$: $\sin 165°$, $\cos 75°$, $\cos 285°$; and these are equal to $-\sin 15°$: $\sin 195°$, $\sin 345°$, $\cos 105°$, $\cos 255°$.

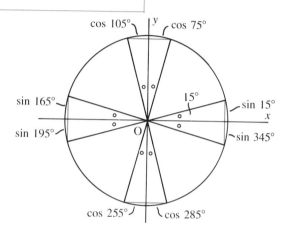

QUESTIONS

4. a) Use a calculator to check the value of $\sin 15°$ found above.
   b) Find $\sin 15°$ in another way.
   c) Use the sum and difference identities to calculate some other values.

5. a) Substitute $22.5°$ for x in the identity $\cos 2x = 2 \cos^2 x - 1$, and use the result to determine the exact value of $\cos 22.5°$.
   b) Determine the exact value of $\sin 22.5°$ in a similar way.

6. Repeat *Question 5* for a different value of x and determine the exact values of the cosine and the sine of another angle.

7. a) Derive the identities for $\cos \frac{x}{2}$ and $\sin \frac{x}{2}$ stated above.
   b) Derive an identity for $\tan \frac{x}{2}$.

8. *Using some ingenuity*
   a) Determine the exact value of $\sin 18°$ using this method.
      By a cofunction identity, $\sin 36° = \cos 54°$, or $\sin 2(18°) = \cos 3(18°)$. Expand $\sin 2(18°)$ using the identity for $\sin 2x$. Then expand $\cos 3(18°)$ by first obtaining an identity for $\cos 3x$ by writing $\cos 3x = \cos (2x + x)$ and expanding. Hence, obtain an equation for $\sin 18°$, and solve it.
   b) Using the result of part a), find the exact value of $\cos 18°$ and $\sin 36°$.

9. a) List some angles whose function values can be determined by using the methods above and combinations of them.
   b) What are some of the advantages and disadvantages of using algebraic methods to determine values of trigonometric functions?

Using a Table

To keep pace with progress in navigation and astronomy in the 17th and 18th centuries, mathematicians required increasingly more accurate values of trigonometric functions. Methods of calculation were developed, and extensive tables of values were calculated manually. An example of such a table is shown below. For more accurate results, much larger tables were used. As with tables of logarithms, some of these occupied entire volumes of several hundred pages. Almost always, the sine function was listed first.

Notice that the first column of the table contains angles from 0° to 45°. For these angles, the headings at the top of the table are used. For example, cos 15° = 0.966

For values of θ between 45° and 90° we use the headings at the *bottom* of the table. Hence, to find cos 70°, we locate 70° in the column at the *right* of the table, and use the cosine column identified by the bottom row of the table. We see that cos 70° = 0.342

Values of Trigonometric Functions

θ	sin	cos	tan	cot	
0	.000	1.000	.000	—	90
5	.087	.996	.087	11.43	85
10	.174	.985	.176	5.671	80
15	.259	.966	.268	3.732	75
20	.342	.940	.364	2.747	70
25	.423	.906	.466	2.145	65
30	.500	.866	.577	1.732	60
35	.574	.819	.700	1.428	55
40	.643	.766	.839	1.192	50
45	.707	.707	1.000	1.000	45
	cos	sin	cot	tan	θ

QUESTIONS

10. Use the table to determine each value.
    a) cos 35°   b) sin 40°   c) cos 65°   d) sin 20°   e) sin 70°
    f) tan 25°   g) cot 70°   h) tan 60°   i) tan 35°   j) cot 55°

11. Choose some values of θ and use your calculator to verify these identities using the table.
    a) $\cos^2\theta + \sin^2\theta = 1$ b) $\cos\theta\,(\sin\theta\tan\theta + \cos\theta) = 1$
    c) $\tan\theta = \dfrac{\sin\theta}{\cos\theta}$ d) $\cot\theta = \dfrac{1}{\tan\theta}$

12. a) Why do you think tables like these were designed so that the column at the left goes from 0° to 45° and not from 0° to 90°?
    b) Explain why it is possible to design the tables in this way.

Using a Table in Degrees and Minutes

In navigation, each degree is subdivided into 60 minutes, and each minute is subdivided further into 60 seconds. Hence, when trigonometric tables were used for navigation, it was necessary to show angles in these units. A small sample from such a table in degrees and minutes is shown below.

Angle	sin	cos	tan	cot	sec	csc	
0° 00'	.0000	1.0000	.0000	—	1.0000	—	90° 00'
10	.0029	1.0000	.0029	343.77	1.0000	343.78	50
20	.0058	1.0000	.0058	171.89	1.0000	171.89	40
30	.0087	1.0000	.0087	114.59	1.0000	114.59	30
40	.0116	.9999	.0116	85.940	1.0001	85.946	20
50	.0145	.9999	.0145	68.750	1.0001	68.757	10
1° 00'	.0175	.9998	.0175	57.290	1.0002	57.299	89° 00'
10	.0204	.9998	.0204	49.104	1.0002	49.114	50
20	.2333	.9997	.2333	42.964	1.0003	42.976	40
40	.6905	.7234	.9545	1.0477	1.3824	1.4483	20
50	.6926	.7214	.9601	1.0416	1.3863	1.4439	10
44° 00'	.6947	.7193	.9657	1.0355	1.3902	1.4396	46° 00'
10	.6967	.7173	.9713	1.0295	1.3941	1.4352	50
20	.6988	.7153	.9770	1.0235	1.3980	1.4310	40
30	.7009	.7133	.9827	1.0176	1.4020	1.4267	30
40	.7030	.7112	.9884	1.0117	1.4061	1.4225	20
50	.7050	.7092	.9942	1.0058	1.4101	1.4183	10
45° 00'	.7071	.7071	1.0000	1.0000	1.4142	1.4142	45° 00'
	cos	sin	cot	tan	csc	sec	Angle

QUESTIONS

13. Determine these values using the table.
    a) sin 44° 10'   b) sec 1° 20'   c) cos 45° 40'   d) tan 89° 30'
    e) csc 1° 10'   f) cot 88° 40'   g) sin 46° 20'   h) sec 89° 50'

14. Describe and account for some patterns in the numbers in the table.

15. a) To save space above, values for angles between 1° 20' and 43° 40' have been deleted from the table. About how many pages of this book would be needed to print the entire table?
    b) The table shows angles increasing in steps of 10'. About how many pages would be needed to print a table for angles increasing in steps of:
    i) 1'   ii) 10"   iii) 1"?

Using a Scientific Calculator

As it has with tables of logarithms, modern technology has rendered tables of trigonometric functions obsolete. If an angle is given in degrees and minutes, you can use your calculator to convert the angle to decimal form, and then determine any trigonometric value in the usual way. For example, to determine cos 23° 38′, proceed as follows:

$$23° \ 38' = \left(23 + \frac{38}{60}\right)°$$
$$= 23.633 \ 333 \ 33°$$

Using the [cos] key, with the calculator in degree mode, we find that the value is approximately 0.916 129 66.

QUESTIONS

16. a) State at least three advantages of using calculators instead of tables to determine values of trigonometric functions.
    b) Do you think there are any disadvantages of using calculators compared with using tables? Explain your answer.

17. Use your calculator to determine each value.
    a) cos 62° 15′   b) sin 49° 23′   c) tan 132° 51′   d) sin 228° 7′

Using a Computer

When a computer is used to determine values of the trigonometric functions, the method depends on the computer. There are sometimes two limitations, both of which can be overcome with the computer. There may be no provision for changing from radian mode to degree mode, as there is with a calculator. And, the chips in the computer may be able to calculate only one trigonometric function, such as the sine function.

QUESTIONS

18. How could you use a computer to convert an angle x to radians if it is given in these units?
    a) degrees   b) degrees and minutes   c) degrees, minutes, and seconds

19. Suppose the chips in a computer can calculate only the sine function. They can, of course, carry out other arithmetic computations.
    a) Describe two different ways in which you could use the computer to calculate the cosine of an angle.
    b) How could you calculate the other trigonometric functions of the angle?

Using an Infinite Series

Credit goes to the Englishman, Brook Taylor (1685–1731) and the Scotsman, Colin Maclaurin (1698–1746) for showing that under certain conditions a function $f(x)$ can be expressed as an infinite series of powers of x. Two important series are these series for cos x and sin x.

$$\cos x = 1 - \frac{x^2}{2!} + \frac{x^4}{4!} - \frac{x^6}{6!} + \dots \qquad \sin x = \frac{x}{1!} - \frac{x^3}{3!} + \frac{x^5}{5!} - \frac{x^7}{7!} + \dots$$

During the 17th and 18th centuries, some mathematicians devoted their careers to using series such as these to construct extensive tables of values of the trigonometric functions by paper-pencil calculation. These series are also used in the programming of the chips in modern scientific calculators. When you use the $\boxed{\sin}$ or $\boxed{\cos}$ keys on a calculator, the calculator determines the value using the above series.

The series contain the factorial sign !, which indicates the product of all natural numbers up to and including the number. For example, $4! = 1 \times 2 \times 3 \times 4$, or 24. We can regard the series as formulas for calculating values of cos x and sin x for real values of x. The formulas are valid only when x is in radians. Hence, to calculate cos 60°, we substitute $\frac{\pi}{3}$ for x in the first formula and obtain:

$$\cos \frac{\pi}{3} \doteq 1 - \frac{1}{2}\left(\frac{\pi}{3}\right)^2 + \frac{1}{24}\left(\frac{\pi}{3}\right)^4 - \frac{1}{720}\left(\frac{\pi}{3}\right)^6$$

$$\doteq 1 - 0.548\ 311\ 4 + 0.050\ 107\ 6 - 0.001\ 831\ 6$$

$$\doteq 0.499\ 964\ 6$$

This is very close to the actual value of 0.5. For a more accurate result, additional terms of the series can be used.

QUESTIONS

20. Write the first six terms of the series for cos x and sin x.

21. Use the result of *Question 20* to calculate each value. Check using the $\boxed{\cos}$ or $\boxed{\sin}$ key on your calculator.

    a) $\cos \frac{\pi}{6}$ b) $\sin \frac{\pi}{2}$ c) $\sin \frac{\pi}{5}$ d) $\cos \pi$

22. How many terms of the series are needed to obtain a value of cos $\frac{\pi}{5}$:

    a) to 2 decimal places   b) to 4 decimal places   c) to 6 decimal places?

Review Exercises

1. Determine $\tan \theta$ to 4 decimal places.
   a) θ is in the second quadrant and $\sin \theta = 0.7429$
   b) $\theta = \frac{7\pi}{3}$
   c) $\theta = 565°$

2. For which values of x is $\tan x$ undefined if $-2\pi \le x \le 2\pi$? Describe the graph of $y = \tan x$ for values of x close to these particular values.

3. Simplify.
   a) $\sin\left(-\frac{\pi}{3}\right)$
   b) $\sec\left(-\frac{\pi}{4}\right)$
   c) $\tan\left(-\frac{2\pi}{3}\right)$
   d) $\cos\left(-\frac{5\pi}{6}\right)$

4. Determine the exact value of each trigonometric function.
   a) $\csc 315°$
   b) $\sec 240°$
   c) $\tan 135°$
   d) $\cot 270°$
   e) $\sec \frac{7\pi}{6}$
   f) $\cot \frac{5\pi}{3}$
   g) $\csc \frac{2\pi}{3}$
   h) $\sec \frac{3\pi}{4}$

5. Prove each identity.
   a) $\sec \theta (1 + \sin \theta) = \tan \theta (1 + \csc \theta)$
   b) $\csc x - \frac{\cot x}{\sec x} = \sin x$
   c) $\cos^2 x = \sin x (\csc x - \sin x)$
   d) $\sec^2 \theta - 1 = (\sin \theta \sec \theta)^2$

6. Prove each identity.
   a) $\cos^2 x = \dfrac{\cot^2 x}{1 + \frac{1}{\tan^2 x}}$
   b) $\dfrac{\sin \theta}{1 - \cos \theta} + \dfrac{\sin \theta}{1 + \cos \theta} = 2 \csc \theta$
   c) $\sin \theta \cot^2 \theta + \cos \theta \tan^2 \theta = \dfrac{\sin^3 \theta + \cos^3 \theta}{\sin \theta \cos \theta}$
   d) $\dfrac{\tan^2 x + 1}{\cot^2 x + 1} = \dfrac{1 - \cos^2 x}{\cos^2 x}$

7. Expand and simplify.
   a) $\cos\left(\frac{\pi}{6} + \frac{\pi}{4}\right)$
   b) $\cos\left(\frac{3\pi}{4} - \frac{\pi}{3}\right)$
   c) $\sin\left(\frac{\pi}{2} + \frac{\pi}{6}\right)$
   d) $\sin\left(\frac{5\pi}{6} - \frac{\pi}{6}\right)$

8. Find an exact expression for each trigonometric ratio.
   a) $\sin \frac{\pi}{12}$
   b) $\cos \frac{13\pi}{12}$
   c) $\cos \frac{7\pi}{12}$
   d) $\sin \frac{23\pi}{12}$

9. Given $\cos \theta = -\frac{2}{5}$ and θ is in Quadrant II, evaluate:
   a) $\sin\left(\theta + \frac{\pi}{6}\right)$
   b) $\cos\left(\theta - \frac{\pi}{4}\right)$.

10. If $\sin \alpha = \frac{3}{4}$ and $\cos \beta = -\frac{3}{5}$, where α and β are in Quadrant II, evaluate:
    a) $\cos (\alpha + \beta)$
    b) $\cos (\alpha - \beta)$
    c) $\sin (\alpha + \beta)$
    d) $\sin (\alpha - \beta)$.

The Simplon tunnel joining Italy and Switzerland was constructed by boring from both ends. When they met, in 1906, the engineers found that the two parts of the tunnel were exactly in line. How was this done? (See Section 9-7 *Example 4*.)

9-1 APPLYING TRIGONOMETRIC FUNCTIONS TO OTHER CIRCLES

In *Chapter 7* we defined the trigonometric functions of an angle in terms of the unit circle. In this section we will apply the definitions to other circles.

Let P be a point on a circle with centre O and radius r. Then P is on the terminal arm of an angle in standard position. We can determine the coordinates of P as follows.

Construct a unit circle with centre O, and let OP intersect this circle at Q. Then the coordinates of Q are $(\cos\theta, \sin\theta)$. Construct similar right triangles PMO and QNO as shown.

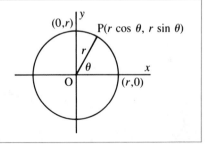

Then,

$$\frac{OM}{OP} = \frac{ON}{OQ} \quad \text{and} \quad \frac{MP}{OP} = \frac{NQ}{OQ}$$

$$\frac{OM}{r} = \frac{\cos\theta}{1} \qquad\qquad \frac{MP}{r} = \frac{\sin\theta}{1}$$

$$OM = r\cos\theta \qquad\qquad MP = r\sin\theta$$

Therefore, the coordinates of P are $(r\cos\theta, r\sin\theta)$.

> The coordinates of any point P on a circle with centre $(0, 0)$ and radius r are
> $(r\cos\theta, r\sin\theta)$
> where P is on the terminal arm of an angle θ in standard position.

Example 1. Point P is on a circle with radius 5 cm. If $\angle PON = 40°$, determine the coordinates of P to two decimal places.

Solution.
$$(r\cos\theta, r\sin\theta) = (5\cos40°, 5\sin40°)$$
$$\doteq (5 \times 0.766\,04, 5 \times 0.642\,79)$$
$$\doteq (3.83, 3.21)$$

The coordinates of P are approximately $(3.83, 3.21)$.

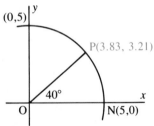

We can use the above result to find the angle between the positive *x*-axis and the line joining the origin to any point on the plane.

Example 2. The point P($-1, -2$) is on the terminal arm of an angle θ.

    a) Determine $\cos \theta$, $\sin \theta$, and $\tan \theta$ to five decimal places, where necessary.

    b) Determine θ to the nearest hundredth of a degree, where $0° \leqslant \theta \leqslant 360°$.

Solution.   a) Draw a diagram and construct a circle with centre $(0, 0)$ passing through P. According to the Pythagorean Theorem, the radius of this circle is

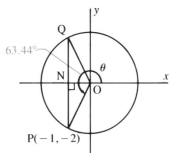

$$r = \sqrt{(-1)^2 + (-2)^2}$$
$$= \sqrt{5}$$

Then, the coordinates of P can be written as $(\sqrt{5} \cos \theta, \sqrt{5} \sin \theta)$. Comparing with the given coordinates, we find

$$\sqrt{5} \cos \theta = -1 \quad \text{and} \quad \sqrt{5} \sin \theta = -2$$
$$\cos \theta = -\frac{1}{\sqrt{5}} \qquad\qquad \sin \theta = -\frac{2}{\sqrt{5}}$$
$$\doteq -0.447\,21 \qquad\qquad\qquad \doteq -0.894\,43$$

Then, $\tan \theta = \dfrac{\sin \theta}{\cos \theta}$

$$= \frac{-\dfrac{2}{\sqrt{5}}}{-\dfrac{1}{\sqrt{5}}}$$
$$= 2$$

    b) To determine θ, use the fact that $\cos \theta = -0.447\,21$. Use the inverse cosine key on your calculator, in degree mode, to obtain $116.56°$. This is the angle corresponding to Q in the diagram above. The reference angle for both points P and Q is
$\angle \text{PON} = \angle \text{QON} = 180° - 116.56°$, or $63.44°$. Hence,
$\theta = 180° + 63.44°$, or $243.44°$.

In *Example 2b*, observe the importance of the diagram. Without the diagram we may have taken θ to be the angle determined by the calculator. We could also have used the sine or tangent values to determine θ.

If we had used $\sin \theta = -0.894\,43$ and the inverse sine key, we would have obtained $-63.44°$. The reference angle is again $63.44°$, and
$\theta = 180° + 63.44° = 243.44°$.

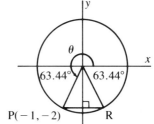

If we had used tan $\theta = 2$ and the inverse
tangent key, we would have obtained
63.44°. Again the reference angle is 63.44°
and $\theta = 243.44°$ as before.

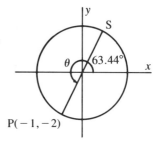

EXERCISES 9-1

Ⓑ

1. Point P is on a circle with radius 10 cm. Determine the coordinates of P to 2 decimal
   places if P is on the terminal arm of each angle in standard position.
   a) 20°   b) 55°   c) 86°   d) 113°   e) 148°   f) 175°
   g) 198°   h) 235°   i) 260°   j) 289°   k) 310°   l) 341°

2. Point P is on a circle with radius 10 cm. Determine the exact coordinates of P if
   P is on the terminal arm of each angle in standard position.
   a) 30°   b) 45°   c) 60°   d) 120°   e) 135°   f) 150°
   g) 210°   h) 225°   i) 240°   j) 300°   k) 315°   l) 330°

3. The point P(5,2) is on the terminal arm of an angle θ.
   a) Determine $\cos \theta$, $\sin \theta$, and $\tan \theta$ to 5 decimal places.
   b) Determine θ to the nearest hundredth of a degree.

4. Repeat *Exercise 3* for the following points.
   a) P($-3,1$)   b) P($-6,-4$)   c) P(4,-1)

5. Each point P is on the terminal arm of an angle θ. Determine θ to the nearest
   hundredth of a degree where $0° \leqslant \theta \leqslant 360°$.
   a) P(11,-6)   b) P($-5,-1$)   c) P($-4,2$)   d) P($-4,-5$)
   e) P(5,-3)   f) P(3,8)   g) P(0,3)   h) P($-4,0$)

6. We used the diagram on page 440 to show that the coordinates of P are
   ($r \cos \theta$, $r \sin \theta$). In this diagram observe that $r > 1$. Do you think that the
   reasoning is valid for $r < 1$? Explain your answer.

7. Use dilatations to show that the coordinates of a point P on a circle with radius r
   and centre O can be written as ($r \cos \theta$, $r \sin \theta$).

Ⓒ

8. Point P is on a circle with centre (0, 0) and radius 8 cm. If OP makes an angle of
   72° with the positive x-axis, determine the coordinates of P to 2 decimal places.

9. Point P is on a circle with centre (0, 0) and radius 6 cm. If the first coordinate of
   P is 4.2, determine the possible second coordinates of P to 2 decimal places.

10. On the coordinate grid, a vertical line is drawn through the point A(5,0). Point Q
    is located on this line such that $\angle QOA = 70°$.
    a) Determine the coordinates of Q to three decimal places.
    b) Find two other ways to solve part a).

9-2 TRIGONOMETRIC RATIOS AND RIGHT TRIANGLES

In the diagram (below left) $\triangle ABC$ is any right triangle in which AB is the hypotenuse and $\angle C = 90°$. Observe that side AC is *opposite* $\angle B$ and side BC is *adjacent* to $\angle B$.

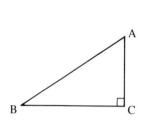 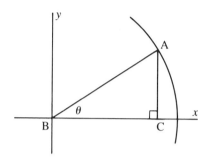

Suppose we draw a coordinate grid on this diagram (above right), with B as the origin and BC on the positive *x*-axis. Draw a circle with centre B and radius AB. Then $\triangle ABC$ lies in the first quadrant, and both coordinates of A are positive. These coordinates are $(AB \cos \theta, AB \sin \theta)$, and they can also be expressed as (BC, CA). Hence,

$$AB \cos \theta = BC \quad \text{and} \quad AB \sin \theta = CA \quad \text{Also, } \tan \theta = \frac{\sin \theta}{\cos \theta}$$
$$\cos \theta = \frac{BC}{AB} \qquad\qquad \sin \theta = \frac{CA}{AB} \qquad\qquad\qquad = \frac{CA}{BC}$$

These results show that if $0° \leq \theta \leq 90°$, the primary trigonometric functions can be expressed as ratios of the lengths of the sides of a right triangle.

$$\sin \theta = \frac{\text{opposite}}{\text{hypotenuse}}$$

$$\cos \theta = \frac{\text{adjacent}}{\text{hypotenuse}}$$

$$\tan \theta = \frac{\text{opposite}}{\text{adjacent}}$$

We can also express the reciprocal ratios in the same way.

$$\csc \theta = \frac{\text{hypotenuse}}{\text{opposite}} \qquad \sec \theta = \frac{\text{hypotenuse}}{\text{adjacent}} \qquad \cot \theta = \frac{\text{adjacent}}{\text{opposite}}$$

These trigonometric ratios can be applied to any right triangle, where $0° < \theta < 90°$.

Example 1. Write the six trigonometric ratios for the two acute angles in the right triangle with sides of length 12, 35, and 37 units.

Solution. Let α and β represent the acute angles.
From the definition of the trigonometric ratios

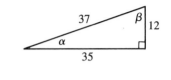

$$\sin \alpha = \frac{12}{37} \qquad \cos \alpha = \frac{35}{37} \qquad \tan \alpha = \frac{12}{35}$$

$$\csc \alpha = \frac{37}{12} \qquad \sec \alpha = \frac{37}{35} \qquad \cot \alpha = \frac{35}{12}$$

$$\sin \beta = \frac{35}{37} \qquad \cos \beta = \frac{12}{37} \qquad \tan \beta = \frac{35}{12}$$

$$\csc \beta = \frac{37}{35} \qquad \sec \beta = \frac{37}{12} \qquad \cot \beta = \frac{12}{35}$$

The next two examples show how we can use the trigonometric ratios to determine unknown sides and angles in right triangles.

Example 2. The top of a cliff has an angle of elevation of 36° when measured from a point 175 m from its base. How high is the cliff?

Solution. Let h metres represent the height of the cliff.

Then, $\tan 36° = \dfrac{h}{175}$

$\qquad\qquad h = 175 \tan 36°$

Use your calculator.

$h \doteq 127.144\ 94$

The cliff is about 127 m high.

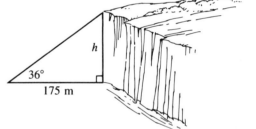

Example 3. A 35 m cable is attached to a TV tower at a height of 30 m. What is the angle of elevation of the cable?

Solution. Let θ be the angle of elevation.

Then, $\sin \theta = \dfrac{30}{35}$

Use your calculator.

$\theta \doteq 58.997\ 281$

The angle of elevation is about 59°.

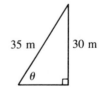

Example 4. Determine.　　a) cos (Arctan 1)　　　b) tan $\left(\text{Sin}^{-1}\frac{2}{3}\right)$

Solution.　　a) Recall that Arctan 1 means the angle whose tangent is 1, or 45°.
cos (Arctan 1) means the cosine of the angle whose tangent is 1.
That is, the cosine of 45°, or $\frac{1}{\sqrt{2}}$

Hence, cos (Arctan 1) $= \frac{1}{\sqrt{2}}$

　　b) Similarly, tan $\left(\text{Sin}^{-1}\frac{2}{3}\right)$ means the tangent of the angle whose sine
is $\frac{2}{3}$.

Draw the right △ABC shown in
which the hypotenuse has length
3 units and one leg has length 2 units.
Then, sin $A = \frac{2}{3}$ so ∠A is an angle
whose sine is $\frac{2}{3}$. We must find the
tangent of this angle. The length of
the other leg is $\sqrt{3^2 - 2^2} = \sqrt{5}$.
Hence, tan $A = \frac{2}{\sqrt{5}}$

Therefore, tan $\left(\text{Sin}^{-1}\frac{2}{3}\right) = \frac{2}{\sqrt{5}}$

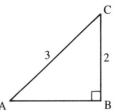

EXERCISES 9-2

(A)

1. Write the ratios sin θ, cos θ, and tan θ for each triangle.
　a)　　　　　　　　　　b)　　　　　　　　　　c)

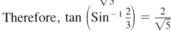

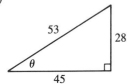

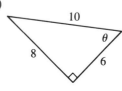

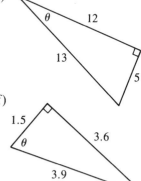

　d)　　　　　　　　　　e)　　　　　　　　　　f)

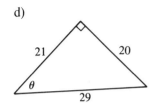

2. Write expressions for the six trigonometric ratios of each angle.
　a) ∠A　　　　　b) ∠B

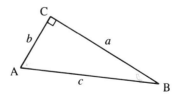

3. The lengths of the sides of △PQR are 9, 40, and 41 units. If ∠Q = 90°, find:
   a) the primary trigonometric ratios for the smallest angle
   b) the measures of the two smaller angles to 1 decimal place.

Ⓑ

4. Large shopping malls make use of ramps, steps, and escalators to move people from one level to another. Find the angle of inclination to the nearest degree of each conveyor.
   a) ramp   b) steps   c) escalator

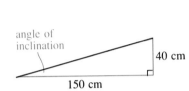
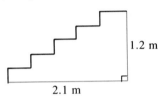
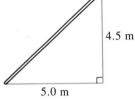

5. A wheelchair ramp (below left) is 4.2 m long and rises 0.7 m. What is its angle of inclination to 1 decimal place?

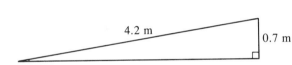
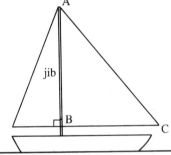

6. The guy wire for a jib sail (above right) is 3.7 m in length. It is attached at point A. The foot of the guy wire is 1.1 m from the mast AB. What is the angle of elevation of the guy wire to 1 decimal place?

7. In *Exercise 6*, the mast AB is 3.53 m long and the boom BC is 3.20 m. Find the measure of ∠C to 1 decimal place.

8. Determine.
   a) $\sin(\text{Arctan } 1)$ b) $\cos\left(\text{Sin}^{-1}\frac{1}{2}\right)$ c) $\tan\left(\text{Cos}^{-1}\frac{1}{2}\right)$ d) $\cos\left(\text{Tan}^{-1}\frac{\sqrt{3}}{2}\right)$
   e) $\tan\left(\text{Cos}^{-1}\frac{3}{4}\right)$ f) $\cos\left(\text{Arcsin }\frac{4}{5}\right)$ g) $\sin\left(\text{Tan}^{-1}\frac{5}{3}\right)$ h) $\tan(\text{Arcsin } 0.25)$

Ⓒ

9. Determine each value, and compare your results with *Exercise 8*.
   a) $\sin(\text{Arctan } -1)$ b) $\cos\left(\text{Sin}^{-1}-\frac{1}{2}\right)$ c) $\tan\left(\text{Cos}^{-1}-\frac{1}{2}\right)$
   d) $\cos\left(\text{Tan}^{-1}-\frac{\sqrt{3}}{2}\right)$ e) $\tan\left(\text{Cos}^{-1}-\frac{3}{4}\right)$ f) $\cos\left(\text{Arcsin }-\frac{4}{5}\right)$

10. Find the measures of the acute angles to 1 decimal place in a right triangle if its sides have lengths a, $a + d$, $a + 2d$.

11. Let $P(x,y)$ be any point on a circle with centre O and radius r, corresponding to an angle θ in standard position. The circle intersects the x-axis at A(r,0) and C($-r$,0).
    a) Express the lengths of AP and CP as functions of r and θ.
    b) Check the results of part a) when $\theta = 0°$, 90°, 180°, and 270°.

An 8 cm by 8 cm square is cut into 4 pieces, as shown. The pieces are then rearranged to form a 5 cm by 13 cm rectangle.
a) Are the areas of the figures equal?   b) Explain where the error is.

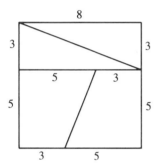
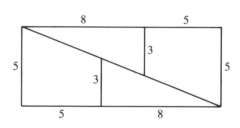

Identities for sin 2θ, cos 2θ, and tan 2θ can be established using the diagram of the unit circle shown. Since $\triangle$ONP is a right triangle with hypotenuse 1 unit, then ON = cos 2θ and PN = sin 2θ. Similarly, since $\triangle$MCO is a right triangle with hypotenuse 1 unit, then CM = cos θ and MO = sin θ.

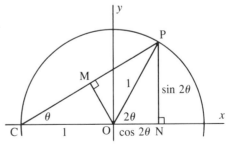

1. If $\angle$MCO $= \theta$, explain why $\angle$PON $= 2\theta$.

2. Write two different expressions for the length of CP. Use the results to establish an identity for cos 2θ in terms of cos θ.

3. Use the results of *Question 2* to establish identities for sin 2θ and tan 2θ in terms of functions of θ.

9-3 SOLVING RIGHT TRIANGLES

We have learned how to find the height of a cliff given the angle of inclination of the cliff at a given distance. This amounted to finding the length of one side of a right triangle given the length of another side and the measure of an angle. Finding all the unknown sides and angles of a triangle is called *solving the triangle*. We can solve a right triangle if we know either:

● the lengths of any two sides, or
● the length of one side and the measure of an acute angle.

    The following example shows how we solve a right triangle given the lengths of two sides.

Example 1. Solve △ABC given AB = 25, AC = 18, and ∠C = 90°. Give the answers to 1 decimal place.

Solution.   From the Pythagorean Theorem

$$BC^2 = AB^2 - AC^2$$
$$= 25^2 - 18^2$$
$$= 301$$
$$BC = \sqrt{301}$$
$$\doteq 17.349$$

To find ∠A, we write $\cos A = \dfrac{18}{25}$ Use a calculator.

$$\angle A \doteq 43.9°$$

Since ∠A + ∠B = 90°, then ∠B ≐ 46.1°
We summarize these results in a table.

AB	AC	BC	∠A	∠B	∠C
25	18	17.3	43.9°	46.1°	90°

    In *Example 1*, we used the Pythagorean Theorem to calculate the unknown side, and then the ratio of any two sides to determine an unknown angle. The next example shows how we can solve a right triangle given only the length of one side and the measure of an acute angle.

Example 2. Solve △DEF given that ∠E = 90°, ∠D = 37°, and EF = 12. Give the answers to the nearest whole number.

Solution.   By definition of the tangent and sine ratios

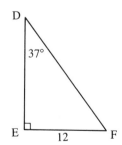

$$\tan 37° = \frac{12}{DE}$$

$$DE = \frac{12}{\tan 37°}$$ Use a calculator.

$$\doteq 15.92$$

$$\sin 37° = \frac{12}{\text{DF}}$$

$$\text{DF} = \frac{12}{\sin 37°}$$

$$\doteq 19.94$$

Since $\angle D = 37°$, then $\angle F = 90° - 37°$, or $53°$
We summarize these results in a table.

EF	DE	DF	$\angle D$	$\angle E$	$\angle F$
12	16	20	37°	90°	53°

In *Example 2*, once we found DE we could have used the fact that EF = 12 and applied the Pythagorean Theorem to calculate DF.

The next examples show how we can find all the primary trigonometric ratios, given only one of them.

Example 3. If $\tan \theta = \dfrac{5}{12}$, find $\cos \theta$ and $\sin \theta$.

Solution. Sketch a right triangle with shorter sides 5 and 12, and hypotenuse h. Label the angle θ.
Using the Pythagorean Theorem
$$h = \sqrt{5^2 + 12^2}$$
$$= \sqrt{169}$$
$$= 13$$
Then, $\cos \theta = \dfrac{12}{13}$ and $\sin \theta = \dfrac{5}{13}$

Example 4. If $\sin \theta = \dfrac{a}{b}$, find expressions for $\cos \theta$ and $\tan \theta$.

Solution. Sketch a right triangle with side a opposite θ, and hypotenuse b.
It follows from the Pythagorean Theorem that the third side has length $\sqrt{b^2 - a^2}$.
So, $\cos \theta = \dfrac{\sqrt{b^2 - a^2}}{b}$ and

$$\tan \theta = \dfrac{a}{\sqrt{b^2 - a^2}}$$

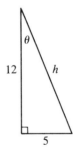

EXERCISES 9-3

Ⓐ

1. Solve each triangle. Give the answers to 1 decimal place.

a)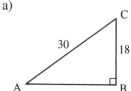

b)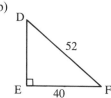

c)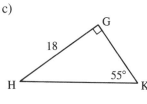

d)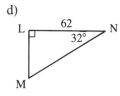

e)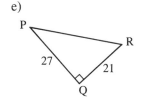

f)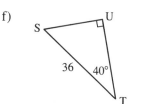

2. Solve △XYZ if ∠Y = 90° and:
   a) XY = 24, XZ = 35
   c) XZ = 51, YZ = 13
   e) YZ = 32, ∠X = 64°
   b) XY = 16, ∠X = 27°
   d) XZ = 72, ∠Z = 52°
   f) XY = 45, YZ = 20.
   Give the answers to 1 decimal place.

3. Find the other two primary trigonometric ratios for each value of θ.

   a) $\sin \theta = \dfrac{8}{17}$ b) $\cos \theta = \dfrac{7}{25}$ c) $\tan \theta = \dfrac{20}{21}$

   d) $\sin \theta = \dfrac{15}{32}$ e) $\cos \theta = \dfrac{19}{23}$ f) $\tan \theta = \dfrac{43}{112}$

Ⓑ

4. Find expressions for the other primary trigonometric ratios for each value of θ.

   a) $\sin \theta = \dfrac{p}{q}$ b) $\cos \theta = \dfrac{a}{a + 2}$ c) $\tan \theta = \dfrac{x - y}{x + y}$

5. At a point 28 m away, the angle of elevation of a building is 65° (below left).
   a) How tall is the building?
   b) How far is the observer's eye from the top of the building?

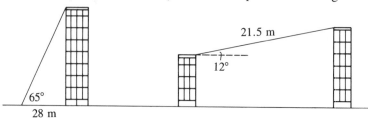

6. A tightrope walker attaches a cable to the roofs of two adjacent buildings (above right). The cable is 21.5 m long and the angle of inclination is 12°.
   a) How far apart are the buildings?   b) What is the difference in their heights?

7. A rectangle has length 10 cm and width 6 cm. Find the acute angle to the nearest degree between the diagonals.

8. The length of rectangle ABCD is three times its width. Points M and N are the midpoints of the longer sides AB and DC.
   a) Find ∠MAN.
   b) If P is the midpoint of AD, find ∠MPN.
   Give the answers to the nearest degree.

9. A funnel is placed in a glass, as shown. If the glass is 14.5 cm tall and 7.6 cm in diameter, how high is the vertex of the funnel above the bottom of the glass?

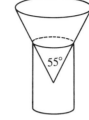

10. Prior to 1982, visitors to the observation deck of the Peace Tower in Ottawa had to ride two elevators. The Memorial Chamber at the base of the tower made a vertical assent impossible. A new elevator system carries visitors up the first 24.2 m by travelling a path inclined at 10° to the vertical. It then rises vertically for the balance of the trip.
    a) How long is the elevator shaft that runs on the incline?
    b) By how far is the elevator displaced horizontally by the incline?
    c) What is the slope of the incline to 2 decimal places?

11. Two office towers are 31.7 m apart. From the shorter one, the angle of elevation to the top of the other is 27.5°, while the angle of depression to the base is 78.2°. Find the height of each tower.

©—

12. The diagram (below left) shows how the ancient Greeks constructed line segments of lengths $\sqrt{2}, \sqrt{3}, \sqrt{4}, \sqrt{5}, \ldots$ As the process continues, the triangles turn about point A, as shown.
    a) Find these angles to 1 decimal place.
       i)   ∠CAB   ii) ∠DAB   iii) ∠EAB   iv) ∠FAB
    b) How many triangles can be drawn without overlapping?

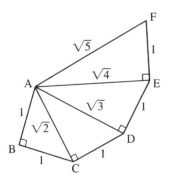

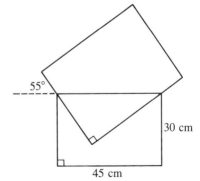

13. A box is resting inside a second box (above right). How high is the lowest corner of the first box above the bottom of the second box?

MATHEMATICS AROUND US

The Spiral Tunnels

When British Columbia entered into the Canadian Confederation on July 20, 1871, the federal government agreed to build a railway to link the province with the rest of Canada. The railway was completed in 1885. The track through the mountains was kept to a maximum gradient of 2.2% (a rise of 2.2 m in 100 m of track) with one exception — the section of track between Hector, B.C. and Field, B.C. There, a rise of 297 m in only 6.6 km was necessary. This section became known as Big Hill. Taking trains up and down this hill required additional locomotives, and on the downhill run there was always the danger of runaway trains.

The only way to reduce the gradient of Big Hill to 2.2% was to lengthen the track between the two towns. This was done in 1907–1909 when a pair of spiral tunnels was built into the mountains. These tunnels are the only ones of their kind in North America. As many as 15 trains a day pass through the tunnels in each direction. The long freight trains can be seen coming out of a tunnel before they have finished going in.

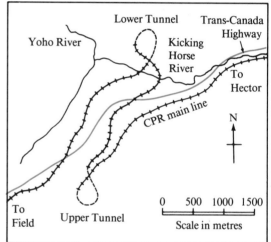

QUESTIONS

1. What was the gradient of the track on Big Hill?

2. By how much did the track have to be lengthened to reduce the gradient to 2.2%?

3. The train in the photograph is passing through Lower Tunnel, which is about 880 m long and curves through 288°. Each car in the train is about 12.2 m long.
   a) How many cars are in the train?
   b) What is the difference in height between the two sections of track shown in the photograph?
   c) If the speed of the train is 40.5 km/h, how long does it take to pass completely through the tunnel?

4. What is the radius of the spiral?

9-4 APPLICATIONS OF THE TRIGONOMETRIC RATIOS

In *Section 9-3* we learned how to solve a right triangle given either:
- the lengths of any two sides; or
- the length of one side and the measure of an acute angle.

In this section we apply these techniques to the solutions of various problems. In each case we solve for an unknown side or an unknown angle rather than solving for all sides and angles.

Example 1. The Great Pyramid in Egypt has a square base of side length 230 m. If the angle of elevation of the sides is 52°, what is the height of the pyramid?

Solution. Let h metres represent the height.
Then, in $\triangle ABC$

$$\frac{h}{115} = \tan 52°$$

$$h = 115 \tan 52°$$

$$\doteq 147.193\ 29$$

The pyramid is about 147 m high.

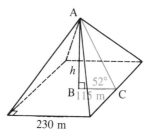

Example 2. A fireman's ladder is inclined at an angle of 58°. The ladder is 10 m long measured from the foot to the top rung, where a fireman is standing. How high is the fireman above the ground?

Solution. Let h metres represent the height of the top rung.

Then, $\dfrac{h}{10} = \sin 58°$

$$h = 10 \sin 58°$$

$$\doteq 8.48$$

The fireman is about 8.5 m above the ground.

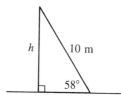

Example 3. The world's longest suspension bridge is across the Humber Estuary in England. The towers of this bridge reach about 135 m above the level of the bridge. The angles of elevation of the towers seen from the centre of the bridge and either end are 10.80° and 18.65° respectively. How long is the Humber Estuary Bridge?

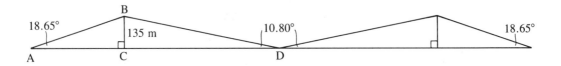

Solution. The length of the bridge is double the length of AD.

$$\frac{135}{AC} = \tan 18.65° \qquad \text{and} \qquad \frac{135}{CD} = \tan 10.8°$$

$$AC = \frac{135}{\tan 18.65°} \qquad\qquad CD = \frac{135}{\tan 10.8°}$$

$$AD = AC + CD$$

$$= \frac{135}{\tan 18.65°} + \frac{135}{\tan 10.8°}$$

$$= 135\left(\frac{1}{\tan 18.65°} + \frac{1}{\tan 10.8°}\right)$$

$$\doteq 1107.68$$

The length of the bridge is about 2(1107.68 m), or about 2215 m.

EXERCISES 9-4

(B)

1. When spraying a crop with pesticides, a farmer uses a boom sprayer pulled by a tractor. The nozzles are 50 cm apart and spray at an angle of 70°. How high should the sprayer be set above the top of the crop to provide an even distribution of the pesticide?

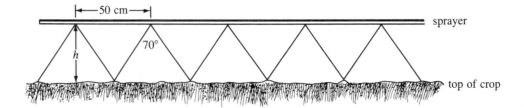

2. A hemispherical bowl of diameter 20 cm contains some liquid with a depth of 4 cm. Through what angle with the horizontal may the bowl be tipped before the liquid begins to spill out?

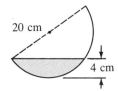

3. The Calgary Tower is 190 m high and casts a shadow 84 m long. Find the angle to the nearest degree which the sun's rays make with the ground.

4. A television antenna is supported by a guy wire connected to the mast. The angle of elevation of the guy wire is 39°, and the angle of elevation of the top of the antenna is 53°. If the guy wire is fixed to the ground 7 m from the base of the mast, find to the nearest tenth of a metre:
   a) the height of the antenna
   b) the distance from the top of the antenna to where the guy wire is connected.

5. The picture tube in a color television set is 50 cm wide, and has a deflection angle of 90° (below left).
   a) Calculate the least possible depth of a cabinet that could hold the tube.
   b) The manufacturer advertises that by increasing the deflection angle to 100°, the cabinet can be made smaller. Find the decrease in depth of the cabinet allowed by the larger deflection angle.

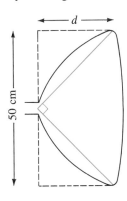
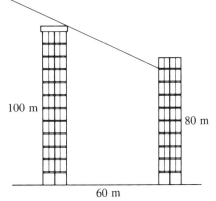

6. Two apartment buildings 100 m and 80 m high are 60 m apart (above right). The sun casts a shadow of the 100 m building on the 80 m building.
   a) If the angle of elevation of the sun is 22°, calculate the height of the shadow on the 80 m building to the nearest metre.
   b) If the angle of elevation of the sun changes at a constant rate of 15°/h, calculate the total time that the 80 m building is partly in the shadow of the 100 m building.

7. Donna measured the angle of elevation of a church steeple and found it to be 10°. Then she walked 100 m towards the steeple and measured the angle of elevation again; this time it was 20°. Find the height of the steeple, assuming that the ground is level.

8. Trigonometry can be used to find the circumference of the Earth. From the top of a mountain 5 km high the angle between the horizon and the true vertical is 87.73°. Use the diagram to calculate:
   a) the radius
   b) the circumference of the Earth.

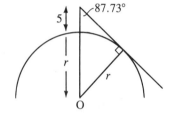

9. Assume that the method of *Exercise 8* is used with measurements taken from a satellite at an altitude of 200 km. If the Earth's radius is 6370 km, find the angle between the horizon and the true vertical to 2 decimal places.

10. Angle parking allows more cars to park along a given street than does parallel parking. However, the cars use more of the street width when angle parked.

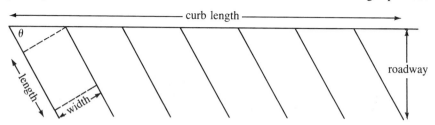

   a) If each car requires a space 2.7 m wide, how much curb length would be required to park 20 cars if θ is: i) 30° ii) 50° iii) 60°?
   b) If 20 cars had to be parked in 60 m of curb length, what would be the value of θ?
   c) If each car requires a space 6.5 m long, how much of the roadway is given up for parking if θ is: i) 30° ii) 50° iii) 60°?

---

11. The measure of angle θ in *Exercise 10* depends upon the amount of roadway K that can be used for parking. The relationship between θ and K is given by $\dfrac{2.7 \cos \theta}{K - 6.5 \sin \theta} = 1$. If $K = 6.9$ m, find the value of θ to the nearest degree.

12. On a sunny day, the shadows of stationary objects move slowly across the ground. This is caused by the apparent motion of the sun across the sky, due to the rotation of the Earth. Assume that the sun rises due east at 6 A.M., and sets due west at 6 P.M.
   a) Find the length of the shadow of a 150 m building at:
      i) 8 A.M.   ii) 10:30 A.M.   iii) 2 P.M.   iv) 5:30 P.M.
   b) At what times during the day is the shadow of a 150-m building 90 m long?
   c) Directly to the west of a 400-m building there is a 300-m building a distance of 200 m away. Calculate the total time during the day that the space between the buildings is entirely in shadow.

13. The top of a cylindrical oil storage tank, 55.3 m high and 28.4 m in diameter, is reached by a spiral stairway that circles the tank exactly once. Calculate the angle of inclination of the stairway to the nearest degree.

MATHEMATICS AROUND US

Designing Windows to Save Energy

One energy-saving idea is to design houses with recessed windows on the south side facing the sun. Sunlight will enter the window in winter when the sun's angle is low, but it will be completely blocked in the summer when its angle is much higher. In the northern hemisphere the highest angle of elevation of the sun occurs at noon around June 21. At that time the angle of elevation, in degrees, is $l + 23.5$, where l is the latitude of the location.

The diagram shows a particular window with a height of 1.00 m. The window is recessed so that the sun's rays are completely blocked when the sun is at its highest elevation in the summer. In the winter, when the sun is at its lowest elevation, much of the window is still exposed to the sun. The depth of the recess depends on the latitude of the location.

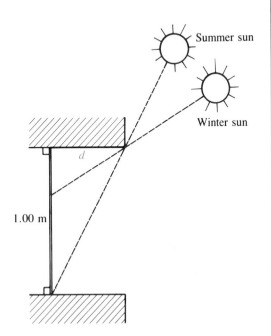

QUESTIONS

1. Express the depth d metres of the recess as a function of the latitude l.

2. Draw a graph of d against l.

3. Determine the value of d for your latitude, for a window 1.00 m high.

4. Around December 21 in the northern hemisphere, the highest angle of elevation, in degrees, is $l - 23.5$. For your latitude, determine the percent of the window that is in sunlight at that time.

Extend the Problem

"(No) problem whatever is completely exhausted. There remains always something to do; with sufficient study and penetration, we can improve any solution, and, in any case, we can always improve our understanding of the solution."

George Polya

George Polya, a former professor of mathematics at Stanford University, gained worldwide recognition for his skills as a teacher. Polya is suggesting that when we have solved a problem, we may also think of related problems. These may often be obtained by generalizing some condition of the problem, or changing some part of the problem to make a new problem. For example, some of the ways in which the Pythagorean Theorem can be extended are given below.

The Pythagorean Theorem states that the areas of the squares constructed on the sides of a right triangle are related:

area of the
square on the $=$ the squares on the
hypotenuse

sum of the areas of
the squares on the
other two sides

$$a^2 = b^2 + c^2$$

First extension
The lengths of the sides of a right triangle satisfy the equation $x^2 + y^2 = z^2$. Find integral values of x, y, and z which satisfy this equation. These are called *Pythagorean triples*.

Second extension

Can you find integral values of x, y, and z which satisfy equations such as these?

$$x^2 + y^2 + z^2 = w^2 \qquad x^3 + y^3 + z^3 = w^3$$
$$x^2 + y^2 = z^2 + w^2 \qquad x^3 + y^3 = z^3 + w^3$$
$$x^{-1} + y^{-1} = z^{-1} \qquad x^{\frac{1}{2}} + y^{\frac{1}{2}} = z^{\frac{1}{2}}$$

Third extension

The Pythagorean Theorem can be used to find the distance between any two points in the plane. How could you find the distance between any two points in three dimensions?

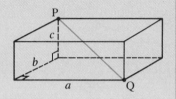

Fourth extension

The Pythagorean Theorem relates the lengths of the sides of any right triangle. If $\triangle ABC$ is not a right triangle, how are the lengths of its sides related?

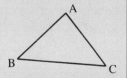

Fifth extension

If figures other than squares are constructed on the sides of a right triangle, does the area relation still hold for these figures?

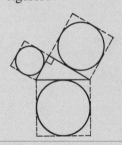
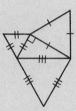
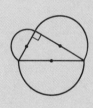

PROBLEMS

(B)

1. The Earth's equatorial diameter is 12 756 km. The polar diameter is about 0.33% less than this. What is the polar diameter?

2. ABCD is a square with sides 6 cm. Points M and N are located on sides AD and AB respectively, such that MC = NC and ∠MCN = 60°. Determine the length of MN.

3. Let k be a positive rational number. Prove that $k + \frac{1}{k}$ is a natural number if, and only if, $k = 1$.

4. A square with sides of length s is given. A regular octagon is formed by cutting off four corner isosceles triangles as shown. Express x as a function of s.

5. An equilateral triangle with sides of length s is divided into three regions with equal areas by two segments of lengths x and y parallel to one of the sides. Find equations expressing x and y as functions of s.

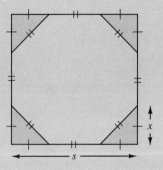

(C)

6. If the sides of a triangle are in the ratio 3 : 4 : 5, the triangle is right-angled. Find out something about a triangle whose sides are in the ratio 4 : 5 : 6, and prove your result.

7. Two vertices of an equilateral triangle are A(1, 8) and B(5, 2). Find the possible coordinates of the third vertex.

8. Four quarter circles are inscribed in a square with sides of 6 cm using the vertices as centres. Calculate the areas of the regions x, y, and z.

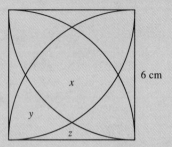

(D)

9. A triangle is inscribed in a circle, and P is any point on the circle. Prove that the distance from P to the farthest vertex of the triangle is equal to the sum of its distances to the other two vertices if, and only if, the triangle is equilateral.

9-5 THE AREA OF A TRIANGLE

The area A of a triangle can be found using the formula $A = \frac{1}{2}bh$ where b is the base and h is the height, or altitude. If the height of the triangle is not known, the sine ratio can be used to find the area.

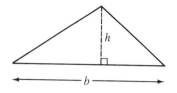

Example 1. Find the area of $\triangle XYZ$ if $\angle Y = 55°$, $YZ = 23$ cm, and $XY = 18$ cm.

Solution. Draw the altitude XW, perpendicular to YZ.
To find the length of XW, use right $\triangle XYW$.

$$\sin 55° = \frac{XW}{XY}$$

$$XW = XY \sin 55°$$

$$\text{Area of } \triangle XYZ = \frac{1}{2}(\text{base})(\text{height})$$

$$= \frac{1}{2}(YZ)(XW)$$

$$= \frac{1}{2}(YZ)(XY \sin 55°)$$

$$= \frac{1}{2}(23)(18 \sin 55°)$$

$$\doteq 169.6$$

The area of $\triangle XYZ$ is approximately 170 cm².

In an obtuse triangle, this same method can be used to find the area.

Example 2. Find the area of $\triangle PQR$ if $\angle Q = 125°$, $QR = 23$ cm, and $PQ = 18$ cm.

Solution. Draw the altitude PS, perpendicular to RQ extended.
To find the length of PS, use right $\triangle PSQ$, where $\angle PQS = 180° - 125°$.

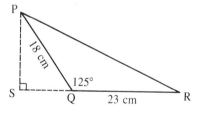

$$\sin (180° - 125°) = \frac{PS}{PQ}$$

$$PS = PQ \sin (180° - 125°)$$

$$= PQ \sin 125°$$

$$\text{Area } \triangle PQR = \frac{1}{2}(\text{base})(\text{height})$$

$$= \frac{1}{2}(QR)(PS)$$

$$= \frac{1}{2}(QR)(PQ \sin 125°)$$

$$= \frac{1}{2}(23)(18 \sin 125°)$$

$$\doteq 169.6$$

The area of $\triangle PQR$ is approximately 170 cm².

We can extend the method of *Examples 1* and *2*, to find the area of any triangle.
In each △ABC,

Area $= \frac{1}{2}bh$

$= \frac{1}{2}b(a \sin C)$

$= \frac{1}{2}ab \sin C$

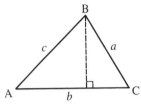
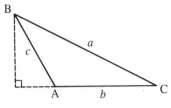

If two sides *b* and *c*, and the contained angle *A* of △ABC are known, then

$$\text{Area } \triangle ABC = \frac{1}{2}bc \sin A$$

EXERCISES 9-5

Ⓐ

1. Use the sine ratio to find an expression for the length of the altitude of each triangle.

   a)   b)   c)   d)

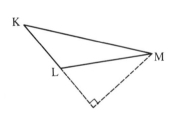

Ⓑ

2. Find the area of each triangle.

   a)   b)   c)

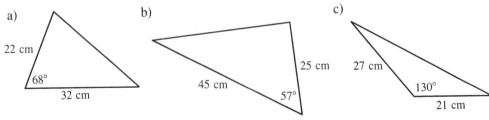

3. Find the area of each △ABC.
   a) ∠B = 28°, AB = 12, BC = 15
   b) ∠C = 52°, BC = 48, AC = 18
   c) ∠A = 110°, AB = 35, AC = 20
   d) ∠B = 140°, BC = 65, AB = 25
   e) ∠C = 81°, BC = 14.5, AC = 6.5

4. Find the area of each triangle.

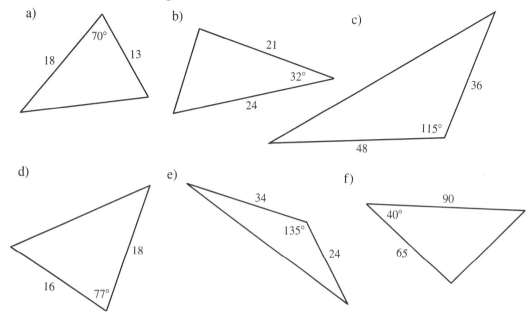

5. Two sides of a triangular field have lengths 85 m and 63 m. The angle between these sides is 62.3°. Find the area of the field.

6. Find the area of an equilateral triangle with side length 21.6 cm.

7. A triangular sail is made to fit along the full length of the 4.20 m mast and the 2.85 m boom. The angle between the boom and the mast is 86.5°. How much material is used in the sail?

8. Find the area of a parallelogram with sides of length 23.7 cm and 15.2 cm, and one angle of 105.4°.

9. The sail on a windsurfer has the dimensions shown (below left). If the "window" is made of clear plastic, how much nylon is required to make the sail?

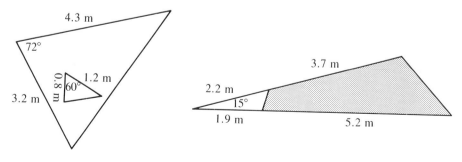

10. Find the area of the shaded part of the triangle (above right).

11. A triangular section of a lawn in a park is to be covered with sod. Two sides of the triangle measure 28.3 m and 19.6 m. The angle between these sides is 115°.
    a) Find the area to be covered in sod.
    b) If sod costs $2.75/m², how much will it cost to buy sufficient sod?

12. A piece of carpet has the shape of a parallelogram with sides 3.2 m and 2.1 m. The angle between these sides is 81°. If carpet remnants are priced at $7.50/m², how much does this piece cost?

13. The base of a tetrahedron is an equilateral triangle with sides 12 cm. The faces of the tetrahedron are isosceles triangles with equal sides 18 cm and vertical angle 39°. Find the surface area of the tetrahedron.

14. a) Find the area of the cedar deck shown in the diagram (below left).
    b) If the cedar costs $52.50/m², how much did the deck cost?

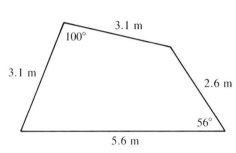

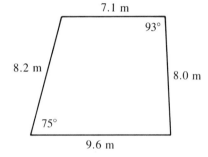

15. The foundation of a condominium unit is shown in the diagram (above right). Find its area.

16. The end wall of a hotel lobby is to be covered with wallpaper costing $8.25/m². Find the cost of the wallpaper.

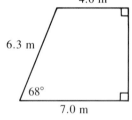

17. Two sides of a triangle have lengths 28.2 cm and 18.8 cm. The angle between them is 41.5°. Find the lengths of the sides of an isosceles right triangle with the same area.

---

18. The edges of a pyramid with a square base are 15 cm long. Find:
    a) the surface area
    b) the volume
    c) the angle that each edge makes with the base
    d) the angle that each face makes with the base.

19. The diagonals of a quadrilateral are a and b units in length, with angle θ between them. Prove that the area of the quadrilateral is $\frac{1}{2}ab \sin \theta$.

9-6 THE LAW OF COSINES

Previously in this chapter we solved right triangles given the lengths of any two sides, or the length of one side and the measure of an acute angle. In this section, we will study the Law of Cosines, which will enable us to solve certain oblique triangles; that is, triangles that contain no right angles.

A triangle is uniquely determined by two sides and the contained angle. The following example shows how to calculate the remaining side.

Example 1. In $\triangle ABC$, $AB = 8$, $AC = 5$, and $\angle A = 35°$; find the length of BC to 1 decimal place.

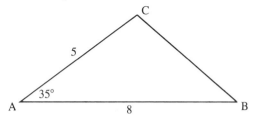

Solution. Construct CN perpendicular to AB and let $BC = a$, $CN = h$, and $AN = x$.

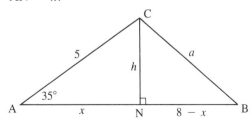

Apply the Pythagorean Theorem to $\triangle CNB$ and $\triangle CNA$.

$a^2 = h^2 + (8 - x)^2 \ldots ①$

$5^2 = h^2 + x^2 \ldots ②$

Subtract ② from ①.

$a^2 - 5^2 = 64 - 16x$

$\quad a^2 = 89 - 16x$

$\qquad = 89 - 16(5 \cos 35°)$ Since $\frac{x}{5} = \cos 35°$

$\quad a^2 \doteq 23.4678$

$\qquad a \doteq 4.844$

The length of BC is approximately 4.8.

Now we consider the general cases of $\triangle ABC$ where $\angle A$ is acute and where $\angle A$ is obtuse.

In both cases, construct CN perpendicular to AB or AB extended; let CN = h, and AN = x. Apply the Pythagorean Theorem to △CNB and △CNA.

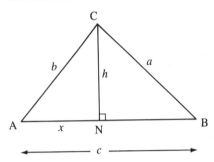

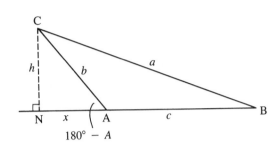

For the acute triangle
$$a^2 = h^2 + (c - x)^2$$
$$b^2 = h^2 + x^2$$
Subtract.
$$a^2 - b^2 = c^2 - 2cx$$
$$a^2 = b^2 + c^2 - 2cx$$
$$= b^2 + c^2 - 2c(b \cos A)$$
$$= b^2 + c^2 - 2bc \cos A$$

For the obtuse triangle
$$a^2 = h^2 + (c + x)^2$$
$$b^2 = h^2 + x^2$$
Subtract.
$$a^2 - b^2 = c^2 + 2cx$$
$$a^2 = b^2 + c^2 + 2cx$$
$$= b^2 + c^2 + 2c(b \cos (180° - A))$$
$$= b^2 + c^2 - 2bc \cos A$$

In both cases, $a^2 = b^2 + c^2 - 2bc \cos A$

Similarly, by letting BN = x we can prove that $b^2 = a^2 + c^2 - 2ac \cos B$, and by constructing a perpendicular from A to BC we can prove that $c^2 = a^2 + b^2 - 2ab \cos C$.

The Law of Cosines
In any △ABC
$$a^2 = b^2 + c^2 - 2bc \cos A$$
$$b^2 = a^2 + c^2 - 2ac \cos B$$
$$c^2 = a^2 + b^2 - 2ab \cos C$$

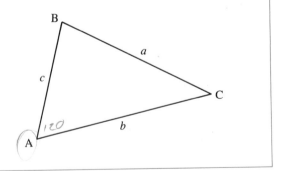

We can use the Law of Cosines to find the third side of a triangle when two sides and the contained angle are given.

Example 2.   In △ABC, AB = 10 and AC = 8; find the length of BC to 1 decimal place for each value of ∠A.
a) ∠A = 50°   b) ∠A = 130°

Solution. In each case we use the Law of Cosines in the form
$a^2 = b^2 + c^2 - 2bc \cos A$.

a)

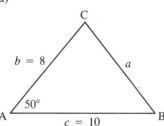

b)

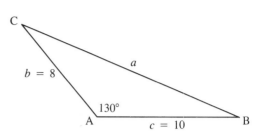

For the acute triangle

$a^2 = 8^2 + 10^2 - 2(8)(10)(\cos 50°)$
$\doteq 61.153\ 982$
$a \doteq 7.8201$

The length of BC is about 7.8.

For the obtuse triangle

$a^2 = 8^2 + 10^2 - 2(8)(10)(\cos 130°)$
$\doteq 266.846\ 02$
$a \doteq 16.3354$

The length of BC is about 16.3.

Example 2 and the diagrams below suggest that the Pythagorean Theorem is a special case of the Law of Cosines.

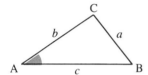
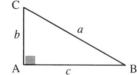
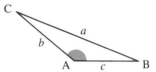

If $\angle A < 90°$, $\cos A > 0$
and $a^2 < b^2 + c^2$

If $\angle A = 90°$, $\cos A = 0$
and $a^2 = b^2 + c^2$

If $\angle A > 90°$, $\cos A < 0$
and $a^2 > b^2 + c^2$

The Law of Cosines can also be used to find any angle of a triangle when its three sides are given.

Example 3. In $\triangle PQR$, $PQ = 7$, $QR = 8$, and $RP = 10$; find the measure of $\angle R$ to the nearest degree.

Solution. To find $\angle R$, use the Law of Cosines in this form.

$$r^2 = p^2 + q^2 - 2pq \cos R$$
$$7^2 = 8^2 + 10^2 - 2(8)(10) \cos R$$
$$49 = 164 - 160 \cos R$$
$$160 \cos R = 115$$
$$\cos R = \frac{115}{160}$$
$$\angle R \doteq 44.0486$$

To the nearest degree, $\angle R = 44°$

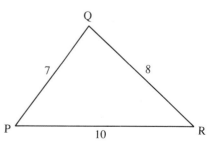

Example 4. A tunnel is to be built through a hill to connect points A and B in a straight line. Point C is chosen so that it is visible from both A and B, and measurement shows that $\angle C = 63°$, $CA = 2$ km, and $CB = 5$ km.
Find the length of AB to 2 decimal places and the measure of $\angle A$ to 1 decimal place.

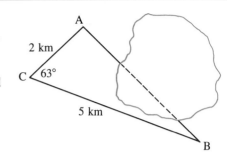

Solution. By the Law of Cosines
$$c^2 = a^2 + b^2 - 2ab \cos C$$
$$= 5^2 + 2^2 - 2(5)(2)(\cos 63°)$$
$$\doteq 19.920\ 19$$
$$c \doteq 4.4632$$
The distance from A to B, through the hill, is approximately 4.46 km.
To find $\angle A$, we use the Law of Cosines in this form.
$$a^2 = b^2 + c^2 - 2bc \cos A$$
Substitute the given values of a and b, and the (non-rounded) values of c and c^2.
$$5^2 \doteq 2^2 + 19.920\ 19 - 2(2)(4.463\ 204) \cos A$$
Solve for $\cos A$.
$$\cos A \doteq -\frac{1.079\ 81}{17.853\ 216}$$
Since $\cos A$ is negative, $\angle A$ is obtuse.
$$\angle A \doteq 93.5°$$

EXERCISES 9-6

(A)

1) Find the third side of each triangle to 1 decimal place.

a)

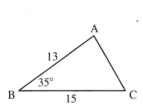

b)

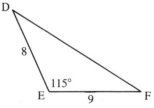

c)

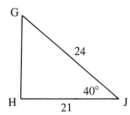

2) Use the given information to find the third side of $\triangle ABC$ to 1 decimal place.
a) $\angle B = 42°$, $a = 6$, $c = 4$
b) $\angle A = 130°$, $b = 15$, $c = 11$
c) $\angle C = 95°$, $a = 18$, $b = 27$
d) $\angle B = 28°$, $a = 17$, $c = 15$
e) $\angle A = 105°$, $b = 7.4$, $c = 10.2$

3. Find θ to 1 decimal place.

a)

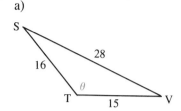

b)

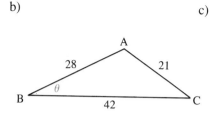

c)

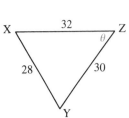

4. For a triangle with sides of the given lengths, find to 1 decimal place the measure of: i) the smallest angle   ii) the largest angle.

a) 7, 9, 14   b) 6, 11, 15   c) 23, 31, 52
d) 28, 45, 53   e) 8.3, 9.7, 12.5   f) 14, 55, 61

(B)

5. Use the given information to find the third side of $\triangle PQR$.

a) $\angle Q = 72°$, $p = 4.3$, $r = 2.9$
b) $\angle P = 112°$, $PQ = 25$, $PR = 33$
c) $\angle R = 98°$, $PR = 17.4$, $QR = 21.3$

6. A roof truss (below left) is to span 8.2 m. One piece of the truss is 6.8 m in length and set at an angle of 35°. How long is the other piece of the truss?

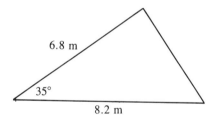

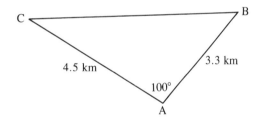

7. A radar station at A (above right) is tracking ships at B and C. How far apart are the two ships?

8. To find the distance across a marsh, a surveyor locates point C as shown in the diagram (below left). If $\angle C$ is 65°, how far is it across the marsh?

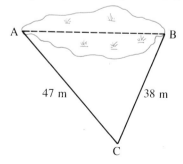

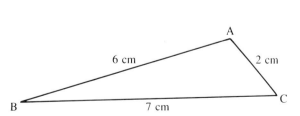

9. Find the size of each angle in $\triangle ABC$ (above right).

10. In parallelogram ABCD, AB = 4 cm and BC = 7 cm. If ∠B = 65°, how long is each diagonal to 1 decimal place?

11. Given the points P(5,8), Q(3,2), and R(7,5), calculate ∠PQR to the nearest degree.

12. The sides of a parallelogram measure 18.0 cm and 10.0 cm. The diagonals measure 14.7 cm and 25.1 cm. Find the size of each angle in the parallelogram.

13. A radar tracking station locates a fishing trawler at a distance of 5.4 km, and a passenger ferry at a distance of 7.2 km. At the station, the angle between the two boats is 118°. How far apart are they?

14. In a circle with diameter 12 cm, the chord AB subtends an angle of 140° at the centre. How long is the chord?

15. In a circle with diameter 21.4 cm, the chord AB subtends an angle of 42° at a point C on the circumference. How long is the chord?

16. Calculate, to the nearest degree, the smallest angle in the triangle formed by the points O(0,0), A(4,3), and B(3,4).

17. In a circle of radius 10 cm, AB is an arc of length 10 cm. How long is the chord AB to 1 decimal place?

18. Calculate, to 1 decimal place, the largest angle in the triangle formed by the points P(2,7), Q(8, − 3), and R(− 5,1).

19. Find the area of each △ABC with the given lengths of sides.
    a) 17 cm, 29 cm, 23 cm
    b) 32 cm, 19 cm, 15 cm
    c) 12 cm, 35 cm, 37 cm

20. The triangle formed by the points J(5,7), K(− 7, − 1), and L(8, − 4) is inscribed in a circle. Find the size of the angle at the centre of the circle subtended by KL.

21. Twelve points are equally spaced around a circle of radius *r*. Express these lengths in terms of *r*.
    a) AB   b) AC   c) AD
    d) AE   e) AF   f) AG

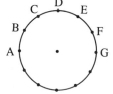

22. Two ships leave a port, sailing at 17 km/h and 21 km/h. The angle between their directions of travel from the port is 38°. How far apart are the ships after 2 h?

23. The goal posts of a hockey net are 1.8 m apart. The puck is shot from a point which is 9.2 m from one post and 10.8 m from the other post. Within what angle must the puck travel to score a goal?

24. In the diagrams below, ABCD is a square with side length 3 cm and △PBC is equilateral. Find the length of AP.

a)

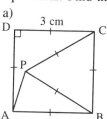

b)

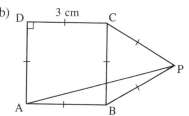

25. ABCD is a square of side 1 unit. Equilateral triangles are constructed on the sides of the square.
    a) Find the length of EH.
    b) Find the area of △EDH.

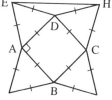

26. Find the values of x and y.

a)

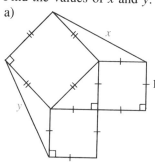

b)

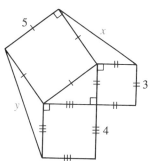

Ⓒ

27. For the diagram (below left), show that $x^2 + y^2 = 5c^2$.

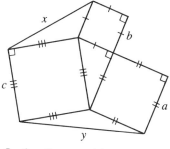

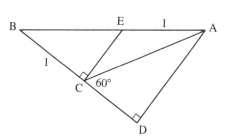

28. In the diagram (above right), EC is perpendicular to BD, ∠ACD = 60°, and AE = BC = 1 unit. Find the lengths of BE and CA.

USING TECHNOLOGY

Periodic Functions, Part II

Applications

The trigonometric functions are useful for illustrating natural phenomena which change in a periodic manner. The changing times of sunsets during the year, the frequency of sunspots, and the volume of air in the lungs can often be understood better if we model them as graphs.

The approximate number of hours of daylight in Montreal can be expressed by the formula $h = 3.75 \sin \dfrac{2\pi x}{365} + 12$, where x is the number of days after March 21. On March 21 (when $x = 0$), the number of daylight hours is 12 and the length of daytime equals the length of nighttime.

a) Enter the above equation on the functions menu of your graphing calculator. Set the viewing window to be $[-1, 365]$ by $[-1, 18]$ and graph the function.

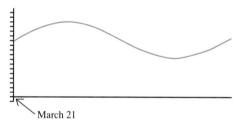

March 21

b) Use the TRACE feature to determine the day on which the maximum number of hours of daylight will occur. What date is this? How many hours of daylight are there on this date?

c) What is the other date on which there will be exactly 12 daylight hours?

d) On which date will there be the fewest daylight hours?

e) Consult an almanac or an encyclopedia and find the meanings of the following terms: summer solstice, winter solstice, vernal equinox, autumnal equinox.

f) The graph in part a) represents a year that begins on March 21 and ends on March 20, a period of 365 days. March 21 is the eightieth day of the normal calendar year. To produce a graph that begins on January 1, we would have to introduce a phase shift of 80 days into the original equation. Recall that in the equation $y = \sin k(x - p)$, the phase shift is p. With a phase shift of 80 days, our original equation becomes $h = 3.75 \sin \dfrac{2\pi(x - 80)}{365} + 12$. Graph this equation on your graphing calculator. With the TRACE feature verify that the dates of the solstices and equinoxes match those found from the original equation.

An Infinite Series Revisited

For a certain interval in its domain, the function $y = \sin x$ can be approximated by the function $y = x - \dfrac{x^3}{6} + \dfrac{x^5}{120}$, where x is in radians.

a) Display the graphs of $Y_1 = \sin X$ and $Y_2 = X - \dfrac{X^3}{6} + \dfrac{X^5}{120}$ together on your graphing calculator. For which interval of the domain are the graphs close together?

b) Compare the graph of $Y_1 = \sin X$ with the graph of $Y_3 = Y_2 - \dfrac{X^7}{5040}$. For which interval of the domain are the graphs close together?

c) Follow the pattern of terms in Y_2 and Y_3. Make a new function Y_4 that will approximate the sine function even more closely. Display the graphs of Y_1 and Y_4 together on your graphing calculator.

Patterns and Exploration I

When two sine functions with the same amplitude but different periods are added, some interesting patterns can be observed in the resulting graph. This is particularly interesting if the periods of the two sine functions are almost equal.

a) Graph $Y_1 = \sin 4X + \sin 5X$.

b) Graph $Y_2 = \sin 6X + \sin 7X$ on a different screen.

c) Describe what you think the graph of $Y_3 = \sin 9X + \sin 10X$ will look like and then graph Y_3.

Patterns and Exploration II

Other interesting patterns can be observed when a sine function and a cosine function with the same period are added: $y = a \sin x + b \sin x$.

a) Graph each function separately on your graphing calculator.
   i) $Y_1 = \sin X + \cos X$ ii) $Y_2 = \sin X - \cos X$ iii) $Y_3 = 2 \sin X + \cos X$

b) Use the TRACE feature to determine the amplitude of each function and record your results.

c) Determine a relationship between the amplitude and the values of a and b. (Hint: think of the Pythagorean theorem).

d) Verify your answer by checking the graph of $Y_4 = 2 \sin X + 3 \cos X$.

9-7 THE LAW OF SINES

There are some triangles that cannot be solved using the Law of Cosines; that is, triangles for which only one side is known.

A triangle is uniquely determined by two angles and a particular side. The following example shows how to find the other sides of such a triangle.

Example 1. In $\triangle ABC$, $\angle A = 30°$, $BC = 5$, and $\angle B = 65°$; find the length of AC to 1 decimal place.

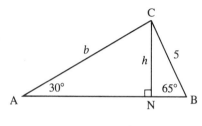

Solution. Construct CN perpendicular to AB, and let $CN = h$ and $AC = b$.

In right $\triangle ANC$

$$\frac{h}{b} = \sin 30°, \text{ or } h = b \sin 30°$$

In right $\triangle BNC$

$$\frac{h}{5} = \sin 65°, \text{ or } h = 5 \sin 65°$$

That is, $b \sin 30° = 5 \sin 65°$

$$b = \frac{5 \sin 65°}{\sin 30°}$$

$$\doteq 9.063$$

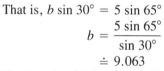

The length of AC is approximately 9.1.

Now we consider the general cases of $\triangle ABC$ where $\angle A$ is acute and $\angle A$ is obtuse. In both cases, construct CN perpendicular to AB or AB extended, and let $CN = h$.

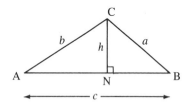   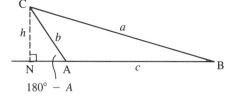

For the acute triangle
$$h = b \sin A$$
and $h = a \sin B$

For the obtuse triangle
$$h = b \sin (180° - A)$$
$$= b \sin A$$
and $h = a \sin B$

In both cases, $b \sin A = a \sin B$

$$\frac{\sin A}{a} = \frac{\sin B}{b}$$

Similarly, by constructing a perpendicular from A to BC, we can show

that $\dfrac{\sin B}{b} = \dfrac{\sin C}{c}$.

The Law of Sines
In any $\triangle ABC$
$$\frac{\sin A}{a} = \frac{\sin B}{b} = \frac{\sin C}{c}$$

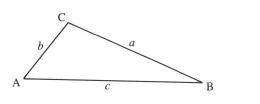

We can use the Law of Sines to find the remaining sides of a triangle when two angles and one side are given.

Example 2. Solve $\triangle PQR$, given that $\angle P = 57°$, $\angle Q = 73°$, and $QR = 24$. Give the answers to 1 decimal place.

Solution. $\angle R = 180° - (73° + 57°)$
$\qquad = 50°$

By the Law of Sines
$$\frac{\sin P}{p} = \frac{\sin Q}{q} = \frac{\sin R}{r}$$
$$\frac{\sin 57°}{24} = \frac{\sin 73°}{q} = \frac{\sin 50°}{r}$$

To find q
$$\frac{\sin 57°}{24} = \frac{\sin 73°}{q}$$
$$q = \frac{24 \sin 73°}{\sin 57°}$$
$$\doteq 27.366\ 304$$
$$\doteq 27.4$$

To find r
$$\frac{\sin 57°}{24} = \frac{\sin 50°}{r}$$
$$r = \frac{24 \sin 50°}{\sin 57°}$$
$$\doteq 21.921\ 679$$
$$\doteq 21.9$$

We summarize these results in a table.

$\angle P$	$\angle Q$	$\angle R$	p	q	r
57°	73°	50°	24	27.4	21.9

The Law of Sines actually represents three equations. Each equation relates four variables.
$$\frac{\sin A}{a} = \frac{\sin B}{b} \qquad \frac{\sin B}{b} = \frac{\sin C}{c} \qquad \frac{\sin A}{a} = \frac{\sin C}{c}$$

To use the Law of Sines, we must know the values of three of the four variables in any equation. Then, we must select the equation relating these three variables and solve for the unknown variable.

Since no single equation above contains the three variables a, b, and C we cannot use the Law of Sines to solve a triangle given only that information. As explained in *Section 9-6*, the Law of Cosines is used in this situation.

To apply the Law of Sines to solve a triangle we must know the measure of one angle and the length of the opposite side, plus one other angle or side.

Example 3. Solve $\triangle ABC$ given $\angle B = 48°$, $b = 9$, and $c = 11$. Give the answers to 1 decimal place.

Solution. Use the Law of Sines to find $\angle C$.

$$\frac{\sin C}{c} = \frac{\sin B}{b}$$

$$\sin C = \frac{11 \sin 48°}{9}$$

$$\doteq 0.908\ 288\ 1$$

$$\angle C \doteq 65.3°$$

Since $\sin C = \sin (180° - C)$, $\angle C$ could be 114.7°.
That is, there are two different triangles which satisfy the given conditions.
We proceed to solve the triangle for both values of $\angle C$.

If $\angle C = 65.3°$
Then $\angle A = 180° - 48° - 65.3°$
$= 66.7°$

To find a

$$\frac{a}{\sin A} = \frac{c}{\sin C}$$

$$a = \frac{11 \sin 66.7°}{\sin 65.3°}$$

$$\doteq 11.120\ 329$$

$$\doteq 11.1$$

If $\angle C = 114.7°$
Then $\angle A = 180° - 48° - 114.7°$
$= 17.3°$

To find a

$$\frac{a}{\sin A} = \frac{c}{\sin C}$$

$$a = \frac{11 \sin 17.3°}{\sin 65.3°}$$

$$\doteq 3.600\ 544$$

$$\doteq 3.6$$

We summarize these results in tables and draw a triangle to illustrate each case.

$\angle A$	$\angle B$	$\angle C$	a	b	c
66.7°	48°	65.3°	11.1	9	11

$\angle A$	$\angle B$	$\angle C$	a	b	c
17.3°	48°	114.7°	3.6	9	11

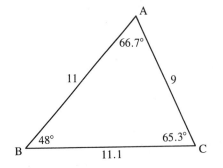

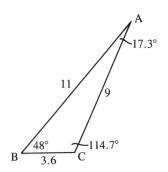

The Ambiguous Case

If we superimpose the two triangles obtained in *Example 3*, we discover why, given two sides and an angle other than the contained angle, there are two solutions.

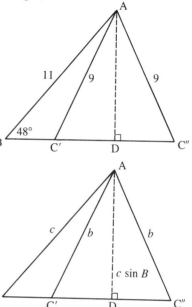

The vertex C of △ABC can be placed in position C′ or its mirror image in AD, C″ without affecting the given values; that is, ∠B and the lengths *b* and *c*.

The case in which two triangles are possible is called the *ambiguous case*.

How can we tell when we have an ambiguous case; that is, two solutions?

Consider △ABC where ∠B, *b*, and *c* are given. The length of AD, the perpendicular from A to BC, is *c* sin B.

Case I If *b* < *c* sin B, then there is no triangle possible because AD is the shortest distance from A to BC″.

Case II If *b* = *c* sin B, then *b* is the length of AD; that is, △ABC is the right triangle △ABD.

Case III If *b* > *c* sin B, then there are two triangles provided *b* < *c*. If b > c, then C can be only in position C″ and not C′.

These cases are summarized in the following statement.

> If △ABC is known to exist; and the measure of ∠B, the length *b*, and the length *c* are given, then there are exactly two different triangles which satisfy these conditions provided *c* sin B < *b* < *c*. Otherwise, there is exactly one triangle.

Example 4. A tunnel through the mountains is to be constructed to join A and B. Point C is 12.6 km from B. A cannot be seen from B or from C. Point D is 10.3 km from C and 6.7 km from A; ∠ADC = 125° and ∠DCB = 142°.

          a) Find the length of the tunnel AB.
          b) Find the angle between:
             i) AB and AD   ii) AB and CB.

Solution.   a) First, use the Law of Cosines in △ACD to find AC.

$$d^2 = a^2 + c^2 - 2ac \cos D$$
$$= 10.3^2 + 6.7^2 - 2(6.7)(10.3)(\cos 125°)$$
$$\doteq 230.145\ 02$$
$$d \doteq 15.1705$$

Then, use the Law of Sines in △ACD to find ∠C.

$$\frac{\sin C}{c} = \frac{\sin D}{d}$$

$$\sin C = \frac{6.7 \sin 125°}{15.1705}$$

$$\doteq 0.361\ 775\ 7$$

$$\angle C \doteq 21.2°$$

Subtract to find $\angle ACB$.

$$\angle ACB = 142° - 21.2°$$

$$= 120.8°$$

Use the Law of Cosines in $\triangle ABC$ to find AB.

$$c^2 = a^2 + b^2 - 2ab \cos C$$

$$= 12.6^2 + 15.1705^2 - 2(15.1705)(12.6)(\cos 120.8°)$$

$$\doteq 584.6563$$

$$c \doteq 24.180$$

The tunnel is approximately 24.2 km in length.

b) Use the Law of Sines in $\triangle ABC$ to find $\angle A$.

$$\frac{\sin A}{a} = \frac{\sin C}{c}$$

$$\sin A = \frac{12.6 \sin 120.8°}{24.180}$$

$$\doteq 0.447\ 597$$

$$\angle A \doteq 26.6°$$

i) The angle between AB and AD is $\angle DAB$.

$$\angle DAB = \angle BAC + \angle DAC$$

$$\angle BAC = 26.6°$$

In $\triangle ADC$

$$\angle DAC = 180° - 125° - 21.2°$$

$$= 33.8°$$

$$\angle DAB = 26.6° + 33.8°$$

$$= 60.4°$$

ii) The angle between AB and CB is $\angle ABC$.

In $\triangle ABC$, $\angle ABC = 180° - 120.8° - 26.6°$

$$= 32.6°$$

These examples show that we can solve any triangle using the Laws of Sines and/or Cosines given:

- the length of one side and the measures of any two angles; or
- the lengths of two sides and the measure of any one angle; or
- the lengths of three sides.

If we are given only the measures of 3 angles, then there is an infinite number of similar triangles with this shape; the lengths of the sides of the triangles can be expressed only in terms of one of the sides of the triangle. That is, the Laws of Sines and Cosines enable us to solve any triangle given any three pieces of data except the measures of the three angles. In all but the ambiguous case, the solution is unique.

The fact that the sets of conditions SSS, AAS, and SAS determine unique triangles is a direct consequence of the corresponding congruence theorems. That is, if there were another triangle satisfying any of these three conditions (such as SSS) it would be congruent to any triangle satisfying these conditions. The SSA condition is not a congruence condition and, as shown in the ambiguous case above, does not guarantee a unique solution.

These results are summarized below.

Number of Sides Given	Number of Angles Given	Method of Solution of the Triangle
1	2	Law of Sines
2	1 not contained	Law of Sines, ambiguous case
2	1 contained	Law of Cosines
3	0	Law of Cosines

EXERCISES 9-7

1. Find the length of AB to 1 decimal place.

   a)   b)   c)

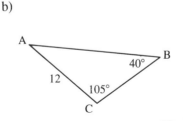
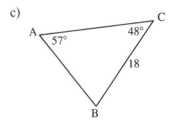

2. Find θ to 1 decimal place.

   a)   b)   c)

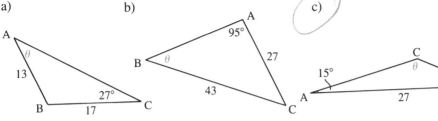

3. a) In $\triangle ABC$, $\angle A = 65°$, $\angle B = 40°$, and $a = 15$; find b.
   b) In $\triangle PQR$, $\angle P = 52°$, $\angle Q = 73°$, and $q = 27$; find p.
   c) In $\triangle ABC$, $\angle B = 27°$, $\angle C = 64°$, and $b = 14$; find c.
   d) In $\triangle ABC$, $\angle A = 38°$, $\angle B = 77°$, and $b = 16.5$; find c.
   e) In $\triangle XYZ$, $\angle Y = 84°$, $\angle Z = 33°$, and $z = 9.2$; find x.
   Give the answers to 1 decimal place.

(B)

4. Solve each △PQR. Give the answers to 1 decimal place.
   a) ∠P = 105°, p = 12, q = 9   b) ∠Q = 63°, q = 20, r = 17
   c) ∠P = 112°, p = 32, r = 25   d) ∠R = 78°, r = 42, p = 28

5. Solve each △ABC. Give the answers to 1 decimal place.
   a) ∠A = 35°, a = 12, b = 15   b) ∠B = 55°, b = 11, c = 13
   c) ∠C = 78°, b = 19, a = 24   d) ∠B = 42°, b = 22, c = 27
   e) ∠A = 39°, c = 32, b = 45   f) ∠B = 124°, b = 27, a = 13

6. Solve each △XYZ. Give the answers to 1 decimal place.
   a) ∠X = 72°, ∠Z = 50°, x = 34   b) ∠X = 46.4°, y = 21, z = 29
   c) ∠Y = 54°, x = 22, y = 19   d) ∠Z = 61°, y = 6.3, x = 7.8

7. A bridge AB (below left) is to be built across a river. The point C is located 62.0 m
   from B, and ∠ABC = 74° while ∠ACB = 48°. How long will the bridge be?

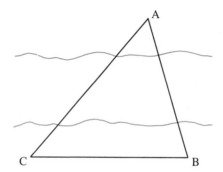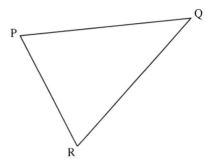

8. Two ships at P and Q (above right) are 32.0 km apart. How far is each ship from
   a lighthouse at R if ∠P = 68° and ∠Q = 42°?

9. A triangular park measures 251 m along one side (below left). Find the lengths of
   the other two sides if they form angles of 32° and 56° with the first side.

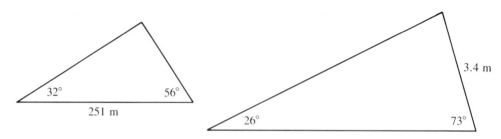

10. The roof lines of a ski chalet make angles of 26° and 73° with the horizontal (above
    right). The shorter roof line is 3.4 m long. Find the length of the other roof line.

11. Two girls intend to swim from a dock at D, to the island at I, and back to a dock at K (below left). The docks are 168 m apart. The angles between the line joining each dock to the island, and the line joining the docks are 64° and 70°. How far must the girls swim?

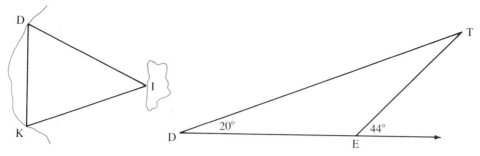

12. From points D and E (above right) the lines of sight to a tree at T make angles of 20° and 44° respectively, with DE. If DE is 62 m, how far is the tree from D, and from E?

13. Two guy wires 17.0 m and 10.0 m in length are fastened to the top of a TV tower from two points M and N on level ground. The angle of elevation of the longer wire is 28.1°.
    a) How far apart are M and N?
    b) How tall is the tower?

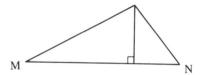

14. In the diagram (below left)
    a) Find the length of BC.
    b) Find the length of the altitude from A.

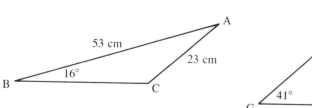

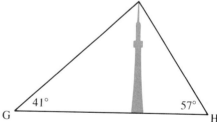

15. From points G and H, the angles of elevation of the top of the CN tower are 41° and 57° respectively (above right). If the distance between G and H is 995 m, find the height of the tower.

16. Bijan observes the angle of elevation of an ultra-light airplane to be 52°. At the same instant the angle of elevation for Therese is 36°. Bijan and Therese are 325 m apart on level ground and in the same vertical plane as the ultra-light.
    a) How far is each person from the ultra-light?
    b) How high is the ultra-light?

17. In the diagram (below left), ABCD is a square of side 1 unit. Point P is such that
    ∠PAD = 30° = ∠PCD. Find the length to 1 decimal place of: a) PD   b) PC.

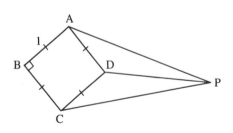

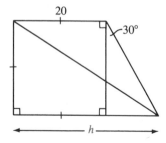

18. In the diagram (above right), find the value of *h*.

19. In a molecule of water (below left), the two hydrogen atoms and one oxygen atom
    are bonded in the shape of a triangle. The nuclei of the atoms are separated by
    the distances shown. Calculate the bond angles.

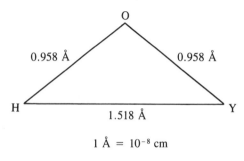

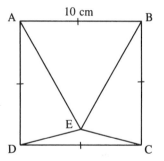

20. Square ABCD (above right) has sides of length 10 cm. Point E is inside the square
    so that ∠CDE = ∠DCE = 15°. Find the length of AE.

21. In △ABC, AC = 2, AB = 3, and BC = 4. Prove that:

    a) $\sin B = \frac{1}{2} \sin A$ 　　　　　　　 b) $\sin C = \frac{3}{4} \sin A$.

22. Prove that in any △ABC the constant of proportionality for the Sine Law is the
    diameter of the circumscribing circle.

23. An isosceles △ABC has vertical ∠C = 20°. Points M and N are taken on AC and
    BC so that ∠ABM = 60° and ∠BAN = 50°. Prove that ∠BMN = 30°.

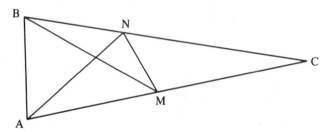

INVESTIGATE

Relating the Laws of Cosines and Sines to Right Triangles

Earlier in this chapter we defined the primary trigonometric ratios in terms of the sides of a right triangle.

$\sin \theta = \dfrac{\text{opposite}}{\text{hypotenuse}}$

$\cos \theta = \dfrac{\text{adjacent}}{\text{hypotenuse}}$

$\tan \theta = \dfrac{\text{opposite}}{\text{adjacent}}$

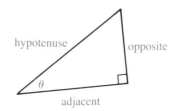

Then we used these definitions to develop the Laws of Cosines and Sines for any triangle.

The Law of Cosines
$a^2 = b^2 + c^2 - 2bc \cos A$
$b^2 = a^2 + c^2 - 2ac \cos B$
$c^2 = a^2 + b^2 - 2ab \cos C$

The Law of Sines
$\dfrac{\sin A}{a} = \dfrac{\sin B}{b} = \dfrac{\sin C}{c}$

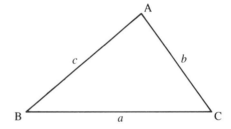

The purpose of this investigation is to find out what happens if the Laws of Cosines and Sines are applied to a right triangle.

1. Suppose one of the angles in △ABC is a right angle.
    a) Investigate what happens if the Law of Sines is applied to this triangle. Does it matter which of the three angles is the right angle?
    b) Investigate what happens if the Law of Cosines is applied to the same triangle. Does it matter which angle is the right angle?

2. Try to use the results of *Question 1* to develop the expressions above for $\sin \theta$, $\cos \theta$, and $\tan \theta$ in terms of opposite, adjacent, and hypotenuse.

3. Do you think that we could define the primary trigonometric ratios by starting with the Laws of Cosines and Sines and then applying them to a right triangle? Explain your answer.

9-8 APPLICATIONS OF THE LAWS OF COSINES AND SINES

In *Sections 9-5, 9-6,* and *9-7,* we learned how to find the area of a triangle and to solve a right triangle using the Law of Cosines and the Law of Sines.

In this section we apply these laws, as well as the trigonometric ratios, to the solutions of various problems. To complete the exercises:
- copy the diagram given, or draw the diagram suggested by the problem;
- mark all measures that have been given;
- decide on the method of solution—Law of Cosines, Law of Sines, or trigonometric ratios;

and then proceed with the calculation.

Example.   A water bomber is sent to help fight a small forest fire. The diagram shows the situation when the target is "bombed." Observers at A and C note the angles of elevation of the bomber. Find the height of the bomber to the nearest metre.

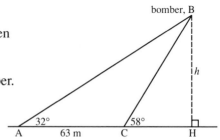

Solution.   Since we know (or can find easily) two angles and one side of $\triangle ABC$, we shall use the Law of Sines to find BC, and then a trigonometric ratio in $\triangle BCH$ to find BH.

Calculate $\angle B$.

$\angle A = 32°$; $\angle C = 180° - 58° = 122°$; so
$\angle B = 180° - 32° - 122° = 26°$

Use the Law of Sines in $\triangle ABC$ to find BC.

$$\frac{\sin A}{a} = \frac{\sin B}{b}$$

$$a = \frac{b \sin A}{\sin B}$$

$$a = \frac{63 \sin 32°}{\sin 26°}$$

$$\doteq 76.1567$$

In $\triangle BCH$,

$$\sin \angle BCH \doteq \frac{h}{76.1567}$$

$$h \doteq 76.1567(\sin 58°)$$

$$\doteq 64.5846$$

The water bomber was at a height of about 65 m.

EXERCISES 9-8

Ⓑ

1. The diagram shows a chairlift which is 700 m long and inclined at an angle of 38°. The base of the chairlift is 20 m from the end of the ski run.

   a) How long is the ski run?

   b) What is the inclination of the ski run?

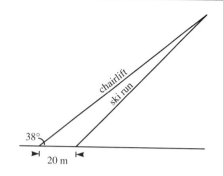

2. A conveyor belt at a farm carries bales of feed from ground level to the loft of a barn which is 8.2 m high. The conveyor belt is at an angle of 50°. How long is the conveyor belt?

3. A triangular building lot is at the intersection of two roads which meet at an angle of 108°. The frontage on one street is 15.8 m, and the frontage on the second street is 10.2 m.

   a) What is the area of the lot?

   b) What is the length of the third side of the lot?

4. A radio transmission antenna is located on the top of a building. An observer located 20.0 m from the building at ground level measures the angle of elevation to the top of the mast as 59°, and the angle of elevation to the bottom of the mast as 52°. How high is the mast?

5. An undersea mine has an entry tunnel of length 1.1 km, and the floor of the tunnel has an angle of depression of 22°. The sea floor slopes at an angle of depression of 8°. At the end of the entry tunnel, what is its depth below sea level? Give the answer to the nearest metre.

6. The diagram (below left) shows the relative positions of three cities in the province of Quebec. How far is it from Chicoutimi to Sherbrooke?

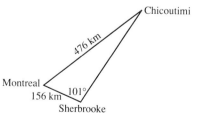

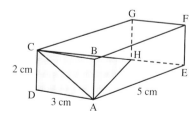

7. The diagram (above right) shows a solid rectangular prism with dimensions 5 cm by 3 cm by 2 cm. Section ACDH is cut off. What is the measure of ∠ACH? Give the answer to the nearest tenth of a degree.

8. A new transmission line is being installed to connect two cities, but it must be diverted since a direct route would take it over a provincial wild-life sanctuary (below left). Aerial survey shows that the most efficient route will be when ∠RAC = 138° and ∠CBS = 152°. The direct route AB is 12.4 km. By how much does the diversion increase the length of the transmission line?

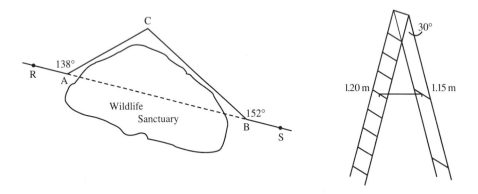

9. For the step ladder (above right)
   a) Find the angle of inclination of the steps to the nearest degree.
   b) Find the width of the ladder on the floor.

10. A hovercraft is crossing a channel from A to B at a speed of 25 km/h (below left). The wind is blowing directly from the east at a speed of 6 km/h. Experience has shown that the hovercraft must start at A and head in a direction which is at 70° to the bank of the channel, to make landfall at B. How long will the journey take if the distance from A to B is 32.8 km?

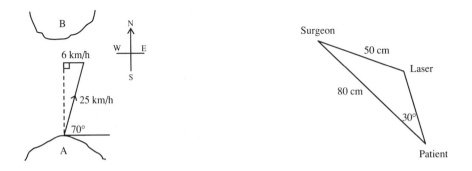

11. To treat glaucoma, a laser is placed directly in front of the patient (above right). The surgeon stands 80 cm from the patient on a line that makes an angle of 30° with the line between the laser and the patient. The surgeon is 50 cm from the laser. How far is the patient from the laser?

12. A vertical pole of height 10 m is located on the side of a hill. When the sun is at an angle of elevation of 31°, the length of the shadow down the hill is 25 m. Find the angle of inclination of the hill to the nearest degree.

13. On the par-3 second hole of a golf course, the distance from the tee to the flag is 246 m, and the direct shot is over a lake. To avoid the water, a golfer aims left of the flag at an angle of 18° and hits her tee shot a distance of 115 m. How far is the ball from the flag?

Ⓒ

14. A symmetric roof framework is to be made using 2 by 4 wood in the shape shown (below). Some of the measurements are known and included on the diagram. What is the total length of wood required to make the framework? Give your answer to the nearest metre.

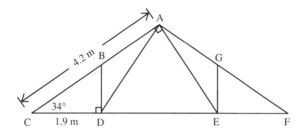

15. In a rugby game, the home side scored a try at a distance of 15 m from the left touch line (below). To kick the conversion, the player must place the ball anywhere on the line that is parallel to the touch line and 15 m from it.

   a)   i) Find the "angle of success" (between left and right goal posts) if the ball is 8 m from the goal line. Give the answer to 1 decimal place.

      ii) By how much does this angle increase if the ball is 25 m from the goal line? Give the answer to 1 decimal place.

   b) The greatest distance the kicker can kick is 40 m. What is the maximum distance the kicker can be from the goal line? Give the answer to the nearest tenth of a metre.

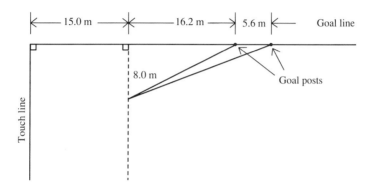

Review Exercises

1. The point P is on a circle centre (0,0) with radius 10 cm. Determine the coordinates of P to 2 decimal places if P is on the terminal arm of each angle in standard position.
   a) 40°   b) 110°   c) 235°   d) 300°   e) 312°

2. Each of the following points is on the terminal arm of an angle θ. Determine $\sin \theta$, $\cos \theta$, and $\tan \theta$ to 5 decimal places, and θ to the nearest hundredth of a degree.
   a) P(3,7)   b) Q(-4,1)   c) R(-2,-3)   d) S(6,-2)

3. Determine each value.
   a) $\cos (\mathrm{Tan}^{-1} \sqrt{3})$ b) $\sin \left(\mathrm{Arccos} \, \frac{1}{\sqrt{2}} \right)$ c) $\tan \left(\mathrm{Cos}^{-1} \frac{\sqrt{3}}{2} \right)$ d) $\sin \left(\mathrm{Arcsin} \, \frac{3}{5} \right)$

4. Given θ is an acute angle, find the values of the other two primary trigonometric ratios.
   a) $\cos \theta = \frac{8}{17}$ b) $\tan \theta = \frac{12}{5}$ c) $\cos \theta = \frac{11}{21}$ d) $\sin \theta = \frac{5}{9}$

5. Solve $\triangle ABC$, if $\angle B = 90°$, and:
   a) AB = 15, BC = 27
   b) AC = 18, BC = 10
   c) AB = 42, $\angle C = 72°$
   d) AC = 12, $\angle A = 35°$.
   Give the answers to 1 decimal place where necessary.

6. Find the area of each triangle to 1 decimal place.
   a)   b)   c)

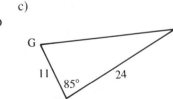

7. Solve each $\triangle PQR$. Give the answers to 1 decimal place.
   a) $\angle Q = 75°$, $r = 8$, $p = 11$
   b) $\angle R = 52°$, $r = 28$, $q = 25$
   c) $\angle P = 38°$, $\angle Q = 105°$, $p = 32$
   d) $r = 17$, $p = 14$, $q = 26$

8. A wheelchair ramp 8.2 m long rises 94 cm. Find its angle of inclination to 1 decimal place.

9. The angle of elevation of the sun is 68° when a tree casts a shadow 14.3 m long. How tall is the tree?

10. Two identical apartment buildings are 41.3 m apart. From her balcony, Kudo notices that the angle of elevation to the top of the adjacent building is 57°. The angle of depression to the base of the building is 28°. Find the height of the buildings.

1. Convert from radians to degrees. Give each answer to 2 decimal places where necessary.

   a) $\frac{3\pi}{4}$
   b) $-\frac{7\pi}{6}$
   c) 2.7 radians
   d) $-\frac{11\pi}{3}$

2. Convert from degrees to radians. Give each answer to 2 decimal places where necessary.

   a) $210°$
   b) $-225°$
   c) $147°$
   d) $270°$

3. Each point P is on the terminal arm of an angle θ.

   a) Find $\sin \theta$, $\cos \theta$, and $\tan \theta$.   i) $P(3, 1)$ ii) $P(-5, -2)$ iii) $P(6, -4)$

   b) Find each value of θ in degrees to 1 decimal place.

4. State the exact values of the six trigonometric ratios of each angle.

   a) $\frac{5\pi}{6}$
   b) $\frac{\pi}{3}$
   c) $\frac{7\pi}{4}$
   d) $\frac{4\pi}{3}$
   e) $\frac{11\pi}{6}$

5. State the amplitude, period, phase shift, and vertical translation for each function.

   a) $y = 2 \sin 3\left(\theta - \frac{\pi}{6}\right)$
   b) $y = \frac{1}{2} \cos \left(2\theta + \frac{\pi}{2}\right) - 1$

6. Prove each identity.

   a) $\sin^4\theta - \cos^4\theta = 2 \sin^2\theta - 1$
   b) $\frac{\csc \theta}{\sec^2 \theta} = \csc \theta - \sin \theta$

7. Expand and simplify.

   a) $\sin \left(\frac{\pi}{6} + \frac{\pi}{4}\right)$
   b) $\cos \left(\frac{\pi}{3} - \frac{\pi}{4}\right)$
   c) $\tan \left(\frac{\pi}{3} + \frac{\pi}{4}\right)$

8. If $\sin \alpha = \frac{2}{3}$ and $\cos \beta = -\frac{1}{4}$, where α and β are in Quadrant II, evaluate:

   a) $\cos (\alpha + \beta)$
   b) $\sin (\alpha - \beta)$
   c) $\cos 2\alpha$
   d) $\cos (\alpha - \beta)$.

9. Each point P is on the terminal arm of angle θ. Find $\sin \theta$, $\cos \theta$, and $\tan \theta$ to 3 decimal places.

   a) $P(4, 9)$
   b) $P(8, -15)$
   c) $P(-4, 7)$
   d) $P(-6, -5)$

10. Find each value of θ in *Exercise 9* to 1 decimal place.

11. Solve $\triangle PQR$, if $\angle Q = 90°$ and:

    a) $PQ = 11$, $QR = 8$
    b) $QR = 26$, $\angle P = 28°$.

    Give the answers to 1 decimal place where necessary.

12. Solve $\triangle XYZ$ if:

    a) $XY = 7$, $YZ = 5$, and $\angle Y = 110°$

    b) $x = 3.7$, $y = 4.1$, and $\angle X = 58°$.

    Give the answers to 1 decimal place where necessary.

PROBLEM SOLVING

The Pigeonhole Principle

"Society is not static, and the basics are not eternal."

Shirley Hill

The population of Canada is about 25 million. Prove that at least two people in Canada have the same number of hairs on their heads.

Understand the problem
● Can we do this without counting the hairs on everybody's head?
● Do we have to determine which people have the same number of hairs on their heads?

Think of a strategy
● Is it possible for someone to have 25 million hairs on her or his head?

Carry out the strategy
● Estimate the greatest number of hairs that could be on somebody's head.
● Is it possible for every person in Canada to have a different number of hairs on her or his head?

Look back
● Since there are more people than possible numbers of hairs, it follows that at least two people have the same number of hairs on the head. This kind of reasoning makes use of a principle called the pigeonhole principle.

> **The Pigeonhole Principle**
> If n objects are to be placed in $k < n$ boxes, then some box contains at least two objects.

● In the above problem, $n > 25\ 000\ 000$ (the number of Canadians), and $k < 25\ 000\ 000$ (the possible number of hairs on the head). Since $n > k$, there must be at least two people with the same number of hairs on the head.
● Of course, we have no idea who the people are with the same number of hairs on the head!

The pigeonhole principle is a very useful problem solving strategy. It can be used to solve a surprisingly wide variety of problems.

PROBLEMS

Ⓑ

1. How many cards must you draw from a deck of playing cards to be certain that you will have:
   a) at least two red cards or two black cards
   b) at least two cards from the same suit?

2. Given any 5 different natural numbers, prove that at least two of them leave the same remainder when divided by 4.

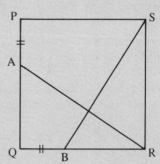

3. In square PQRS, A and B are points on the sides PQ and QR such that PA = QB. Prove that RA = SB and RA is perpendicular to SB.

4. PQRS is any parallelogram. Prove that $PQ^2 + QR^2 + RS^2 + SP^2 = PR^2 + QS^2$.

5. Prove that for every acute angle θ, $\sin \theta + \dfrac{1}{\sin \theta} \geq 2$.

6. The arithmetic mean of a set of 30 numbers is 65. If 10 numbers having a mean of 60 are discarded, what is the mean of the remaining numbers?

Ⓒ

7. Five points are randomly located in a square with sides 1 unit long. Prove that at least two of the points are no more than $\dfrac{\sqrt{2}}{2}$ units apart.

8. A circle has radius r. Three arcs of circles with radius r are drawn to intersect at the centre and on the circumference of the given circle as shown. Determine the shaded area as a function of r.

Ⓓ

9. Here are ten different numbers less than 100:
   18, 33, 38, 50, 59, 64, 68, 75, 81, 97.
   Notice that there are two sets of numbers with the same sum:
   18 + 50 + 68 + 75 = 211 and 33 + 81 + 97 = 211.
   Prove that this always occurs. That is, prove that for any selection of ten different numbers less than 100 it is always possible to find two sets of numbers with the same sum.

THE MATHEMATICAL MIND

Problems Computers Can't Solve

Even the world's fastest supercomputers have limitations. Some practical problems require so much computation that one would need a computer as large as the universe, operating for as long as the age of the universe.

The Travelling Salesman Problem
Bob sells farm machinery and lives in Goderich, Ontario. He must make calls in each town shown on the map. What is the shortest distance he could travel before returning home?

This problem can be solved by systematic trial. But for 100 towns it would take the world's fastest computers centuries to solve the problem. No one has yet been able to give a general solution for any number of cities.

If a solution is ever found, it could be applied to similar problems such as making deliveries, collecting money from vending machines, and routing telephone calls.

> What is the shortest route which passes through each town?

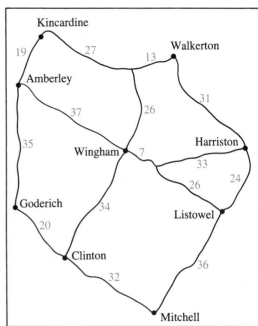

The Bin-Packing Problem
A manufacturer has items with masses as indicated. What is the least number of bins needed to pack the items if each bin can hold no more than 1 kg?

For a small number of items this problem can also be solved by systematic trial. But for 100 items the number of possible packings is so great that even if all the computing power in the world were available, it is very unlikely that the problem would ever be solved.

If a general solution is found, it could be applied to similar problems such as cutting material with the least amount of waste, and scheduling television commercials.

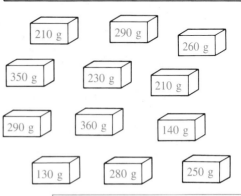

> What is the least number of 1 kg bins needed to pack the items with masses indicated?

There are elaborate algorithms (step-by-step procedures) for solving these problems, but they are not much better than the simplest one: list all the possibilities and choose the best one. But it can be shown that the time required to do this is an exponential function of the size of the problem, n. For example, in the two problems on the opposite page, $n = 9$ (there are 9 towns) and $n = 12$ (there are 12 items). For larger values of n, say 100, this algorithm is far too slow, even for the world's fastest supercomputers.

The travelling salesman problem and the bin-packing problem are examples of what are known as *NP-complete* problems. This concept was introduced in 1971 by Stephen Cook of the University of Toronto. These are a certain kind of problem that some computer scientists think can never be solved. Since 1971, Stephen Cook has gained worldwide recognition for his work on the problem of showing what computers cannot do.

Mathematicians think that our inability to discover an efficient algorithm for such problems is inherent in the nature of the problems themselves, because the time required to solve the problem is an exponential function of the size of the problem.

QUESTIONS

1. Use systematic trial to solve the two problems on the opposite page.

2. A carpenter is making wooden inserts for windows. He needs pieces of trim as follows.
   44 cm (4 pieces)
   59 cm (6 pieces)
   74 cm (6 pieces)
   88 cm (4 pieces)
   145 cm (3 pieces)
   The total length of the pieces is less than 18 m. Determine if it is possible to cut them from six 3 m lengths of trim.

3. If the time required to solve a problem is a polynomial function of the size of the problem, then the problem can be solved by a computer in a reasonable time. To see why, compare polynomial and exponential functions as follows.
   A polynomial function $y = f(x)$ and an exponential function $y = g(x)$ are given. Use a calculator to evaluate each function for $x = 10, 50, 100,$ and 300.
   a) $f(x) = x^2$ and $g(x) = 2^x$
   b) $f(x) = x^3$ and $g(x) = 1.5^x$
   c) $f(x) = x^{10}$ and $g(x) = 1.1^x$

4. Based on the results of *Question 3*, what conclusion might you make about how the values of exponential and polynomial functions compare for large values of the variable?

THE MATHEMATICAL MIND

Pascal's Triangle

This triangular array of numbers has interested mathematicians for centuries. It was called the "Precious Mirror of the Four Elements" by Shi-Chieh, a Chinese mathematician of the thirteenth century. But the triangle carries the name of the great French mathematician Blaise Pascal (1623-1662) because of his work with the properties of the triangle.

```
                        1
1st row ──▶  1        1  ──1st diagonal
2nd row ──▶ 1      2      1  ──2nd diagonal
          1      3      3      1
        1      4      6      4      1
      1      5     10     10      5      1
    1      6     15     20     15      6      1
  1      7     21     35     35     21      7      1
```

   Each row of the triangle starts and ends with a 1. The other numbers in each row can be obtained from the previous row. For example, in the 5th row, each of the numbers 5, 10, 10, and 5 is the sum of the two numbers immediately above it. This is the *defining property* of the triangle. As a consequence of this property, Pascal's triangle has many other properties and applications. A few of these are suggested below. As you work with the triangle, you may notice others.

1. Use the defining property to write out the triangle down to the 10th row.

2. Add the numbers in each row. What do you notice?

3. Why do the numbers 1, 2, 3, 4, . . . appear in the first diagonal?

4. Add the first few numbers in the first diagonal. Can you find the sum in the triangle? Try to explain the result using the defining property.

5. a) What is the second number in the 50th row? How can you determine the second number in any row?

   b) What is the third number in the 50th row? How can you determine the third number in any row?

Pascal's triangle and combinations

Pascal's triangle is useful because it contains the values of $\binom{n}{r}$. For example, the number of combinations of 6 things taken 2 at a time is $\binom{6}{2}$, which is equal to 15. Look for the *3rd number* in the 6th row of the triangle; you will find that this is also 15.

6. Why is $\binom{6}{2}$ the third number in the sixth row, not the second number?

7. Use Pascal's triangle to evaluate each expression.

   a) $\binom{4}{2}$ b) $\binom{6}{4}$ c) $\binom{7}{3}$ d) $\binom{8}{5}$ e) $\binom{9}{4}$

8. The triangle is symmetric, since numbers equidistant from the ends of each row are equal.

   a) Evaluate $\binom{8}{3}$ and $\binom{8}{5}$.

   b) Explain why the number of ways of choosing 3 items from a set of 8 items should be the same as the number of ways of choosing 5 items from the same set of 8 items.

   c) Prove algebraically that $\binom{n}{r} = \binom{n}{n-r}$.

9. We can explain why Pascal's triangle contains the values of $\binom{n}{r}$ by showing that the defining property is also a property of $\binom{n}{r}$.

   a) Evaluate $\binom{8}{3}$ and $\binom{7}{3} + \binom{7}{2}$.

   b) Explain why the number of ways of choosing 3 items from a set of 8 items should be the same as the number of ways of choosing 3 items from a set of 7 items *plus* the number of ways of choosing 2 items from a set of 7 items.

   c) Prove algebraically that $\binom{n}{r} = \binom{n-1}{r} + \binom{n-1}{r-1}$.

10. You may have discovered that the sum of the numbers in each row of Pascal's triangle is a power of 2.

    a) Evaluate $\binom{5}{0} + \binom{5}{1} + \binom{5}{2} + \binom{5}{3} + \binom{5}{4} + \binom{5}{5}$.

    b) What does the sum in part a) represent, with respect to choosing items from a set of 5 items?

    c) Using the meaning from part b), explain why the sum in part a) should be a power of 2.

11. Find a formula for the greatest number in the nth row of Pascal's triangle.

THE MATHEMATICAL MIND

Staircase Series

More than two thousands years ago, the ancient Greeks knew the sums for certain series. Though their algebraic development was not sufficiently advanced to be of much help, they were able to give geometric representations of such series.

For the series of natural numbers: $1 + 2 + 3 + 4 + \ldots$, they could find the sum of any number of terms geometrically. For example, the sum of the first 8 terms can be represented by the squares in a *staircase* pattern:

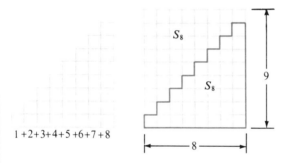

$1 + 2 + 3 + 4 + 5 + 6 + 7 + 8$

They arranged two of these patterns to form an 8 by 9 rectangle, as in the diagram. If S_8 represents the sum of the first 8 terms, then $2S_8$ represents the area of the rectangle.

$$2S_8 = 8 \times 9$$
$$= 72$$
$$S_8 = 36$$

The sum of the first 8 terms is 36.

With the efficiency of algebra available, if S_n represents the sum of the first n terms, then $2S_n$ represents the area of the rectangle.

$$2S_n = n(n + 1)$$
$$S_n = \frac{n(n + 1)}{2}$$

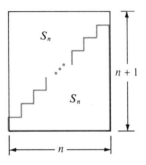

1. a) Represent geometrically the sum of the series: $1 + 3 + 5 + 7$.

   b) If the nth odd number can be written $2n - 1$, find an expression for the sum of the first n odd numbers.

2. a) Represent geometrically the sum of the series: $2 + 4 + 6 + 8$.

   b) If the nth even number can be written $2n$, find an expression for the sum of the first n even numbers.

3. a) Represent geometrically the sum of the series: $3 + 6 + 9 + 12$.

   b) If the nth multiple of 3 can be written $3n$, find an expression for the sum of the first n multiples of 3.

THE MATHEMATICAL MIND

Infinity

The concept of infinity has intrigued mathematicians and non-mathematicians alike for centuries.

Infinity in Language

Great fleas have little fleas upon
   their backs to bit 'em
And little fleas have lesser fleas,
   and so *ad infinitum*,
And the great fleas themselves, in turn,
   have greater fleas to go on,
While these again have greater still,
   and greater still, and so on.
               A. de Morgan

I could be bounded in a nutshell and
count myself a king of infinite space.
            William Shakespeare

The notion of infinity is our greatest
friend; it is also the greatest enemy of
our peace of mind.
            James Pierpont

Infinity in Art

Circle Limit III
By Maurits Escher

Infinity in Mathematics

About two hundred years ago mathematicians noticed some strange results when they began to work with infinite quantities. Here is a small sample of some of the difficulties they encountered. Some of the world's greatest mathematicians were surprised by results such as these, and it was many years before the concept of infinity was understood.

In arithmetic
Natural numbers: 1, 2, 3, 4, . . .
Even numbers: 2, 4, 6, 8, . . .
Since the natural numbers include both odd and even numbers, there appear to be twice as many natural numbers as even numbers. But the natural numbers can be paired with the even numbers as shown above. This suggests that there are the same number of even numbers as natural numbers!

In geometry

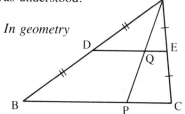

D and E are midpoints of two sides of △ABC. Since BC is twice as long as DE, it contains twice as many points as DE. But any point P on BC can be paired with a corresponding point Q on DE by joining PA. This suggests that DE contains the same number of points as BC!

Examples like the two above convinced mathematicians that when they deal with infinite sets, they need to define what is meant by the ''number'' of quantities in those sets.

In arithmetic

$$\frac{1}{3} = 0.333\ 333\ .\ .\ .\ ,\ \text{or } 0.\overline{3}$$

$$\frac{2}{3} = 0.666\ 666\ .\ .\ .\ ,\ \text{or } 0.\overline{6}$$

Add. $\overline{1} = \overline{0.999\ 999}\ .\ .\ .\ ,\ \text{or } 0.\overline{9}$

But 0.999 999 . . . is never exactly equal to 1; no matter how many 9s we take, this expression will always be less than 1. How can a quantity that is less than 1 be equal to 1? The answer is that we can make 0.999 999 . . . as close to 1 as we like by taking enough 9s. This is what we mean when we write 1 = 0.999 999 . . ., or $0.\overline{9}$.

In algebra
Consider the infinite series
$1 + 2 + 4 + 8 + 16 + . . .$
Let $S = 1 + 2 + 4 + 8 + 16 + . . .$
$\quad S = 1 + 2(1 + 2 + 4 + 8 + 16 + . . .)$
$\quad S = 1 + 2S$
Hence, $S = -1$
But, how can a series of infinitely many positive terms have a sum of -1? The answer, of course, is that it can't. Yet, the algebra above appears correct. Hence, mathematicians began to realize that they cannot assume that familiar algebraic operations can always be performed with infinite quantities.

QUESTIONS

1. Consider the quotation by A. de Morgan. What does de Morgan mean by "ad infinitum?"

2. In his quotation, A. de Morgan describes the infinitely large and the infinitely small. How does Escher's print, Circle Limit III, illustrate the infinitely large and the infinitely small?

3. This quotation appeared in Readers' Digest magazine some years ago.

   "High up in the North, in the land called Svetjod, there stands a rock. It is a thousand miles long and a thousand miles high. Once every thousand years a little bird comes to sharpen its beak. When the rock has thus been worn away, then a single day of eternity will have gone by."

   According to this quotation, how long is a "single day of eternity"? Make any assumptions that seem reasonable.

4. Here is another example of an infinite series that can lead to absurd results.
   Let $S = 1 - 1 + 1 - 1 + 1 - 1 + \ldots$
   $$S = (1 - 1) + (1 - 1) + (1 - 1) + \ldots$$
   $$S = 0 + 0 + 0 + \ldots$$
   $$S = 0$$
   Assuming that the rules of algebra apply, demonstrate that:
   a) $S = 0.5$ b) $S = 1$.

In *Question 4*, and the series on the previous page, one reason for the absurd results is that the sum S does not exist. But there are other examples of series for which the corresponding sum S *does* exist, and yet similar contradictory results can be obtained!

5. Here is a "proof" of the formula for the sum of an infinite geometric series.
   Let $S = a + ar + ar^2 + ar^3 + \ldots$
   $$S = a + r(a + ar + ar^2 + \ldots)$$
   $$S = a + rS$$
   $$S(1 - r) = a$$
   $$S = \frac{a}{1 - r} \quad (\text{if } r \neq 1)$$

   Although this "proof" leads to the correct formula, it is not a valid proof of the formula. Explain the error.

COMPUTER POWER

The Snowflake Curve and Fractal Geometry

About a hundred years ago, mathematicians devised some strange curves to serve as counterexamples to disprove certain intuitive ideas about geometry. For example, we might think that a figure cannot have an infinite perimeter. But in 1906, Helge von Koch came up with a curve to show that it can! To visualize this curve, we construct a sequence of polygons S_1, S_2, S_3, . . . as follows.

S_1 is an equilateral triangle.

To obtain S_2, construct an equilateral triangle on each side of S_1 and remove the base.

S_3 is obtained from S_2 in the same way as S_2 is obtained from S_1.

S_1

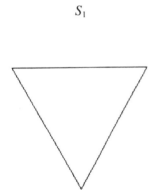

S_2

S_3

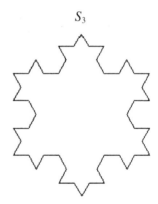

Continue in the same way to obtain the other polygons of the sequence.

S_4 S_5

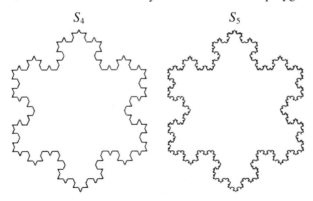

• • •

It can be proved that these polygons come closer and closer to a certain limiting curve, called the *snowflake curve*.

QUESTIONS

1. Assume that the equilateral triangle S_1 has sides 3 cm long.
   a) Calculate the perimeters of the five polygons shown.
   b) Calculate the areas of the five polygons.
   c) Calculate the area of the region enclosed by the snowflake curve, and explain why this region has an infinite perimeter.

2. Write recursive definitions for the sequence of:
   a) polygons $S_1, S_2, S_3, \ldots$ b) perimeters $P_1, P_2, P_3, \ldots$
   c) areas $A_1, A_2, A_3, \ldots$

Some computer languages are well suited for displaying figures defined recursively on the screen. The two LOGO procedures below define a command called SNOWFLAKE. (On some computers it may be necessary to replace SETPOS in the second line with SETXY:)

```
TO SNOWFLAKE :X
CS PU SETPOS [-90 52] RT 90 PD
MAKE "SIZE 180
MAKE "N 5 - :X
MAKE "X 1
REPEAT :N [MAKE "X :X * 3]
REPEAT 3 [DRAW :SIZE :X RT 120]
END

TO DRAW :SIZE :X
IF :SIZE < :X [FD :SIZE STOP]
DRAW :SIZE / 3 :X LT 60
DRAW :SIZE / 3 :X RT 120
DRAW :SIZE / 3 :X LT 60
DRAW :SIZE / 3 :X
END
```

3. If you have a computer with LOGO, experiment with the SNOWFLAKE command. For example, to display the polygon S_3 on the screen, type SNOWFLAKE 3. Try to get the best example you can within the limitations of your computer screen.

The snowflake curve is one of several weird curves that were introduced early in the 20th century. Another curve passes through every point inside a square! Still another intersects itself at every one of its points! At the time, these curves were dismissed by mathematicians as little more than pathological curiosities. No one would have thought that 70 years later they would be an important part of a new kind of geometry called *fractal geometry*.

Fractal geometry was introduced in 1977 by Benoit B. Mandelbrot for the purpose of modelling natural phenomena that are irregular (or crinkled) over several different size scales. Examples include coastlines, the surface of the lungs, the network of arteries and veins in the body, the branching structure of plants, the thermal agitation of molecules in a fluid (Brownian motion), sponges, and even the rings of Saturn.

Fractal geometry deals with novel kinds of curves and surfaces with a fractional dimension! For example, the snowflake curve is not two-dimensional because it does not include the points inside it. And, it is not one-dimensional either because it zigzags infinitely often. We can find the dimension of the snowflake curve as follows.

A key feature of the snowflake curve is its self-similarity. This means that parts of it are similar to larger copies of themselves. For example, the two parts shown are similar. The larger part is a $3\times$ enlargement of the smaller, and 4 copies of the smaller part are needed to make the enlargement.

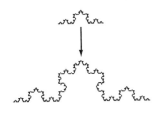

Consider what happens with simpler self-similar figures such as a line segment, a square, or a cube.

- In *1 dimension*, to make a $3\times$ enlargement of a line segment, we used 3^1, or 3 copies.

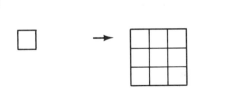

- In *2 dimensions*, to make a $3\times$ enlargement of a square, we need 3^2, or 9 copies.

- In *3 dimensions*, to make a $3\times$ enlargement of a cube, we need 3^3, or 27 copies.

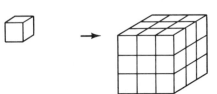

Observe that, in each case, the number of copies needed to make the enlargement is a power of the scale factor, and the exponent is the number of dimensions.

4. Let x represent the dimension of the snowflake curve. Use the above observation to write an exponential equation in x. Solve the equation to obtain the dimension of the snowflake curve.

Fractal geometry is a new and complicated branch of geometry that is accessible only with computers. Computers are needed to handle the enormous computations involved in recursive processes, and to display the intricate results. The example below provides one small glimpse of this new world. It is a set of points that is studied in fractal geometry.

5. Examine the illustration carefully.
   a) Describe as many patterns in it as you can find.
   b) Find as many examples of self-similarity as you can.

Answers

See Teacher's Resource Book for graphs.

Chapter 1

Exercises 1-1, page 4

1. a, c, d

2. a) 10 **b)** 1.6 **c)** 0.3 **d)** $\dfrac{7}{9}$ **e)** $\dfrac{11}{6}$

3. a) $\sqrt{30}$ **b)** $\sqrt{21}$ **c)** $56\sqrt{6}$ **d)** $15\sqrt{42}$
e) $-96\sqrt{77}$ **f)** $75\sqrt{70}$

4. a) $3\sqrt{2}$ **b)** $2\sqrt{3}$ **c)** $5\sqrt{2}$ **d)** $4\sqrt{5}$
e) $4\sqrt{7}$ **f)** $2\sqrt{33}$

5. a) $30\sqrt{2}$ **b)** $140\sqrt{2}$ **c)** $48\sqrt{15}$
d) $-108\sqrt{10}$ **e)** $-180\sqrt{2}$ **f)** $140\sqrt{5}$

6. Mixed radicals: b, d, f
Entire radicals: a, c, e
a) $4\sqrt{2}$ **b)** $\sqrt{24}$ **c)** $7\sqrt{2}$ **d)** $\sqrt{45}$
e) $8\sqrt{5}$ **f)** $\sqrt{405}$

7. a) 180 **b)** $720\sqrt{3}$ **c)** $108\sqrt{5}$ **d)** $-360\sqrt{5}$

8. Estimates may vary. **a)** 5.5 **b)** 14.1
c) 11.2 **d)** 0.95 **e)** 12.2 **f)** 1.6

9. a) $2\sqrt{10}, 4\sqrt{3}, 5\sqrt{2}, 3\sqrt{6}, 2\sqrt{14}$
b) $-4\sqrt{6}, -4\sqrt{5}, -5\sqrt{3}, -6\sqrt{2}, -2\sqrt{17}$
c) $6\sqrt{3}, 4\sqrt{7}, 5\sqrt{5}, 3\sqrt{14}, 8\sqrt{2}$

11. 16 cm^2

12. a) $5\sqrt{3}$ **b)** $7\sqrt{2}$ **c)** $4\sqrt{3}$ **d)** $-8\sqrt{3}$
e) $2\sqrt[3]{7}$ **f)** $\dfrac{3}{4}\sqrt{12}$

Exercises 1-2, page 8

1. a) $3\sqrt{5}$ **b)** $3\sqrt{3}$ **c)** $5\sqrt{2}$ **d)** $13\sqrt{7}$
e) $8\sqrt{10}$ **f)** $9\sqrt{3}$

2. a) $2\sqrt{2}$ **b)** $7\sqrt{3}$ **c)** $5\sqrt{6}$ **d)** $-2\sqrt{2}$
e) $8\sqrt{7}$ **f)** $\sqrt{5}$

3. a) $2\sqrt{3}$ **b)** $26\sqrt{6}$ **c)** $9\sqrt{7}$ **d)** 0
e) $63\sqrt{6}$ **f)** $-4\sqrt{5}$

4. a) $\sqrt{15} + \sqrt{21}$ **b)** $28\sqrt{6} - 12\sqrt{15}$
c) $10\sqrt{6a} + 20\sqrt{6b}$ **d)** $90\sqrt{3} - 63\sqrt{15}$
e) $8\sqrt{2y} - 6y$ **f)** 154

5. a) $1 + \sqrt{15}$ **b)** $-32 + \sqrt{35}$
c) $15x - \sqrt{xy} - 6y$ **d)** $30 - 14\sqrt{6}$
e) $192 + 90\sqrt{2}$ **f)** $16m - 46\sqrt{mn} + 15n$

6. a) $3\sqrt{7}$ **b)** $-\dfrac{1}{3}\sqrt{5}$ **c)** $-3\sqrt{13}$ **d)** $6\sqrt{14}$
e) $-\dfrac{2}{5}\sqrt{11}$ **f)** $-15\sqrt{17}$ **g)** $8\sqrt{5}$ **h)** $\dfrac{2}{3}\sqrt{5}$

7. a) $2\sqrt{5}$ **b)** $27\sqrt{2}$ **c)** $-11\sqrt{6}$ **d)** $19\sqrt{2}$
e) $-17\sqrt{10}$ **f)** $10\sqrt{5}$

8. a) $12\sqrt{14} - 30$ **b)** -72 **c)** $30(\sqrt{3} - \sqrt{2})$
d) $36\sqrt{2} + 8\sqrt{21} - 60$ **e)** $35a - 35\sqrt{2a}$
f) $32\sqrt{2b} - 16\sqrt{3b} - 24b$

9. a) 3 **b)** $9m - 4n$ **c)** -32
d) $104 - 60\sqrt{3}$ **e)** $49x + 56\sqrt{xy} + 16y$
f) $404\sqrt{2} + 60\sqrt{42}$

10. a) 8 **b)** $-6\sqrt{3}$ **c)** $-\dfrac{1}{2}$ **d)** $4\sqrt{5}$
e) $\dfrac{15}{4}\sqrt{2}$ **f)** $-\dfrac{20}{3}\sqrt{2}$ **g)** $\sqrt{2}$ **h)** $\sqrt{3}$

11. a) i) $\sqrt{2}$ **ii)** $\sqrt{3}$ **b)** 4

12. a) i) 2 **ii)** $\sqrt{5}$ **b) i)** 9 **ii)** 8

13. $\dfrac{2\sqrt{3}}{3}$

Exercises 1-3, page 11

1. a) $\dfrac{2\sqrt{5}}{5}$ **b)** $\dfrac{7\sqrt{11}}{11}$ **c)** $-\dfrac{4\sqrt{3}}{3}$ **d)** $\dfrac{5\sqrt{14}}{7}$
e) $-2\sqrt{30}$ **f)** $\dfrac{12\sqrt{35}}{35}$ **g)** $3\sqrt{10}$
h) $-\dfrac{5\sqrt{21}}{3}$

2. a) $\dfrac{3\sqrt{30}}{10}$ **b)** $\sqrt{10}$ **c)** $-3\sqrt{6}$ **d)** $\dfrac{5\sqrt{6}}{4}$
e) $\dfrac{4\sqrt{21}}{3}$ **f)** $\dfrac{\sqrt{21}}{2}$ **g)** $\dfrac{4\sqrt{30}}{3}$ **h)** $\dfrac{27}{4}$

3. a) $\dfrac{6 + 4\sqrt{3}}{3}$ **b)** $\dfrac{35 - 3\sqrt{7}}{7}$ **c)** $\dfrac{20 - 2\sqrt{5}}{5}$
d) $2\sqrt{6} - 1$ **e)** $\dfrac{8\sqrt{30} + 5}{5}$ **f)** $3\sqrt{5} - 1$
g) $\dfrac{10\sqrt{3} + 3\sqrt{2}}{3}$ **h)** $\dfrac{\sqrt{6}}{2}$

4. a) $\dfrac{\sqrt{15} + \sqrt{6}}{3}$ **b)** $\dfrac{\sqrt{35} - \sqrt{15}}{4}$
c) $\dfrac{8\sqrt{11} + \sqrt{55}}{59}$ **d)** $\dfrac{2\sqrt{30} - 2\sqrt{15}}{3}$
e) $\dfrac{-30\sqrt{2} - 25\sqrt{6}}{13}$ **f)** $\dfrac{4\sqrt{105} + 4\sqrt{70}}{5}$
g) $\dfrac{30\sqrt{3} - 6\sqrt{6}}{23}$ **h)** $\dfrac{3\sqrt{55} + 15}{2}$

5. a) $\dfrac{\sqrt{6}}{2}$ **b)** $\dfrac{32 + 7\sqrt{6}}{10}$ **c)** $\sqrt{15}$

d) $\dfrac{42 + 17\sqrt{5}}{29}$ **e)** $\dfrac{27 - 7\sqrt{21}}{30}$

f) $\dfrac{13\sqrt{2} - 3\sqrt{7}}{25}$

6. a) $\dfrac{5x\sqrt{y}}{y}$ **b)** $\dfrac{3\sqrt{m^2 - mn}}{m - n}$ **c)** $\dfrac{3\sqrt{2a + b}}{2a + b}$

d) $\dfrac{x\sqrt{x} - x}{x - 1}$ **e)** $\dfrac{2\sqrt{6}x + 2\sqrt{3}}{2x^2 - 1}$ **f)** $\dfrac{-3 - \sqrt{x}}{9 - x}$

g) $\dfrac{2\sqrt{5}a + 2a\sqrt{a}}{5 - a}$ **h)** $\dfrac{5x(\sqrt{x} - \sqrt{3})}{x - 3}$

7. a) $\dfrac{\sqrt{2}}{2}$ **b)** $\dfrac{\sqrt{3}}{6}$ **c)** $\dfrac{\sqrt{2}}{10}$ **d)** $\sqrt{2} + 1$

e) $\sqrt{3} - \sqrt{2}$ **f)** $\dfrac{2\sqrt{5} + 3\sqrt{2}}{2}$

8. a) 4 **b)** $\dfrac{2\sqrt{5} + 4\sqrt{2}}{3}$ **c)** $5\sqrt{2} - 2$

d) $\dfrac{2\sqrt{x}}{x - y}$ **e)** $\dfrac{2m\sqrt{n}}{m - n}$ **f)** $\dfrac{3a\sqrt{2a} + 5ab}{2a - b^2}$

9. a) $\dfrac{1}{2\sqrt{2}}$ **b)** $\dfrac{5}{3\sqrt{5}}$ **c)** $\dfrac{1}{y\sqrt{x}}$ **d)** $\dfrac{x - 1}{x(\sqrt{x} - 1)}$

e) $\dfrac{a - 4b}{\sqrt{a}(\sqrt{a} - 2\sqrt{b})}$ **f)** $\dfrac{-m + 4n^2}{(\sqrt{m} - \sqrt{n})(\sqrt{m} + 2n)}$

g) $\dfrac{x - y}{(\sqrt{x} + \sqrt{y})^2}$ **h)** $\dfrac{4a - 9b}{(2\sqrt{a} + 3\sqrt{b})^2}$

Exercises 1-4, page 14

1. a, b, d, h **2.** a, c, d, g, h
3. b, c—rational; a, d, e, f—irrational
4. a) $\mathbb{Q}', \mathbb{R}$ **b)** $\mathbb{Q}, \mathbb{R}$ **c)** $\mathbb{N}, \mathbb{Z}, \mathbb{Q}, \mathbb{R}$
d) $\mathbb{Q}', \mathbb{R}$ **e)** $\mathbb{Q}, \mathbb{R}$ **f)** $\mathbb{Q}', \mathbb{R}$ **g)** $\mathbb{Q}', \mathbb{R}$
h) $\mathbb{Q}', \mathbb{R}$

6. Answers may vary. Examples are:
a) 2.579 18 and 2.579 181 181 118...
b) $-6.327\ 329$ and $-6.327\ 329\ 010\ 010\ 001...$
c) 4.190 15 and 4.190 151 151 115...

7. a) $\dfrac{4}{9}, \dfrac{6}{9}$ **b)** $\sqrt{0.999\ 999\ 9}$

8. a) $\mathbb{N}, \mathbb{Z}, \mathbb{Q}, \mathbb{R}$ **b)** $\mathbb{Z}, \mathbb{Q}, \mathbb{R}$ **c)** $\mathbb{Q}, \mathbb{R}$
d) $\mathbb{N}, \mathbb{Z}, \mathbb{Q}, \mathbb{R}$ and $\mathbb{Z}, \mathbb{Q}, \mathbb{R}$ **e)** $\mathbb{Q}', \mathbb{R}$
f) No solution

Exercises 1-5, page 19

1. a) ± 2.74 **b)** ± 2.24 **c)** ± 2.26
2. a) $2, 7$ **b)** $5, -3$ **c)** $-2.5, -3$ **d)** $-0.8, 3$
3. a) $2 \pm \sqrt{3}$ **b)** $\dfrac{11 \pm \sqrt{41}}{4}$ **c)** No real roots

4. a) $-4, 28$ **b)** $-\dfrac{1}{4}, \dfrac{7}{3}$ **c)** $\dfrac{1}{5}, -1$

d) No real roots **e)** 1, 2 **f)** $\dfrac{12 \pm \sqrt{313}}{13}$

5. a) i) 2.56 m **ii)** 5.76 m **b) i)** 4.0 m/s
ii) 4.8 m/s
6. a) 4.5 m/s **b)** 6.3 m/s **c)** 10.0 m/s
7. a) 2 distinct real roots **b)** 2 distinct real roots
c) No real roots **d)** One double root
e) 2 distinct real roots **f)** No real roots
8. a) $x^2 - 10x + 21 = 0$
b) $x^2 - 5x - 36 = 0$
c) $3x^2 + 13x - 10 = 0$
d) $8x^2 + 10x + 3 = 0$
e) $2x^2 + 3x = 0$ **f)** $x^2 - 4x - 1 = 0$
9. a) $\pm 4\sqrt{6}$ **b)** -1.6 **c)** 9
10. a) $m \geqslant 6\sqrt{2}, \ m \leqslant -6\sqrt{2}$ **b)** $m \leqslant 0.9$
c) $m \geqslant 2\sqrt{3}, \ m \leqslant -2\sqrt{3}$
11. Some answers may vary. **a)** $\pm 13, \pm 8, \pm 7$
b) 3,4 **c)** 0, 4, 10, 18,...
12. a) 1413 km **b)** 455 km
13. a) 629.757 184 3 or $-635.157\ 184\ 3$
b) 3461.401 917 or $-3466.801\ 917$
14. a) $(3\sqrt{5} - 3)$ cm **b)** $(27\sqrt{5} - 45)$ cm^2
15. The left side is always positive and hence cannot equal zero.
16. There are no real numbers with this property.

Exercises 1-6, page 24

1. a) 16 **b)** 9 **c)** 16 **d)** 6.25 **e)** 1
f) 9
2. a) 23 **b)** 53 **c)** 37 **d)** 4 **e)** 4
f) $\dfrac{10}{3}$

3. a) $\dfrac{49}{18}$ **b)** $\dfrac{14}{5}$ **c)** No solution **d)** $\dfrac{19}{4}$
e) 3 **f)** 4

4. a, c, e **5.** $a = \sqrt{d^2 - b^2}$

6. a) 1 **b)** $\dfrac{19}{5}$ **c)** 1.5 **d)** No solution

e) $-\dfrac{1}{3}$ **f)** -4

7. a) 6 **b)** 9 **c)** 9 **d)** 1 **e)** 3 **f)** 11

8. a) 1 **b)** 7 **c)** 1 **d)** 3 **e)** 7 **f)** 5

9. a) 4, 5 **b)** 1, −11 **c)** 8 **d)** 9 **e)** 6
f) 7

10. a) $d = \left(\dfrac{v + 7}{8.2}\right)^2$ **b) i)** 67 m **ii)** 140 m

    iii) 240 m **c) i)** 51 km/h **ii)** 75 km/h
    iii) 93 km/h

11. a) $l = \dfrac{T^2 g}{4\pi^2}$ **b)** $a = \dfrac{v^2 - u^2}{2s}$ **c)** $W = \dfrac{2gE}{V^2}$

   d) $c = \dfrac{vm}{\sqrt{m^2 - M^2}}$ **e)** $k = \dfrac{F}{m(v^2 + u^2)}$

   f) $E = \dfrac{h^2 - 2ae^2 m}{2a^2 m}$

12. $h = \sqrt{\left(\dfrac{A}{\pi r} - r\right)^2 - r^2}$

13. 20 cm, 21 cm, 29 cm **14.** 9, 16

15. $h = 2r \pm \sqrt{4r^2 - c^2}$

16. a) $h = r$ **b)** $c \leqslant 2r$ **17.** c, d, e

Exercises 1-7, page 28

1. a) 1.7 **b)** 2.3 **c)** −2.7, −1.1, 0.5, 3.3
   d) −2.9, −1.4, 0, 1.4, 2.9

2. a) 0, ±3.2 **b)** 3.6, 2 **c)** −2, −1.5, 3.7
   d) 4

3. a) −3.5, −0.7, 4.2 **b)** 2.3 **c)** ±1.2, ±3.7
   d) −2.3, 3.2

4. a) 1.6 **b)** 3.5 **c)** −3.3, −0.6, 1.2, 2.7
   d) −2.1, 3.2

5. There could be 2 negative roots which are
approximately equal, or there could be no real
roots. **9.** About 4.5 s

10. a) i) $x^3 - 12x + 10 = 0$
   ii) $x^3 - 12x + 20 = 0, x^3 - 12x - 20 = 0$
   b) i) $-16 < k < 16$ **ii)** $k = \pm 16$
   iii) $k > 16; k < -16$

11. a)

n	1	2	3	4	5	6
$n^3 + n^2$	2	12	36	80	150	252

n	7	8	9	10
$n^3 + n^2$	392	576	810	1100

  b) 7 **c)** No

12. About 7.9 cm by 5.3 cm by 11.8 cm

Mathematics Around Us, page 32

1. 4.5, 18 **2.** 4 km **3.** The graph would be
stretched vertically by a factor of 4.

Exercises 1-8, page 35

1. a) 0, 2, −5 **b)** 0, $-\dfrac{3}{2}$, 4 **c)** 0, −3, −7

   d) 0, $-\dfrac{7}{3}, \dfrac{3}{2}$ **e)** 0, ±2 **f)** 0, −2, −3

2. a) 0 **b) i)** $-\dfrac{1}{2}$, 3 **ii)** $\pm\dfrac{3}{2}$ **iii)** $\dfrac{5}{2}$, 3

   iv) 0, $-\dfrac{2}{3}$, −4 **v)** 0, $\pm\dfrac{5}{3}$ **vi)** 3, 4

3. a) 2 **b)** −5, ±3 **c)** $-2, \dfrac{1}{2}$, 3 **d)** $\pm 2, \dfrac{2}{3}$

4. a) −2, 3, −4 **b)** 1 **c)** 1, 2, $-\dfrac{3}{2}$

   d) $-\dfrac{1}{2}, \pm\dfrac{3}{2}$

5. a) 2 **b)** ±3, 2 **c)** $-1, \dfrac{-4 \pm \sqrt{6}}{2}$ **d)** $\dfrac{2}{3}$

6. a) −2, −3, −4 **b)** −4, −5, −6

7. a) 3 **b)** −5

8. 10 cm by 6 cm by 1 cm or $\left(\dfrac{9 - \sqrt{21}}{2}\right)$ cm by
   $(3 + \sqrt{21})$ cm by $(\sqrt{21} - 1)$ cm

9. ±22, ±23

10. a) $x^3 - 8x^2 + 17x - 10 = 0$
   b) $x^3 - 3x^2 - 3x + 1 = 0$
   c) $2x^4 - x^3 - 19x^2 + 9x + 9 = 0$
   d) $4x^3 - 8x^2 - 23x - 11 = 0$

11. a) 13; 5, $-\dfrac{1}{2}$ **b)** −104; $\pm\dfrac{2}{5}$, −2

   c) 20; $\dfrac{9 \pm \sqrt{57}}{6}$ **d)** 23; $-\dfrac{1}{3}, 3 \pm \sqrt{2}$

12. a) ±1, ±2 **b)** 2

13. a) 1, 5, 14, 30 **b)** 24

The Mathematical Mind, page 37

1. a) 0.327 480 0 **b)** −0.673 593 1
   c) −0.568 946 4

Problem Solving, page 39

1. Typical results are: **a)** $3^2 + 4^2 + 12^2 = 13^2$;
$1^2 + 2^2 + 2^2 = 3^2$
b) $3^3 + 4^3 + 5^3 = 6^3$; $1^3 + 6^3 + 8^3 = 9^3$
c) $8^2 + 1^2 = 7^2 + 4^2$; $5^2 + 5^2 = 7^2 + 1^2$
d) $12^3 + 1^3 = 10^3 + 9^3$; $9^3 + 15^3 = 2^3 + 16^3$

2. $\sqrt{33}$

4. **a) i)** $2(R + r)$ **ii)** $2(R - r)$ **b) i)** $\dfrac{D + d}{4}$

ii) $\dfrac{D - d}{4}$ **c)** $A = \dfrac{\pi^2(D^2 - d^2)}{4}$,
$V = \dfrac{\pi^2(D^2 - d^2)(D - d)}{32}$

5. Rotate the curve 90° inside the circle.

6. 5, 2

8. The line passes from upper left to lower right through the centre, inclined at an angle of 45° to the horizontal.

Review Exercises, page 40

1. **a) i)** $2\sqrt{6}$ **ii)** $3\sqrt{5}$ **iii)** $4\sqrt{7}$ **iv)** $11\sqrt{5}$
b) i) $\sqrt{63}$ **ii)** $\sqrt{50}$ **iii)** $\sqrt{80}$ **iv)** $\sqrt{294}$

2. **a)** 60 **b)** 120 **c)** $-60\sqrt{42}$

3. **a)** $3\sqrt{30} + 16 - 10\sqrt{3}$
b) $8\sqrt{10} + 16\sqrt{6} - 12\sqrt{3}$
c) $14\sqrt{30} - 6\sqrt{13} - 4\sqrt{7}$

4. **a)** $-3\sqrt{x}$ **b)** $5\sqrt{2x} - 3\sqrt{3y}$
c) $6\sqrt{2x} + 12\sqrt{x} + 3\sqrt{2}$

5. **a)** $4\sqrt{6}$ **b)** $168\sqrt{2} - 105\sqrt{6}$
c) $132 - 72\sqrt{2}$

6. **a)** $3\sqrt{6}$ **b)** $-\dfrac{16\sqrt{5}}{5}$ **c)** $\sqrt{10}$ **d)** $3 + \sqrt{5}$

e) $\dfrac{42 - 4\sqrt{7} + 6\sqrt{14} - 4\sqrt{2}}{5}$ **f)** $\dfrac{9}{2}(\sqrt{10} - \sqrt{6})$

7. **a)** $7, -2$ **b)** $4, -8$ **c)** $1, -\dfrac{1}{3}$ **d)** $\dfrac{5}{2}, -\dfrac{2}{3}$

8. **a)** 6 **b)** 5 **c)** No solution

9. **a)** $m = 4$ or -3 **b)** $m > 4$ or $m < -3$
c) $-3 < m < 4$

10. a **11.** Yes **12. a)** -2.9 **b)** $0, \pm 3$

13. **a)** $1, \pm 2$ **b)** $-1, 2, 3$ **c)** -2 **d)** $1, 2, \pm 2$

Chapter 2

Exercises 2-1, page 46

1. **a)** Yes **b)** No **c)** Yes
2. **a)** D: $[0, +\infty$; R: $[1, 7]$ **b)** Not a function
c) D: $\mathbb{R}^*$; R:$\mathbb{R}^*$
3. **a)** Yes **b)** No **c)** Yes
4. **a)** D: $]-2, 4]$; R: $[-2, 2]$
b) D: $\mathbb{R}$; R: $[0, +\infty$ **c)** D: $[-2, +\infty$; R: $[0, +\infty$
5. **a)** D: $\mathbb{R}$; R: $\mathbb{R}$; yes
b) D: $\mathbb{R}$; R: $\{-5\}$; yes
c) D: 4; R: $\mathbb{R}$; no
6. **a)** -1 **b)** 5 **c)** 11 **d)** 1 **e)** -11
f) 2
7. **a)** $-17, 18, -4.5$ **b)** $4, 11, -4.75$
c) $6, 20, -0.25$
8. **a)** $-3, 2, -2$ **b)** $4, -2, -1$
9. **a)** 30 **b)** 24 **c)** 0 **d)** 10 **e)** 2
f) 1.25
10. **a)** -5 **b)** -8 **c)** -20 **d)** -6 **e)** -50
f) -8
11. **a)** $2a + 1$ **b)** $6a + 1$ **c)** $3 + 2y$
d) $2x + 3$ **e)** $3 - y$ **f)** $1 + y$ **g)** $4 - z$
h) $6 - 2x$ **i)** $4x + 2$ **j)** $15 - 5n$
k) $-6x - 3$ **l)** $2a - 6$
12. **a)** D: $\mathbb{R}$; R:$\mathbb{R}$
b) D: $\mathbb{R}$; R: $[0, +\infty$
c) D: $[0, +\infty$; R: $[0, +\infty$;
13. **a)** -4 **b)** -7 **c)** 8 **d)** 6 **e)** 6
f) 3
14. **a)** 1.5 **b)** 2 **c)** $\dfrac{2}{3}$ **d)** -3

Exercises 2-2, page 50

1. **a), c), d), e)** Yes **b), f)** No
2. **b)** D: all real numbers; $y \geqslant 5$
3. **b)** D: all real numbers; $y \geqslant -7$
4. **b)** $t \geqslant 0$; $0 \leqslant h \leqslant 82$ **c)** 51.4 m
5. **b)** 42.5 cm
6. **a)** D: all real numbers; $y \geqslant 0.5$
b) D: all real numbers; $y \leqslant 5$
7. **b)** 289 m/s, 13 068 m
8. **a)** 593.5 m **b)** 11.5 s
9. **a)** Height is quadrupled.
b) Height is multiplied by 9.
10. **a)** $A = \pi x^2 - 20x\pi + 100\pi$
c) $0 < x < 10$

11. a) $A = (16 - 4\pi)r^2$ **b)** $A = (2\sqrt{2} - 1)\pi r^2$
12. 2 min, 8.5 h, 9 days, 15 years
13. a) $k \doteq 1.56$ m/s^2 **b)** 66 m

Exercises 2-3, page 53

1. b) The vertex is on the y-axis. When q is positive, the vertex is q units above the x-axis. When q is negative, it is q units below the x-axis.
2. a) iii   **b)** iv   **c)** ii   **d)** i
3. a) $y = x^2 + 5$ **b)** $y = x^2$ **c)** $y = x^2 - 2$
   d) $y = x^2 - 6$
4. a) i) up   **ii)** $(0, 1)$ **iii)** 1
   b) i) up   **ii)** $(0, -4)$ **iii)** -4 **iv)** ± 2
   c) i) up   **ii)** $(0, 3)$ **iii)** 3
   d) i) up   **ii)** $(0, -6)$ **iii)** -6 **iv)** ± 2.5
5. a) i) up   **ii)** $(0, 5)$ **iii)** 5
   b) i) up   **ii)** $(0, -3)$ **iii)** -3 **iv)** ± 1.7
   c) i) up   **ii)** $(0, 2)$ **iii)** 2
   d) i) up   **ii)** $(0, 4)$ **iii)** 4
7. a) $y = x^2 + 2$ **b)** $y = x^2 - 9$
   c) $y = x^2 + 5$

Exercises 2-4, page 57

2. a) When $p < 0$, the graph of $y = (x - p)^2$ is to the left of that of $y = x^2$.
   b) When $p > 0$, the graph of $y = (x - p)^2$ is to the right of that of $y = x^2$.
3. a) iii   **b)** i   **c)** iv   **d)** ii
4. a) $y = (x + 2)^2$ **b)** $y = (x - 3)^2$
   c) $y = (x + 4)^2$ **d)** $y = (x - 5)^2$
5. a) i) $(-2,0)$ **ii)** $x + 2 = 0$ **iii)** up
   iv) 4
   b) i) $(-1,0)$ **ii)** $x + 1 = 0$ **iii)** up
   iv) 1
   c) i) $(3,0)$ **ii)** $x - 3 = 0$ **iii)** up   **iv)** 9
   d) i) $(4,0)$ **ii)** $x - 4 = 0$ **iii)** up   **iv)** 16
6. a) $y = (x + 2)^2$ **b)** $y = (x + 1)^2$
   c) $y = (x - 3)^2$ **d)** $y = (x - 4)^2$
7. a) i) $(-3,0)$ **ii)** $x + 3 = 0$ **iii)** up
   iv) 9
   b) i) $(8,0)$ **ii)** $x - 8 = 0$ **iii)** up   **iv)** 64
   c) i) $(2,0)$ **ii)** $x - 2 = 0$ **iii)** up   **iv)** 4
   d) i) $(-4,0)$ **ii)** $x + 4 = 0$ **iii)** up
   iv) 16
10. a) $y = (x - 4)^2$ **b)** $y = (x + 3)^2$
   c) $y = (x - 7)^2$

Mathematics Around Us, page 59

1. 0.44 s   **2.** 96 cm   **3.** 81 cm   **4.** 379 km/h

The Mathematical Mind, page 61

2. $f(x) = \begin{cases} x + 2, x < -2 \\ x^2, \quad -2 \leqslant x \leqslant 2 \\ x + 2, x \geqslant 2 \end{cases}$

3. Answers may vary.
4. Answers may vary, for example,
$$f(x) = \begin{cases} 1, \text{ if } x \text{ is rational} \\ -1, \text{ if } x \text{ is irrational} \end{cases}$$

Exercises 2-5, page 65

1. b) The parabola is expanded more: as a increases when $a > 0$; and as a decreases when $a < 0$.
2. a) iii   **b)** ii   **c)** i   **d)** iv
4. a) $y = 2x^2$ **b)** $y = -x^2$ **c)** $y = -\frac{1}{4}x^2$
   d) $y = 6x^2$
5. a) $y = -2.5x^2$ **b)** $y = \frac{5}{9}x^2$ **c)** $y = \frac{4}{27}x^2$
   d) $y = -3x^2$
6. $y = \frac{3}{4}x^2$

Exercises 2-6, page 67

1. a) i   **b)** iii   **c)** iv   **d)** ii
3. a) i) $(5,2)$ **ii)** $x - 5 = 0$ **iii)** 27
   b) i) $(-3,-8)$ **ii)** $x + 3 = 0$ **iii)** 10
   iv) $-1, -5$ **c) i)** $(-1,4)$ **ii)** $x + 1 = 0$
   iii) 0   **iv)** $0, -2$ **d) i)** $(2,-8)$
   ii) $x - 2 = 0$ **iii)** -6 **iv)** $6, -2$
7. a) $y = 2(x - 4)^2 - 1$ **b)** $y = -\frac{1}{3}(x + 2)^2 + 3$

   c) $y = -\frac{1}{2}(x + 3)^2 + 2$ **d)** $y = (x - 3)^2 - 4$
8. a) $y = (x - 3)^2 - 1$ **b)** $y = -2(x + 1)^2 + 4$
   c) $y = 3(x - 2)^2 - 27$
10. a) $y = x^2 + 5$ **b)** $y = -\frac{1}{2}x^2 + 3$

Exercises 2-7, page 74

1. a) $y = (x - 3)^2 - 1$ **b)** $y = (x + 5)^2 - 11$
   c) $y = 2(x + 1)^2 + 5$ **d)** $y = -2(x - 1)^2 + 7$
   e) $y = 3(x - 4)^2 - 8$ **f)** $y = -5(x + 2)^2 - 10$

Exercises 2-8, page 77

1. a) max., 4, 1   b) min., −4, 3
  c) min., −1, −2   d) max., 2, −3
  e) min., −8, 6   f) max., 3, 2

2. a) 5, min., 3   b) −3, min., −1
  c) 4, max., 1   d) −6, max., −2
  e) −9, min., 0   f) 7, max., 0
  g) −2, min., 3   h) 7, min., 2
  i) $\dfrac{25}{8}$, max., $\dfrac{5}{4}$

3. a) D: $\mathbb{R}$; R: $[2, +\infty$ b) D: $\mathbb{R}$; R: $-\infty, 80]$
  c) D: $\mathbb{R}$; R: $[-0.5, +\infty$

4. 125   **5.** 32   **6.** $1500

7. a) 256 m, 8 min   b) D: [0,16]; R: [−256,0]

8. $99 000 000   **9.** a) 250 km/h   b) 375 L/h

10. a) 4.8 m   b) 0.6 s   c) 1.58 s   d) 3 m

11. a) 9 A   b) 40.5 W

12. a) 40 m   b) 1 s   c) 3.8 s   d) 35 m
  e) $h = -5t^2 + 10t$

13. a) 1650 m   b) 18 s   c) 37 s

14. $b = \pm 2\sqrt{ac}, a > 0, c \geqslant 0$

Exercises 2-9, page 83

1. 4, −4   **2.** 6, 6   **3.** 30, 30   **4.** 10, −10

5. 8, 8   **6.** 14, 14   **7.** 9, 3

8. 7, −9   **9.** 150 m by 300 m   **10.** 5000 m²

11. a) 400 m²   b) 20 m by 20 m

12. 100 m by 150 m   **13.** $15

14. 70¢   **15.** 12.5 cm   **16.** 28.125 cm²

17. 300 m by 200 m   **18.** 14.1 cm, 15.9 cm

19. $\dfrac{1}{2}$ **20.** $\dfrac{p^2}{16}$ units²   **22.** 3.33

Exercises 2-10, page 86

1. a) Increasing on $\mathbb{R}$
  b) Increasing on [4, 8]; decreasing on $-\infty, 0]$
  c) Increasing on $-\infty, -2] \cup [0, +\infty$; decreasing on [−2, 0]
  d) Increasing on $[0, +\infty$; decreasing on $-\infty, 0]$
  e) Increasing on $-\infty, 0]$; decreasing on $[0, +\infty$
  f) Increasing on $[-2, +\infty$

2. a) Increasing on $[2, +\infty$; decreasing on $-\infty, 2]$
  b) Increasing on $-\infty, \dfrac{2}{3}]$; decreasing on $[\dfrac{2}{3}, +\infty$
  c) Increasing on $[\dfrac{3}{4}, +\infty$; decreasing on $-\infty, \dfrac{3}{4}]$
  d) Increasing on $-\infty, -\dfrac{2}{3}]$; decreasing on $[-\dfrac{2}{3}, +\infty$

  e) Increasing on $[\dfrac{1}{3}, +\infty$; decreasing on $-\infty, \dfrac{1}{3}]$
  f) Increasing on $-\infty, -20]$; decreasing on $[-20, +\infty$

3. [$0, $20]

4. a) $2   b) 4 months   c) 8 months

5. 12 days

6. a) 12 000   b) 10 years   c) 1990

Exercises 2-11, page 90

1. a) {−1, 1, 3}   b) {−3, 2.5}   c) {−6, 2}

2. a) {−4, 6}   b) {−1, 4}   c) {4}
  d) {−1.5, 2}   e) $\left\{\dfrac{2 \pm \sqrt{2}}{2}\right\}$ f) No zeros

3. a) {0, 1.5}   b) {−1, 2.5}   c) No solution

4. a) $f(x) = -\dfrac{1}{4}(x^2 + 2x - 15)$
  b) $f(x) = 2(x^2 - 8x + 12)$
  c) $f(x) = -x^2 + x + 2$
  d) $f(x) = -\dfrac{1}{2}(x^2 - x - 6)$
  e) $f(x) = -5(x^2 - 12x + 32)$

5. $f(x) = \dfrac{1}{3}(x^2 - 2x - 8)$

6. a) 6 s, 14 s   b) After 20 s

7. 4 s   **8.** a) 10 s, 20 s   b) 30.2 s

9. a) $1 200 000   b) 20   c) $400 000

10. $h(t) = -\dfrac{25}{4}t^2 + 25t$ **11.** 36 m

12. 20.2 min

Exercises 2-12, page 94

1. a) $f(x) > 0$ on $]-2, 2[\cup]4, +\infty$;
   $f(x) < 0$ on $-\infty, -2[\cup]2, 4[$
  b) $f(x) > 0$ on $-\infty, 0[\cup]4, +\infty$;
   $f(x) < 0$ on $[0, 4[$
  c) $f(x) > 0$ for $\forall x \in \mathbb{R}$

2. a) i) {−3, 5}
  iii) $f(x) > 0$ on $-\infty, -3[\cup]5, +\infty$;
   $f(x) < 0$ on $]-3, 5[$
  b) i) {−3, 4}
  iii) $f(x) > 0$ on $]-3, 4[$;
   $f(x) < 0$ on $-\infty, -3[\cup]4, +\infty$
  c) i) {0.5, 2}
  iii) $f(x) > 0$ on $-\infty, 0.5[\cup]2, +\infty$;
   $f(x) < 0$ on $]0.5, 2[$

3. a) $x < -2$ or $x > 3$ **b)** $0 \leqslant x \leqslant 2$
c) $x < 0$ or $x > 5$ **d)** $x \leqslant -2$ or $x \geqslant 4$

e) $x = \dfrac{2}{3}$ **f)** $-3 \leqslant x \leqslant 8$ **g)** No solution

h) $-\dfrac{5}{2} < x < \dfrac{4}{3}$ **i)** $x \in \mathbb{R}$

4. a) $-\infty, -2\,[\,\cup\,]\,6, +\infty$ **b)** $[0, 4]$ **c)** $\forall x \in \mathbb{R}$
5. a) $]0, 5[$ **b)** $]5, 8]$
6. 5 months   **7. a)** 30   **b)** Between 4 and 30
8. Between 4000 and 8000 seeds   **9.** 2 s
10. a) $x < 1$ or $x > 5$ **b)** $-2 < x < 7$
11. a) $]-3, 1\,[\,\cup\,]\,3, +\infty$ **b)** $[-5, 0]\cup[2, +\infty$
c) $-\infty, -1\,[\,\cup\,]\,0, 1[$ **d)** $[0, 1]\cup[2, +\infty$

Problem Solving, page 97

1. \$12.50
2. Answers may vary. Typical answers are:
$2^1 + 5^2 = 3^3; 4^1 + 11^2 = 5^3$

3. $\dfrac{1}{2}$ **4.** $0.25x^2$

5. There are four possibilities: 192, 384, 576; 219,
438, 657; 327, 654, 981; 273, 546, 819
6. 7, 3   **7. a)** 11   **b)** 2, 4, 6
9. $\pm 2, -1, -5$ **10.** $a + b + c + d$

Review Exercises, page 98

1. a) $\mathbb{R}; y \leqslant 9$ **b)** $\mathbb{R}; y \geqslant -9$
2. a) 2.78 m   **b)** 3.26 m
3. a) $y = (x + 2)^2$ **b)** $y = (x - 5)^2$
c) $y = (x + 6)^2$

4. a) $y = 4x^2$ **b)** $y = -2x^2$ **c)** $y = \dfrac{3}{2}x^2$

d) $y = \dfrac{5}{3}x^2$ **e)** $y = -\dfrac{3}{2}x^2$ **f)** $y = \dfrac{3}{4}x^2$

g) $y = \dfrac{4}{5}x^2$ **h)** $y = -2x^2$

5. a) $y = -(x + 3)^2 + 4$
b) $y = 2(x - 2)^2 - 2$

c) $y = \dfrac{1}{2}(x - 4)^2 - 4$

7. 10, \$40   **8.** 11, -13 **9.** 90¢

Chapter 3

Exercises 3-1, page 102

1. a) ± 5 **b)** ± 2 **c)** 0   **d)** No solution
2. a) $-5, 9$ **b)** $-1, -7$ **c)** $4, -6$ **d)** 7

e) $2, -\dfrac{2}{3}$ **f)** No solution   **g)** $9, -7$

h) $11, -1$ **i)** $3, -\dfrac{5}{3}$

3. a) 1   **b)** No solution   **c)** $-1, 7$ **d)** $\dfrac{1}{2}$

e) No solution   **f)** $\dfrac{1}{3}, \dfrac{1}{5}$

4. a) 1   **b)** $\dfrac{1}{2}$ **c)** 1   **d)** $\dfrac{1}{12}$

e) No solution   **f)** 0

5. a) $3, -5$ **b)** $1, -5$ **c)** $3.5, -1.5$ **d)** $\dfrac{4}{3}$

e) No solution   **f)** $-1.5, 4.5$
6. a) No solution   **b)** 4   **c)** No solution
d) 3
7. a) ± 2 **b)** $1, -5$ **c)** $0, -2$
d) No solution   **e), f)** All real numbers

8. a) $14, -3$ **b)** $\dfrac{1}{4}, \dfrac{1}{6}$ **c)** $5, -1$

d) $\{x \,|\, 1 \leqslant x \leqslant 3, x \in \mathbb{R}\}$

9. a) ± 4 **b)** $\dfrac{1}{2}$

c) No solution   **d)** All real numbers
10. a) $0, 5$ **b)** $\{x \,|\, 1 \leqslant x \leqslant 4, x \in \mathbb{R}\}$
c) No solution

Exercises 3-2, page 104

1. a) $-3 < x < 3$ **b)** $x > 4$ or $x < -4$
c) $-6 \leqslant x \leqslant 6$ **d)** $-3 < x < 7$

e) $x \geqslant \dfrac{8}{5}$ or $x \leqslant -\dfrac{8}{5}$

f) $-10 \leqslant x \leqslant 8$
2. a) $-3 \leqslant x \leqslant 5$ **b)** $x > 6$ or $x < -8$

c) $-5 < x < 4$ **d)** $-\dfrac{4}{3} < x < 2$

e) $x \geqslant 7$ or $x \leqslant -13$
f) $x \geqslant 3$ or $x \leqslant -2.5$
3. a) $\mathbb{R}$ **b)** $-1 \leqslant x \leqslant 6$

c) $x > \dfrac{1}{5}$ or $x < -1$ **d)** $\dfrac{1}{4} < x < \dfrac{3}{2}$

e) No solution   **f)** $x < \dfrac{1}{2}$

4. a) $-5 < x < 4$ **b)** $-6 \leqslant x \leqslant 2$
c) $x > 6$ or $x < -1.5$ **d)** $x > 1$
e) No solution **f)** $x > \dfrac{1}{2}$

5. a) $x \geqslant 2$ or $x \leqslant -\dfrac{8}{7}$
b) $-1 < x < 5$ **c)** $\mathbb{R}$ **d)** $x > 1$ **e)** $x = 2$
f) No solution

6. a) $-2 < x < 3$ **b)** $-\dfrac{17}{5} \leqslant x \leqslant 19$
c) No solution **d)** $-1 \leqslant x \leqslant 1$
7. a) $x < 5$ **b)** $x > 8$ or $x < -8$
c) $x > -\dfrac{7}{3}$ or $x < -13$ **d)** No solution

8. a) $5 - x + \dfrac{1}{x-2}$ **b)** $2 < x \leqslant 3.7808$

9. Answers may vary. Typical inequalities are:
a) $|x - 2| > x - 2$ **b)** $|x| > 0$
c) $|x - 1| < 2$ **d)** $|x - 1| > 2$
10. Answers may vary. Typical inequalities are:
a) $|x - 3| \geqslant 3 - x$ **b)** $|x - 2| \leqslant 2$
c) $|x - 2| > 2$ **d)** $|x - 2| > 0$
11. Answers may vary. Typical inequalities are
a) $|2 - 3x| < 3x - 4$ **b)** $|x + 1| > x - 1$
c) $|6 - 3x| \leqslant x - 2$

Exercises 3-3, page 108

1. a) 4 **b)** 4 **c)** 0 **d)** 11
4. a) D: $\mathbb{R}$; R: $[3, +\infty$; zeros: none; minimum: 3;
increasing on $[1, +\infty$; decreasing on $-\infty, 1]$;
$f(x) > 0$ for $\forall x \in \mathbb{R}$
b) D: $\mathbb{R}$; R: $[-2, +\infty$; zeros: $\{-7, 5\}$;
minimum: -2: increasing on $[-1, +\infty$;
decreasing on $-\infty, -1]$;
$g(x) > 0$ for $-\infty, -7 [\cup] 5, +\infty$;
$g(x) < 0$ for $]-7, 5[$
c) D: $\mathbb{R}$; R: $-\infty, 2]$; zeros: $\{-1.5, -0.5\}$;
maximum: 2; increasing on $-\infty, -1]$;
decreasing on $[-1, +\infty$;
$h(x) > 0$ for $]-1.5, -0.5[$;
$h(x) < 0$ for $-\infty, -1.5 [\cup] -0.5, +\infty$
5. a) $f(x) = 3|x - 2| + 1$; D: $\mathbb{R}$; R: $[1, +\infty$
b) $g(x) = -|x - 2| + 4$; D: $\mathbb{R}$; R: $-\infty, 4]$
c) $f(x) = |x - \dfrac{1}{2}| - 3$; D: $\mathbb{R}$; R: $[-3, +\infty$
6. a) $-3, 7$ **b)** No zeros **c)** 0, 3
7. a) $\dfrac{1}{3}, 1$ **b)** $-1, \dfrac{7}{3}$ **c)** $\dfrac{2}{3}$ **d)** No solution

8. a) $-\infty, -1 [\cup] 2, +\infty$ **b)** $[-1, 2]$
c) $-\infty, -3] \cup [4, +\infty$ **d)** No solution
9. Increasing on $-\infty, 1]$; decreasing on $[1, +\infty$
10. a) $f(x) = 2|x - 2| - 3$ **b)** $\{0.5, 3.5\}$
11. \$2.50 **12.** 30 min

Exercises 3-4, page 112

3. a) D: $\mathbb{R}_+$; R: $[-1, \infty$; zero: $\dfrac{1}{4}$; minimum: -1;
increasing on $[0, +\infty$
b) D: $[-1, +\infty$; R: $-\infty, 2]$; zero: 3, maximum: 2;
decreasing on $[-1, \infty$
c) D: $-\infty, 2]$; R: $-\infty, 1]$; zero: 1; maximum: 1;
increasing on $-\infty, 2]$
4. a) $\left[\dfrac{1}{3}, +\infty\right.$ **b)** $[-1.5, +\infty$ **c)** $-\infty, 2]$
5. a) D: $[-2.5, +\infty$; R: $[-3, +\infty$; zero: 2;
minimum: -3; increasing on $[-2.5, +\infty$
b) D: $[2, +\infty$; R: $-\infty, -1]$; zero: none;
maximum: -1; decreasing on $[2, +\infty$
6. a) 2.5 **b)** -12 **7. a)** 5 **b)** No solution
8 Decreasing on $-\infty, 2]$ **9.** $[-1, 3[$
10. $f(x) = \sqrt{2x + 4} + 1$
11. b) 10.7 m/s **c)** 20.1 m
12. b) 10 000 **c)** 2012

Problem Solving, page 115

2. Parallelograms **3.** $x^2 - 2px + q^2 = 0$
4. a) i) $(n - 2)^3$ **ii)** $6(n - 2)^2$ **iii)** $12(n - 2)$
iv) 8 **b)** $(n - 2)(n^2 + 2n + 4)$

Exercises 3-5, page 118

1. $\left(2, -\dfrac{1}{3}\right), \left(-\dfrac{1}{9}, 6\right), \left(\dfrac{1}{2}, -\dfrac{4}{3}\right)$
4. D: $\mathbb{R}^*$; R: $\mathbb{R}^*$; asymptotes: $x = 0$ and $y = 0$
a) Decreasing on $\mathbb{R}^*$ **b)** Increasing on $\mathbb{R}^*$
c) Decreasing on $\mathbb{R}^*$
5. $f(x) = -\dfrac{4}{3x}$ **6. a)** $f(x) = \dfrac{3}{2x}$ **b)** $f(x) = -\dfrac{2}{x}$
7. 20 **8. a)** $120 \, \Omega$ **b)** 1.5 A

Exercises 3-6, page 126

1. a) 3 **b)** -6 **c)** 3 **d)** 3 **e)** -5
f) -3 **g)** 9 **h)** 5
2. a) -4 **b)** 3 **c)** 3 **d)** -1 **e)** -2
f) 1.5 **g)** -3 **h)** -3.5
3. D: $\mathbb{R}$ **a)** R: $\{y = 3k, k \in \mathbb{Z}\}$
b), c), d) R: $\mathbb{Z}$

4. a) i) 1; 2   **ii)** left
iii) R: $\{y = 2k + 1, k \in \mathbb{Z}\}$
b) i) 1; 1   **ii)** left   **iii)** R: $\mathbb{Z}$
c) i) 1; 0.5   **ii)** left
iii) R: $\{y = \frac{1}{2}k, k \in \mathbb{Z}\}$
d) i) 0.5; 1   **ii)** right   **iii)** R: $\mathbb{Z}$
e) i) 1; 2   **ii)** right
iii) R: $\{y = 2k + 1, k \in \mathbb{Z}\}$
f) i) 3; 4   **ii)** left
iii) R: $\{y = 4k + 2, k \in \mathbb{Z}\}$ All D: $\mathbb{R}$
5. a) i) $4.00   **ii)** $9.00   **iii)** $11.00
6. b) R: {2.50, 3.00, 3.50, 4.00, 4. 50, 5.00, 5.50, 6.00, 6.50, 7.00}   **c)** $12.50
7. a) i) $3.00   **ii)** $5.00   **iii)** $7.00
c) $C(t) = -2[-t] - 1$

Exercises 3-7, page 129

1. a) ii   **b)** i   **c)** iii   **3. a)** ii   **b)** iv
5. a) D: $\mathbb{R}$; R: $[1, +\infty$ **b)** D: $\mathbb{R}$; R: $-\infty, -2]$
c) D: $[-1, +\infty$; R: $[-3, +\infty$
d) D: $-\infty, 1]$; R: $-\infty, 3]$
e) D: $\mathbb{R}$; R: $\{y = 2k + 1, k \in \mathbb{Z}\}$
f) D: $\mathbb{R}$; R: $\{y = 1 + 1.5k, k \in \mathbb{Z}\}$

Mathematics Around Us, page 131

3. a) i) Growth of corn plant   **ii)** Wind speed
iii) Survival rate

Exercises 3-8, page 134

1. a) Square-root   **b)** Inverse-variation
c) Greatest integer   **d)** Absolute-value
2. d
3. b) i) $6.00   **ii)** $10.00
c) i) 6 months   **ii)** $4.00
4. 7.1 s   **5.** 14.4 L
7. a) i) 7.5°C   **ii)** 2 P.M.   **b)** 12 h
8. a) 1.74 s   **b)** 1.50 m
9. a) i) 12 years   **ii)** 9 years   **iii)** 6.9 years
b) 18%
10. b) $15.50   **11.** 84 km
12. a) 30 000 L   **b)** 10 000 L   **c)** 8 h
d) D: [0, 12]; R: [10 000, 50 000]
13. b) 1 m   **c)** 5.3 m
14. a) $200   **b)** $500   **d)** $8000
15. 34 min 23 s   **16. a)** 333 m/s   **b)** 11.7°C
17. 18 units^2 **18.** $200   **19.** 7 years 9 months
20. b) 6   **c)** 9 days   **d)** 9 days   **e)** 6 days

Review Exercises, page 138

1. b) i) D: $\mathbb{R}$; R: $\mathbb{R}$ **ii)** D: $\mathbb{R}$; R: $\mathbb{R}$
iii) D: $\mathbb{R}^*$; R: $\mathbb{R}^*$ **iv)** D: $\mathbb{R}$; R: $\mathbb{Z}$
2. a) iii   **b)** ii   **c)** i   **d)** iv
6. a) D: $\mathbb{R}$; R: $-\infty, 2]$ **b)** D: $[1, +\infty$; R: $[3, +\infty$
c) D: $\mathbb{R}^*$; R: $\mathbb{R}^*$
d) D: $\mathbb{R}$; R: $\{y = 1 + 2.5 k, k \in \mathbb{Z}\}$

Cumulative Review, Chapters 1, 2, and 3, page 139

1. a) $13\sqrt{3}$ **b)** $-8\sqrt{2} - 4\sqrt{6}$
c) $6\sqrt{35} + 32\sqrt{15}$ **d)** 28

2. a) $\frac{11}{2}$ **b)** $\frac{12\sqrt{7}}{35}$ **c)** $8 - 3\sqrt{2}$ **d)** $\frac{30 + 2\sqrt{10}}{5}$

3. a) $\frac{1}{2}$ **b)** $\frac{9}{7}$ **c)** $\frac{7}{3}, -2$ **d)** $\frac{-2 \pm 3\sqrt{2}}{2}$

e) $-\frac{3}{5}, -1$ **f)** $-\frac{1}{2}, 3$

4. a) 1 double root   **b)** 2 distinct real roots
c) No real roots
5. $4x^2 + 5x - 6 = 0$

6. a) $k = \pm 2\sqrt{6}$ **b)** $k < -\frac{25}{8}$

7. a) 9   **b)** 6   **c)** 4   **d)** $\frac{6 - \sqrt{11}}{2}$

8. a) No real roots   **b)** 0   **c)** $-1, -2, 3$

d) $\frac{3}{2}, \pm 2$ **e)** 1, 3, 2, 2   **f)** $-\frac{5}{3}, 3$

9. a) $-6, 4$ **b)** $-5, 3$ **c)** $-7, 5$
11. a) i) $(-7, 0)$ **ii)** $x + 7 = 0$ **iii)** up   **iv)** 147
b) i) $(3, 4)$ **ii)** $x - 3 = 0$ **iii)** down   **iv)** -14
c) i) $\left(\frac{1}{2}, -\frac{3}{4}\right)$ **ii)** $x - \frac{1}{2} = 0$ **iii)** down
iv) -1
d) i) $(-6, 3)$ **ii)** $x + 6 = 0$ **iii)** up   **iv)** 15

12. a) $y = \frac{7}{4}x^2$ **b)** $y = 12(x + 1)^2 + 4$

c) $y = -3(x + 3)^2 - 2$ **d)** $y = \frac{5}{4}(x - 3)^2 - \frac{5}{4}$

13. 500 m^2
14. a) $4, -3$ **b)** No solution   **c)** $2, -10$
d) No solution

15. a) $1, \frac{1}{3}$ **b)** $2, -1$ **c)** 6   **d)** -1.375

16. a) D: $\mathbb{R}$; R: $-\infty, 6]$ **b)** D: $[-2.5, \infty$; R: $[-3, \infty$
c) D: $\mathbb{R}^*$; R: $\mathbb{R}^*$ **d)** D: $\mathbb{R}$; R: $\mathbb{Z}$

Chapter 4

Exercises 4-1, page 144

1. a) The locus is a circle with centre $(0,0)$ and radius 2.
 b) The locus is a circle with centre $(0,2)$ and radius 2.
 c) The locus is a straight line with zero slope and y-intercept 3.
 d) The locus is a straight line with slope $\frac{1}{2}$ and y-intercept 3.
 e) The locus is a straight line with slope -1 and y-intercept 1.
 f) The locus is a pair of parallel lines with infinite slope and x-intercepts 2 and -2.
2. a) The locus is a straight line parallel to the x-axis, with y-intercept -5.
 b) The locus is a straight line parallel to the y-axis, with x-intercept -2.
 c) The locus is a circle, centre the origin and radius 7.
 d) The locus is a straight line with slope 1 and y-intercept 2.
 e) The locus is a circle, centre $(1,-4)$ and radius 4.
 f) The locus is a circle, centre $(1,0)$ and radius 1.
3. a) A circle, centre $B(0,3)$ and radius 6
 b) $x^2 + (y - 3)^2 = 36$
4. a) $(x + 1)^2 + (y - 2)^2 = 25$
 b) A circle, centre $C(-1,2)$ and radius 5
 c) $5, -1$
5. a) A straight line with slope $\frac{2}{3}$, passing through $M(3,-1)$.
 b) A parabola with vertex $(0,0)$ and axis of symmetry the y-axis. The parabola opens up.
 c) A parabola with vertex $(3,0)$ and axis of symmetry $x = 3$; it opens down, and is congruent to $y = -\frac{1}{4}x^2$.
6. a) $y = \frac{1}{4}(x - 2)^2 + 4$
 b) A parabola with vertex $(2,4)$ and axis of symmetry $x = 2$; it opens up and is congruent to $y = \frac{1}{4}x^2$.
 c) 13
7. a) $5x - 2y - 13 = 0$; the perpendicular bisector of AB
 b) $x^2 + y^2 = 16$; a circle, centre $(0,0)$ radius 4
 c) $x + y = 3$; a straight line through A and B

8. a) $y = \frac{1}{2}x^2 - 2$
 b) A parabola, vertex $(0,-2)$, axis of symmetry the y-axis, which opens up and is congruent to $y = \frac{1}{2}x^2$
 c) ± 6
9. a) $x^2 + y^2 = 25$
 b) A circle, centre $(0,0)$ and radius 5
 c) $\pm\sqrt{21}$
10. a) $x^2 + y^2 = 16$
 b) A circle, centre $(0,0)$ and radius 4
11. $x^2 + y^2 = 25$. See graph of *Exercise 9c*).
12. a) $y^2 - 9 = 0$ **b)** $x^2y^2 = 36$
 c) $|x| + |y| = 5$
 d) $(x - y - 3)(y - x - 3) = 0$
 e) $|y| = |x|$ **f)** $\dfrac{x^2}{3} + \dfrac{(y - 4)^2}{4} = 1$
13. $y(x - 9) = 0$
14. a) $3x^2 + 4y^2 = 48$ **b)** $15x^2 - y^2 = 15$
15. $5x + 3y - 17 = 0$

Exercises 4-2, page 150

1. a, c, e, f
2. a) Circle   **b)** Ellipse   **c)** Hyperbola
 d) Parabola   **e)** Ellipse   **f)** Hyperbola
3. b) Answers may vary.
4. a) Hyperbola
 b) Hyperbola, parabola or ellipse
 c) Hyperbola

Exercises 4-3, page 154

1. a) Yes   **b)** No   **c)** Yes   **d)** No
2. a) $8; (0,0)$ **b)** $2\sqrt{3}; (0,0)$ **c)** $9; (3, -4)$
 d) $\sqrt{5}; (-2,1)$ **e)** $\sqrt{15}; (-4,0)$ **f)** $4\sqrt{3}; (0,6)$
3. a) $x^2 + y^2 = 9$ **b)** $x^2 + y^2 = 49$
 c) $(x - 5)^2 + (y - 3)^2 = 16$
 d) $(x + 2)^2 + (y - 6)^2 = 25$
 e) $(x - 4)^2 + y^2 = 36$
 f) $x^2 + (y + 3)^2 = 81$ **g)** $x^2 + y^2 = 5$
 h) $(x - 3)^2 + (y + 5)^2 = 10$
4. a) $x^2 + y^2 - 6x + 4y - 12 = 0$
 b) $x^2 + y^2 - 2x - 12y + 7 = 0$
 c) $x^2 + y^2 + 8x - 4y + 9 = 0$
 d) $x^2 + y^2 + 10x = 0$
5. a) $(x - 2)^2 + (y + 5)^2 = 16$
 b) $(x + 4)^2 + (y - 3)^2 = 50$
7. a) $x^2 + y^2 = 36$ **b)** $\pm 2\sqrt{5}$
8. a) $3 \pm 2\sqrt{6}$ **b)** $2 \pm 2\sqrt{6}$

9. a) 3; (5,−2)   **b)** 5; (3,1)   **c)** Not a circle

d) $\sqrt{4.5}$; $\left(-\dfrac{1}{2}, -\dfrac{1}{2}\right)$ **e)** $\dfrac{\sqrt{65}}{4}$; $\left(1, -\dfrac{3}{4}\right)$

f) Not a circle

11. $G^2 + F^2 - C > 0$ **a) i)** $F = 0$ **ii)** $G = 0$
iii) $G = 0; F = 0$ **b)** $C = 0$ **c) i)** $C = G^2$
ii) $F^2 = C$ **iii)** $G^2 = F^2 = C$

12. To avoid fractions in the formulas for the coordinates of the centre, and the radius

13. a) $(x + 2)^2 + y^2 = 16$ **b)** Circle

14. a) $(x - 3)^2 + (y + 2)^2 = 25$
b) $(x - 1)^2 + (y - 2)^2 = 17$
c) $(x - 3)^2 + (y - 4)^2 = 5$

15. $x^2 + y^2 = 2x - 2y$

16. a) Not intersect   **b)** Not intersect
c) Intersect   **d)** Not intersect

17. $\sqrt{G_1^2 + F_1^2 - C_1} + \sqrt{G_2^2 + F_2^2 - C_2} \geq$
$\sqrt{(G_2 - G_1)^2 + (F_2 - F_1)^2} \geq$
$\left|\sqrt{G_1^2 + F_1^2 - C_1} - \sqrt{G_2^2 + F_2^2 - C_2}\right|$

18. $(x - 1)^2 + (y - 5)^2 = 25$

19. $\left(x - \dfrac{a}{2}\right)^2 + \left(y - \dfrac{b}{2}\right)^2 = \dfrac{a^2 + b^2}{4}$

20. $a_1 a_2 = b_1 b_2$

Exercises 4-4, page 157

1. a) 24   **b)** $6\sqrt{3}$ **c)** $\sqrt{421}$

2. b) i) 10   **ii)** $5\sqrt{3}$ **iii)** $4\sqrt{3}$

3. a) 8   **b)** $\sqrt{37}$ **c)** $2\sqrt{2}$

4. a) $4x + 3y - 25 = 0$ **b)** $3x - 4y - 40 = 0$
c) $x + 2y - 5 = 0$ **d)** $3x + 2y + 13 = 0$

5. b) i) $2\sqrt{5}$ **ii)** $\sqrt{65}$ **iii)** $2\sqrt{10}$

6. a) $\sqrt{33}$ **b)** $2\sqrt{17}$ **c)** $\sqrt{73}$
d) $2\sqrt{14}$

7. 7   **8.** $(4, \pm 2\sqrt{6})$

9. a) $x - 3y + 10 = 0$ **b)** $y + 4 = 0$
c) $x + y - 2\sqrt{2} = 0$ **d)** $3x - \sqrt{2}\,y - 11 = 0$

10. $2x - 3y - 13 = 0$

11. $5x + 2y + 29 = 0, 5x + 2y - 29 = 0$

12. b) $\sqrt{40}$

13. a) 61.6 m   **b)** 3.8 km   **14.** 3.5 cm

15. a) $(x - 1.8)^2 + (y - 2.2)^2 = 2.08$
b) $3x + 2y - 4.6 = 0$

16. 1.5 km

17. $12x - 5y - 144 = 0; 12x + 5y + 144 = 0$

18. a) $x^2 + (y - 5)^2 = 25$ **b)** 10 units

19. a) $(x - 105)^2 + (y - 15)^2 = 225$ **b)** 2.1 m

20. a) $4\sqrt{2}$ **b)** $(-2\sqrt{2}, 2\sqrt{2})$
c) $24 + 16\sqrt{2}$

21. a) $\sqrt{(x_1 - h)^2 + (y_1 - k)^2 - r^2}$ **b) i)** 7
ii) $2\sqrt{6}$ **iii)** 0   **iv)** No solution
c) (0,6) is on the circle. (0,0) is inside the circle.

22. $x_1 x + y_1 y = r^2$ **23.** 4

Exercises 4-5, page 163

1. a) Yes   **b)** No   **c)** No   **d)** Yes

2. a) $(1, 0); x = -1$ **b)** $(3, 0); x = -3$

c) $\left(-\dfrac{3}{2}, 0\right); x = \dfrac{3}{2}$ **d)** $(0, 2); y = -2$

e) $\left(0, -\dfrac{1}{2}\right); y = \dfrac{1}{2}$ **f)** $\left(0, \dfrac{3}{4}\right); y = -\dfrac{3}{4}$

g) $\left(-\dfrac{9}{4}, 0\right); x = \dfrac{9}{4}$ **h)** $\left(0, -\dfrac{5}{4}\right); y = \dfrac{5}{4}$

3. a) $(2, 0); x = -2$ **b)** $\left(-\dfrac{3}{4}, 0\right); x = \dfrac{3}{4}$

c) $(0, 1); y = -1$ **d)** $\left(0, -\dfrac{5}{2}\right); y = \dfrac{5}{2}$

4. a) i) $y^2 = 16x$ **ii)** $y^2 = -24x$
iii) $x^2 = 12y$ **b)** $x^2 = -32y$

5. a) $x^2 = \dfrac{1}{2}y$ **b)** $x^2 = \dfrac{8}{3}y$ **c)** $x^2 = \dfrac{8}{5}y$
d) $x^2 = -8y$

6. a) $y^2 = \dfrac{16}{5}x$ **b)** $y^2 = \dfrac{25}{3}x$ **c)** $y^2 = \dfrac{36}{5}x$
d) $y^2 = \dfrac{49}{3}x$

7. a) i) $x^2 = 8y$ **ii)** $x^2 = 5y$ **iii)** $x^2 = -3y$
iv) $x^2 = -7y$
b) If a parabola passes through (a, a), then $x^2 = ay$.

8. $y^2 = 20x$ **9.** $x^2 = 4py$

10. a) $A = x(25 - x)$

13. a) $(3p, \pm p\sqrt{12})$ **b)** $(p, \pm 2p)$

Exercises 4-6, page 170

1. a) $(3, 2); y = 2$; right
b) $(2, -1); y = -1$; left
c) $(-1, -5); x = -1$; up
d) $(4, 1); x = 4$; down   **e)** $(0, 3); y = 3$; right
f) $(0, 2); x = 0$; up

2. a) $y^2 + 6y - 2x + 11 = 0$
b) $y^2 - 2y + x + 4 = 0$
c) $x^2 + 10x + 4y + 17 = 0$
d) $x^2 - 4x - 3y + 4 = 0$

3. a) $(x - 1)^2 = 3(y + 3)$
   b) $(x + 3)^2 = -5(y - 2)$
   c) $(y + 2)^2 = 4(x - 5)$
   d) $(y - 1)^2 = -3(x + 2)$

4. a) $(1, -2); (2, -2); y + 2 = 0; x = 0$
   b) $(-4, 3); \left(-\dfrac{9}{2}, 3\right); y - 3 = 0; x = -\dfrac{7}{2}$
   c) $(3, -2); \left(3, -\dfrac{3}{2}\right); x - 3 = 0; y = -\dfrac{5}{2}$
   d) $(0, 1); \left(0, \dfrac{1}{4}\right); x = 0; y = \dfrac{7}{4}$
   e) $(2, 0); (0, 0); y = 0; x = 4$
   f) $(0, -1); (0, 0); x = 0; y = -2$

5. a) $(y - 2)^2 = 8(x - 1)$
   b) $(y - 3)^2 = -12(x + 1)$
   c) $(x - 2)^2 = 12(y + 3)$

6. a) $y^2 = 4(x - 2)$ **b)** Parabola

7. $(x + 1)^2 = -8(y - 4)$ **8.** $y^2 = 12x - 12$

10. a) $k = 0; h = -p$ **b)** $h = 0; k = -p$

Exercises 4-7, page 175

1. a) Yes   **b)** Yes   **c)** No   **d)** Yes

2. a) $(4, 0), (-4, 0); (\sqrt{7}, 0), (-\sqrt{7}, 0); 8; 6$
   b) $(6, 0), (-6, 0); (\sqrt{11}, 0), (-\sqrt{11}, 0); 12; 10$
   c) $(0, 3), (0, -3); (0, \sqrt{5}), (0, -\sqrt{5}); 6; 4$
   d) $(0, 7), (0, -7); (0, \sqrt{33}), (0,-\sqrt{33}; 14; 8$
   e) $(8, 0), (-8, 0); (4\sqrt{3}, 0), (-4\sqrt{3}, 0); 16; 8$
   f) $(0, 5), (0, -5); (0, 4), (0, -4); 10; 6$

3. a) $\dfrac{x^2}{25} + \dfrac{y^2}{9} = 1$ **b)** $\dfrac{x^2}{64} + \dfrac{y^2}{36} = 1$
   c) $\dfrac{x^2}{20} + \dfrac{y^2}{16} = 1$ **d)** $\dfrac{x^2}{49} + \dfrac{y^2}{9} = 1$
   e) $\dfrac{x^2}{25} + \dfrac{y^2}{9} = 1$ **f)** $\dfrac{x^2}{36} + \dfrac{y^2}{20} = 1$

4. a) i) $\dfrac{x^2}{9} + \dfrac{y^2}{4} = 1$ **ii)** $6; 4; (\pm 3, 0); (\pm\sqrt{5}, 0)$
   b) i) $\dfrac{x^2}{16} + \dfrac{y^2}{4} = 1$ **ii)** $8; 4; (\pm 4, 0); (\pm 2\sqrt{3}, 0)$
   c) i) $\dfrac{x^2}{9} + \dfrac{y^2}{16} = 1$ **ii)** $8; 6; (0, \pm 4); (0, \pm\sqrt{7})$
   d) i) $\dfrac{x^2}{16} + \dfrac{y^2}{25} = 1$ **ii)** $10; 8; (0, \pm 5); (0, \pm 3)$
   e) i) $\dfrac{x^2}{1} + \dfrac{y^2}{9} = 1$ **ii)** $6; 2; (0, \pm 3); (0, \pm 2\sqrt{2})$
   f) i) $\dfrac{x^2}{3} + \dfrac{y^2}{2} = 1$
   ii) $2\sqrt{3}; 2\sqrt{2}; (\pm\sqrt{3}, 0); (\pm 1, 0)$

5. $\dfrac{x^2}{9} + \dfrac{y^2}{5} = 1$ **6.** $\dfrac{x^2}{b^2} + \dfrac{y^2}{a^2} = 1$

7. a) $\dfrac{x^2}{100} + \dfrac{y^2}{25} = 1$ **b)** ± 8 **c)** $\pm\dfrac{5}{2}\sqrt{3}$

8. Yes   **9. a)** $\dfrac{x^2}{16} + \dfrac{y^2}{12} = 1$ **b)** Ellipse

14. a) $C < 0 < A < B$ or $B < A < 0 < C$
   b) $C < 0 < B < B < A$ or $A < B < 0 < C$

Problem Solving, page 180

1. 12 edges, 8 vertices
3. b) One of the angles is a reflex angle.
4. 6%

5. $DE = \sqrt{\dfrac{x}{2}}$

7. Approximately 2.0565

Exercises 4-8, page 187

1. a) Yes   **b)** No   **c)** Yes   **d)** No

2. a) $(2, 0), (-2, 0); (2\sqrt{5}, 0), (-2\sqrt{5}, 0); 4; 8$
   b) $(5, 0), (-5, 0); (\sqrt{34}, 0), (-\sqrt{34}, 0); 10; 6$
   c) $(9, 0), (-9, 0); (\sqrt{130}, 0), (-\sqrt{130}, 0); 18; 14$

3. a) $\dfrac{x^2}{36} - \dfrac{y^2}{9} = 1$ **b)** $\dfrac{x^2}{9} - \dfrac{y^2}{4} = 1$
   c) $\dfrac{x^2}{20} - \dfrac{y^2}{16} = 1$ **d)** $\dfrac{x^2}{25} - \dfrac{y^2}{49} = 1$
   e) $\dfrac{x^2}{4} - \dfrac{y^2}{5} = 1$ **f)** $\dfrac{x^2}{49} - \dfrac{y^2}{49} = 1$

4. a) i) $\dfrac{x^2}{4} - \dfrac{y^2}{9} = 1$
   ii) $4; 6; (\pm 2, 0); (\pm\sqrt{13}, 0); y = \pm\dfrac{3}{2}x$
   b) i) $\dfrac{x^2}{36} - \dfrac{y^2}{4} = 1$
   ii) $12; 4; (\pm 6, 0); (\pm 2\sqrt{10}, 0); y = \pm\dfrac{1}{3}x$
   c) i) $\dfrac{x^2}{9} - \dfrac{y^2}{25} = 1$
   ii) $6; 10; (\pm 3, 0); (\pm\sqrt{34}, 0); y = \pm\dfrac{5}{3}x$
   d) i) $\dfrac{x^2}{4} - \dfrac{y^2}{16} = 1$
   ii) $4; 8; (\pm 2, 0); (\pm 2\sqrt{5}, 0); y = \pm 2x$
   e) i) $\dfrac{x^2}{12} - \dfrac{y^2}{4} = 1$
   ii) $4\sqrt{3}; 4; (\pm 2\sqrt{3}, 0); (\pm 4, 0); y = \pm\dfrac{1}{\sqrt{3}}x$

f) i) $\dfrac{x^2}{5} - \dfrac{y^2}{4} = 20$

ii) $2\sqrt{5}$; 4; $(\pm\sqrt{5}, 0)$; $(\pm 3, 0)$; $y = \pm\dfrac{2}{\sqrt{5}}x$

5. $8x^2 - y^2 = 32$

6. a) $\dfrac{x^2}{6} - \dfrac{y^2}{2} = 1$ **b)** $\pm 3\sqrt{2}$ **c)** ± 1

7. a) $\dfrac{x^2}{9} - \dfrac{y^2}{9} = 1$ **b)** $(\pm 2\sqrt{3}, 0)$; $y = x$, $y = -x$

8. a) $3x^2 - y^2 = 12$ **b)** Hyperbola

Exercises 4-9, page 192

1. a) Yes   **b)** Yes   **c)** No   **d)** Yes

2. a) $(0, 3), (0, -3)$; $(0, 5), (0, -5)$; 6; 8

   b) $(0, 5), (0, -5)$; $(0, \sqrt{29}), (0, -\sqrt{29})$; 10; 4

   c) $(0, 6), (0, -6)$; $(0, 10), (0, -10)$; 12; 16

3. a) $\dfrac{x^2}{16} - \dfrac{y^2}{9} = -1$ **b)** $\dfrac{x^2}{15} - \dfrac{y^2}{49} = -1$

   c) $\dfrac{x^2}{9} - \dfrac{y^2}{27} = -1$ **d)** $\dfrac{x^2}{7} - \dfrac{y^2}{25} = -1$

   e) $\dfrac{x^2}{4} - \dfrac{y^2}{16} = -1$

4. a) i) $\dfrac{x^2}{9} - \dfrac{y^2}{4} = -1$

   ii) 4; 6; $(0, \pm 2)$; $(0, \pm\sqrt{13})$; $y = \pm\dfrac{2}{3}x$

   b) i) $\dfrac{x^2}{16} - \dfrac{y^2}{4} = -1$

   ii) 4; 8; $(0, \pm 2)$; $(0, \pm 2\sqrt{5})$; $y = \pm\dfrac{1}{2}x$

   c) i) $\dfrac{x^2}{25} - \dfrac{y^2}{16} = -1$

   ii) 8; 10; $(0, \pm 4)$; $(0, \pm\sqrt{41})$; $y = \pm\dfrac{4}{5}x$

   d) i) $\dfrac{x^2}{25} - \dfrac{y^2}{100} = -1$

   ii) 20; 10; $(0, \pm 10)$; $(0, \pm 5\sqrt{5})$; $y = \pm 2x$

   e) i) $\dfrac{x^2}{50} - \dfrac{y^2}{25} = -1$

   ii) 10; $10\sqrt{2}$; $(0, \pm 5)$; $(0, \pm 5\sqrt{3})$; $y = \pm\dfrac{1}{\sqrt{2}}x$

   f) i) $\dfrac{x^2}{8} - \dfrac{y^2}{6} = -1$

   ii) $2\sqrt{6}$; $4\sqrt{2}$; $(0, \pm\sqrt{6})$; $(0, \pm\sqrt{14})$; $y = \pm\dfrac{\sqrt{3}}{2}x$

5. $\dfrac{x^2}{8} - \dfrac{y^2}{1} = -1$ **6.** $\dfrac{x^2}{b^2} - \dfrac{y^2}{a^2} = -1$

8. $A > 0, B < 0, C > 0$ or $A < 0, B > 0, C < 0$

9. a) Typical answer: $\dfrac{x^2}{4} - \dfrac{y^2}{9} = 1$; $\dfrac{x^2}{4} - \dfrac{y^2}{9} = -1$

   b) Change the sign of the constant term.

Exercises 4-10, page 196

1. a) $y = \dfrac{1}{2160}x^2$ **b)** 42 cm

2. $y = -\dfrac{1}{64}x^2$

3. Typical answers: **a)** $y = -\dfrac{15.3}{1225}x^2$ **b)** 14 m

4. a) $9x^2 + 25y^2 = 225$ **b)** About 5.50 m

5. a) $15\,625x^2 + 22\,500y^2 = 351\,562\,500$

   b) About 123.9 m

6. 5.4 m

7. 44 m

8. a) 800 km   **b)** 2000 km

Exercises 4-11, page 198

1. Answers may vary.   **a)** $(0,0)$ **b)** $(10,10)$
   c) $(1,0)$ **d)** $(0,0)$ **e)** $(0,20)$ **f)** $(10,10)$

2. Answers may vary.   **a)** $(2,1)$ inside
   b) $(0,2)$ inside   **c)** $(0,2)$ outside

3. a) $(x + 2)^2 + (y - 1)^2 \leqslant 4$
   b) $y < (x + 1)^2 - 2$
   c) $y \leqslant -(x + 1)^2 + 5$

4. a) $x^2 - \dfrac{y^2}{4} \leqslant 1$ **b)** $\dfrac{x^2}{4} + \dfrac{y^2}{16} > 1$

   c) $\dfrac{x^2}{4} - \dfrac{y^2}{4} \leqslant -1$ **d)** $\dfrac{x^2}{25} + \dfrac{4y^2}{9} \leqslant 1$

7. a) $x \geqslant 4$; $y \in \mathbb{R}$ **b)** $x \in \,]-1, 7\,[$; $y \in \,]0, 8[$
   c) $x \in \mathbb{R}$; $y \in \mathbb{R}$ **d)** $x \in [-3, 3]$; $y \in \mathbb{R}$
   e) $x \in \mathbb{R}$; $y > -4$
   f) $x \in \,]-\infty, -3] \cup [3, \infty]$; $y \in \mathbb{R}$

8. a) $(x - 4)^2 + (y - 1)^2 \leqslant 9$; $(x - 10)^2 + (y - 4)^2 \leqslant 9$;
   $(x - 9)^2 + (y + 1)^2 \leqslant 9$ **b)** $(7, 0)$

9. $\left(\dfrac{x}{20}\right)^2 + \left(\dfrac{y}{30}\right)^2 > 1$; $x \in [-26, 26]$; $y \in [-36, 36\,]$

10. $\dfrac{x^2}{25} + \dfrac{y^2}{16} \leqslant 1$

11. Answers may vary. With the origin at the centre of
   the base of the tunnel, $y < 4.5 - \dfrac{1}{8}x^2$, $y \geqslant 0$

12. a) $x^2 + y^2 \leqslant 25 \cap \dfrac{x^2}{4} - \dfrac{5y^2}{64} \leqslant 1$
   b) $x \in [-3, 3]$; $y \in [-5, 5]$

Review Exercises, page 202

1. a) Circle   b) Straight line   c) Parabola   d) Straight line
2. a) Ellipse   b) Parabola   c) Circle   d) Hyperbola   e) Circle   f) Hyperbola
3. a) No; parabola   b) Yes; circle   c) No; hyperbola   d) No; ellipse
4. a) $(0, 0)$; 2.5   b) $(2, -3)$; 5
5. a) $y = \frac{1}{8}x^2$ b) $y = -1.5x^2$
6. a) $\frac{x^2}{9} + \frac{y^2}{25} = 1$ b) $\frac{x^2}{9} + \frac{y^2}{36} = 1$
7. a) $\frac{x^2}{16} - \frac{y^2}{64} = 1$ b) $\frac{x^2}{16} - \frac{y^2}{49} = 1$
8. $y = -\frac{1}{64}x^2$ 9. $\frac{x^2}{900} + \frac{y^2}{625} = 1$
10. $x^2 - y^2 = -380.25$

Chapter 5

Exercises 5-1, page 207

1. a) 1   b) $\frac{1}{5}$ c) $\frac{8}{125}$ d) $\frac{1}{8}$ e) $\frac{1}{16}$ f) 1   g) 4   h) $\frac{16}{81}$ i) $\frac{1}{64}$ j) $\frac{9}{25}$ k) 81   l) $\frac{64}{27}$

2. a) 3   b) $\frac{1}{9}$ c) 2.5   d) 5   e) 5   f) $\frac{1}{2}$ g) $\frac{1}{1000}$ h) 2   i) $\frac{7}{5}$ j) $\frac{1}{9}$ k) 0.5   l) 2

3. a) $\frac{1}{216}$ b) 9   c) 4   d) $\frac{1}{32}$ e) $\frac{1}{243}$ f) $\frac{27}{8}$ g) $\frac{125}{27}$ h) $\frac{1}{1000}$ i) $\frac{4}{25}$ j) $\frac{125}{27}$ k) 32   l) $\frac{1}{27}$

4. a) 32   b) $\frac{1}{125}$ c) $\frac{1}{243}$ d) 8000   e) 8   f) 8   g) 1   h) $\frac{32}{3125}$ i) 2   j) $\frac{16}{81}$ k) $\frac{8}{27}$ l) 1

5. a) 3.278   b) 16.442   c) 5.481   d) 8.000   e) 121.268   f) 3.386   g) 0.480   h) 0.170   i) 68.470   j) 10.600   k) 0.150   l) 0.700

6. a) m^{-6} b) x^5 c) $-45a^7$ d) $-14s^{15}$ e) $-9m^5$ f) $\frac{64n}{5}$

7. a) $\frac{x^{-1}}{49}$ b) $\frac{s^{-\frac{1}{4}}}{3}$ c) $-3m^{-2}$ d) $-3a^{\frac{3}{5}}$ e) $n^{\frac{1}{60}}$ f) $-4x^{\frac{3}{4}}$

8. a) 5   b) 7   c) $\frac{17}{72}$ d) 0   e) 11   f) $\frac{1}{2}$ g) 256   h) $\frac{33}{16}$ i) 2.7

9. a) i) 8000   ii) 22 627   iii) 2828   b) i) 1000   ii) 1414   iii) 630

10. a) $P = 24.3(1.0185)^t$ b) 20.2 million

11. a) $N = 100(10)^{\frac{t}{7}}$ b) 3.7×10^8

12. a) $-7a^9b^{-8}$ b) $20m^{-7}n^3$ c) $9x^9y^{-12}$ d) $12a^3b^{-4}c^{-4}$ e) $10n^4$ f) $\frac{15x^{-4}z^5}{2}$

13. a) $-4b^{\frac{1}{3}}$ b) $\frac{5mn^{-\frac{5}{6}}}{2}$ c) $x^{\frac{4}{5}}y^{\frac{3}{5}}$ d) $a^{-\frac{9}{2}}y^{\frac{11}{4}}$ e) $m^{-\frac{5}{6}}n^{\frac{8}{9}}$ f) $a^{-1}b^2$

14. a) $-3m^{\frac{1}{3}}n^{-\frac{1}{2}}$ b) $-42a^{\frac{1}{6}}b^{\frac{1}{6}}$ c) $-2x^{-\frac{5}{4}}$ d) $2a^{-1}b^{\frac{3}{10}}c^{-\frac{7}{15}}$ e) $-\frac{2a^{\frac{1}{4}}c^{-3}}{21}$ f) $-\frac{40x^{-\frac{7}{4}}z^{\frac{7}{4}}}{9}$

15. a) 16   b) 32   c) $\frac{1}{1024}$ d) $\frac{1}{4096}$

16. a) $-\frac{16}{9}$ b) $\frac{59\,049}{4096}$ c) 1.5   d) 2187

17. a) $a^{\frac{9}{2}}$ b) $4a^{-4}$ c) $216a^{39}$

18. a) $6x^9$ b) $\frac{4x^{-12}}{27}$ c) $\frac{9x^3}{4}$

19. a) 1   b) s^{8n} c) a d) $m^{bc-ac-ab}$ e) x^{-2a+2} f) $\frac{a^{x-4y}}{9}$ g) $x^{-\frac{a}{6}}$ h) $m^{-\frac{5n}{6}}n^{-\frac{3m}{4}}$ i) $a^{-\frac{10x}{3}}$

20. a) 31.544   b) 36.462   c) 25.955   d) 1.823   e) 0.013   f) 0.064   g) 3.416   h) 3.040

21. a) i) 4   ii) 0.25   iii) 0.25   iv) 4   v) 2   vi) 0.5   vii) 0.5   viii) 2

22. a) $5^{\frac{4}{3}}$ b) 2^{2x+1} c) 2^{2x+2}

Mathematics Around Us, page 210

1. a) i) 19   ii) 62   b) i) 58   ii) 57   c) i) 72   ii) 85
2. 155   3. Answers may vary.

Exercises 5-2, page 212

1. a) 49   b) 64   c) 16   d) 8   e) 81   f) 25   g) 8   h) 243
2. a) 5   b) 5   c) 4   d) 4   e) 7   f) 3   g) 3   h) 3   i) 4

3. a) 1 **b)** 4 **c)** 7 **d)** −1 **e)** 2 **f)** 0

4. a) 0 **b)** −2 **c)** 1 **d)** −2

5. 8 years **6.** 9.7 years

7. a) 1 **b)** 0 **c)** $\frac{4}{3}$ **d)** −1 **e)** $\frac{5}{2}$ **f)** $\frac{3}{2}$

g) $-\frac{2}{3}$ **h)** $-\frac{1}{2}$ **i)** $\frac{5}{2}$

8. a) 2 **b)** 3 **c)** 3 **d)** 6 **e)** 3 **f)** 3

g) 2 **h)** 0 **i)** $-\frac{1}{2}$

9. 4 months **10. a)** $25 \times 2^{\frac{n}{5}}$ **b)** About 43 years

11. a) $\frac{3}{2}$ **b)** −2 **c)** 6

12. a) 1.56 **b)** 2.84 **c)** 2.51

Exercises 5-3, page 216

1. a) About 9 years **b)** About 14 years

3. About 45 years **5.** About 6 bounces

7. About 27 m **9.** $P = 80(2)^{\frac{n}{20}}$

10. $P = 300(2)^{\frac{d}{5}}$

11. $P = 100(0.95)^n$

12. $C = 100(0.5)^n$

Mathematics Around Us, page 218

1. a) 10 000 **b)** 10 000 000

3. a) 316 **b)** 10 000 **c)** 31 623

4. a) 8 **b)** 7943

5. a) Trumpet, clarinet
  b) Bassoon, 3; flute, 5; trumpet, clarinet, 6

6. 316 **7. a)** 100 **b)** 2.5

8. a) $t = 8(0.5)^{\frac{d-90}{5}}$ **b) i)** 2 h **ii)** 2 min, 28 s

Problem Solving, page 221

1. 7.75 cm^2

2. a) Powers of 6 **b)** Powers of 12

3. $(20 + 10\sqrt{3})$ cm

4. $3x − 4y + 2 = 0, 3x − 4y + 22 = 0$

5. There are two angles such that one is double the other.

6. a) $n!$ **c)** $\frac{(2n)!}{2^n(n!)}$

7. $\dfrac{b}{\sqrt{b^2\cos^2\theta + a^2\sin^2\theta}}$

Exercises 5-4, page 225

1. a) iv **b)** iii **c)** i **d)** ii

2. Answers may vary.

3. a)

x	−2	−1	0	1	2
3^x	0.11	0.33	1	3	9
$\left(\frac{1}{3}\right)^x$	9	3	1	0.33	0.11

5. a) 6 **b)** 2 **c)** 8 **d)** 4 **e)** $\frac{1}{8}$ **f)** 6

g) 7 **h)** 27

6. Asymptote: $y = 0$
  a), b), c) Vertical intercept: 1; D: $\mathbb{R}$; R: $\mathbb{R}_+^*$; increasing on $\mathbb{R}$
  d) Vertical intercept: −1; D: $\mathbb{R}$; R: $\mathbb{R}_-^*$; decreasing on $\mathbb{R}$
  e) Vertical intercept: 1; D: $\mathbb{R}$; R: $\mathbb{R}_+^*$; decreasing on $\mathbb{R}$

7. D: $\mathbb{R}$; increasing on $\mathbb{R}$
  a) Vertical intercept: 1; R: $\mathbb{R}_+^*$; asymptote $y = 0$
  b) Vertical intercept: 2; R: $]1, \pm\infty$; asymptote $y = 1$
  c) Vertical intercept: 0; R: $]−1, +\infty$; asymptote $y = −1$
  d) Vertical intercept: 2; R: $\mathbb{R}_+^*$; asymptote $y = 0$
  e) Vertical intercept: 0.5; R: $\mathbb{R}_+^*$; asymptote $y = 0$

8. D: $\mathbb{R}$
  a) R: $\mathbb{R}_+$; $y = 0$ **b)** R: $]2, +\infty$; $y = 2$
  c) R: $]−2, +\infty$; $y = −2$

9. a) $f(x) = 4^{x-2} − 1$ **b)** $g(x) = 0.2^x + 2$
  c) $h(x) = 3^{x+1} + 4$

10. a) i) $y = −5$ **ii)** $\mathbb{R}$ **iii)** $]−5, +\infty$
  iv) increasing
  b) i) $y = 3$ **ii)** $\mathbb{R}$ **iii)** $]3, +\infty$
  iv) decreasing
  c) i) $y = −2$ **ii)** $\mathbb{R}$ **iii)** $]−2, +\infty$
  iv) increasing

11. a) $a \in \mathbb{R}, x = 0$ or $a = 1, x \in \mathbb{R}$
  b) $a > 1, x > 0$ or $0 < a < 1, x < 0$
  c) $0 < a < 1, x > 0$ or $a > 1, x < 0$

The Mathematical Mind, page 227

1. b) $x = r\sqrt[3]{2}$ **c)** $y = r\sqrt[3]{4}$

Mathematics Around Us, page 228

1. About 78.6% **2.** 15 600 years

3. a) About 1900 years **b)** About 3100 years
  c) About 4000 years **d)** About 11 900 years
  e) About 31 700 years

Exercises 5-5, page 231

1. a) 2 **b)** 3 **c)** 6 **d)** 1 **e)** −1

f) −3 **g)** 0 **h)** $\frac{1}{3}$ **i)** 5 **j)** $\frac{1}{5}$ **k)** $\frac{2}{3}$

l) n

2. a) $10^{0.6990}$ **b)** $10^{1.2553}$ **c)** $10^{1.7952}$
d) $10^{3.6882}$ **e)** $10^{-0.6021}$ **f)** $10^{-0.0969}$
g) $10^{-1.6990}$ **h)** $10^{-2.2218}$

3. a) 5 **b)** 9 **c)** 1

4. a) 12 **b)** −7 **c)** −12

5. a) $10\,000 = 10^4$ **b)** $10 = 10^1$
c) $0.01 = 10^{-2}$

6. a) $\log 1000 = 3$ **b)** $\log 1 = 0$
c) $\log 0.001 = -3$

7. 600

8. a) 100 **b)** 100 000 **c)** 0.001 **d)** 1
e) 10 **f)** 10^{10}

9. a) 4 **b)** 5 **c)** −3 **d)** 100 **e)** 20
f) 0.2

10. a) i) 0.301 03 **ii)** 1.301 03 **iii)** 2.301 03
iv) 3.301 03 **v)** −0.698 97 **vi)** −1.698 97
vii) −2.698 97 **viii)** −3.698 97
b) Answers may vary.

Exercises 5-6, page 235

1. a) $\log 42$ **b)** $\log 4$ **c)** $\log 24$ **d)** $\log 7$
e) $\log 84$ **f)** $\log 0.5$ **g)** $\log 10$
h) $\log 90$ **i)** $\log 21$ **j)** $\log 28$

2. Answers may vary. Typical answers:
a) $\log 2 + \log 5$ **b)** $\log 3 + \log 7$
c) $\log 4 + \log 7$ **d)** $\log 3 + \log 12$
e) $\log 3 + \log 3$ **f)** $\log 4 + \log 11$
g) $\log 3 + \log 19$ **h)** $\log 11 + \log 11$

3. Answers may vary. Typical answers:
a) $\log 10 - \log 2$ **b)** $\log 16 - \log 2$
c) $\log 24 - \log 2$ **d)** $\log 26 - \log 2$
e) $\log 20 - \log 2$ **f)** $\log 42 - \log 2$
g) $\log 34 - \log 2$ **h)** $\log 80 - \log 2$

4. a) $2 \log 3$ **b)** $2 \log 5$ **c)** $3 \log 2$
d) $3 \log 3$ **e)** $3 \log 10$ **f)** $5 \log 2$
g) $3 \log 7$ **h)** $7 \log 2$

5. a) $\log 36$ **b)** $\log 64$ **c)** $\log 81$
d) $\log 49$ **e)** $\log 243$ **f)** $\log 16$
g) $\log 216$ **h)** $\log 100\,000$

6. a) 1.477 12 **b)** 3.477 12 **c)** −0.522 88
d) −2.522 88 **e)** 0.954 24 **f)** 1.908 48
g) 0.238 56 **h)** 0.095 42

7. a) 2.795 88 **b)** 0.232 99 **c)** −0.698 97
d) −1.397 94

8. a) 0.8451 **b)** 2.8451 **c)** −1.1549
d) −0.1549 **e)** 5.8451 **f)** −2.1549

9. a) $3 + \log a + \log b$ **b)** $2 \log a + \log b$
c) $\log a + \frac{1}{2} \log b$ **d)** $\log a - 2 \log b$
e) $\frac{1}{2} \log a - \log b$ **f)** $\frac{1}{3} \log a - 2 \log b$

10. a) $1 + 2 \log x$ **b)** $\frac{1}{2} \log x$ **c)** $\frac{1}{2} + \log x$

d) $\frac{1}{2} + \frac{1}{2} \log x$ **e)** $1 + \frac{1}{2} \log x$

11. a) $\log \left(\dfrac{xy}{z}\right)$ **b)** $\log \left(\dfrac{m}{np}\right)$ **c)** $\log \left(\dfrac{ab}{cd}\right)$

d) $\log \left(\dfrac{a^2 + ab}{a - b}\right)$

12. a) $\log (a^2 b^5)$ **b)** $\log (x^3 y^{\frac{1}{2}})$ **c)** $\log \left(\dfrac{m^2 n}{p^5}\right)$

d) $\log \left(\dfrac{x^{\frac{1}{2}}}{y^2 z}\right)$ **e)** $\log \left(\dfrac{a^3 b^{\frac{1}{2}}}{c^{\frac{5}{4}}}\right)$ **f)** $\log \left(\dfrac{a^{10} c^{\frac{1}{2}}}{b^3 d}\right)$

13. a) $\log \left(\dfrac{x + 3}{x - 1}\right), x \neq 1$

b) $\log \left(\dfrac{2x - 7}{x + 3}\right), x \neq -3$

c) $\log \left(\dfrac{a + 2}{a - 2}\right), a \neq 2$

d) $\log \left(\dfrac{8a + 15}{2a + 3}\right), a \neq -1.5$

14. a) $x + y$ **b)** $y - x$ **c)** $1 + x + y$
d) $2x + y$ **e)** $x + 2y$ **f)** $2x + 2y$
g) $2x + 2y - 1$ **h)** $-x - y$

15. a) $3^{1.7712437}$ **b)** $2^{2.3219281}$ **c)** $2^{4.8579809}$
d) $8^{2.0889288}$ **e)** $0.5^{-1.5849625}$ **f)** $6^{-0.4456556}$

16. a) 3.459 **b)** 2.579 **c)** 0.898 **d)** 2.365
e) −0.415 **f)** −0.398

17. a) 0.630 929 8 **b)** 1.160 964
c) −0.564 575 **d)** −0.464 973 5
e) −1.547 952 1 **f)** 0.769 124

18. a) $\log y = 1 + \log x$ **b)** $\log y = -\log x$

c) $\log y = 2 \log x$ **d)** $\log y = \frac{1}{2} \log x$

e) $\log y = 1 + \frac{1}{2} \log x$

f) $\log y = \frac{1}{2} + \frac{1}{2} \log x$

19. a) $x > 2$ **b)** $x > 0$ **c)** $x > 5$
20. a) 3 **b)** 6 **c)** 101

21. a) $y = \dfrac{x + 2}{3x}$; $\{x \mid x > 0, x \in \mathbb{R}\}$

  b) $y = 100 + \dfrac{100}{x}$; $\{x \mid x > 0, x \in \mathbb{R}\}$

  c) $y = 10^x$; $\mathbb{R}$

22. a) 3376 **b)** 6533 **c)** 39 751 **d)** 65 050

23. a) $3.056\ 912 \times 10^{79}$ **b)** 80

24. a) 218 **b)** 2083 **c)** 20 734

  d) Answers may vary.

Mathematics Around Us, page 238

1. a) It's the logarithm of the distance in metres.
  b) The number increases by 3, the distance is 10^3
  times as great

2. a) 3 **b)** 39

3. a) 5 **b)** km and cm

4. 2 cm **5.** 1 week **7.** 4.8

8. a) 6 **b)** 8 **c)** 12

9. 1.3×10^{26} m **10.** 2.0×10^{26} m **11.** 99.9%

Exercises 5-7, page 244

1. a) $x \doteq 3.3 \log\left(\dfrac{y}{5}\right)$ **b)** $x = \log\left(\dfrac{y}{1.3}\right)$

  c) $x \doteq 78 \log\left(\dfrac{y}{8.2}\right)$ **d)** $x \doteq -3.3 \log\left(\dfrac{y}{6.4}\right)$

  e) $x \doteq 2.3 \log\left(\dfrac{y}{3.5}\right)$

  f) $x \doteq -5.7 \log\left(\dfrac{y}{2.75}\right)$

2. a) $n \doteq 30 \log\left(\dfrac{A}{500}\right)$

  b) i) 11.9 years; $500 will amount to $1250 in
  nearly 12 years
  ii) -4.6 years; $350 invested about 4.6 years ago
  will amount to $500 now
  d) $\{A \mid A > 0, A \in \mathbb{R}\}$; $\mathbb{R}$

3. a) $n \doteq -6.5 \log\left(\dfrac{h}{2}\right)$

  b) i) 3; after 3 bounces, the height is about 0.7 m
  ii) 8; after 8 bounces, the height is about 0.12 m
  d) $\mathbb{N}$

4. a) $P = 6800(1.018)^n$ **b)** $n \doteq 129 \log\left(\dfrac{P}{6800}\right)$

  c) i) 17 **ii)** -12
  d) They are inverses of each other.

5. a) 3:20 P.M. **b)** 5:04 P.M. **c)** 8:57 A.M.

7. a) See page 246.

Exercises 5-8, page 249

1. a) $f^{-1}(x) = \log x$; horizontal intercept: 1; D: $\mathbb{R}_+^*$;
  R: $\mathbb{R}$; asymptote: $x = 0$; increasing on $\mathbb{R}_+^*$
  $f(x) = 10^x$; vertical intercept: 1; D: $\mathbb{R}$; R: $\mathbb{R}_+^*$;
  asymptote: $y = 0$; increasing on $\mathbb{R}$
  b) $g^{-1}(x) = \log_{0.4} x$; horizontal intercept: 1;
  D: $\mathbb{R}_+^*$; R: $\mathbb{R}$; asymptote: $x = 0$; decreasing on $\mathbb{R}_+^*$
  $g(x) = (0.4)^x$; vertical intercept: 1; D: $\mathbb{R}$; R: $\mathbb{R}_+^*$,
  asymptote: $y = 0$; decreasing on $\mathbb{R}$
  c) $h^{-1}(x) = \log_{\frac{3}{2}} x$; same properties as part a)

  $h(x) = \left(\dfrac{3}{2}\right)^x$; same properties as part a)

  d) $k^{-1}(x) = \log_{\frac{1}{5}} x$; same properties as part b)

  $k(x) = \left(\dfrac{1}{5}\right)^x$; same properties as part b)

2. a) See *Exercise 1a)*.

  b) $g^{-1}(x) = \left(\dfrac{1}{2}\right)^x$; see *Exercise 1b)*

  c) $h^{-1}(x) = \left(\dfrac{5}{4}\right)^x$; see *Exercise 1a)*

  d) $k^{-1}(x) = \left(\dfrac{2}{3}\right)^x$; see *Exercise 1b)*

3. a) $f^{-1}(x) = \log_5 x$ **b)** $g^{-1}(x) = \log_{\frac{3}{4}} x$

4. a), b) See Exercises 5-7, *Exercise 6*.
  c) $f^{-1}(x) = \log_3 x$

5. c) $g^{-1}(x) = \log_{\frac{1}{2}} x$

6. a) Horizontal intercept: 1; D: $]0, +\infty[$; R: $\mathbb{R}$;
  asymptote: $x = 0$; increasing on $]0, +\infty[$
  b) Horizontal intercept: 0; D: $]-1, +\infty[$; R: $\mathbb{R}$;
  asymptote: $x = -1$; increasing $]-1, +\infty[$
  c) Horizontal intercept: 0.5; D: $]0, +\infty[$; R: $\mathbb{R}$;
  asymptote: $x = 0$; decreasing on $]0, +\infty[$

7. a) 2 **b)** $\dfrac{1}{3}$ **c)** $\dfrac{1}{9}$ **d)** 36 **e)** $\dfrac{1}{5}$ **f)** 10

8. $(0.548, 0.548)$

9. a) $0 < a < 1$ **b)** Answers may vary.

Exercises 5-9, page 251

2. a) $g(x) = \log_4 (x - 2) - 1$　　**b)** $g(x) = \log_{0.2} x - 2$
c) $g(x) = \log_2 (x + 3)$

3. a) Horizontal intercept: 2.125; D: $]2, +\infty$; R: $\mathbb{R}$;
asymptote: $x = 2$; increasing on $]2, +\infty$
b) Horizontal intercept: -0.75; D: $]-1, +\infty$;
R: $\mathbb{R}$; asymptote: $x = -1$; decreasing on $]-1, +\infty$
c) Horizontal intercept: 81; D: $]0, +\infty$; R: $\mathbb{R}$;
asymptote: $x = 0$; increasing on $]0, +\infty$
d) Horizontal intercept: $-\frac{7}{3}$; D: $]-3, +\infty$; R: $\mathbb{R}$;
asymptote: $x = -3$; decreasing on $]-3, +\infty$
e) Vertical intercept: 1.5; D: $\mathbb{R}$; R: $]1, +\infty$;
asymptote: $y = 1$; increasing on $\mathbb{R}$
f) Vertical intercept: -2.75; D: $\mathbb{R}$; R: $]-3, +\infty$;
asymptote: $y = -3$; decreasing on $\mathbb{R}$

4. a) $f^{-1}(x) = 3^{x-2} + 1$; D: $\mathbb{R}$; R: $]1, +\infty$
b) $g^{-1}(x) = -\left(\frac{1}{2}\right)^{x-4} + 2$; D: $\mathbb{R}$; R: $-\infty, 2[$
c) $h^{-1}(x) + \log_4 (x - 5) + 1$; D: $]5, +\infty$; R: $\mathbb{R}$

5. a) Vertical intercept: 2; horizontal intercept: 1.5;
D: $-\infty, 2[$; R: $\mathbb{R}$; asymptote: $x = 2$;
decreasing on $-\infty, 2[$
b) Horizontal intercept: $\left(\frac{1}{2}\right)^{\frac{2}{3}}$; D: $]0, +\infty$; R: $\mathbb{R}$;
asymptote: $x = 0$; decreasing on $]0, +\infty$
c) Horizontal intercept: 2; D: $]1.5, +\infty$; R: $\mathbb{R}$;
asymptote: $x = 1.5$; decreasing on $]1.5, +\infty$

Exercises 5-10, page 253

1. a) $8 = 2^3$　　**b)** $32 = 2^5$　　**c)** $\frac{1}{4} = 2^{-2}$
d) $625 = 5^4$　　**e)** $9 = 3^2$　　**f)** $3 = 9^{\frac{1}{2}}$

2. a) 4　　**b)** 2　　**c)** 3　　**d)** 2　　**e)** -1　　**f)** 1
g) 0　　**h)** 4

3. a) 8; 6; 2; 1; $-4, -8$　　**b)** 4; 3; 1; 0.5; $-2, -4$

4. a) $\frac{1}{2}$　　**b)** 4　　**c)** 2　　**d)** 4　　**e)** -3
f) -2　　**g)** 1.5　　**h)** 6

5. a) 1.465　　**b)** 0.712　　**c)** 5.644　　**d)** 1.544
e) 2.377　　**f)** 0.750

6. a) $\log_6 36 = 2$　　**b)** $\log_4\left(\frac{1}{16}\right) = -2$
c) $\log_3 243 = 5$　　**d)** $\log_7 343 = 3$
e) $\log_8 2 = \frac{1}{3}$　　**f)** $\log_2 1 = 0$
g) $\log_5 0.04 = -2$　　**h)** $\log_4\left(\frac{1}{2}\right) = -\frac{1}{2}$
i) $\log_{\frac{1}{2}}\left(\frac{1}{4}\right) = 2$　　**j)** $\log_{\frac{2}{3}}\left(\frac{3}{2}\right) = -1$

k) $\log_{\frac{1}{9}}\left(\frac{1}{81}\right) = 2$　　**l)** $\log_x z = y$

7. a) $400 = 20^2$　　**b)** $\frac{1}{49} = 7^{-2}$　　**c)** $4 = 8^{\frac{2}{3}}$
d) $36^2 = 6^4$　　**e)** $8 = (0.5)^{-3}$　　**f)** $s = r^t$

8. a) 2　　**b)** 0　　**c)** 4　　**d)** 9　　**e)** 8　　**f)** 81

9. a) 512　　**b)** $\frac{1}{4}$　　**c)** -1　　**d)** 10　　**e)** $\frac{1}{4}$
f) $\frac{1}{5}$

10. a) $3x + 2y$　　**b)** $6x + 2y$

11. a) $2^x - x$　　**b)** $\frac{2^x}{x}$

12. a) 14　　**b)** 132 878

13. a) i) 3; $\frac{1}{3}$　　**ii)** 2; $\frac{1}{2}$　　**b)** $\log_a b = \dfrac{1}{\log_b a}$

Exercises 5-11, page 261

1. a) 2　　**b)** 1　　**c)** 3　　**d)** 3　　**e)** 3　　**f)** 4

2. Answers may vary. Typical answers:
a) $\log_3 10 + \log_3 2$　　**b)** $\log_7 5 + \log_7 9$
c) $\log_5 10 + \log_5 9$　　**d)** $\log_{12} 2 + \log_{12} 3$
e) $\log_8 5 + \log_8 15$　　**f)** $\log_{20} 3 + \log_{20} 13$

3. Answers may vary. Typical answers:
a) $\log_4 22 - \log_4 2$　　**b)** $\log_3 24 - \log_3 2$
c) $\log_9 10 - \log_9 2$　　**d)** $\log_6 14 - \log_6 2$
e) $\log_{11} 42 - \log_{11} 2$　　**f)** $\log_2 26 - \log_2 2$

4. a) 2　　**b)** 3　　**c)** 2　　**d)** 5

5. a) 7　　**b)** 7　　**c)** 6　　**d)** 3　　**e)** 2　　**f)** 1

6. a) $3 \log_3 2$　　**b)** $2 \log_5 6$　　**c)** $3 \log_2 3$
d) $5 \log_6 2$　　**e)** $4 \log_{12} 3$　　**f)** $3 \log_4 5$

7. a) $\log_2 125$　　**b)** $\log_7 16$　　**c)** $\log_3 262\ 144$
d) $\log_{12} 1024$　　**e)** $\log_2 14\ 348\ 907$

8. a) 4　　**b)** $\frac{5}{3}$　　**c)** 1.5　　**d)** 2.5　　**e)** 1
f) -1.5　　**g)** 1.5　　**h)** 1.75

9. a) 4.3219　　**b)** 4.6438　　**c)** 1.3219
d) 1.1610

10. a) 5　　**b)** 3　　**c)** 2　　**d)** 1

11. a) 6.2877　　**b)** 3.0959　　**c)** $-0.547\ 95$
d) 2.1918

12. a) $y = x^2$; $\{x \mid x > 0, x \in \mathbb{R}\}$
b) $y = (x + 1)^2(x - 1)$; $\{x \mid x > 1, x \in \mathbb{R}\}$
c) $y = 3(x + 3)^2 + 3$; $\{x \mid x > -3, x \in \mathbb{R}\}$

13. a) i) 11.550 747　　**ii)** 8.228 819
iii) 4.906 891　　**iv)** 1.584 963
v) $-1.736\ 966$　　**vi)** $-5.058\ 894$
vii) $-8.380\ 822$　　**viii)** $-11.702\ 750$

14. a) $3x$ **b)** $1 + 3x$ **c)** $0.5x$ **d)** $1 + 1.5x$
15. a) $2 + x$ **b)** $2 + 2x$ **c)** $1 + 1.5x$
d) $\frac{1}{3}x - 1$

16. a) 6 **b)** 4 **c)** 10 **d)** 12
17. a) 7 **b)** 11 **c)** 0 **d)** 4
18. a) 8 **b)** 9 **c)** 2 **d)** 6 **e)** 2 **f)** 5
19. a) 100 **b)** 18 **c)** 3 **d)** 4 **e)** 3
f) 2

20. a) 10.079 **b)** 114.036

21. b) $\dfrac{1}{\log_a x} + \dfrac{1}{\log_b x} = \dfrac{1}{\log_{ab} x}$

Exercises 5-12, page 266

1. \$3814.48 **2.** About 12.9%
3. In 1990, about $\$3.52 \times 10^{13}$
4. Between 10 and 11 years
5. Between 6 and 7 years
6. a) $P = 100(0.65)^d$; $P = 100(0.95)^d$;
$P = 100(0.975)^d$ **b)** 1.6 m; 13.5 m; 27.4 m
c) 10.7 m; 89.8 m; 181.9 m
7. a) About 60% **b)** About 90
8. 11 300 **9.** About 1.9% **10.** 3960
11. 2620 **12.** 48 min
14. a) 93 years **b)** 186 years
15. For iodine − 131 **b) i)** $P = 100(0.5)^n$
ii) $P = 100(0.5)^{\frac{t}{8.1}}$ **c) i)** 55% **ii)** 7.7%
iii) 2.7×10^{-12}% **d) i)** 27 days **ii)** 81 days
For cesium − 144 **b) i)** $P = 100(0.5)^n$
ii) $P = 100(0.5)^{\frac{t}{282}}$ **c) i)** 98% **ii)** 93%
iii) 41% **d) i)** 937 days **ii)** 2810 days
16. a) 99.7% **b)** 97.2% **c)** 74.9% **d)** 5.6%
17. a) 8.8 g **b)** 15 g **c)** 4.1 g **d)** 2.0 g
18. Between 9 and 10 years
19. a) $T = 80(0.5)^{\frac{t}{5}} + 20$ **b)** 15 min
20. a) $c = 100(0.5)^{\frac{t}{5}}$ **b) i)** 16.6 h **ii)** 33.2 h
21. a) $L = 2.00(1.2)^n$ **b)** 18
22. a) $\dfrac{5}{6}$ **b)** $t = 0.120\left(\dfrac{5}{6}\right)^n$ **c)** 26 **d)** 229 m
23. a) 2018 **b) i)** 2065 **ii)** 2050
iii) 2142 is the year when demand exceeds supply

Exercises 5-13, page 272

1. a) i) $P_4 = P_0(5)$ **ii)** $P_6 = P_0(5)^{1.5}$
b) About 2.2
2. About 1.9 **3.** About 2.6 **4.** 5
5. a) About 4 **b)** About 3 **c)** About 13
6. a) 6 or 7 times as frequent **b)** 36 to 49 times
as frequent **c)** 216 to 343 times as frequent
7. 20
8. a) 10 **b)** Answers may vary
c) i) 50 **ii)** 501
9. 8

10. a) $\dfrac{P_2}{P_1} = (0.95)^{\frac{h_2 - h_1}{300}}$ **b)** About 15.7%

11. a) $\dfrac{N_2}{N_1} = 4^{\frac{t_2 - t_1}{3}}$ **b) i)** 10 times as many
ii) 102 times as many **iii)** 1024 times as many

Investigate, page 273

2.718 281 8

The Mathematical Mind, page 275

1. a) $e^{0.6931471} \doteq 2$ **b)** $e^{1.3862944} \doteq 4$
c) $e^{3.4011974} \doteq 30$ **d)** $e^{4.6051702} \doteq 100$
e) $e^{9.0768090} \doteq 8750$ **f)** $e^{-0.6931472} \doteq 0.5$
g) $e^{-2.3025851} \doteq 0.1$ **h)** $e^{-7.7287358} \doteq 0.000\,44$

2. a) 1.609 437 9 **b)** 2.708 050 2
c) 3.987 130 5 **d)** 5.583 496 3 **e)** 0
f) −1.386 294 4 **g)** −2.385 966 7
h) −8.111 728 1

3. a) 2.718 281 8 **b)** 4.953 032 4
c) 20.085 537 **d)** 90.017 131
e) 1.390 968 1 **f)** 0.367 879 4
g) 0.246 597 0 **h)** 0.110 803 2

4. a) $\ln 15$ **b)** $\ln 20$ **c)** $\ln 36$ **d)** $\ln 9$
e) $\ln 7$ **f)** $\ln 5$

5. a) i) 1 **ii)** 2 **iii)** −3 **iv)** 0.2
b) $\ln e^n = n$

6. a) 4 **b)** 22 **c)** 145 **d)** 72 382
e) 48 254 942

7. a) 4 **b)** 9 **c)** 42 **d)** 10 478
e) 4 657 079

8. a) 3.912 023

Mathematics Around Us, page 278

1. a) 57 million; 0.7%   **b)** 20 million; 3.0%
   c) 2.6 million; 3.8%
2. a) $P = 770e^{0.016t}$ **b) i)** 903.6 million
   ii) 2001   **iii)** 1958
3. a) 99.8%   **b)** 4.53×10^9 years
4. a) 17 600 m; 25 500 m   **b)** 5.9 kPa
   c) $h \doteq -6452 \ln\left(\dfrac{P}{130}\right)$

Review Exercises, page 279

1. a) $\dfrac{1}{4}$ **b)** 3   **c)** 8   **d)** 25   **e)** 3.375
   f) 3.375   **g)** 1   **h)** 0.000 32
2. a) i) 4000   **ii)** 45 255   **b) i)** 125   **ii)** 44
3. a) $5x^3y^{-2}$ **b)** $\dfrac{m^2n}{2}$ **c)** $\dfrac{25a^{-4}b^{-7}}{8}$ **d)** $\dfrac{9y^{-\frac{4}{3}}}{25}$
   e) $-\dfrac{3a^{-\frac{1}{4}}b^{-\frac{1}{3}}}{5}$ **f)** $\dfrac{3m^{-\frac{5}{2}}n^{-\frac{1}{6}}}{2}$
4. a) 1   **b)** $\dfrac{2m^{6x-4y}}{3}$ **c)** $a^x b^{\frac{x}{2}}$
5. $2351.18   **6.** About 20.7%
7. About 12.25 years
8. a) $1000 = 10^3$ **b)** $\sqrt{10} = 10^{\frac{1}{2}}$ **c)** $81 = 3^4$
9. a) $\log 10\,000 = 4$ **b)** $\log 0.001 = -3$
   c) $\log_5 625 = 4$
10. a) 100   **b)** 0.000 01   **c)** 8   **d)** 27
   e) -2 **f)** 32
11. a) $\log x + 2 \log y$ **b)** $\log x + \dfrac{1}{2} \log y$
   c) $1 + 3 \log x + 2 \log y$
   d) $\dfrac{1}{3}[\log x + 2 \log y]$
   e) $\log x - \dfrac{1}{2} \log y$
   f) $2 \log x - \dfrac{1}{3} \log y$
12. a) $\log\left(\dfrac{xy}{z}\right)$ **b)** $\log\left(\dfrac{x^2}{y}\right)$ **c)** $\log(x^3y^5)$
   d) $\log(x^{\frac{1}{2}}y^3)$ **e)** $\log(2x - 3)(y + 5)$
   f) $\log \dfrac{(x + y)^3}{x - y}$
13. a) $3^{1.8927893}$ **b)** $6^{1.7737056}$ **c)** $1.3^{9.4712085}$
   d) $2^{-0.358454}$
14. a) 1.3652   **b)** 0.7879   **c)** 1.9650
   d) 2.2541   **e)** 2.2876   **f)** 0.8072
   g) -0.5204 **h)** 3.5547
15. a) 4   **b)** 4   **c)** 5   **d)** -3 **e)** -3
   f) 10   **g)** -3 **h)** 3

16. a) 4   **b)** 4   **c)** 3   **d)** 3
17. a) See graph for Exercises 5-7, *Exercise 6*.
   b) See answers for Exercises 5-8, *Exercise 3a)*.
   c) See *Example 1*, Section 5-8.
18. a) 76 days   **b)** 116 days
19. a) 64.7%   **b)** 536 days
20. a) $N = 1000(2)^{\frac{n}{2}}$ **b)** 1991
21. 19

Chapter 6

Exercises 6-1, page 285

1. b) i) 3.5 cm   **ii)** 2.1 cm   **iii)** 5.7 cm
2. a) $15°, 140°, 25°, 40°$ **b)** $64°, 72°, 28°, 76°$
3. $\triangle PQR \cong \triangle PSR$ (HL); $\triangle PQT \cong \triangle PST$ (SAS);
   $\triangle QRT \cong \triangle SRT$ (SAS)
4. a) If a quadrilateral is a rectangle, then it is a
   square. False
   b) If a quadrilateral has congruent diagonals, then
   it is a rectangle. False
5. a) $\triangle ABD \sim \triangle CED$
   c) $\dfrac{m\overline{AB}}{m\overline{CE}} = \dfrac{m\overline{BD}}{m\overline{ED}} = \dfrac{m\overline{AD}}{m\overline{CD}}$ **d)** 3.5 cm, 4.9 cm
6. 17.8 m

Exercises 6-2, page 290

1. The centre   **2.** $2R$ **4. b)** Yes
6. An infinite number
7. a) $\overline{OB}, \overline{OE}, \overline{OC}$ **b)** $\overline{EC}$ **c)** $\overline{DA}$ **d)** $\overline{AB}$
   e) $\overparen{EBC}, \overparen{EDC}$ **f)** $\angle BOC, \angle EOC$
8. a) 6   **b)** 1
9. a) $120°$ **b)** $120°$ **c)** $180°$ **d)** 14
10. a) 51 cm   **b)** About 68 cm   **c)** About 31 cm

Exercises 6-3, page 294

1. a) 9.8   **b)** 5.7   **c)** 6
2. a) $45°$ **b)** 2.2   **c)** 4.5
3. About 6 cm   **4. a)** 8   **b)** 2.1   **c)** 4.1
6. 2   **7.** 3 cm
8. $115°, 115°, 65°, 65°$ **9.** $82°$
10. 34 cm   **14.** $\dfrac{3\sqrt{3}R^2}{2}$

Exercises 6-4, page 301

1. a) ∠ACB, ∠ADB, ∠AEB   **b)** ∠CBD, ∠CAD
  c) ∠DAE, ∠DBE   **d)** ∠CAB
2. a) 90°   **b)** 180°
3. a) 60°   **b)** 55°   **c)** 20°
4. a) 90°, 50°, 40°   **b)** 28°, 62°, 90°
  c) 45°, 90°, 45°
5. a) 51°   **b)** 138°
6. 120°, 30°   **7. a)** 40°   **b)** 160°   **c)** 160°
8. 100°, 100°
9. $\dfrac{\sqrt{5}}{2}$ cm
11. a) 43°   **b)** 86°   **c)** 32°
13. a) 38°   **b)** 104°   **c)** 104°   **d)** 52°
14. a) 48°   **b)** 98°   **c)** 96°   **15.** 54°, 108°
16. 119°, 119°, 61°, 61°   **17.** 66°, 118°, 114°, 62°

Problem Solving, page 305

1. 10 cm   **2. a)** 22   **b)** $12\sqrt{2}$ **c)** $\dfrac{22}{49}$
3. There are many solutions, two of which are 184,
  369, 752 and 926, 741, 358
4. a) 147 m   **5.** 1610 L   **6.** None

Exercises 6-5, page 312

1. a) 7   **b)** 18°   **c)** 130°
2. a) 200°   **b)** 70°   **c)** 40°   **d)** 13°   **e)** 84°
  f) 25°
3. a) 30°   **b)** 75°   **c)** 60°
4. a) 60°   **b)** 60°   **c)** 7 cm   **5.** 44 cm
6. a) 102°, 51°   **b)** 78°, 62°   **c)** 25°, 85°
7. 98°, 73°, 82°, 107°   **8.** 108°, 36°, 72°, 36°
9. 150°   **10.** 84°   **11.** 72°   **12.** 6°, 134°

Exercises 6-6, page 320

1. 100°   **2.** 12 cm   **3.** 28 cm   **6.** 7.3, 12.2
7. a) 242°   **b)** 8   **c)** 17.9
8. a) 70°, 70°   **b)** 40°, 25°   **9.** 98°, 94°
10. 154.3 cm
11. a) 56.6 cm²   **b)** 30.9 cm²   **12.** 134.4 cm
13. 78.5 cm   **14.** $6(1 + \sqrt{3})$ cm
15. 3 cm, 6 cm, 8 cm
16. $\dfrac{d^2 + R^2 - r^2}{2d}$; $\dfrac{d^2 - R^2 + r^2}{2d}$

Exercises 6-7, page 327

1. a) ±4   **b)** ±6   **c)** ±8   **d)** ±9   **e)** ±12
  f) ±20
2. a) $\pm 2\sqrt{15}$ **b)** $\pm 4\sqrt{15}$ **c)** $\pm 6a\sqrt{2}$ **d)** ±m
  e) $\pm 15x\sqrt{5y}$ **f)** $\pm 12\sqrt{st}$
3. a) 36   **b)** −75   **c)** 18   **d)** 120   **e)** −6
  f) −90
4. 2, 8   **5.** 1.2×10^{-5} cm   **6.** About 124.0 t
7. a) 12   **b)** 4.6   **c)** 12.8
8. a) 2, 4.5 or 8, 8.9   **b)** 3, 10.4   **c)** 11.8, 7.5
9. a) $\overline{PS}$ **b)** $\overline{QP}$ **c)** $\overline{TS}$ **d)** $\overline{PR}$ **e)** $\overline{PS}$
  f) $\overline{QS}$
10. a) 21 cm   **b)** 63 cm²   **11.** 9 m
12. 258 cm²
13. a) 20.5 cm   **b)** 12.8 cm   **14.** $\dfrac{y^2 - x^2}{\sqrt{x^2 + y^2}}$

Review Exercises, page 333

1. a, b, c
2. a) An infinite number   **b)** 2
3. 360°   **4.** About 77 m
5. 10 cm   **6.** 11.3 m

Cumulative Review, Chapters 4, 5, and 6, page 334

1. a) The perpendicular bisector of AB
  b) A circle, centre Q(−2, −3), radius 4 units
2. a) $\dfrac{x^2}{16} + y^2 = 1$ **b)** $\dfrac{x^2}{36} + \dfrac{y^2}{16} = 1$
3. $x^2 - y^2 = -28$
4. a) $4ax^{-2}y^6$ **b)** $\dfrac{9m^{-13}n^{-2}}{2}$
5. a) 0.01   **b)** 9   **c)** 128   **d)** 2.261 859 5
  e) −0.254 412   **f)** 8.186 427 8
6. a) log 6   **b)** $\log\left(\dfrac{2x^2 + 7x - 15}{x + 4}\right)$
7. a) $x - y$ **b)** $x - 2y$ **c)** $1 + x + y$
  d) $3y - x$
8. a) 2.0828   **b)** 0.5207   **c)** 2.0414
  d) −1.0414
9. a) 3   **b)** 3
10. a) 70°, 70°   **b)** 115°, 115°

Chapter 7
Section 7-1, page 336

Estimates may vary.
1. **a) i)** 17:00 h   **ii)** 20:00 h   **iii)** 17:00 h
   b) Approximate dates: **i)** May 20, July 23
   ii) April 12, Aug. 30   **iii)** Mar. 13, Sept. 29
   iv) Feb. 20, Oct. 24
2. Answers may vary.   **3.** 10 to 11 years
4. Typical answers: **a)** 173 m, 58 m   **b)** 6 h
5. Answers may vary.   **6.** Answers may vary.
7. 5 s   **8.** Answers may vary.
9. Sunsets: 1 year; sunspots: 10.5 years; volume and
   pressure of blood: 0.8 s; volume of air: 5 s
10. 15   **11.** Sunspots

Exercises 7-2, page 342

1. **a)** $\frac{\pi}{6}$ **b)** $\frac{\pi}{4}$ **c)** $\frac{\pi}{3}$ **d)** $\frac{\pi}{2}$ **e)** $\frac{2\pi}{3}$
   f) $\frac{3\pi}{4}$ **g)** $\frac{5\pi}{6}$ **h)** π **i)** $\frac{7\pi}{6}$ **j)** $\frac{5\pi}{4}$
   k) $\frac{4\pi}{3}$ **l)** $\frac{3\pi}{2}$ **m)** $\frac{5\pi}{3}$ **n)** $\frac{7\pi}{4}$ **o)** $\frac{11\pi}{6}$
   p) 2π **q)** $\frac{13\pi}{6}$ **r)** $\frac{9\pi}{4}$

2. **a)** 90°   **b)** 135°   **c)** −120°   **d)** 210°
   e) 45°   **f)** −270°   **g)** 315°   **h)** 360°
   i) −300°   **j)** 225°   **k)** 30°   **l)** −330°
3. **a)** 1.75   **b)** 3.93   **c)** 1.00   **d)** −2.18
   e) 1.31x   **f)** 0.33   **g)** −1.13   **h)** 0.43x
   i) 2.62   **j)** 0.52   **k)** 1.00   **l)** −1.57x
4. **a)** 114.6°   **b)** −286.5°   **c)** 183.3°
   d) 103.1°   **e)** −40.1°   **f)** 80.2θ°
   g) 383.9°   **h)** −360x°
5. **a)** 10 cm   **b)** 15 cm   **c)** 9 cm
   d) 30.5 cm   **e)** 21 cm   **f)** 3 cm
6. **a)** 28.3 cm   **b)** 15.7 cm   **c)** 22.0 cm
   d) 34.6 cm   **e)** 50.3 cm   **f)** 37.7 cm
   g) 64.9 cm   **h)** 41.9 cm
7. **a) i)** 15 m   **ii)** 26 m   **b) i)** 47 cm
   ii) 353 cm   **c) i)** 509 mm   **ii)** 1131 mm
8. **a)** 2π **b)** π **c)** $\frac{\pi}{2}$
9. 15 m   **10.** 51 cm   **11.** $\frac{\pi x}{50}$
12. **a)** About 0.0172   **b)** 2 560 000 km
13. **a)** About 87 rad/s   **b)** $\frac{500x}{9d}$ rad/s

14. **a) i)** $R\sqrt{2}$ **ii)** $\frac{\pi R}{2}$ **b)** $\frac{\pi}{2\sqrt{2}}$ **c)** $\frac{R^2(\pi-2)}{4}$
    d) $\frac{R\sqrt{2}}{2}$

Exercises 7-3, page 348

2. **a)** Quadrant IV   **b)** Quadrant I
   c) Quadrant II   **d)** Quadrant II
   e) Quadrant II   **f)** Quadrant II
   g) Quadrant II   **h)** Quadrant I
4. Answers may vary.
   a) $0, 2\pi, -2\pi$ **b)** $\frac{3\pi}{2}, -\frac{\pi}{2}, -\frac{5\pi}{2}$
   c) $\pi, -\pi, -3\pi$ **d)** $-\frac{\pi}{4}, \frac{7\pi}{4}, -\frac{9\pi}{4}$
5.

s	0	$\frac{\pi}{4}$	$\frac{\pi}{2}$	$\frac{3\pi}{4}$	π
$W(s)$	$(1, 0)$	$\left(\frac{1}{\sqrt{2}}, \frac{1}{\sqrt{2}}\right)$	$(0, 1)$	$\left(-\frac{1}{\sqrt{2}}, \frac{1}{\sqrt{2}}\right)$	$(-1, 0)$

s	$\frac{5\pi}{4}$	$\frac{3\pi}{2}$	$\frac{7\pi}{4}$	2π
$W(s)$	$\left(-\frac{1}{\sqrt{2}}, -\frac{1}{\sqrt{2}}\right)$	$(0, -1)$	$\left(\frac{1}{\sqrt{2}}, \frac{-1}{\sqrt{2}}\right)$	$(1, 0)$

6. **a)** $(0, 1)$ **b)** $(-1, 0)$ **c)** $\left(\frac{1}{\sqrt{2}}, \frac{1}{\sqrt{2}}\right)$
   d) $(0, -1)$
7. **a)** 90°, −270°   **b)** 225°, −135°   **c)** 0°, 360°
   d) 45°, −315°
8. **a)** ±0.98   **b)** ±0.94   **c)** ±0.87   **d)** ±0.92
9. **a)** $s \in \,] \, \pi, \frac{3\pi}{2} \, [$ **b)** $s \in \,] \frac{3\pi}{2}, 2\pi \, [$

Exercises 7-4, page 351

1. **a)** 180°, π **b)** 450°, $\frac{5\pi}{2}$ **c)** −90°, $-\frac{\pi}{2}$
   d) −270°, $-\frac{3\pi}{2}$
3. Typical answers: **a)** 410°, −310°
   b) 480°, −240°   **c)** 525°, −195°
   d) 600°, −120°   **e)** $\frac{5\pi}{2}, -\frac{3\pi}{2}$ **f)** $\frac{9\pi}{4}, -\frac{7\pi}{4}$
   g) $\frac{8\pi}{3}, -\frac{4\pi}{3}$ **h)** $\frac{7\pi}{2}, -\frac{\pi}{2}$

4. Typical answers: **a)** $420°, -300°$
b) $150°, -570°$ **c)** $\dfrac{13\pi}{4}, -\dfrac{3\pi}{4}$ **d)** $\dfrac{3\pi}{2}, -\dfrac{5\pi}{2}$

5. Typical answers: **a)** $3\pi, -\pi$ **b)** $\dfrac{5\pi}{2}, -\dfrac{3\pi}{2}$

c) $\dfrac{5\pi}{3}, -\dfrac{7\pi}{3}$ **d)** $0, -4\pi$ **6. a)** 1   **b)** First

7. a) 1; second   **b)** 1; fourth   **c)** 2; second
   d) 2; fourth   **9. a)** 1   **b)** First

10. a) 0; between second and third
   b) 0; between third and fourth
   c) 1; between fourth and first
   d) 1; between first and second

12. a) $45° + 360°n$ **b)** $150° + 360°n$
   c) $240° + 360°n$ **d)** $-30° + 360°n$

   e) $\pi + 2\pi n$ **f)** $-\dfrac{\pi}{4} + 2\pi n$

   g) $\dfrac{5\pi}{2} + 2\pi n$ **h)** $1 + 2\pi n$

14. b) $\mathbb{R}; \{y \mid 0 \leqslant y < 2\pi, y \in \mathbb{R}\}$

Exercises 7-5, page 356

1. a) 0.939 69   **b)** 0.615 66   **c)** $-0.544\ 64$
   d) $-0.866\ 03$ **e)** 0.809 02   **f)** $-0.224\ 95$

2. a) 0.070 74   **b)** $-0.702\ 71$ **c)** 0.932 70
   d) $-0.416\ 15$ **e)** 0.841 47   **f)** $-0.322\ 54$

4. a) $-0.573\ 58$ **b)** Answers may vary. $235°$,
$485°, 595°$

5. a) $-0.631\ 27$ **b)** Answers may vary.
$5.6 + 2\pi, 5.6 + 4\pi, 5.6 - 2\pi$

6. a) Positive   **b)** Negative   **c)** Negative
   d) Negative   **e)** Positve   **f)** Negative

7. a) 0.292 371 704; 0.956 304 756   **b)** 1

8. 1

9. a) 0.6470   **b)** 0.9223   **c)** -0.9901
   d) -0.7160

Exercises 7-6, page 359

2. a) $\dfrac{1}{\sqrt{2}}$ **b)** $\dfrac{1}{\sqrt{2}}$ **c)** $-\dfrac{1}{\sqrt{2}}$ **d)** $-\dfrac{1}{\sqrt{2}}$ **e)** $\dfrac{1}{2}$

   f) $\dfrac{1}{2}$ **g)** $-\dfrac{1}{2}$ **h)** $-\dfrac{1}{2}$ **i)** $\dfrac{\sqrt{3}}{2}$ **j)** $\dfrac{\sqrt{3}}{2}$

   k) $-\dfrac{\sqrt{3}}{2}$ **l)** $-\dfrac{\sqrt{3}}{2}$

3. a) $\dfrac{1}{\sqrt{2}}$ **b)** $-\dfrac{1}{\sqrt{2}}$ **c)** $-\dfrac{1}{\sqrt{2}}$ **d)** $\dfrac{1}{\sqrt{2}}$

   e) $\dfrac{\sqrt{3}}{2}$ **f)** $-\dfrac{\sqrt{3}}{2}$ **g)** $-\dfrac{\sqrt{3}}{2}$ **h)** $\dfrac{\sqrt{3}}{2}$ **i)** $\dfrac{1}{2}$

   j) $-\dfrac{1}{2}$ **k)** $-\dfrac{1}{2}$ **l)** $\dfrac{1}{2}$

5. a) $\dfrac{\sqrt{3}}{2}$ **b)** $\dfrac{1}{2}$ **c)** $\dfrac{1}{\sqrt{2}}$ **d)** $\dfrac{1}{\sqrt{2}}$ **e)** $\dfrac{\sqrt{3}}{2}$

   f) $-\dfrac{1}{2}$ **g)** $\dfrac{1}{\sqrt{2}}$ **h)** $-\dfrac{1}{\sqrt{2}}$

6. a) 1   **b)** 1   **c)** 1

7. b) The equation holds.

Problem Solving, page 361

1. 2.4 cm   **2.** $(65 + 20\pi)$ cm   **3.** 36

4. 2 min 7 s   **5.** $4\sqrt{2}, \dfrac{8\sqrt{2}}{3}, \dfrac{8\sqrt{2}}{3}$ **6.** 260

8. $x > 1.25$

Exercises 7-7, page 365

2. a) $\cos \theta = 1, 0.5, 0, -0.5, -1$
   b) $\cos \theta = -0.5, 0, 0.5, 1$
   d) i) $\,]\,\pi, 2\pi\,[$ **ii)** $\,]\,0, \pi\,[$

5. a) $y = 1$ when $\theta = \dfrac{\pi}{2}$ and $-\dfrac{3\pi}{2}$

   b) $y = -1$ when $\theta = \dfrac{3\pi}{2}$ and $-\dfrac{\pi}{2}$

   c) $\{y \mid -1 \leqslant y \leqslant 1\}$ **d)** 0
   e) $0, \pm\pi, \pm 2\pi$

   f) $\ldots]-\dfrac{3\pi}{2}, -\dfrac{\pi}{2}\,[\,;\,]\,\dfrac{\pi}{2}, \dfrac{3\pi}{2}\,[\ldots$

   g) $\ldots]-2\pi, -\dfrac{3\pi}{2}\,[\,;\,]-\dfrac{\pi}{2}, \dfrac{\pi}{2}\,[\,;\,]\,\dfrac{3\pi}{2}, 2\pi\,[\ldots$

6. a) $y = 1$ when $\theta = 0$ and $\pm 2\pi$
   b) $y = -1$ when $\theta = \pm\pi$

   c) $\{y \mid -1 \leqslant y \leqslant 1\}$ **d)** 1   **e)** $\pm\dfrac{\pi}{2}, \pm\dfrac{3\pi}{2}$

   f) $\ldots]-2\pi, -\pi\,[\,;\,]\,0, \pi\,[\ldots$
   g) $\ldots]-\pi, 0\,[\,;\,]\,\pi, 2\pi\,[\ldots$

7. a, c   **8.** Answers may vary.

Exercises 7-8, page 373

2. a) $y = 1.5 \sin x$; $1.5; -1.5; 1.5$
   b) $y = 0.5 \cos x$; $0.5, -0.5, 0.5$

3. a) $y = \sin x + 0.5$; $0.5; 1.5; -0.5; 0.5$
   b) $y = \cos x - 1$; $-1; 0; -2; 0$

4. a) 5; −5; $\{y \mid −5 \le y \le 5\}$
b) 3; −3; $\{y \mid −3 \le y \le 3\}$
c) 7; 1; $\{y \mid 1 \le y \le 7\}$
d) −1; −5; $\{y \mid −5 \le y \le −1\}$
e) 2; −6; $\{y \mid −6 \le y \le 2\}$
f) 3.5; 2.5; $\{y \mid 2.5 \le y \le 3.5\}$
g) −0.5; −1.5; $\{y \mid −1.5 \le y \le −0.5\}$
h) 4; 0; $\{y \mid 0 \le y \le 4\}$
i) 6; 0; $\{y \mid 0 \le y \le 6\}$
5. a) $a + q$; $\frac{\pi}{2}, \frac{5\pi}{2}, \ldots$ **b)** $q − a$; $\frac{3\pi}{2}, \frac{7\pi}{2}, \ldots$
6. a) $a + q$; 0, π, 2π,…
b) $q − a$; π, 3π,…
7. $y = \sin x + 1$; $y = \sin x − 1$

Exercises 7-9, page 376

2. Typical answers: $\frac{\pi}{3}$, $y = \sin\left(x − \frac{\pi}{3}\right)$; $−\frac{5\pi}{3}$,
$y = \sin\left(x + \frac{5\pi}{3}\right)$

3. Typical answers: $\frac{5\pi}{6}$, $y = \cos\left(x − \frac{5\pi}{6}\right)$;
$−\frac{7\pi}{6}$, $y = \cos\left(x + \frac{7\pi}{6}\right)$

5. a) D: $\mathbb{R}$; R: $\{y \mid 1 \le y \le 5, y \in \mathbb{R}\}$
b) D: $\mathbb{R}$; R: $\{y \mid 0 \le y \le 4, y \in \mathbb{R}\}$
c) D: $\mathbb{R}$; R: $\{−5 \le y \le 3, y \in \mathbb{R}\}$
d) D: $\mathbb{R}$; R: $\{y \mid −6 \le y \le 2, y \in \mathbb{R}\}$
6. Answers may vary.
 a) $\pm 2\pi, \pm 4\pi, \ldots$ **b)** $−\frac{\pi}{2}, \frac{3\pi}{2}, \ldots$
7. Answers may vary.
 a) $\frac{\pi}{2}, \frac{5\pi}{2}, \ldots$ **b)** $\pm 2\pi, \pm 4\pi, \ldots$
8. a) $f(x) = a + q$ when $x = p + \frac{\pi}{2}$; $p − \frac{3\pi}{2}$;…
 b) $f(x) = −a + q$ when $x = p + \frac{3\pi}{2}$; $p − \frac{\pi}{2}$;…
9. a) $f(x) = a + q$ when $x = p$; $\pm 2\pi + p$;…
 b) $f(x) = −a + q$ when $x = \pm\pi + p$;…

Exercises 7-10, page 379

2. a) $y = \sin 3x$ **b)** $y = \sin 6x$
3. a) 2, π **b)** 3, 4π **c)** 4, π
 d) 4, 4π **e)** 5, π **f)** 3, $\frac{2\pi}{3}$

4. a) 5; $\frac{2\pi}{3}$; π **b)** 2; $\frac{\pi}{2}$; $−\frac{\pi}{2}$ **c)** 2.5; $\frac{\pi}{3}$; $\frac{2\pi}{3}$
 d) 0.5; $\frac{2\pi}{5}$; $−\frac{5\pi}{4}$

5. a) 1; π; $\frac{\pi}{3}$ **b)** 2; $\frac{2\pi}{3}$; $\frac{\pi}{2}$ **c)** 4; 4π; −π
 d) 0.5; 4π; $\frac{5\pi}{4}$

6. b) Answers may vary.
 d) Answers may vary.

7. a) $\frac{2\pi}{3}$ **b)** 4π **c)** π
8. a) $y = \sin(−x)$ is a reflection of $y = \sin x$ in the
 y-axis.
 b) $y = \cos(−x)$ is the same graph as $y = \cos x$.

Exercises 7-11, page 387

1. a) About 4.0 m; 1.7 m
 b) 4.9 m at 7:06 A.M. and 7:30 P.M.
2. About 2.3 m
3. a) $y = 4 \cos \dfrac{2\pi(t − 8.00)}{12.4}$ **b)** About 2.1 m

4. a) $y = 4.6 \cos \dfrac{2\pi(t − 4.50)}{12.4} + 5$
 b) 1.2 m, 7.7 m
5. a) $y = 1.4 \cos \dfrac{2\pi(t − 4.50)}{12.4} + 5$
 b) 3.9 m, 5.8 m
6. a) The angle would have to be converted from
 radians to degrees.
8. Answer may vary. $y = 2000 \sin \dfrac{\pi t}{5} + 3000$
9. b) $y = 80 \sin \dfrac{\pi t}{5}$
10. a) $y = 0.5 \sin \dfrac{\pi t}{50}$; $y = 0.5 \sin \dfrac{\pi t}{25}$;
 $y = 0.5 \sin \dfrac{3\pi t}{50}$; $y = 0.5 \sin \dfrac{2\pi t}{25}$
11. b) Typical answer:
 $y = 0.4 \cos \dfrac{2\pi(t − 0.6)}{1.2} + 0.5$ or
 $y = 0.4 \sin \dfrac{2\pi(t − 0.3)}{1.2} + 0.5$
 c) i) 0.50 m **ii)** About 0.85 m **iii)** 0.10 m
12. a) i) 40 cm **ii)** 0 cm **iii)** 0.05 s
 b) 72 000
13. b) Typical answer: $h = 25 \cos \dfrac{2\pi(t − 25)}{50} + 26$
 c) i) 18 m **ii)** 46 m **iii)** 18 m **iv)** 18 m

14. b) Typical answer: $y = 16.5 \cos \frac{2\pi t}{5} + 29$

   c) i) 45.5 cm   **ii)** 15.7 cm   **iii)** 15.7 cm

15. a) Typical answer:

   $d = 2.5 \cos \frac{2\pi(n - 172)}{365} + 149.7$

   b) i) 148.8 million km   **ii)** 151.3 million km
   iii) 150.5 million km

16. a) Answers may vary.   **b)** Feb. 16 and Oct. 23

17. a) 6:56 A.M.   **b)** 9:02 A.M.

Review Exercises, page 390

1. a) 60°   **b)** −315°   **c)** 150°   **d)** 269.3°

2. a) $\frac{3\pi}{4}$ **b)** $\frac{3\pi}{2}$ **c)** $\frac{11\pi}{6}$ **d)** −0.82

3. About 35 cm

5. a) $-\frac{\sqrt{3}}{2}; -\frac{1}{2}$ **b)** $\frac{1}{\sqrt{2}}; -\frac{1}{\sqrt{2}}$ **c)** $-\frac{1}{2}; \frac{\sqrt{3}}{2}$

   d) $\frac{1}{\sqrt{2}}; \frac{1}{\sqrt{2}}$ **e)** $0; -1$ **f)** $\frac{\sqrt{3}}{2}; \frac{1}{2}$

6. a) 0.9924   **b)** −0.9689
   c) −0.8081   **d)** 0.5691

7. a) $-\frac{\sqrt{3}}{2}$ **b)** $\frac{\sqrt{3}}{2}$ **c)** $\frac{1}{\sqrt{2}}$ **d)** $-\frac{1}{\sqrt{2}}$

   e) $-\frac{\sqrt{3}}{2}$ **f)** $\frac{\sqrt{3}}{2}$

8. See Section 7-7.

   a) $\sin \theta$: 1 at $-\frac{3\pi}{2}, \frac{\pi}{2}$; $\cos \theta$; 1 at 0, $\pm\ 2\pi$

   b) $\sin \theta$: − 1 at $-\frac{\pi}{2}, \frac{3\pi}{2}$; $\cos \theta$: −1 at $\pm\ \pi$

   c) $\sin \theta$: y-intercept 0, θ-intercepts $\pm\ 2\pi$,
   $\pm\ \pi$, 0; $\cos \theta$: y-intercept 1,
   θ-intercepts $\pm\frac{3\pi}{2}, \pm\frac{\pi}{2}$

9. a) $3; \pi; \frac{\pi}{4}; -4$ **b)** $2; \frac{2\pi}{5}; -\frac{\pi}{3}; 1$

Chapter 8

Exercises 8-1, page 395

1. a) 0.624 87   **b)** 19.081 14   **c)** −0.466 31
   d) 2.050 30   **e)** −1.37638

2. a) 1.557 41   **b)** −2.185 04   **c)** 0.374 59
   d) −1.268 44   **e)** 0.350 16

3. Answers may vary.

4. a) 3.732 05   **b)** Answers may vary. 255°,
   435°, −105°

5. a) Negative   **b)** Negative   **c)** Positive
   d) Positive   **e)** Negative

6. a) 0.8608   **b)** −0.6801   **c)** 0.0998
   d) −2.8557

7. a) −1   **b)** 1   **c)** −1   **d)** $\sqrt{3}$ **e)** −$\sqrt{3}$
   f) $\sqrt{3}$ **g)** −$\sqrt{3}$ **h)** $\frac{1}{\sqrt{3}}$ **i)** $-\frac{1}{\sqrt{3}}$ **j)** $\frac{1}{\sqrt{3}}$

9. a) $\tan \theta = -\frac{\sqrt{1 - \cos^2\theta}}{\cos \theta}$ **b)** $\tan \theta = -\frac{\sin \theta}{\sqrt{1 - \sin^2\theta}}$

10. Answers may vary.

Exercises 8-2, page 398

3. a) No   **b)** D: any angle in standard position
   except odd values of $\frac{\pi}{2}$; R: $\mathbb{R}$ **c)** 0

   d) $\ldots 0, \pm\pi, \pm2\pi, \ldots$

   e) $\ldots]-\frac{\pi}{2}, \frac{\pi}{2} [;] \frac{\pi}{2}, \frac{3\pi}{2} [\ldots$

   f) No intervals

4. c, d, e   **5.** Answers may vary.

7. Odd function

Exercises 8-3, page 401

1. a) 1.064   **b)** −1.031   **c)** −11.474
   d) 28.654   **e)** 14.301

2. a) 1.016   **b)** −12.767   **c)** −1.800
   d) 1.120   **e)** −30.123

3. a) $\sqrt{2}$ **b)** 2   **c)** $\sqrt{3}$ **d)** 2   **e)** 1
   f) $-\frac{2}{\sqrt{3}}$ **g)** −$\sqrt{2}$ **h)** −1   **i)** −2   **j)** −2
   k) $-\frac{1}{\sqrt{3}}$ **l)** $\sqrt{2}$ **m)** $-\frac{2}{\sqrt{3}}$ **n)** $\frac{1}{\sqrt{3}}$ **o)** $\frac{2}{\sqrt{3}}$

5. Answers may vary.   **6.** Answers may vary.

7. a) $2\pi, \pi$ **b)** $2\pi, -\pi$

Exercises 8-4, page 407

5. b) $\frac{1}{1 + \cos \theta} + \frac{1}{1 - \cos \theta} = 2 \csc^2\theta$

6. b) $\cot^2 x (1 + \tan^2 x) = \csc^2 x$

7. b) Answers may vary.
   $(\csc^2\theta - 1)(1 + \tan^2\theta) = \csc^2\theta$

9. $\dfrac{1}{1 + \sec x} + \dfrac{1}{1 - \sec x} = -2 \cot^2 x$

   $\dfrac{1}{1 + \csc x} + \dfrac{1}{1 - \csc x} = -2 \tan^2 x$

   $\dfrac{1}{1 + \tan x} + \dfrac{1}{1 - \tan x} = \dfrac{2}{1 - \tan^2 x}$

   $\dfrac{1}{1 + \cot x} + \dfrac{1}{1 - \cot x} = \dfrac{2}{1 - \cot^2 x}$

10. Answers may vary.

Exercises 8-5, page 413

4. a) $\sin(180° - \theta) = \sin\theta$; $\csc(180° - \theta) = \csc\theta$;
$\cos(180° - \theta) = -\cos\theta$;
$\sec(180° - \theta) = -\sec\theta$;
$\tan(180° - \theta) = -\tan\theta$; $\cot(180° - \theta) = -\cot\theta$
b) $\sin(-\theta) = -\sin\theta$; $\csc(-\theta) = -\csc\theta$;
$\cos(-\theta) = \cos\theta$; $\sec(-\theta) = \sec\theta$;
$\tan(-\theta) = -\tan\theta$; $\cot(-\theta) = -\cot\theta$
c) $\sin\left(\dfrac{\pi}{2} - \theta\right) = \cos\theta$; $\csc\left(\dfrac{\pi}{2} - \theta\right) = \sec\theta$;

$\cos\left(\dfrac{\pi}{2} - \theta\right) = \sin\theta$; $\sec\left(\dfrac{\pi}{2} - \theta\right) = \csc\theta$;

$\tan\left(\dfrac{\pi}{2} - \theta\right) = \cot\theta$; $\cot\left(\dfrac{\pi}{2} - \theta\right) = \tan\theta$

5. Answers may vary. **a)** $-\cos 70°$
b) $-\sin 40°$ **c)** $-\tan 20°$ **d)** $\cos 20°$
e) $-\sin 50°$ **f)** $-\tan 75°$ **g)** $-\cot 80°$
h) $-\sec 5°$ **i)** $-\sin 35°$ **j)** $-\sec 20°$
k) $\csc 65°$

6. $\sin x = \sin(\pi - x)$; $\sin(\pi - x) = -\sin(\pi + x)$

7. a) $\sin 1.2$ **b)** $-\cos 1.2$ **c)** $-\sin 1.2$
d) $-\cos 1.2$ **e)** $\tan 1$ **f)** $\cot 1$
g) $\csc 1.5$ **h)** $-\sec 1.5$ **i)** $\cos 1.2$
j) $-\sin 1.2$ **k)** $-\cot 1$ **l)** $\sec 1$

8. a) $\dfrac{\sqrt{3}}{2}$ **b)** $-\dfrac{1}{2}$ **c)** $-\dfrac{1}{\sqrt{2}}$ **d)** $-\dfrac{1}{\sqrt{2}}$

e) $-\dfrac{1}{2}$ **f)** $\dfrac{\sqrt{3}}{2}$ **g)** $\dfrac{1}{\sqrt{3}}$ **h)** $-\dfrac{1}{\sqrt{3}}$

9. a) $\dfrac{\sqrt{3}}{2}$ **b)** $-\dfrac{1}{2}$ **c)** $-\dfrac{1}{\sqrt{3}}$ **d)** $-\dfrac{2}{\sqrt{3}}$

10. a) $\dfrac{1}{\sqrt{2}}$ **b)** $-\dfrac{1}{\sqrt{2}}$ **c)** $-\dfrac{\sqrt{3}}{2}$ **d)** $-\dfrac{\sqrt{3}}{2}$

e) $-\sqrt{3}$ **f)** $\sqrt{3}$ **g)** $\sqrt{2}$ **h)** $\dfrac{1}{\sqrt{3}}$

12. a) $\sin 20°$ **b)** $\cos 10°$ **c)** $\cot 35°$
d) $\sec 25°$ **e)** $\cos 40°$ **f)** $-\sin 25°$
g) $-\cos 25°$ **h)** $-\csc 25°$

13. a) $\tan(\pi - x) = -\tan x$; $\csc(\pi - x) = \csc x$;
$\sec(\pi - x) = -\sec x$; $\cot(\pi - x) = -\cot x$
b) $\tan\left(\dfrac{\pi}{2} - x\right) = \cot x$; $\csc\left(\dfrac{\pi}{2} - x\right) = \sec x$;

$\sec\left(\dfrac{\pi}{2} - x\right) = \csc x$; $\cot\left(\dfrac{\pi}{2} - x\right) = \tan x$

15. b) i) $\sin(\pi + x) = -\sin(\pi - x)$;
$\sin\left(\dfrac{3\pi}{2} + x\right) = \sin\left(\dfrac{3\pi}{2} - x\right)$;
$\sin(2\pi + x) = -\sin(2\pi - x)$
ii) $\cos(\pi + x) = \cos(\pi - x)$;
$\cos\left(\dfrac{3\pi}{2} + x\right) = -\cos\left(\dfrac{3\pi}{2} - x\right)$;
$\cos(2\pi + x) = \cos(2\pi - x)$

Exercises 8-6, page 422

2. a) 1 **b)** 0 **c)** $\dfrac{1}{2}$ **d)** $\dfrac{1}{2}$

3. a), b), c) $-\dfrac{1}{2}$ **4. a, b)** $\dfrac{1}{\sqrt{2}}$ **5. b)** $\dfrac{1 + \sqrt{3}}{2\sqrt{2}}$

6. a) $\dfrac{1 - \sqrt{3}}{2\sqrt{2}}$ **b)** $\dfrac{\sqrt{3} - 1}{2\sqrt{2}}$ **c)** $\dfrac{\sqrt{3} - 1}{2\sqrt{2}}$

d) $\dfrac{1 + \sqrt{3}}{2\sqrt{2}}$

9. a) $-\cos x$ **b)** $\cos x$ **c)** $\sin x$ **d)** $\sin x$

10. a) $\dfrac{4\sqrt{3} + 3}{10}$ **b)** $\dfrac{7}{5\sqrt{2}}$ **c)** $\dfrac{3 + 4\sqrt{3}}{10}$

11. a) $\dfrac{\sqrt{15} - 2}{6}$ **b)** $\dfrac{-2 - \sqrt{15}}{6}$ **c)** $\dfrac{\sqrt{5} - 2}{3\sqrt{2}}$

12. a) $\dfrac{3 - \sqrt{21}}{8}$ **b)** $\dfrac{3 - \sqrt{21}}{8}$ **c)** $\dfrac{-\sqrt{7} - 3}{4\sqrt{2}}$

13. b) i) $\cos x$ **ii)** $\sqrt{3}\cos x$
c) $\sin(x + y) + \sin(x - y) = 2\sin x \cos y$

14. a) $-\dfrac{16}{65}$ **b)** $\dfrac{56}{65}$ **c)** $\dfrac{63}{65}$ **d)** $-\dfrac{33}{65}$

15. a) $\dfrac{4\sqrt{5} - 6}{15}$ **b)** $\dfrac{4\sqrt{5} + 6}{15}$ **c)** $\dfrac{-3\sqrt{5} - 8}{15}$

d) $\dfrac{8 - 3\sqrt{5}}{15}$

16. a) $\beta = 0$ or $\alpha = -\beta$ **b)** $\alpha = -\beta = \dfrac{\pi}{3}$
c) $\beta = 0$ or $\alpha = -\beta$

18. b) i) $\sin x \sin y = -\dfrac{\cos(x + y) - \cos(x - y)}{2}$

ii) $\sin x \cos y = \dfrac{\sin(x + y) + \sin(x - y)}{2}$

iii) $\cos x \sin y = \dfrac{\sin(x + y) - \sin(x - y)}{2}$

19. b)

$$\text{i)} \ \cos x - \cos y = -2 \sin\left(\frac{x+y}{2}\right) \sin\left(\frac{x-y}{2}\right)$$

$$\text{ii)} \ \sin x + \sin y = 2 \sin\left(\frac{x+y}{2}\right) \cos\left(\frac{x-y}{2}\right)$$

$$\text{iii)} \ \sin x - \sin y = 2 \cos\left(\frac{x+y}{2}\right) \sin\left(\frac{x-y}{2}\right)$$

Problem Solving, page 426

2. a) i) 2   **ii)** 4   **iii)** 7   **b)** No

5. $3x - 4y - 9 = 0$; $3x - 4y - 29 = 0$

6. $4x + 3y - 6 = 0$; $4x + 3y - 21 = 0$

7. 22 units^2

Exercises 8-7, page 429

3. a) $\sin 1.2$ **b)** $\sin 6$ **c)** $\sin 4$ **d)** $\cos 0.9$
   e) $\cos 10$ **f)** $\cos 6$

4. a) $\sin \dfrac{\pi}{3}$ **b)** $\cos \dfrac{\pi}{5}$ **c)** $\cos 1$

5. $\dfrac{\sqrt{3}}{2}; -\dfrac{1}{2}$ **6.** 1; 0

8. a) $\dfrac{4\sqrt{2}}{9}$ **b)** $\dfrac{7}{9}$ **c)** $\dfrac{4\sqrt{2}}{7}$

9. a) $-\dfrac{\sqrt{3}}{2}; -\dfrac{1}{2}; \sqrt{3}$ **b)** $\dfrac{4\sqrt{5}}{9}; \dfrac{1}{9}; 4\sqrt{5}$

   c) $\dfrac{24}{25}; \dfrac{7}{25}; \dfrac{24}{7}$

11. b) $\cos^2 x = \dfrac{\cos 2x + 1}{2}$

13. b) $\csc 2\theta - 1 = \dfrac{(\sin \theta - \cos \theta)^2}{\sin 2\theta}$

14. a) $\dfrac{1 - \cos 2x}{\sin 2x} = \tan x$ **b)** $\dfrac{\sin 2x}{1 + \cos 2x} = \tan x$

   c) $\dfrac{\sin 2x}{1 - \cos 2x} = \cot x$

15. a) $-\dfrac{3}{4}$

16. b) Answers may vary.   **c)** $x = 0, \pm\pi, \pm 2\pi, \ldots$

17. b) Answers may vary.   **c)** $x \doteq 1.95, 4.34, \ldots$

Investigate, page 430

$\sin 3x = 3 \sin x - 4 \sin^3 x$; $\cos 3x = 4 \cos^3 x - 3 \cos x$

The Mathematical Mind, page 433

4. a) 0.258 819

5. a) $\dfrac{\sqrt{\sqrt{2} + 2}}{2}$ **b)** $\dfrac{1}{\sqrt{\sqrt{2} + 4}}$

7. b) $\tan \dfrac{x}{2} = \pm\sqrt{\dfrac{1 - \cos x}{1 + \cos x}}$

8. a) $\dfrac{-1 + \sqrt{5}}{4}$

   b) $\sqrt{\dfrac{5 + \sqrt{5}}{8}}; \dfrac{(-1 + \sqrt{5})(\sqrt{5 + \sqrt{5}})}{4\sqrt{2}}$

10. a) 0.819   **b)** 0.643   **c)** 0.423   **d)** 0.342
   e) 0.940   **f)** 0.466   **g)** 0.364   **h)** 1.732
   i) 0.700   **j)** 0.700

13. a) 0.6967   **b)** 1.0003   **c)** 0.6988
   d) 114.59   **e)** 49.114   **f)** 0.2333
   g) 0.7234   **h)** 343.78

15. a) 6.5   **b) i)** 65   **ii)** 390   **iii)** 3900

17. a) 0.465 614 5   **b)** 0.759 081 9
   c) $-1.078\ 013\ 2$
   d) $-0.744\ 505\ 8$

20. $\cos x = 1 - \dfrac{x^2}{2!} + \dfrac{x^4}{4!} - \dfrac{x^6}{6!} + \dfrac{x^8}{8!} - \dfrac{x^{10}}{10!}$

   $\sin x = \dfrac{x}{1!} - \dfrac{x^3}{3!} + \dfrac{x^5}{5!} - \dfrac{x^7}{7!} + \dfrac{x^9}{9!} - \dfrac{x^{11}}{11!}$

21. a) 0.866 025 4   **b)** 1   **c)** 0.587 785 2
   d) $-1.001\ 829$

22. a) 3   **b)** 4   **c)** 5

Review Exercises, page 438

1. a) -1.1098 **b)** 1.7321   **c)** 0.4663

2. $-\dfrac{3\pi}{2}, -\dfrac{\pi}{2}, \dfrac{\pi}{2}, \dfrac{3\pi}{2}$; descriptions may vary

3. a) $-\dfrac{\sqrt{3}}{2}$ **b)** $\sqrt{2}$ **c)** $\sqrt{3}$ **d)** $-\dfrac{\sqrt{3}}{2}$

4. a) $-\sqrt{2}$ **b)** -2 **c)** -1 **d)** 0   **e)** $-\dfrac{2}{\sqrt{3}}$

   f) $-\dfrac{1}{\sqrt{3}}$ **g)** $\dfrac{2}{\sqrt{3}}$ **h)** $-\sqrt{2}$

7. a) $\dfrac{\sqrt{3} - 1}{2\sqrt{2}}$ **b)** $\dfrac{\sqrt{3} - 1}{2\sqrt{2}}$ **c)** $\dfrac{\sqrt{3}}{2}$ **d)** $\dfrac{\sqrt{3}}{2}$

8. a) $\dfrac{\sqrt{3}-1}{2\sqrt{2}}$ **b)** $\dfrac{-\sqrt{3}-1}{2\sqrt{2}}$ **c)** $\dfrac{1-\sqrt{3}}{2\sqrt{2}}$

d) $\dfrac{1-\sqrt{3}}{2\sqrt{2}}$

9. a) $\dfrac{3\sqrt{7}-2}{10}$ **b)** $\dfrac{-2+\sqrt{21}}{5\sqrt{2}}$

10. a) $\dfrac{3\sqrt{7}-12}{20}$ **b)** $\dfrac{3\sqrt{7}+12}{20}$ **c)** $\dfrac{-9-4\sqrt{7}}{20}$

d) $\dfrac{-9+4\sqrt{7}}{20}$

Chapter 9

Exercises 9-1, page 442

1. a) $(9.40, 3.42)$ **b)** $(5.74, 8.19)$
c) $(0.70, 9.98)$ **d)** $(-3.91, 9.21)$
e) $(-8.48, 5.30)$ **f)** $(-9.96, 0.87)$
g) $((-9.51, -3.09)$ **h)** $(-5.74, -8.19)$
i) $(-1.74, -9.85)$ **j)** $(3.26, -9.46)$
k) $(6.43, -7.66)$ **l)** $(9.46, -3.26)$

2. a) $(5\sqrt{3}, 5)$ **b)** $(5\sqrt{2}, 5\sqrt{2})$ **c)** $(5, 5\sqrt{3})$
d) $(-5, 5\sqrt{3})$ **e)** $(-5\sqrt{2}, 5\sqrt{2})$ **f)** $(-5\sqrt{3}, 5)$
g) $(-5\sqrt{3}, -5)$ **h)** $(-5\sqrt{2}, -5\sqrt{2})$
i) $(-5, -5\sqrt{3})$ **j)** $(5, -5\sqrt{3})$
k) $(5\sqrt{2}, -5\sqrt{2})$ **l)** $(5\sqrt{3}, -5)$

3. a) $0.928\,48;\ 0.371\,39;\ 0.400\,000$ **b)** $21.80°$

4. a) $-0.948\,68;\ 0.316\,23;\ -0.333\,33;\ 161.57°$
b) $-0.832\,05;\ -0.554\,70;\ 0.666\,67;\ 213.69°$
c) $0.970\,14;\ -0.242\,54;\ -0.250\,000;\ 345.96°$

5. a) $331.39°$ **b)** $191.31°$ **c)** $153.43°$
d) $231.34°$ **e)** $329.04°$ **f)** $69.44°$
g) $90.00°$ **h)** $180.00°$

8. $(2.47, \pm7.61)$ **9.** ±4.28

10. a) $(5.000, 13.737)$

Exercises 9-2, page 445

1. a) $\dfrac{28}{53}; \dfrac{45}{53}; \dfrac{28}{45}$ **b)** $\dfrac{8}{10}; \dfrac{6}{10}; \dfrac{8}{6}$ **c)** $\dfrac{5}{13}; \dfrac{12}{13}; \dfrac{5}{12}$

d) $\dfrac{20}{29}; \dfrac{21}{29}; \dfrac{20}{21}$ **e)** $\dfrac{8}{17}; \dfrac{15}{17}; \dfrac{8}{15}$

f) $\dfrac{3.6}{3.9}; \dfrac{1.5}{3.9}; \dfrac{3.6}{1.5}$

2. a) $\sin A = \dfrac{a}{c}; \cos A = \dfrac{b}{c}; \tan A = \dfrac{a}{b}; \csc A = \dfrac{c}{a};$

$\sec A = \dfrac{c}{f}; \cot A = \dfrac{b}{a}$

b) $\sin B = \dfrac{b}{c}; \cos B = \dfrac{a}{c}; \tan B = \dfrac{b}{a}; \csc B = \dfrac{c}{b};$

$\sec B = \dfrac{c}{a}; \cot B = \dfrac{a}{b}$

3. a) The smallest angle is P. $\sin P = \dfrac{9}{41};$

$\cos P = \dfrac{40}{41}; \tan P = \dfrac{9}{40}$ **b)** $12.7°, 77.3°$

4. a) $15°$ **b)** $30°$ **c)** $42°$

5. $9.6°$ **6.** $72.7°$ **7.** $47.8°$

8. a) $\dfrac{1}{\sqrt{2}}$ **b)** $\dfrac{\sqrt{3}}{2}$ **c)** $\sqrt{3}$ **d)** $\dfrac{2}{\sqrt{7}}$ **e)** $\dfrac{\sqrt{7}}{3}$

f) $\dfrac{3}{5}$ **g)** $\dfrac{5}{\sqrt{34}}$ **h)** $\dfrac{1}{\sqrt{15}}$

9. a) $-\dfrac{1}{\sqrt{2}}$ **b)** $\dfrac{\sqrt{3}}{2}$ **c)** $-\sqrt{3}$ **d)** $\dfrac{2}{\sqrt{7}}$

e) $-\dfrac{\sqrt{7}}{3}$ **f)** $\dfrac{3}{5}$

10. $53.1°, 36.9°$

11. a) $r\sqrt{\cos^2\theta + \sin^2\theta + 1 - 2\cos\theta};$
$r\sqrt{2 + 2\cos\theta}$

Investigate, page 447

a) No   **b)** Answers may vary.

Investigate, page 447

2. $2\cos\theta; \sqrt{2 + 2\cos2\theta}; \cos2\theta = 2\cos^2\theta - 1$

3. $\sin2\theta = 2\cos\theta\sin\theta; \tan2\theta = \dfrac{2\cos\theta\sin\theta}{2\cos^2\theta - 1}$

Exercises 9-3, page 450

1. a) AB $= 24, \angle A = 36.9°, \angle C = 53.1°$
b) DE $= 33.2, \angle D = 50.3°, \angle F = 39.7°$
c) $\angle H = 35°,$ GK $= 12.6,$ HK $= 22.0$
d) $\angle M = 58°,$ LM $= 38.7,$ MN $= 73.1$
e) PR $= 34.2, \angle P = 37.9°, \angle R = 52.1°$
f) $\angle S = 50°,$ SU $= 23.1,$ UT $= 27.6$

2. a) YZ $= 25.5, \angle X = 46.7°, \angle Z = 43.3°$
b) $\angle Z = 63°,$ YZ $= 8.2,$ XZ $= 18.0$
c) XY $= 49.3, \angle X = 14.8°, \angle Z = 75.2°$
d) $\angle X = 38°,$ XY $= 56.7,$ YZ $= 44.3$
e) $\angle Z = 26°,$ XY $= 15.6,$ XZ $= 35.6$
f) XZ $= 49.2, \angle Z = 66.0°, \angle X = 24.0°$

3. a) $\cos\theta = \dfrac{15}{17}$, $\tan\theta = \dfrac{8}{15}$

b) $\sin\theta = \dfrac{24}{25}$, $\tan\theta = \dfrac{24}{7}$

c) $\sin\theta = \dfrac{20}{29}$, $\cos\theta = \dfrac{21}{29}$

d) $\cos\theta = \dfrac{\sqrt{799}}{32}$, $\tan\theta = \dfrac{15}{\sqrt{799}}$

e) $\sin\theta = \dfrac{\sqrt{168}}{23}$, $\tan\theta = \dfrac{\sqrt{168}}{19}$

f) $\sin\theta = \dfrac{43}{\sqrt{14\,393}}$, $\cos\theta = \dfrac{112}{\sqrt{14\,393}}$

4. a) $\cos\theta = \dfrac{\sqrt{q^2 - p^2}}{q}$, $\tan\theta = \dfrac{p}{\sqrt{q^2 - p^2}}$

b) $\sin\theta = \dfrac{2\sqrt{a+1}}{a+2}$, $\tan\theta = \dfrac{2\sqrt{a+1}}{a}$

c) $\sin\theta = \dfrac{x-y}{\sqrt{2x^2 + 2y^2}}$, $\cos\theta = \dfrac{x+y}{\sqrt{2x^2 + 2y^2}}$

5. a) 60 m **b)** 66 m

6. a) 21.0 m **b)** 4.5 m

7. 62° **8. a)** 34° **b)** 37° **9.** 7.2 cm

10. a) 24.6 m **b)** 4.3 m **c)** 5.67

11. 151.7 m, 168.2 m

12. a) i) 45.0° **ii)** 80.3° **iii)** 110.3°
iv) 136.8° **b)** 16

13. 8.9 cm

Mathematics Around Us, page 452

1. 4.5% **2.** 6.9 km

3. a) About 90 **b)** About 20 m
c) About 3 min

4. About 130 m

Exercises 9-4, page 454

1. About 36 cm **2.** 37° **3.** 66°

4. a) 9.3 m **b)** 3.6 m

5. a) 25 cm **b)** 4 cm

6. a) 76 m **b)** 2 h 42 min

7. 34.2 m **8. a)** 6367 km **b)** 40 003 km

9. 75.83°

10. a) i) 108 m **ii)** 70.5 m **iii)** 62.4 m
b) 64° **c) i)** 5.6 m **ii)** 6.7 m **iii)** 7.0 m

11. 56°, 79°

12. a) i) 260 m **ii)** 62 m **iii)** 87 m
iv) 1139 m **b)** 9:52 A.M. and 2:08 P.M.
c) 7 h and 59 min **13.** 32°

Mathematics Around Us, page 457

1. $d = \cot(23.5° + l)$
3., 4. Answers will vary.

Problem Solving, page 460

1. 12 714 km **2.** $6\sqrt{2}(1 - \tan 15°)$ cm

4. $\dfrac{s}{2 + \sqrt{2}}$ **5.** $x = \sqrt{\dfrac{1}{3}}s$; $y = \sqrt{\dfrac{2}{3}}s$

7. $(3 + 3\sqrt{3}, 5 + 2\sqrt{3})$ or $(3 - 3\sqrt{3}, 5 - 2\sqrt{3})$

8. $36 - 36\sqrt{3} + 12\pi$; $-36 + 18\sqrt{3} + 3\pi$;
$36 - 9\sqrt{3} - 6\pi$

Exercises 9-5, page 462

1. a) $b\sin C$, or $c\sin B$ **b)** $e\sin F$, or $f\sin E$
c) $h\sin J$ **d)** $l\sin K$

2. Answers to the nearest square centimetre
a) 326 cm² **b)** 472 cm² **c)** 217 cm²

3. Answers to the nearest square unit **a)** 42
b) 340 **c)** 329 **d)** 522 **e)** 47

4. Answers to the nearest square unit **a)** 110
b) 134 **c)** 783 **d)** 140 **e)** 288
f) 1880

5. 2371 m² **6.** 202.0 cm² **7.** 5.97 m²

8. 347 cm² **9.** 6.2 m² **10.** 4.9 m²

11. a) 251.4 m² **b)** $691.35 **12.** About $50

13. 368.2 cm² **14. a)** 10.8 m² **b)** $565.30

15. 66.4 m² **16.** $280

17. 18.7 cm, 18.7 cm, 26.5 cm

18. a) 615 cm² **b)** 796 cm³ **c)** 45° **d)** 55°

Exercises 9-6, page 468

1. a) 8.6 **b)** 14.3 **c)** 15.6

2. a) 4.0 **b)** 23.6 **c)** 33.7 **d)** 8.0
e) 14.1

3. a) 129.1° **b)** 26.4° **c)** 53.6°

4. a) i) 25.2° **ii)** 121.6° **b) i)** 20.0°
ii) 121.0° **c) i)** 13.4° **ii)** 148.4°
d) i) 31.9° **ii)** 90° **e) i)** 41.6°
ii) 87.6° **f) i)** 12.5° **ii)** 108.9°

5. a) 4.4 **b)** 48 **c)** 29.3 **6.** 4.7 m

7. 6.0 km

8. About 46 m **9.** 112.0°, 15.4°, 52.6°

10. 6.4 cm, 9.4 cm **11.** 35°

12. 55°, 55°, 125°, 125° **13.** 10.8 km

14. 11.3 cm **15.** 14.3 cm **16.** 16°

17. 9.6 cm **18.** 80.4°

19. a) 195 cm²   **b)** 91 cm²   **c)** 210 cm²
20. 143°
21. a) $r\sqrt{2 - \sqrt{3}}$ **b)** r **c)** $r\sqrt{2}$ **d)** $r\sqrt{3}$
    e) $r\sqrt{2 + \sqrt{3}}$ **f)** $2r$
22. About 26 km
23. 4.7°
24. a) $3\sqrt{2 - \sqrt{3}}$ cm   **b)** $3\sqrt{2 + \sqrt{3}}$ cm
25. a) $\sqrt{2 + \sqrt{3}}$ cm   **b)** 0.25 cm²
26. a) $\sqrt{5}$ cm, $\sqrt{5}$ cm   **b)** $2\sqrt{13}$ cm, $\sqrt{73}$ cm
28. $\sqrt[3]{2}$, $\sqrt[3]{4}$

Exercises 9-7, page 479

1. a) 22.2   **b)** 18.0   **c)** 15.9
2. a) 36.4°   **b)** 38.7°   **c)** 140.6°
3. a) 10.6   **b)** 22.2   **c)** 27.7   **d)** 15.3
    e) 15.1
4. a) $\angle Q = 46.4°$, $\angle R = 28.6°$, $r = 5.9$
   b) $\angle R = 49.2°$, $\angle P = 67.8°$, $p = 20.8$
   c) $\angle R = 46.4°$, $\angle Q = 21.6°$, $q = 12.7$
   d) $\angle P = 40.7°$, $\angle Q = 61.3°$, $q = 37.7$
5. a) $\angle B = 45.8°$, $\angle C = 99.2°$, $c = 20.7$ or
     $\angle B = 134.2°$, $\angle C = 10.8°$, $c = 3.9$
   b) $\angle C = 75.5°$, $\angle A = 49.5°$, $a = 10.2$ or
     $\angle C = 104.5°$, $\angle A = 20.5°$, $a = 4.7$
   c) $c = 27.3$, $\angle B = 42.9°$, $\angle A = 59.1°$
   d) $\angle C = 55.2°$, $\angle A = 82.8°$, $a = 32.6$ or
     $\angle C = 124.8°$, $\angle A = 13.2°$, $a = 7.5$
   e) $a = 28.5$, $\angle C = 45.0°$, $\angle B = 96.0°$
   f) $\angle A = 23.5°$, $\angle C = 32.5°$, $c = 17.5$
6. a) $\angle Y = 58°$, $y = 30.3$, $z = 27.4$
   b) $x = 21.0$, $\angle Y = 46.4°$, $\angle Z = 87.2°$
   c) $\angle X = 69.5°$, $\angle Z = 56.5°$, $z = 19.6$ or
     $\angle X = 110.5°$, $\angle Z = 15.5°$, $z = 6.3$
   d) $z = 7.3$, $\angle X = 69.2°$, $\angle Y = 49.8°$
7. 54.3 m   **8.** 31.6 km, 22.8 km
9. 133 m, 208 m   **10.** 7.4 m   **11.** About 429 m
12. 106 m, 52 m   **13. a)** 21 m   **b)** 8 m
14. a) 33 m   **b)** 15 cm   **15.** 553 m
16. a) 191 m, 256 m or 929 m, 693 m
   b) 151 m or 546 m
17. a) 1.9   **b)** 2.7   **18.** $20\left(1 + \dfrac{1}{\sqrt{3}}\right)$
19. $\angle O = 104.8°$, $\angle Y = \angle H = 37.6°$ **20.** 10 cm

Exercises 9-8, page 485

1. a) 684 m   **b)** 39°   **2.** 10.7 m
3. a) 76.6 m²   **b)** 21.3 m
4. 7.7 m   **5.** 269 m   **6.** 421 km   **7.** 78.1°
8. 2.6 m   **9. a)** 70°   **b)** 61 cm
10. 1 h 21 min   **11.** 39 cm or 99 cm   **12.** 11°
13. 141 m   **14.** 24 m
15. a) i) 6.1°   **ii)** 2.1°   **b)** 33.5 m

Review Exercises, page 488

1. a) (7.66, 6.43)   **b)** (−3.42, 9.40)
   c) (−5.74, −8.19)   **d)** (5.00, −8.66)
   e) (6.69, −7.43)
2. a) 0.91915; 0.393 92; 2.333 33; 66.80°
   b) 0.24253; −0.970 14; −0.250 00; 165.96°
   c) −0.832 05; −0.554 70; 1.500 00; 236.31°
   d) −0.316 23; 0.948 68; −0.333 33; 341.57°
3. a) $\dfrac{1}{2}$ **b)** $\dfrac{1}{\sqrt{2}}$ **c)** $\dfrac{1}{\sqrt{3}}$ **d)** $\dfrac{3}{5}$
4. a) $\sin \theta = \dfrac{15}{17}$; $\tan \theta = \dfrac{15}{8}$
   b) $\sin \theta = \dfrac{12}{13}$; $\cos \theta = \dfrac{5}{13}$
   c) $\sin \theta = \dfrac{8\sqrt{5}}{21}$; $\tan \theta = \dfrac{8\sqrt{5}}{11}$
   d) $\cos \theta = \dfrac{2\sqrt{14}}{9}$; $\tan \theta = \dfrac{5}{2\sqrt{14}}$
5. a) 29.1°; 60.9°; 30.9   **b)** 33.7°; 56.3°; 15.0
   c) 18°; 44.2, 13.6   **d)** 6.9, 9.8, 55°
6. a) 47.3 units²   **b)** 33.7 units²
   c) 131.5 units²
7. a) 40.9°, 64.1°, 11.8   **b)** 44.7°, 83.3°, 35.3
   c) 37.0°, 50.2, 31.3   **d)** 36.8°, 29.6°, 113.7°
8. 6.6°   **9.** 35.4 m   **10.** 85.6 m

Cumulative Review, Chapters 7, 8, and 9, page 489

1. a) 135°   **b)** −210°   **c)** 154.70°
   d) −660°
2. a) $\dfrac{7\pi}{6}$ **b)** $-\dfrac{5\pi}{4}$ **c)** 2.57   **d)** $\dfrac{3\pi}{2}$
3. a) i) $\dfrac{1}{\sqrt{10}}$; $\dfrac{3}{\sqrt{10}}$; $\dfrac{1}{3}$ **ii)** $-\dfrac{2}{\sqrt{29}}$; $-\dfrac{5}{\sqrt{29}}$; $\dfrac{2}{5}$
   iii) $-\dfrac{2}{\sqrt{13}}$; $\dfrac{3}{\sqrt{13}}$; $-\dfrac{2}{3}$ **b) i)** 18.4°   **ii)** 201.8°
   iii) 326.3°

4. The ratios are given in this order: sine, cosecant, cosine, secant, tangent, cotangent.

a) $\dfrac{1}{2}$; 2; $-\dfrac{\sqrt{3}}{2}$; $-\dfrac{2}{\sqrt{3}}$; $-\dfrac{1}{\sqrt{3}}$; $-\sqrt{3}$

b) $\dfrac{\sqrt{3}}{2}$; $\dfrac{2}{\sqrt{3}}$; $\dfrac{1}{2}$; 2; $\sqrt{3}$; $\dfrac{1}{\sqrt{3}}$

c) $-\dfrac{1}{\sqrt{2}}$; $-\sqrt{2}$; $\dfrac{1}{\sqrt{2}}$; $\sqrt{2}$; -1, -1

d) $-\dfrac{\sqrt{3}}{2}$; $-\dfrac{2}{\sqrt{3}}$; $-\dfrac{1}{2}$; -2; $\sqrt{3}$; $\dfrac{1}{\sqrt{3}}$

e) $-\dfrac{1}{2}$; -2; $\dfrac{\sqrt{3}}{2}$; $\dfrac{2}{\sqrt{3}}$; $-\dfrac{1}{\sqrt{3}}$; $-\sqrt{3}$

5. a) 2; $\dfrac{2\pi}{3}$; $\dfrac{\pi}{6}$; 0 **b)** $\dfrac{1}{2}$; π; $-\dfrac{\pi}{4}$; -1

7. a) $\dfrac{1+\sqrt{3}}{2\sqrt{2}}$ **b)** $\dfrac{1+\sqrt{3}}{2\sqrt{2}}$ **c)** $\dfrac{\sqrt{3}+1}{1-\sqrt{3}}$

8. a) $\dfrac{\sqrt{5}-2\sqrt{15}}{12}$ **b)** $\dfrac{5\sqrt{3}-2}{12}$ **c)** $\dfrac{1}{9}$

d) $\dfrac{\sqrt{5}+2\sqrt{15}}{12}$

9. a) 0.914; 0.406; 2.250
  b) -0.882, 0.471, -1.875
  c) 0.868; -0.496; -1.750
  d) -0.640, -0.768, 0.833

10. a) 66.0° **b)** 298.1° **c)** 119.7°
  d) 219.8°

11. a) 36.0°; 54.0°; 13.6 **b)** 62°; 55.4; 48.9

12. a) 28.3°; 41.7°; 9.9
  b) 70.0°; 52.0°; 3.4 or 110.0°, 12.0°, 0.9

Problem Solving, page 491

1. a) 3 **b)** 5 **6.** 67.5 **8.** $\dfrac{3\sqrt{3}r^2}{2}$

The Mathematical Mind, page 493

1. Shortest route is: Goderich—Clinton—Mitchell—Listowel—Harriston—Walkerton—Wingham—Kincardine—Amberley—Goderich (289 km); Items packed: {360 g, 350 g, 290 g}, {280 g, 260 g, 250 g, 210 g}, {290 g, 230 g, 210 g, 140 g, 130 g}
2. Typical answer: 3 pieces cut into 145 cm, 88 cm, 59 cm; 2 pieces cut into 59 cm, 74 cm, 74 cm, 44 cm, 44 cm; 1 piece cut into 59 cm, 74 cm, 74 cm, 88 cm

3. a) 100; 2500; 10 000; 90 000; 1024; 1.126×10^{15}; 1.268×10^{30}; 2.037×10^{90}
  b) 1000; 125 000; 1 000 000; 27 000 000; 57.7; 637 621 500; 4.066×10^{17}, 6.720×10^{52}
  c) 10^{10}; 9.766×10^{16}; 10^{20}; 5.905×10^{24}; 2.594; 117.4; 13 781; 2.617×10^{12}

The Mathematical Mind, page 494

1. 8th row: 1, 8, 28, 56, 70, 56, 28, 8, 1
  9th row: 1, 9, 36, 84, 126, 126, 84, 36, 9, 1
  10th row: 1, 10, 45, 120, 210, 252, 210, 120, 45, 10, 1
2. The sum in the nth row is 2^n.
3. Answers may vary.
4. The sum of the first n numbers in the first diagonal is the nth number in the second diagonal.
5. a) 50; it is the same as the row number.
  b) 1225; it is the sum of all preceding row numbers.
6. Answers may vary.
7. a) 6 **b)** 15 **c)** 35 **d)** 56 **e)** 126
8. a) 56; 56 **b)** Answers may vary.
9. a) 56; 56 **b)** Answers may vary.
10. a) 32 **b), c)** Answers may vary.

11. $\dfrac{n!}{\left(\dfrac{n-1}{2}\right)!\left(\dfrac{n+1}{2}\right)!}$ if n is odd

  $\dfrac{n!}{\left(\dfrac{n}{2}\right)!\left(\dfrac{n}{2}\right)!}$ if n is even

The Mathematical Mind, page 496

1. a) A rectangle, 8 by 4 **b)** n^2
2. a) A rectangle, 8 by 5 **b)** $n(n+1)$
3. a) A rectangle, 12 by 5 **b)** $\dfrac{3n(n+1)}{2}$

Computer Power, page 501

1. a) 9 cm, 12 cm, 16 cm, $21.\overline{3}$ cm, $28.\overline{4}$ cm
  b) Approximately 3.897 11 cm², 6.495 19 cm², 7.072 54 cm², 7.200 84 cm², 7.229 35 cm²

c) $\dfrac{117\sqrt{3}}{28}$ cm²

2. a) Descriptions may vary.
  b) $P_1 = 9$ cm, $P_n = \tfrac{4}{3}P_{n-1}$, $n > 1$

c) $A_1 = \dfrac{9\sqrt{3}}{4}$, $A_2 = \dfrac{15\sqrt{3}}{4}$, $A_n = A_{n-1} + \tfrac{2}{9}B_{n-1}$,

  where $B_2 = \dfrac{6\sqrt{3}}{4}$, $n > 2$

4. 1.261 859 5

Index